WEST SUSSEX

Crawley

East Grinstead

Horsham

Ardingly Resr

River Ouse

T h e   W e a l d

Haywards Heath

Burgess Hill

East Sussex

Storrington

River Adur

Henfield

Steyning

Shoreham by Sea

Worthing

Lancing

ENGLISH CHANNEL

| 0 Km | 5 | 10 |
| 0 Miles | 3 | 6 |

This book is dedicated to the memory of Stuart Hughes. His energy and enthusiasm was the genesis of this project; he sadly died before seeing it concluded.

Stuart Hughes.

Lavington Common in July

BIRDS OF
SUSSEX

Editor: Paul James

Assistant Editor: John Newnham
Habitat and Illustrations Editor: Chris Corrigan
Photograph Editor and Production: Alan Perry

Sussex Ornithological Society

Published in June 1996 by the Sussex Ornithological Society

ISBN 0 9528466 0 8

British Library Cataloguing-in-Publication Data. A catalogue record for this book is available from the British Library.

Camera ready copy prepared by Dilmun Secretarial Services, Hartley Wintney, Hook, Hampshire.

Printed by BAS Printers Limited, Over Wallop, Hampshire.

Contents

Publication of this book has been aided by
financial assistance from :

Barons (BMW), East Sussex County Council,
Lord Egremont, Mrs. Margaret Hughes,
J & L Hutchinson, Keats Harding,
The National Rivers Authority, M J O'Brien,
Potter Owtram & Peck, Sun Alliance and
West Sussex County Council.

The Hadden bequest to the SOS supported the
inclusion of the coloured artwork by John Reaney.

We wish to thank the other individuals and
companies who also made donations.

Acknowledgements

For any society or voluntary organisation it is a major and daunting task to conceive and bring to fruition a project such as a County Avifauna. A large number of members of the Sussex Ornithological Society were involved in the production of this book but special thanks must also go to all those who contributed, either by undertaking the field work for the Sussex Tetrad Atlas, or by submitting the records on which the species accounts in the Systematic List are largely based.

A great many people, to whom sincere thanks are due, contributed their expertise and enthusiasm to this project:

Chris Corrigan, Robert Edgar, Ann Griffiths, Tony Marr, Sarah McKenzie and Tony Whitbread wrote the introductory chapters, which were typed by Andrew South. Ian Dawson, Richard Porter and Michael Shrubb assisted with the 'Sussex Ornithology - Its History and Personalities' chapter.

Val Bentley, Barry Collins, Tony Cook, John E S Cooper, Jon Curson, Derek Crawley, Anne de Potier, Robert Edgar, Richard Fairbank, John Hobson, Clive Hope, Roger Jackson, Charles James, Paul James, Chris Janman, Martin Kalaher, Richard Kelly, Roy Leverton, Leonard Manns, Mike Mason, John Newnham, Joe Nobbs, Tim Parmenter, Sarah Patton, Robin Pepper, Michael Prince, Graham Roberts, Roy Sanderson, Roy Sandison, Mike Scott-Ham, Matthew Sennitt, Dave Smith, Tim Toohig, Barrie Watson, Peter Whitcomb, Tony Wilson and Barry Yates wrote the species accounts for the systematic list. Richard Fairbank undertook the preparation of the species accounts for most of the very scarce and rare birds and, in this respect, he would like to thank his family for allowing him the time to extensively research previously unpublished information for many records. Particular thanks are due to the many individuals who readily provided him with details relating to their records and especially to Mike Rogers who offered much encouragement and also dug out answers to specific queries from countless *British Birds Rarities Committee* files. John E S Cooper provided the ringing summaries for most of the species accounts in the Systematic List and Mike Mason extracted the wildfowl and wader count data for the county into a readily accessible form. Dave Burges and John Houghton made available previously unpublished breeding information which has been incorporated into the relevant species accounts. John F Cooper and Tim Parmenter allowed Richard Fairbank access to their extensive libraries and Charles James answered many queries relating to the text. Jeremy Adams allowed access to the collection at the Booth Museum of Natural History and also provided data on specimens held there.

Val Bentley, Mike Scott-Ham and the Society's network of 10-km square stewards organised the Sussex Tetrad Atlas and Leonard Manns and Iris Simpson input much of this information gathered onto computer.

John Reaney provided the artwork, both colour and black-and-white, and Dennis Bright, Mike Read, Andy Williams and Roger Wilmshurst the photographs. D M Turner-Ettlinger and Tony Marr made available a selection of historical photographs.

Barrie Watson undertook the unenviable task of producing the bibliography and John Irons and John Newnham the gazetteer. Barrie also commented on the first drafts of the species accounts as did Colin Brooks and especially John Fairbank on those relating to the rarer species. Richard Fairbank, John Irons, Paul Outhwaite, Tim Parmenter and Barry Yates spent many hours reading and correcting the proofs of the text.

David Gumn, of B A S Printers who printed the book, offered expert advice on layout and production as did Anne Hallowes, the type setter. Tim Parmenter provided technical assistance with the printing of the photographs.

Iris Simpson and Leonard Manns organised the sales and distribution.

John Clark and John Eyre, editors of the Birds of Hampshire, offered many helpful suggestions which enabled a number of potential pitfalls to be sidestepped, as did John Gooders.

To all these people we are greatly indebted.

Ringing data were provided by the BTO Ringing Scheme. The BTO wishes to acknowledge the support given by the Joint Nature Conservation Committee (on behalf of the Countryside Council for Wales, English Nature and Scottish Natural Heritage), DOE (NI), the National Parks and Wildlife Service (Ireland) and the ringers themselves. Ringing costs for seabirds are currently subsidised by JNCC's seabird monitoring programme. Crown Copywright is reproduced with the permission of the Controller of HMSO.

Finally, special thanks are due to the patient families, friends and work colleagues of the members of the Avifauna Committee, all of whom will no doubt be as delighted as they are that the book has finally been published.

Chris Corrigan, Paul James, John Newnhan and Alan Perry

Foreword

It is a pleasure to write a short foreword to this new book on the *Birds of Sussex*.

The modest contribution of D D Harber and myself to the task of collating data and presenting it in a useful form in our *Guide to the Birds of Sussex* (1963) makes me particularly interested in the present volume. Our aim then was to simplify the preparation of the *Sussex Bird Report* by having a trustworthy baseline. The major publication prior to the 1963 book was Walpole-Bond's majestic work which gathered together all, or nearly all, the printed records, although he admitted some were unacceptable.

After the last war, interest in birds in the county greatly increased but before that such awareness was not always the case. The truth is that in the days immediately following the Second World War there were few people in Sussex doing more than egg-collecting or what we now think of as twitching. It therefore fell to me to take over the Sussex Report when the *South Eastern Bird Report* organised by Ralph Whitlock collapsed. Similarly, someone had to help with the British Trust for Ornithology when they were seeking to establish contacts and representatives at county level.

With the publication of the annual *Sussex Bird Report* the amount of information on status has progressively increased and so too the number of observers. In addition it has been possible to organise through the Sussex Ornithological Society enquiries either specific to the county or on behalf of national organisations. This has led to a huge amount of data being available allowing a clearer picture of the changing status of species to be seen (including extinction of some breeding species such as the Cirl Bunting and the arrival of new ones as for example Cetti's Warbler).

The present volume is the first fully cooperative effort but I would particularly thank, on behalf of the Society, the small committee consisting of Paul James, John Newnham, Chris Corrigan and Alan Perry who have spent much time and effort in bringing the concept to a conclusion. The many other contributors have been acknowledged elsewhere in this volume. It was however a happy idea to get as many as possible to write the individual species accounts although this must have greatly added to the tribulations of the editor, Paul James.

Grahame des Forges

Sussex Ornithology -
Its History and Personalities

Tony Marr

Sussex is blessed with a well-documented ornithological history, which can be traced back to 1752. It is a fitting introduction to this modern avifauna that we can look back over more than 240 years and, thanks to the literary efforts of the ornithologists of the time, chart the enormous changes that have occurred during the past two centuries. These not only relate to bird numbers and distribution, but also to changes in social history, human population, urbanisation and habitats across the county.

In addition to being well documented, our county's ornithology has produced more than its fair share of great characters and eccentrics. Some have been positive rogues. Many have been larger than life. Above all, they have been achievers, and in recent years Sussex has produced some of the country's finest ornithologists and conservationists, who have moved effortlessly on to the national, and even the international, stage.

We now know that ornithology over the major part of this period was rather different from its modern image. Bird records were substantiated by the gun, the trap and the net, rather than by the binocular, the telescope and the camera. As recently as 1936, one author tells us that he has "enclosed in brackets rare and difficult birds, which have only been seen, knowing as I do from personal experience what absurd mistakes can be made".

Reflecting society at the time, many early ornithologists were men of private means with time on their hands to pursue their interest. These 18th and 19th century workers did not have our advantages in sophisticated optical equipment, so they had to shoot birds to identify them. Although from our modern perspective we may condemn them for this, we need to recognise that collecting specimens has necessarily always played an important role in setting the basic framework for ornithology as a science, in taxonomy and systematics, classification, and distribution. Even today, ornithologists routinely refer to museum collections of skins.

At the other end of the social scale in the county were the professional birdcatchers who, with the aid of decoys, netted thousands of migrants around Brighton for sale either as cage birds or for the table. There were also those who attracted larks passing along the coast in the autumn by a reflecting 'larkglass' or 'twirler', and shot them in huge numbers as they hovered, mesmerised, before the revolving lure (fig. 1).

Shepherds used to supplement their meagre wages by catching Wheatears, a notable delicacy, with horsehair nooses set across specially-constructed 'coops', or tunnels, in the downland turf. The most successful actually made more from Wheatear-catching from July to September than the farmers paid them for the whole year's shepherding.

Most of the birds caught on the Downs found their way to the Brighton or London markets. The poulterers' stalls were regularly trawled by ornithologists for unusual birds, and this resulted in a number of records of rarities, particularly of larks, pipits, finches and buntings. Several of these were additions to the British List, including Little Bunting in 1864, Rustic Bunting in 1867, Black-headed Bunting in 1868, Scarlet Rosefinch and White-winged Lark in 1869, Blyth's Pipit in 1882 and Rock Bunting in 1902.

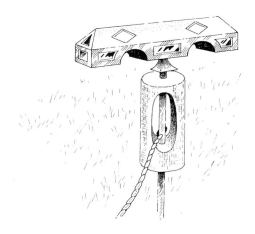

Figure 1. A Larkglass or twirler.

Further inroads upon bird populations were made by egg-collectors, who plundered nests of some of the rarest Sussex birds. Some still suffer this fate; Hobby, Dartford Warbler, and Woodlark are species still favoured by egg-collectors, sadly still active in small (and we hope ever-diminishing) numbers. Other species no longer breed - Stone Curlews, Red-backed Shrikes and Cirl Buntings have now all gone from the county, probably through agricultural or climatic changes rather than egg-collecting, although the latter cannot have helped.

The County Bird Historians

The Sussex Ornithological Society (SOS) was founded in 1962 and its newsletters contain some valuable accounts of the major county bird publications of the last 200 years, including anecdotes about their authors. These articles were written between 1968 and 1982 by the brothers Edwin and Harry Cawkell, themselves notable Sussex ornithologists, and the following summary draws heavily upon their original work.

The 18th Century

There are some half-a-dozen references to various publications on Sussex ornithology between 1752 and 1791, but the first comprehensive account of birdlife in Sussex was provided by William Markwick. His *Aves Sussexiensis*, or *A Catalogue of Birds Found in the County of Sussex*, was read to members of the Linnean Society on May 5th 1795 and published in 1798. It contained 175 species.

Markwick, of Catsfield and Horsham, also kept a natural history journal. The second edition of Gilbert White's *The Natural History of Selborne* (1802) contained a calendar and observations by Markwick, who had been a great friend of White.

An indication of the state of knowledge at the time is revealed by Markwick writing of the Green and Wood Sandpipers in his *Catalogue*. He says that "These birds agree so nearly in size, mode of living, and other respects, that they are with the greatest probability supposed to be only varieties of the same species, perhaps male and female".

The First Half of the 19th Century

About the year 1800, a Mr Woolgar of Lewes made a list of birds observed by him in that neighbourhood, which can be found in Horsfield's *History of Lewes* (1824). However, it was not until 1849 that a comprehensive account of the county's avifauna appeared which superseded Markwick's *Catalogue* of 1795. This was the first edition (of three) of Edward Knox's *Ornithological Rambles in Sussex* (1849). This is a delightful book, with quaint but evocative illustrations from his own drawings (except for the third edition which contained plates by J Wolf). It gives a revealing insight into the era of the shooter and the birdcatcher.

The book includes a "Systematic Catalogue of the Birds of Sussex", but the major part consists of a collection of letters written by Knox to a friend residing "beyond the Tweed". He tells us in the preface that they "owe their appearance in a collected form to a subsequent suggestion that they might become a popular contribution to the Fauna of Sussex, possessing some attractions for the sportsman as well as the ornithologist". How fortunate it is for us now that they were collected and published. They make fascinating, although at times disturbing, reading to modern ornithologists. For example, although he refers to himself as a person for whom "an ardent love of nature has throughout life been his ruling passion", his description of his observations of the autumn migration of Pied Wagtails along the Sussex coast casts some doubt on the nature of his ardour.

"About the latter end of the month, or in the beginning of September", writes Knox, "an early riser, visiting the fields in the neighbourhood of the coast, may observe them flying invariably from west to east, parallel with the shore, and following each other in constant succession. These flights continue from daylight until about ten o'clock in the forenoon; and it is a remarkable fact, that so steadily do they pursue this course, and so pertinacious are they in adhering to it, that even a shot fired at an advancing party, and the death of more than one individual, have failed to induce the remainder to fly in a different direction; for, after opening to the right and left, their ranks have again closed, and the progress towards the east has been resumed as before".

His accounts of the Brighton birdcatchers in action on the Downs and along the coast, already referred to, are graphic and revealing. He distinguishes between the professional trappers, who netted, and the shooters (layabouts, he implied) who shot birds over the 'twirlers'. In describing the latter, he uses phrases such as "this mode of warfare" and "what is called 'good sport' by those who can find amusement in this occupation". He describes how "the infatuated birds advance stupidly to their doom, hover in numbers over the decoy, and present the easiest possible mark to the veriest tyro that ever pulled a trigger". He sees them "hovering over it (the lure) in apparent delight and admiration, patiently suffer themselves to be shot at, and massacred in considerable numbers".

As a historical record, Knox's book is invaluable, and provides the best account we have of what ornithology was all about in the first half of the last century. He also gives some valuable information on habitat and habitat changes in his time. Although Sussex was densely wooded with extensive tracts of swamp and marshland, even then, this was "gradually disappearing before the strides of civilization, while the march of 'agricultural improvement' steadily progresses".

He is one of the very few early writers to give some idea of numbers and distribution for certain species. He describes Ravens nesting in Petworth Park and on the cliffs near Newhaven. Peregrines nested at Newhaven and at Beachy Head, where the cliffs held colonies of Guillemots and Razorbills, "the former on the naked ledge, the latter in the crannies in the face of the cliff".

The Second Half of the 19th Century

Taking us into the second half of that century are the diaries of the Reverend Robert Nathaniel Dennis, one-time rector of East Blatchington. A collection of extracts under the heading *Notes on Sussex Ornithology*, which span the years 1846 to 1852, and 1860 to 1869, were selected by the late Dr Norman Ticehurst and the late W H Mullens (Mullens & Ticehurst 1925).

Unfortunately the journals disappeared after Dennis' death in 1869, and it was not until 1916 that some of them came to light on a second-hand bookstall near Covent Garden, enabling the selection to be made. It is sad that there is a gap between 1852 and 1860, for this may well have been Dennis' most productive period. His journals are full of interesting observations and comment (not all of it ornithological). He was a big, stout man with a white beard, who suffered much from headaches and bilious attacks, becoming something of a recluse towards the end of his life. He was a friend and correspondent of William Borrer, and supplied some of the information for the latters *Birds of Sussex* (1891).

Borrer's book was the county's first real bird history, dedicated by the author to the memory of his father who was a keen botanist. William Borrer was a lifelong Sussex resident, living in Cowfold when his book was published. In his introduction to the 395-page book, he modestly refers to it as "this little account of the 'Birds of Sussex'".

He hoped that his work would "make known the present state of the bird-life of the county", and that the result of his studies "thus presented in this volume, may help those who come after me to enjoy the same pleasure" - that pleasure being "to investigate the works of the Creator, so wonderfully and beautifully displayed in the Natural History of the 'Fowls of the air'".

The work covers 297 species in a comprehensive systematic list, is fascinating reading, and an impressive work. Although much of it is a catalogue of birds shot, it contains a great deal of interesting information for the modern reader. Of particular significance are his remarks about changes in the county in the half-century up to 1891, which he says "have greatly interfered with ornithology in this county, as in others. The whole of Sussex is now intersected with railways, not only inland but along the coast...the whistle of the steam-engine taking the place of that of the Wildfowl and the Wader. The estuaries, formerly abounding in these species, are now far more disturbed by traffic than they used to be; and much of the marsh-land has been brought under cultivation".

He decries changes to Amberley Wild Brooks ("re-echoing with the lowing of cattle instead of the hollow boom of the Bittern"); to the Downs ("once the peaceful haunt of the Bustard and the Lapwing"); and to the cliffs. "The inland aspect of the county, too, is much changed from what it was in former times. Where are the splendid stretches of heather? the sedgy bottoms? and where are the Black Game?" What would he make of it now, just over 100 years on?

Between Knox and Borrer a few bird lists had appeared in other publications, especially the 'Transactions' of the several local natural history societies which existed in Brighton, Chichester, Eastbourne, Hastings and Lewes.

The End of the 19th Century
This was the heyday of the bird shooters and consequently a boom time for taxidermists. The latter included the Pratts and Brazenor of Brighton, Bates of Eastbourne, Bristow of St Leonards, and Ellis of Arundel. Foremost among the shooters was Edward Thomas Booth, whose parents had left him plenty of money which he spent on killing birds with anything from dust shot to the blast of a punt gun.

The marshes near Rye were his early hunting ground (his parents lived at St Leonards), but he soon extended his activities to the Norfolk Broads and then to the Highlands. He was so successful that he established his own private museum collection, which he bequeathed to Brighton Corporation upon his death in 1890, and which one can still visit to this day in Dyke Road.

As well as the fading cases of beautifully mounted birds, Booth left behind him his admirable *Rough Notes* (1881-87), full of excellent observations and fascinating anecdotes. One of these is the story of the punt-gunner who let off his gun and broke all the windows of a public-house because the landlady had "reprimanded him for some unbecoming levity she had detected between him and one of the damsels of her establishment".

The First Half of the 20th Century

In 1905, John Guille Millais provided a list of just over 300 birds for the county in the *Victoria History of Sussex*. Around the same time was the publication of W H Hudson's *Nature in Downland* (1900). Whilst by no means confining himself to birds, Hudson does make some very interesting observations about downland habitats, land-use and birds in Sussex at that period, as well as describing the Wheatear trapping referred to earlier.

There were no more significant publications until 1938, but there was plenty happening in ornithology at the time. It was a period in which Sussex could boast of a whole string of notable ornithologists whose names crop up again and again in the county's records - E C Arnold, the Morris brothers, W Ruskin Butterfield, J B Nichols, Michael Nicoll, and Dr Norman Ticehurst, to name but a few.

Dr Ticehurst was one of the writers for *A Practical Handbook of British Birds* (1919-24), edited by H F Witherby, and the renowned *Handbook of British Birds* (1938-41). The county bird history he wrote for Kent is still regarded as a model of its kind. He lived in St Leonards for many years, and he was such a long-standing editor and recorder for the *Hastings and East Sussex Naturalist* that we can rightly claim him as one of our bird historians.

Arnold was Headmaster of Eastbourne College; author of four books; and a farsighted conservationist who realised that to buy land and preserve habitat was the best way to protect birds. He had a great love of waders (many of which he shot!) and wrote *British Waders* (1924) as well as *Birds of Eastbourne* (1936) and *Bird Reserves* (1940) which are very readable and entertaining books. He combined an unusually racy yet learned style with a superb, and at times scathing, sense of humour.

He purchased land in the Cuckmere Valley and on Pevensey Levels specifically to create bird reserves, which he managed thoughtfully and effectively. Many will not be aware that the nationally famous Salthouse Broad near Cley in Norfolk was acquired by him in 1932 and is of course now known as Arnold's Marsh.

His philosophy was ahead of its time. One can hear modern conservationists saying, as he did over 50 years ago, that "bird protection is nowadays far more a matter of preserving bird haunts than of making laws to protect birds, which may easily, like the Kentish Plover, be exterminated by progress in the form of bungalows, though officially protected by the law".

Arnold had a jaundiced view of politicians, which he expressed in print rather more forcefully than might present day bird conservationists. Writing of wild country being ruined by speculators, he accuses Parliament, "since

13

there are no votes in the business" of "remaining uninterested and supine. At times some minister receives a deputation on the subject, doles out a dose of sympathetic flapdoodle to his visitors, and does exactly nothing after they have retired".

His books deserve a wider audience, and are to be recommended to modern readers with an interest in birds, conservation and Sussex. You will find them full of interesting snippets. For example, in May 1928 at The Mere, Arnold's Pevensey Levels reserve, "a college boy named R S R Fitter" claimed to have seen "an exceptionally bright Sedge Warbler with a light stripe down the centre of its head. If this is true, he of course saw an Aquatic Warbler. I think he probably did, though the date is not a very likely one". R S R Fitter went on to become one of Britain's leading botanists and ornithologists.

Arnold's dislike of anyone without an interest in natural history livens up his writing. He describes a representative from a company who visited him at Eastbourne College to seek permission to erect an electricity pylon on his Pevensey Levels property as a "smart, up-to-date young vandal", representing "the progressive land desecrator". When faced with road "improvements" near one of his reserves, so that "speed maniacs may go faster round sharp corners", he suggests that "it is ridiculous that money should be wasted in providing lethal facilities for a selfish and self-assertive class".

Arnold is very entertaining, and definitely from the mould of many of the great Sussex birdmen. But he was overshadowed by the next to appear on the scene - John Walpole-Bond. His character, his achievements, and his place in Sussex ornithology can all be fairly described as unique.

John Walpole-Bond

John, or Jock, Walpole-Bond, was possibly the county's finest ever field ornithologist. He was also an inveterate egg-collector. These two interests frequently coincided in his generation, and undoubtedly led to a better knowledge of the county's birds as a result.

Walpole-Bond will be remembered above all for his monumental three-volume *A History of Sussex Birds* (1938). It represented the culmination of over thirty years work. In his preface the author states that he was "very far from being satisfied" with the outcome. However, he acknowledged that his work had to come to an end, "or I should have been dead before it was alive", as he put it.

He also acknowledges the work of Michael Nicoll, who apparently had planned a similar book. Nicoll had taken up an appointment abroad, "whereupon he most courteously placed at my disposal all his notes and memoranda". Nicholl is remembered for the book *Nicoll's Birds of Egypt* (1930). (The book was actually written by Richard Meinertzhagen based on the notes prepared by Nicoll before his death).

The copious result was, to quote from the dust-cover, "In three volumes at £5.5s. net the set" and published by Witherby, who produced *The Handbook of British Birds* and most of the major ornithological works of the period. It is a meticulous, and in places candid, appraisal of past records, and a veritable mine of information about the distribution, behaviour, breeding and song of all the county's nesting species.

14

The style is distinctly old-fashioned, even for the period, and quaint to read. To take just two examples from the first species in the book - the Raven. Of the shooting of a bird on Seaford Head in May 1895, he writes that "now usually more than ever are their doting parents wrought up by man's presence on their domain". But some is evocative and poetic, as this description of a day in the life of a Raven family: "Together all leave home at dawn, together all return with eve, a straggling line of croaking animation".

The book is illustrated with very attractive colour paintings of Sussex birds and scenes by Philip Rickman, who died in 1982 at Wilmington. Edwin Cawkell, who with his brother Harry, proof-read the History, tells us that the artist was paid £7 for each of the 53 paintings.

Walpole-Bond financed the publication out of his own pocket. Eight hundred sets of books were printed, and Witherby charged £3000 for the job. It appeared at a bad time, just before the Second World War, and it seemed that Walpole-Bond was going to be significantly out of pocket. But when the war ended and the American soldiers were going home, for some astonishing reason they bought the book in quantity, and it was sold out.

The scale of the book is heroic, as are the exploits and experiences of the author. On the Woodlark, 16 pages with the most moving description of the song one can read anywhere; six pages concerned with the nest and eggs; he clearly had an enormous affection for this "lovable bird". To the Grasshopper Warbler, he devotes over 11 pages; eight of these describe in great detail nests, eggs and breeding habits, from his experience of examining "well over two hundred nests...in situ". And the Cirl Bunting occupies 14 pages - a bird which he describes as being at the time in Sussex "by no means rare..." but "never...really common". The account refers to winter flocks of between six and 60; unfortunately since this was written the species has become extinct as a breeding bird in the county.

Walpole-Bond described himself as "an honest rogue", and from some of the egg-collecting and climbing anecdotes recounted by Edwin Cawkell, this was not far from the truth. When making fair copies of his extensive diaries, he threw the originals away, cutting out certain passages because "they are a record of unsurpassed looting".

When he died in 1958, his obituary in *British Birds* made reference to his outstanding knowledge of British birds, his command of words, his great strength, and his prowess as a fearless cragsman and tree-climber. He was unduly modest about his vast field knowledge of birds, merely saying on one occasion "I've had seven days a week for forty years, I ought to know something".

There are some wonderful stories about him. As a young man at Oxford, he used to take on, and beat, the travelling prize-fighters at fairs. He beat up a burglar who he found in his home. He was quick-tempered, and had a fight over a nest with another collector. He dressed so shabbily that a local parson in Hove once offered him a shilling to buy something better. He received a severe head wound in the 1940s on Seaford Head - an event doubtless not unconnected with his activities as an egg-collector.

It is indeed fortunate that this remarkable man left the legacy of such an outstanding account of the birdlife of the county. At the end of the

Introduction to the History, he writes that his book "will at any rate serve as a groundwork for a future generation of ornithologists to work upon". He would be pleased to know just how grateful we are to him for what he did.

The Hastings Rarities

Walpole-Bond included a total of nearly 450 species and sub-species in the *History* in 1938. A significant number of these were of rare birds from the area around Hastings and St Leonards between 1892 and 1930. Most of these had been shot and brought to local taxidermists in the Hastings area to be stuffed. Many represented the only British records of the species at the time. Some were of pairs, or several birds of the same rare species, seen or shot together.

To illustrate the profusion of these, the following is a list of some of the rarities recorded in the "Hastings area" in 1914 alone:

Bulwer's Petrel, Cory's Shearwater, Cape Verde Little Shearwater, Wilson's Petrel, Little Bittern, Squacco Heron, Ferruginous Duck, Lesser Kestrel, Little Ringed Plover, Caspian Plover, four Asiatic Golden Plovers, four Sociable Plovers, Baird's Sandpiper, Pectoral Sandpiper, Slender-billed Curlew, Upland Sandpiper, two Lesser Yellowlegs, Solitary Sandpiper, two Grey-tailed Tattlers, three Bonaparte's Gulls, two Slender-billed Gulls, Ivory Gull, two Sooty Terns, Noddy Tern, two Tengmalm's Owls, two Alpine Swifts, Tawny Pipit, two Black-eared Wheatears, White's Thrush, two Aquatic Warblers, Icterine Warbler, two Ruppell's Warblers (on the same day), Yellow-browed Warbler, Lesser Grey Shrike, Slender-billed Nutcracker, three Rose-coloured Starlings, four Two-barred Crossbills, three Pine Grosbeaks and Rustic Bunting.

It would be an unlikely year were it for the whole of Sussex - but for a relatively small area, some 20 miles wide by about 15 deep, it was truly unprecedented. To put it in context, 54 individuals of 31 species which are still considered to be national rarities today were recorded in "the Hastings area" in 1914 (all but two of them being in Sussex). By comparison, in 1987, the best year for rarities in Sussex in recent times, there were only 30 individuals of 18 species in the whole county.

For some years, there had been whispers that all was not well with these records. Some ornithologists were entertaining doubts as to the authenticity of this flood of rarities. For example, Harry Witherby, editor of *British Birds*, was very suspicious of the numbers of rarities claimed in this one area.

The main reasons for the doubts and suspicions were as follows:-

1. The sheer volume of rare birds involved, as in the 1914 example above.
2. The oddities of the patterns; where they were found; the unlikely races involved; the occurrence of sedentary species; the frequency of multiple occurrences, and particularly of pairs of adults (improbable in nature but highly prized in collections!); and the very high proportion of major rarities compared to minor ones.
3. The fact that the records patently were often not very well documented or authenticated, and were very widely suspected in their own day for this reason, together with their sheer improbability.
4. Above all, the fact that when Witherby finally laid down clear rules in 1916 for their authentication, which had been sought and were accepted by those involved, the rules were not followed, and the records dried up.

West Pier, Brighton

Amberley Wild Brooks

Two other points are relevant. The first is that there is no doubt that the matter would have been much more quickly, firmly and satisfactorily settled at the time, had not the First World War seriously disrupted things. Witherby, for example, was a serving naval officer, and at the same time trying to keep *British Birds* going. The second is that where information is recorded, some 80-90% of the records are associated with only eight names (other than the taxidermist), and over 70% with two names, as having examined the specimens and/or written them up in the literature. Yet only one of these eight people actually physically obtained any of them. The extraordinary fact is that during the period, there were no other major rarities for the Hastings area other than the Hastings Rarities series. This means that no other observers visited the area, attracted by the masses of extreme rarities, and recorded any for themselves. This is in an era when ornithologists were just as keen on rare birds as many are today. One might well ask why people weren't tramping the area and joining in (they did elsewhere at the time); and why local ornithologists, apparently interested enough to examine and record the specimens, never actually saw or shot any for themselves. To the modern birdwatcher, this is a primary reason for the series' inherent improbability.

The matter remains contentious because it was based on specimens whose existence is not in doubt; many can still be seen in museums such as the Booth Museum in Brighton. However, the weight of modern ornithological opinion is against them on the grounds of sheer implausibility, rather than from any direct proof of fraud.

In about 1954, two of the editors of *British Birds*, Max Nicholson, then Director General of the Nature Conservancy, and James Ferguson-Lees, began an investigation into the Rarities which was to take them nearly eight years. Eventually, in August 1962, the results of their inquiry were published in *British Birds* (a whole issue was devoted to it) and the unusual step was taken to hold a London Press Conference on the subject.

The *British Birds* report - it was prefaced by an editorial "Setting the record straight" - reached the conclusion that the Hastings Rarities "cannot be regarded as reliable. That being so, it appears plain that the records cannot properly stand".

The authors recommended that a list of species and sub-species, including such birds as the Slender-billed Curlew, Black Lark and Masked Shrike be "struck out". Also that further formidable lists of birds obtained and seen in the Hastings area between 1892 and 1930 be regarded as unacceptable, "subject to reinstatement where a particular case is made out".

There has been no satisfactory evidence produced to explain how the specimens were actually obtained, or from where. In the last resort it is usually assumed that birds were imported by ship from abroad, on ice before being skinned.

Eight years after the *British Birds* revelations, a letter was published in the journal in 1970 from R A H Coombes which provides some circumstantial evidence to support this view. He cites an elderly ship's steward, a Mr Parkman, telling him in 1939 that before the First World War, as a hobby and as a sideline, he had collected birds at ports of call, particularly in the Mediterranean and the Middle East, and brought them back to England in the cold storage of his ships. He said that on arrival at a British port he always handed them over to his brother, who disposed of them "at Hastings", and he mentioned "Bristow, the taxidermist" as the destination for the birds.

The upshot for the Sussex avifauna of the British Birds investigation was the removal of 40 species and a further six sub-species from the county list. 14 of these species have subsequently been added as the result of modern records, although not all these are from the extreme eastern end of the county.

A Guide to the Birds of Sussex

The next major work on Sussex ornithology was under the above title, published in 1963, and bringing the record up to date to the end of 1961. The authors were G des Forges and D D Harber. The Guide summarised the status and distribution of all birds which they admitted to the Sussex list, and also gave information under each species on migration. They delayed publication until after the appearance of the *British Birds* article on the Hastings Rarities, and did not include them in this work.

The authors were well qualified to compile this book. Grahame des Forges had edited *Birds in Sussex*, part of the *South Eastern Bird Report*, in 1947. In that year he wrote that "the assistance of Mr J A Walpole-Bond in reading the draft and criticising it, and Mr D D Harber's help in checking all the material, eliminating errors, and in other ways, is gratefully acknowledged. The final responsibility is, however, mine".

The following year, 1948, saw the first *Sussex Bird Report* appear on its own, edited and published (at his own expense) by des Forges, presented, as he announced in his editorial, "with somewhat mixed feelings".

Grahame des Forges was born in Yorkshire, and his lifelong interest in birds received an early boost in the coastal habitats of Norfolk, where he developed a love of waders and taking photographs of them. A lawyer by profession, he came to Sussex in 1936 when he joined the Legal Department of Brighton Corporation. Over the years he spent a lot of time in the field with Walpole-Bond, acquiring a great deal of information from that outstanding man on the status of breeding birds in Sussex (but having no share in egg-collecting activities!).

He subsequently helped set up the (then) Sussex Naturalists' Trust in 1960 and to become its first Chairman; to assist with the launch of the SOS and later to become its President. He was at one time on the Council of the Royal Society for the Protection of Birds (RSPB), and also a member of the Research Group of the International Waterfowl Research Bureau. His contribution to the development of modern ornithology in Sussex, and its continuation over a very long period, has been immense.

In 1949 Denzil Harber formally joined des Forges as co-editor. In 1956 the former took over as sole editor, and produced six reports up to 1961.

The *Guide* was based largely on the contents of these *Sussex Bird Reports* and it reflects their slant and content. There was an emphasis on rarities and migration, and the *Guide* indicated very well where there were gaps in our knowledge of the county's birds. This was particularly in distribution and numbers of breeding species, on which precious little had been done since the publication of 'Walpole-Bond' in 1938.

D.M. Turner-Ettlinger

John 'Jock' Walpole-Bond, author of A History of Sussex Birds (1938) seen here on the Seven Sisters in 1945. Note the "beloved Walpole walking stick and haversack with climbing ropes".

In the acknowledgements in the *Guide*, the authors recognise their "enormous debt to the late J A Walpole-Bond who not only gathered together most thoroughly all printed records up to 1938 but established very accurately the distribution of breeding birds in the county". They go on to admit that "in fact we are much less well informed on breeding distribution today than in 1938". The period covered by the *Guide*, from 1938 to 1961, marks a distinct period in the county's ornithology, with its emphasis on rare birds and migration studies.

The Sussex Bird Report
During the 1950s the 'Sussex Report', as it was affectionately known by devotees, had earned a reputation as an attractive, professional and respected

One of the first big twitches: October 1960 - Desert Wheatear at Selsey Bill.
Left to Right: Steve Knight, Peter Le Brocq, Roy Sandison, Eddie Wiseman,
John Bowers, John Symons, Dave Billett, (unidentified), Richard Porter,
Ewart Jones, Billy Truckle, Gerald Sutton, Martin Port, Graham Rees.

Selsey Bill 1960 - In search of the Desert Wheatear
Left to Right: Mike Nolan (Beachy Head group), Richard Porter,
Julian Harber, Denzil (DD) Harber.

publication. It appeared promptly every spring, and contributors eagerly awaited its arrival through their letterbox.

From 1950 onwards, as its cover design the report had a distinctive, attractive and appropriate drawing of a Peregrine against a background of the Sussex chalk cliffs by D A J Bunce.

The list of contributors to the Sussex Reports over the years reads rather like a "Who's Who" in British ornithology. Most of the observers were Sussex residents; others but passage migrants. Many of the residents were to make later reputations for themselves in national, and even international, ornithological circles. Over the years and decades, Sussex has produced many such people.

It is worth pausing for a moment to acknowledge this point. We can perhaps illustrate it by looking at the list of 63 contributors to the first *Sussex Bird Report*, for 1948.

In alphabetical order the Class of '48 included L P Alder, an enigmatic figure rarely seen, but widely respected for his identification skills and always producing some of the rarest birds (it is claimed that he taught Harber a lot of what he knew, and showed him his first Red-breasted Merganser); he later left the county to work at Slimbridge for the Wildfowl Trust. Stanley Bayliss Smith, who died in 1995, was Headmaster of Brighton College Junior School, a well-known photographer who worked the Sussex coast and author of two books, *British Waders in their Haunts* (1950) and *Wild Wings to the Northlands* (1970). He was also Editor of the *Sussex Bird Report* from 1969 to 1975.

Jeffery Boswall later worked for the BBC and the RSPB, becoming internationally renowned for his film and sound recording work on birds. Dr W R P (Bill) Bourne needs no introduction to modern ornithologists as a man with definite, and often controversial, opinions which appear in the correspondence columns of the birding journals from time to time. His main preoccupations in later life were to be studying seabirds around the world and baiting the ornithological establishment. E M Cawkell and H A R Cawkell have already been quoted extensively in this chapter; Edwin travelled the world for the Foreign Office, and Harry was a journalist with the Brighton Evening Argus who at weekends migrated eastwards to Dungeness in Kent.

Richard S R Fitter has already been mentioned as the schoolboy at Eastbourne College who saw what may have been an Aquatic Warbler on Pevensey Levels. Later he was to co-write the famous *Collins Field Guide* (or *A Pocket Guide to British Birds* to give it its full title) with Richard Richardson, which appeared in 1952. Twenty years later, with Heinzel and Parslow, he co-wrote the successful *Collins Field Guide to The Birds of Britain and Europe with North Africa and the Middle East* (1972). He is also a notable botanist.

A G Glenister was the author *of The Birds of the Malay Peninsula, Singapore and Penang* (1951). Charles James was a loyal Sussex man, of great experience and knowledge, later to be County Recorder for a period. He now lives at Selsey, where he is still in the field nearly every day, and a strong contender to be the doyen of Sussex bird-watchers.

I J Ferguson-Lees was to become editor of *British Birds*, after being a school teacher living in East Sussex. Howard Medhurst is credited with being co-coiner (with Bob Emmett) of the word 'twitcher'. They travelled to rare bird sightings by motorbike, and often were so frozen on arrival they twitched with cold, as much as with excitement.

And J Walpole-Bond appears on the 1948 list - it was only ten years since *A History of Sussex Birds*, and obviously the records published in the report reflected that.

D D Harber

Denzil Dean Harber's contribution to Sussex ornithology may not have been so profound or of such long duration as that of Grahame des Forges, but it was probably more dramatic and certainly more controversial. As the sole editor of the *Sussex Bird Report* for six years, he acquired a certain reputation as a tyrant who wielded the editorial red pen with obvious relish and great severity. He himself wrote of being "in charge of bird records for the county", and it felt like it.

Nevertheless the Report's reputation was high, as most contributors realised it was better to perhaps exclude a few genuine records than to include any doubtful ones. Harber did have an unerring ability to spot a shaky record or description; for example a phrase would sound familiar and he would find it copied from a book, or he would pick out dates or places which were suspicious or unlikely.

He was simply known to us all as Harber, or better still, 'DDH'. He addressed everyone by their surname, to their face and in correspondence, which at first was rather disconcerting. The relationship between Harber and contributors to his bird report was definitely that of headmaster and pupils - many of them recalcitrant and out of order as he saw it, and needing chastisement and correction.

DDH loved the cut and thrust of argument and controversy, and brought to bear his considerable vocabulary and powers of logic to tilt at anyone he disagreed with. He clearly regarded birdwatching and birdwatchers as a source of great entertainment, and he certainly livened it up. His presence at a 'twitch', as it would now be called, was always welcome, and his outrageous and outspoken comments about other observers were hilarious.

He had organised his life around birdwatching, working as an insurance agent for the early part of each week so that he could watch birds for the remainder. He lived for rare birds, and travelled abroad each year on his motor scooter in search of them.

A unique achievement of Harber's was his review in *British Birds* between May and November 1955 of the six volumes of Dementiev's and Gladkov's *The Birds of the Soviet Union* (1955a). This was an epic task, involving translation from Russian, in which DDH was fluent, and one which he tackled with his customary zest and energy.

In June 1959 Harber had become a founder member of the national Rarities Committee, and in 1963 he took over the onerous duties of Secretary. This suited him exactly, and he devoted a great deal of his time to dealing with all correspondence and records with a promptness that was characteristic. As the result of these duties, he relinquished the post of Recorder for the SOS, which he had accepted on the formation of the Society when it took over publication of the *Sussex Bird Report*.

Until the formation of the SOS, the *Sussex Bird Report* under DDH had appeared in a different bright colour each year. The last one with the Peregrine on the cover under his editorship, in 1961, was black. The significance was not lost on the readership; it marked the end of an era.

D D Harber died on 31 August 1966 in the Westminster Hospital in London after a major cancer operation. He was only 57 and left a distinct void after his death. Very sadly, his wife died about a year after his own death. He was undoubtedly the outstanding post-war character in Sussex ornithology, and granted a few more years, would doubtless have left his mark equally forcefully on national ornithology.

The Sussex Ornithological Society

The SOS was formed in 1962, and was the outcome of a measure of disenchantment and frustration felt by a number of younger ornithologists at the time. In their view the *Sussex Bird Report* focussed too much on rarities and migration records (as already referred to above), and they considered that something had to be done urgently to fill the gaps in our knowledge of breeding birds since Walpole-Bond.

We knew very little about the numbers and distribution of the classic Sussex breeding birds - Hobby, Stone Curlew, Woodlark and Cirl Bunting for example. Probably even less was known about waders in the river valleys, Corn Buntings on the Downs and Nightjars in the woodlands of the Weald.

This may have been the main driving force, but there were other reasons for forming a county ornithological society. There was a general need to bring together all the work being carried out in Sussex; to provide a forum for ideas and their dissemination; to educate through meetings, films and lectures; and to assist other organisations in protection and conservation work.

Under the wise and courteous guidance of Dr John Stafford as President, at the time President of the very active and effective Shoreham Ornithological Society, the SOS got off to a flying start, and has never looked back. Work was immediately put in hand under Michael Shrubb and Dr Michael Hollings to survey a range of breeding species. These two made a very effective team, and were well qualified for the task. Shrubb was a farmer at Sidlesham, near Pagham Harbour, with an excellent knowledge of the county's ornithology and a particular interest in its breeding birds. Dr Hollings was a scientist working on plant viruses at the Glasshouse Crops Research Institute at Rustington, where he became Head of Virus Research. He was able to use his professional expertise and disciplined mind to put a sound scientific base under the early efforts, and made an important but largely unseen contribution to the Society's early reports. Together they developed the process of presenting a wealth of data in the reports concisely and clearly.

The Society arranged proper co-ordination of the organised migration studies already being carried out at Selsey Bill in West Sussex, and Beachy Head in East Sussex. Groups of enthusiasts had been regularly watching both headlands since 1959-60, adding a great deal to our knowledge of the county's birds. Watching at Selsey Bill continues to this day while the Beachy Head Ringing Group has also been in continuous operation for over 30 years, with Robert (Bob) Edgar currently at the helm.

Quick action was also taken to provide much needed protection to threatened sites at each end of the county. The Society produced thorough and well-argued reports that led to the creation of nature reserves at Pagham Harbour in the west in 1964, and at Rye Harbour in the east in 1970. In many ways these still represent two of its most tangible and enduring achievements.

There was a steady development of the *Sussex Bird Report* to reflect the increasing scope of members' activities and observations. Its first editor was Tony Sheldon, one of the Selsey Bill watchers. He was able to use his skills as a chartered secretary in the City to produce a comprehensive and professional document, building upon the solid reputation earned for the report by des Forges and Harber.

The Society has always been fortunate in its officers, members of Council, and numerous volunteers and helpers. The work of a number of these is acknowledged at various points in this chapter, particularly in the final section, but there have been many in the essential but unglamourous jobs who deserve recognition and praise. It is always invidious to name individuals, as you offend those who inevitably are omitted, so let us simply offer our greatest thanks to all who have worked so hard in so many jobs to keep the Society going.

For more information and a comprehensive review of the first 25 years of the Society's life, you are referred to *Birds in Sussex 1962-1987*, edited by Grahame des Forges on behalf of the SOS.

The Birds of Sussex

Before long, the knowledge which was accumulating about breeding birds from the Society's surveys reached the point where Michael Shrubb saw the wisdom of bringing all this together in a further county bird book. Thus it was that in 1979, some 16 years after des Forges and Harber, and 41 years after Walpole-Bond, Shrubb's *The Birds of Sussex* (1979) appeared. His experience as the Society's Recorder for seven years equipped him well for the task.

The previous two works had reflected the main ornithological concern of its generation. Walpole-Bond had concentrated very largely on breeding biology, and des Forges and Harber on migration. Shrubb complemented both these by dealing primarily with populations. This was a subject of much greater concern to his generation of ornithologists than to their predecessors, who lacked the organisation needed to gather the necessary information.

At last there were reliable facts and figures on which to base conservation and scientific work. The book dealt with 343 species, of which 118 bred regularly and 13 sporadically. Particular emphasis was placed on breeding and wintering populations, and much previously unpublished data were summarised and included. Initial chapters on bird habitats in Sussex were written by Robert Edgar, and a final chapter by Shrubb dealt with recent changes in the status of birds in Sussex.

It is a coincidence that this present work is appearing just over 16 years after Shrubb, who was 16 years after des Forges and Harber. But this present volume illustrates how our knowledge of our county's birds has continued to grow, to the point where we now need computers to handle the information, and a larger and larger team of volunteers each year to put together the annual report with its systematic list and supporting papers.

The Modern Era

Much has already been said about the ornithological writers who have produced permanent records of the county's birdlife at critical junctures in its history. The point has been made that the contributors to the early *Sussex Bird Reports* were some of the more knowledgeable and active birdwatchers resident in the county who, in many cases, were to go on to greater achievements on a larger ornithological stage.

In addition to those for whom pen-pictures have been provided already, there are a surprising number of more recent Sussex ornithologists who have followed the same course. It is perhaps fitting to end this account of the history of Sussex ornithology by acknowledging some of their achievements.

John Stafford, the Society's first President, served as a member of Guy Mountfort's expeditions to Bulgaria and Hungary, and had five years on the Council of the RSPB. Others who have served the RSPB in this way include Grahame des Forges (once) and Michael Shrubb (twice).

The British Trust for Ornithology (BTO) has also been well served by Sussex ornithologists. Most notable among these is Dr Barrie Watson who was Vice-President from 1977 to 1980, has acted as the BTO representative for Sussex since 1968 and received the Jubilee Medal for long-term service to the Trust in 1989.

Guy Mountfort himself was the Society's second President, for a period of 12 years. His travels to the four corners of the world, his books and his conservation work for the World Wide Fund for Nature (as it is now known) are all renowned. He was a co-author of the famous "Peterson" *Field Guide to the Birds of Britain and Europe* (1954) which is still very popular today, 40 years on. It has sold over two million copies and been translated into 14 languages - no mean feat for a bird book! We should not forget, however, his classic monograph on the Hawfinch, nor his huge programme of ringing and study of birds on his estate at Possingworth Park in East Sussex.

Stuart Hughes, who died so prematurely in 1993, and who served as Vice-President and twice as Assistant Recorder, organised surveys for the BTO. Among the many scientific papers he wrote, some were published in *British Birds*, but it was his remarkable contribution of no fewer than 26 papers in the county bird report which will be his most enduring legacy. He was also a driving force behind the initial work in producing this book.

Our Recorders have been exemplary. Some of Michael Shrubb's contributions in the county have been mentioned already. On the wider scene, he has been on the BTO Council, and in 1991 was the recipient of their Bernard Tucker Medal for services to the Trust. He has written numerous papers as well as books on *Farming and Birds* (1986) and *The Kestrel* (1993). He has retired to Wales, where he is now the editor of the *Welsh Bird Report*.

Tony Prater was the RSPB's South East Regional Officer from 1979 to 1986 as well as SOS Recorder for three years before moving to Norfolk. His books include *Estuary Birds of Britain and Ireland* (1981), *A Guide to the Identification and Ageing of Holarctic Waders* (1977), and the internationally acclaimed *Shorebirds* (1986).

Richard Porter was a long-term Sussex resident from an early age, and the RSPB's first South East Regional Officer. He was involved in the formation of the SOS, and very active in committee and survey work. He subsequently became the RSPB's Head of Species Protection, and now works for them and for BirdLife International on Middle-Eastern conservation. He spearheaded conservation work in Turkey from the mid-1960s, and started what is now the Ornithological Society of the Middle East. He is co-author of three books - *Flight Identification of European Raptors* (1974), which is now translated into five languages, *Birds of the Middle East and North Africa* (1988), and *Red Data Birds in Britain* (1990).

Michael Rogers was County Recorder for five years from 1978 to 1982, and like his predecessor for seven years, Michael Shrubb, he had the ability to summarise a wealth of data into a readable yet concise format. This skill has assisted him in his subsequent role as Secretary to the national British Birds Rarities Committee, a post he has very ably held since 1977.

Two of the early Selsey Bill watchers were Alan Kitson and Ian Willis. Kitson pioneered ornithological studies in Mongolia in the late 1970s, and Willis's work as a bird illustrator and artist has featured in a range of books from *The Shell Guide to the Birds of Britain and Ireland* (1983) to *Birds of the Middle East and North Africa* (1988).

Lord Chelwood was a Sussex resident who contributed immensely to conservation and bird protection through his work over many years for the RSPB (serving as President from 1967 to 1970 as Colonel Sir Tufton Beamish); as Vice President of the Society for the Promotion of Nature Conservation; and as Vice President of the Nature Conservancy Council. He was about to become President of the SOS when he died on 6 April 1989.

Of more modern vintage is Stephen Rumsey from Icklesham in East Sussex, whose intensive and extensive ringing and migration studies in Senegal in West Africa have put that country firmly on the ornithological map. The same approach has yielded remarkable results from his own farm, converted into a nature reserve and run as a ringing station. In 1990 he and his teams ringed more birds on his farm in one year than apparently any other fixed site in the world. The wealth of recoveries, and the number of rare birds trapped there, have added greatly to our knowledge of both Sussex and British birds.

Several ornithological authors currently reside in Sussex. John Gooders has written numerous books over a number of years, pre-eminent among them being the classics *Where to Watch Birds in Britain* (1967) and *Where to Watch Birds in Europe* (1970). Tim Parmenter wrote *A Guide to the Warblers of the Western Palearctic* (1991), and Jon Curson was the author of *New World Warblers: an Identification Guide* (1994) and co-author of *A Guide to the Buntings and North American Sparrows* (1995).

The Shoreham District Ornithological Society

Brief mention has been made of the Shoreham Ornithological Society, whose first president, John Stafford, also became the first President of the SOS. It is fitting, towards the end of this review, to acknowledge the major part that this small yet influential society played by establishing a local meeting place for keen birdwatchers. At the time this was unique in the county in that it concentrated solely on birds.

Launched in January 1953, the Society provided a focus and a discipline for many enthusiastic birdwatchers. Special mention should be made of Miss Catherine Biggs, founder and first Secretary of the Society, whose leadership and enthusiasm inspired many young people to follow her example as a lifelong birdwatcher. Another key figure was Joseph Twort whose meticulous observations of local birds, immense practical knowledge and kindly patience towards over-enthusiastic youngsters (one in particular) will always be remembered and appreciated. Undoubtedly the county society sprang from this local interest, and indeed, many officers of the county body were recruited from the local one.

In 1981 the Society's name was changed to the Shoreham District Ornithological Society (SDOS), to reflect a wider geographical spread of its membership and activities. It continues to thrive, its success being well documented in an ambitious and notable publication *The Birds of Shoreham* (1988), edited by Dr John Newnham, himself an active and energetic personality on the local and county scene and also Assistant Editor of this book.

What of the future?

In this account I have attempted to set out a history of ornithology in Sussex. It is encouraging to note that bird-watching is now more popular than ever before. The SOS continues to be one of the most successful county ornithological societies but despite much progress there is no room for complacency. Birds and their habitats are threatened as never before. Some species such as the Stone Curlew and Cirl Bunting have already been lost. Others, including even such common species as the Skylark, are declining at an alarming rate. Nevertheless, with continued individual and organisational effort we may be able to reverse recent declines and start to make some gains in the approach to the next millenium.

Postscript

It is fitting to end by recording the achievements of Tony Marr himself. Most notably, Tony provided the inspiration and drive which led to the formation of the SOS in 1962. He was its first Secretary (for nearly ten years) during which time the SOS became a well-established and respected organisation. Tony also produced the reports which persuaded the two County Councils to create the successful Local Nature Reserves (LNRs) at Pagham and Rye Harbours.

A very experienced and enthusiastic field observer, he also contributed much to devising and planning the Society's field studies and to the gathering of data. On the wider scene, he has served twice on the Council of the RSPB and is now a member of the British Ornithologists' Union Records Committee (*BOURC*). *Michael Shrubb*

An Introduction To The Habitats Of Sussex

Chris Corrigan

The main purpose of this book is to provide a detailed account of the status and distribution of the bird species which have been recorded in the county. These first sections attempt to provide the background which is needed to complement the detailed species analyses.

This initial introduction sets out a basic description of the physical characteristics of the county. The geology, landform, climate and influence of people all have profound impacts on the habitat types of Sussex, which in turn determine the distribution of any given species.

The Origins and Foundations of Sussex
1. Geology

The modern geology and landforms of Sussex owe their existence to major earth movements which started at the end of the Cretaceous period and continued into the early Tertiary period, over 25 million years ago (Mortimore 1983). These movements were the ripples caused by tectonic plate collisions in the Mediterranean region which also resulted in the formation of the alpine regions of central Europe (Tubbs 1993). This folding process created the most significant geological feature of Sussex which is the Main Wealden Anticline. This is a dome-shaped feature which extends westwards into Hampshire and Wiltshire, north and east into Surrey and Kent and southeast into northern France.

The axis or 'summit' of this anticline crosses northern Sussex in an east-west direction. For this reason the rocks of Sussex tend to dip to the south. It also explains why the oldest rocks tend to be found in the north of the county with younger rocks outcropping towards the south. The structure of the anticline is summarised in fig. 2. To give some sense of the timescales involved, the oldest rocks now exposed at the surface in Sussex were laid down some 145 million years ago in the late Jurassic period (Mortimore 1983).

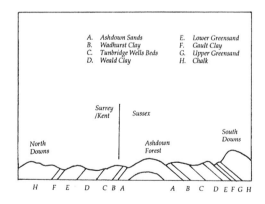

Figure 2. Simplified geology of Sussex

28

When the anticline was originally formed the 'dome' would have been entirely capped by the most recent chalk deposits. However, as shown in fig. 2, during the intervening period the crest has been eroded to reveal the underlying strata which we can see today.

2. Landforms

Sussex can be divided into five main physiographic regions; the High Weald, the Low Weald, the Greensand Ridges and Gault Clay Vale, the South Downs and the Coastal Plain (Williams & Robinson 1983). These are illustrated in fig. 3.

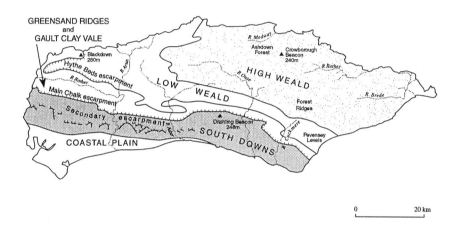

Figure 3. The main physiographic regions of Sussex.

a) The High Weald

The High Weald occupies the northeast part of the county. This area is of considerable landscape value and has been designated as an Area of Outstanding Natural Beauty (AONB).

The underlying rocks include (from upper to lower layers); Tunbridge Wells Sand, Wadhurst Clay and the Ashdown Beds. Taken together these are known as the Hastings Beds and were formed in the Lower Cretaceous period around 125 to 130 million years ago.

The Ashdown Beds have created some of the best scenery in Sussex. This includes the famous Ashdown Forest which reaches an altitude of almost 220 m.

The mixture of clays and sandstones which make up the Hastings Beds have eroded at different rates to form a very dissected landscape. Some of the most characteristic features are the steep sided and well wooded stream valleys called ghylls which are described in more detail in the Woodland section.

29

b) The Low Weald

This is a low-lying band of Weald Clay which runs in a south-easterly direction across the county. The clay is highly impermeable and creates heavy, poorly drained soils with a high level of surface run-off. This is illustrated by the fact that there are 35% more permanent streams on the Weald Clay than there are on the more freely draining Tunbridge Wells Sand of the High Weald (Williams & Robinson 1983).

The traditional Low Weald landscape is one of deciduous woodlands and small pastures. Pevensey Levels is the exception to this where the clay has been covered by deposits of alluvium (Edgar 1979). Although the traditional agricultural use has been grazing, there has been considerable arable conversion in line with recent trends in farming practice. However, yields on these soils are relatively low compared with the better land elsewhere in the county such as the coastal plain. As a result, the arable areas of the Low Weald may be among the first to move out of cereal production in the event of falling prices.

c) The Greensand Ridges and Gault Clay Vale

The Upper Greensand is normally a pale sandstone which occurs in narrow beds up to 1.5 m thick separated by seams of soft silt or marl (Williams & Robinson 1983). This stratum largely underlies the chalk on the scarp slope of the Downs. It forms a terrace or low bench beneath the chalk and above the still lower Gault Clay. This feature is particularly prominent west of the River Arun (Williams & Robinson 1983). The Gault Clay forms a narrow band of lower-lying ground below the chalk escarpment. It produces heavy, poorly drained soils which are difficult to plough. Consequently, the primary land use tends to be a mixture of pasture and woodland.

The Lower Greensand is especially important from an ornithological perspective. It is particularly extensive in the west where it is up to 10 km wide. It produces free draining sandy soils which provide some of the best arable farmland in the county. More significantly, these soils are also suitable for the formation of lowland heathland, one of the most important wildlife habitats in Sussex.

d) The Chalk Downs

Chalk has created some of the most striking landscape features in the county. Indeed the two most famous landmarks are probably the cliffs of the Seven Sisters and the "blunt, bow-headed, whale-backed downs" described by Kipling.

The South Downs cover a distance of 93 km between Beachy Head in the east and the border with Hampshire in the west. They have a maximum width of 9 km and reach a maximum height of 248 m at Ditchling Beacon. The characteristic shape is a steep north-facing scarp slope with a more gentle dip slope to the south.

Although the South Downs form a substantial barrier, four rivers have managed to make deep cuttings through the chalk to reach the sea. Although various theories have been put forward to explain how this could have happened, none have been proven.

The other notable features of the Downs are the coombs or dry valleys. There is some dispute over precisely how these were formed. Williams & Robinson (1983) consider that they must at least have been greatly enlarged and deepened by periglacial erosion caused by meltwater at the end of the last Ice Age. However, the extent of this erosion is subject to considerable disagreement.

Chalk itself is surprisingly resistant to weathering and erosion despite being a relatively soft limestone. It is susceptible to frost weathering but chemical weathering by rainwater would appear to be a more significant factor. The chalk is highly porous and water collects in large underground aquifers. As the rainwater percolates down through the cracks and fissures, it dissolves the chalk (principally calcium carbonate). This process of chemical weathering may have gone on for several million years so the present height of the Downs could be 200 to 300 m less than it was originally (Williams & Robinson 1983).

The ecological value of the South Downs, particularly for plants, is largely the result of the nature and nutrient status of the chalk which is rich in calcium and phosphorus, but poor in potassium and nitrogen. In biological terms, nutrient status and texture are much more important than the age or origin of a deposit (Tubbs 1993). The nature conservation value of chalk grassland is a clear illustration of this principle.

e) The Coastal Plain

The coastal plain occupies the low-lying area in the west of the county between the South Downs and the sea. It is dominated by the Bracklesham Beds, London Clay and Brick Earths (so-called because of their use in brick-making) which produce high quality agricultural land. Much of this area is also built up, but there are still a few remaining woodlands.

In places, sands and gravels overlie the clays. These have been exploited around Chichester forming Chichester Gravel Pits.

3. Climate

Sussex was not covered by ice sheets during the last Ice Age and so was not directly affected by glaciation. However, relicts of this period include the coombs or dry valleys of the South Downs, and the extensive raised beach which forms the coastal plain of West Sussex and southeast Hampshire (Tubbs 1993). These features were formed by erosion from the meltwater which was released as the climate improved.

Fig. 4 illustrates the changes in climate which have taken place since the last glaciation over 10,000 years ago. The climatic optimum from an ecological perspective was the warmer, wetter Atlantic period between 5000 and 7000 years ago. At this time woodland probably reached its maximum extent and would have included the maximum diversity of tree and shrub species (Tubbs 1993).

Climatic changes have continued since the Atlantic period, as indicated in fig. 4. These have been accompanied by various other changes including a general rise in sea-level. The implications of sea-level rise are set out in the Coastal section.

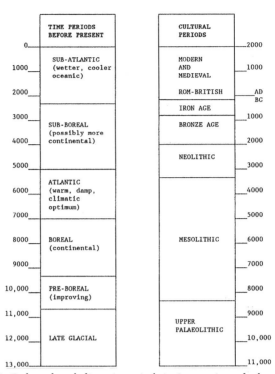

Figure 4. Cultural and climatic periods in Sussex since the last Ice Age.

The climate of Sussex is mainly oceanic in character because it is dominated by westerly airflows. However, being located in southeast England it does have some continental influences. As such, compared with the rest of the country it has warmer summers than most of Britain and a greater temperature range over the year than the west of Britain (Potts & Browne 1983). There is some variation in temperature across the county and the coastal fringe has the mildest winter weather mainly as a result of the moderating influence of the sea. It also tends to have the most sunshine.

Rainfall varies from 70 cm on the Coastal Plain to 100 cm on parts of the South Downs. Rainfall tends to peak in autumn and early winter and is at its lowest in early spring (Potts & Browne 1983).

In ecological terms the inter-relationship between the climate, geology, and the impacts of human occupation have created one of the most interesting counties in Britain (Streeter 1983). The combination of factors listed above has resulted in three main kinds of semi-natural vegetation - woodland; heathland; and chalk scrub and downland. In addition there are the coastal habitats, most notably the intertidal mudflats and saltmarshes, together with the alluvial grazing marshes produced by changing sea levels over the last 1000 years (Streeter 1983).

The individual habitat accounts which follow attempt to build on this background and outline in more detail the origins, importance and threats which are involved in each case.

The Coast

Chris Corrigan

Edgar (1979) estimated that "Sussex has a coastline of 140 km (not including the indentations of the harbours) of which 60% is covered by built-up areas". This picture is still true today and the Sussex coastline remains one of the most built up in the country.

There are four main types of habitat found on the Sussex coast: the intertidal flats and marshes; cliffs; sand dunes and shingle; and the coastal waters themselves.

1. Intertidal Flats and Saltmarshes

These are among the most important habitats in the county for birds. The combination of extensive mudflats and saltmarsh for feeding and roosting, together with the relatively mild winters, make Sussex a favoured location for waders and wildfowl. Chichester and Pagham Harbours are the prime sites and both are internationally important, principally for wintering waders and wildfowl. As such, both have been designated as Special Protection Areas (SPAs) under the European Directive on the Conservation of Wild Birds. In addition, other sites include Littlehampton West Beach, Goring, the Adur Estuary and Rye Bay which includes the stretch of coast between Pett and the Midrips. All these sites (with the exception of Goring) are Sites of Special Scientific Interest (SSSIs) and at times can support nationally important numbers of waders.

Chichester Harbour

Chichester Harbour is easily the largest and most important estuary in Sussex. The Harbour is a large estuarine basin, its complex shape formed by four major arms which were created by land sinking along four small river valleys. The river channels are muddy, whereas the intertidal areas south of Thorney Island consist of sandier sediments (Prater 1981, Cranswick *et al* 1995).

Although the Harbour straddles the county boundary with Hampshire, approximately 70% of the site is in Sussex and, for the purpose of this review, the whole Harbour is considered to be part of Sussex. This is consistent with the approach adopted in the *Sussex Bird Report*.

To illustrate its significance, the Chichester Harbour SSSI covers 3695 ha of which almost 2000 ha are saltmarsh, sandflats and mudflats (Edgar 1979). The remainder of the SSSI includes the open water of the main channel and the associated habitats behind the sea-wall, such as those on Thorney Island.

The primary ornithological value of Chichester Harbour is for migrating and overwintering waders and wildfowl. Typically 55,000 of these birds may be counted in winter. The 5-year mean counts, 1989/90 to 1993/94, are 18,361 wildfowl and 37,144 waders (Cranswick *et al* 1995), making the Harbour the 19th most important estuary in the UK and easily the most important in Sussex.

In general terms the Harbour supports between half (e.g. Ringed Plover) and almost all (e.g. Knot) of the populations of the wader species in the county. In a wider context, the estuary is of national and international importance for a range of wader and wildfowl species. These are listed in table 1.

Internationally Important Numbers	Nationally Important Numbers
Dark-bellied Brent Goose	Little Grebe
Ringed Plover	Shelduck
Grey Plover	Red-breasted Merganser
Dunlin	Sanderling
Bar-tailed Godwit	Black-tailed Godwit
	Redshank

Table 1. Waders and wildfowl present in nationally or internationally important numbers in Chichester Harbour (from Cranswick et al 1995).

For details of the qualifying levels for national and international importance, see Cranswick *et al* (1995).

Of particular significance is the Dark-bellied Brent Goose. In 1979, Edgar estimated that 5% of the world population could be found in Chichester Harbour. Although the Harbour remains an exceptional wintering site for this species, the rate of increase both in Chichester Harbour and Britain as a whole has not matched the increase in the world population (Cranswick *et al* 1995). Consequently, the proportion of the world population which uses the Harbour has declined slightly and is probably now nearer 4%.

Although the wintering and migratory waterfowl are the most significant ornithological feature, the Harbour also supports an interesting and important breeding bird community. The North and South Stake Islands are of particular importance, supporting a colony of more than 1000 pairs of Black-headed Gulls. Common, Sandwich and Little Terns also breed but, in recent years, not in large numbers. Predation, and flooding during particularly high tides, have adversely affected breeding success. Small numbers of Ringed Plovers, Redshanks and Oystercatchers also breed on the saltmarsh and shingle spits.

Around the Harbour are a number of areas which, although behind the sea-wall, are important and integral parts of the site. Thorney Island is one example of such an area. Many of the Brent Geese which use the Harbour feed on the Island's grassland. Thorney Deeps is an important roost site for waders and rapidly increasing numbers of Little Egrets.

This interdependence extends even beyond the areas included within the SSSI. Brent Geese, for example, will also feed on adjacent areas of arable farmland taking advantage of the winter wheat. This is a cause of considerable conflict with the local farming community.

Pagham Harbour

Pagham Harbour is the other important estuarine basin in the county. It is perhaps more accurately described as a tidal inlet rather than an estuary for there is no major river that flows out to sea (Robinson & Williams 1983).

Although it is only approximately one-sixth of the size of Chichester Harbour, it is still an internationally important site. It often supports internationally important numbers of Brent Geese (*ca.* 3000). As with Chichester Harbour, many of these birds feed on the surrounding arable land causing similar conflicts with farmers.

The Harbour was enclosed in 1876 to stop erosion of the cliffs which threatened Pagham Church and provide land for agriculture, but was flooded again by a storm in 1910 (Robinson & Williams 1983).

The central area of the Harbour comprises extensive saltmarsh and tidal mudflats. The SSSI, which covers 616 ha in all, also includes adjoining areas of shingle, open water, reed swamp and lowland wet grassland.

The variety of habitats, its favourable geographical location for migrants and excellent viewing points have made Pagham Harbour one of the most popular and accessible bird-watching sites in the county. Like Chichester Harbour the main interest is wintering waterfowl, but small numbers of birds breed on the saltmarsh. A few pairs of Little Terns also attempt to nest, but these have been unsuccessful in recent years.

Other Sites

There are other areas of habitat of value for birds scattered along the county's coastline. These include Littlehampton West Beach, Goring, the Adur Estuary and Rye Bay. None of these approach either of the Harbours in terms of overall importance. Nevertheless they are an important component in the network of coastal sites used by migrating waders and wildfowl. For example the Adur Estuary has supported nationally important numbers of Ringed Plovers. It also supports upwards of 1500 Dunlin in winter and is a regular resting and feeding site for species such as Knot, Whimbrel and Bar-tailed Godwits on spring and autumn passage. The sandier sediments at Littlehampton West Beach and Goring are favoured by regular flocks of Sanderlings.

Threats

The estuaries of Sussex have not been subject to the direct habitat losses to development which have occurred in estuaries such as the Tees (Fuller 1982). Nevertheless there are great pressures on almost all the sites. This is not surprising given the geographical location in southeast England and proximity to large numbers of people, including relatively short journey times from London.

Chichester Harbour has considerable landscape appeal which is reflected in its designation as an AONB. This is probably one of the factors which has placed it among the most popular sailing locations in the country. The impacts of recreation and other activities such as bait-digging are difficult to quantify. However, the significance of these issues is increasingly being recognised and addressed in estuary management plans.

Sea-level rise

A much more significant issue for the future may be sea-level rise. This is due in part to changing land levels which have followed the disappearance of the huge weight of ice from northern and western parts of Britain after the last glaciation. As a result, land in Scotland and parts of northern England and Wales is rising, while southern England is sinking at 1-2 mm per year (Ministry of Agriculture, Fisheries and Food (MAFF) and the Welsh Office 1993).

As well as changes in land-levels, sea-levels have risen since the Atlantic period, probably due to variations in global temperatures. This has caused, and will continue to cause, the drowning of intertidal areas. One such example was an extensive area off Selsey Bill and the adjoining part of Hampshire which disappeared sometime between the 10th and 14th centuries (Tubbs 1993). Up until recently these losses would have been at least partially offset by an inland migration of intertidal habitats in response to the increasing sea-level. With fixed sea defences along most of the Sussex coast this is no longer possible. This results in 'coastal squeeze' and a net loss of intertidal habitats as they are covered by rising sea-levels and are unable to move inland.

A significant factor in the future will be any further sea-level rises caused by the Greenhouse Effect. Global warming could have a major impact on the climate of Sussex and could significantly add to the problems of 'natural' sea-level rise. Even under existing conditions, the predicted increase in sea-level for southeast England is 6 mm per year (Ministry of Agriculture, Fisheries and Food (MAFF) & the Welsh Office 1993).

At a national level, it has been estimated that over 12,000 ha of intertidal habitats will be lost due to sea-level rise over the next 20 years (Pye & French 1992). A high but unknown proportion of this loss will occur in Sussex. Tubbs (1993) has suggested that by 2030 most of the mudflats in Hampshire outside the sheltered estuaries and harbours will be gone and the areas in the more sheltered sites much reduced. Sussex is suffering equivalent rates of sea-level rise to Hampshire so the impacts are likely to be similar.

2. Sand and Shingle

Shingle

Shingle beaches occupy more of the Sussex coastline than any other habitat. Most are of little ornithological value due to disturbance. The most important area of shingle is found at Rye Harbour LNR, although much has been damaged by gravel extraction. This site has the largest Little Tern colony in Sussex (usually between 35 and 50 pairs). Breeding success is helped by intensive wardening and a series of measures (including electric fencing) to reduce predation. Sandwich Terns breed erratically but Common Terns (typically 45-90 pairs) nest every year. It is also important for its Black-headed Gull colony which held 1050 pairs in 1987 but had declined to only 200 pairs by the early 1990s. There are healthy populations of breeding waders, particularly Ringed Plovers (over 50 pairs). It is now the only site in the county where Wheatears nest regularly (less than ten pairs).

As well as supporting a rich breeding bird community the shingle ridges and pools are important in a wider context. Although smaller and less significant than those at Dungeness, the shingle is an important geomorphological feature in its own right. It is also of botanical interest, supporting rare plants such as least lettuce and sea pea, as well as more typical shingle species such as yellow-horned poppy. Vegetated shingle is a nationally scarce habitat but the coastal shingle in Sussex has lost most of its conservation interest. Sea defence works to protect low-lying land behind the beaches involves re-profiling the beaches using heavy machinery. Apart from any small pockets which can be kept undisturbed, this prevents the establishment of any shingle vegetation.

Human disturbance is also a key factor. A scattering of Ringed Plovers nest along the coast at sites such as Widewater (Lancing Beach) and Brighton Marina. Breeding success, however, is usually very poor. No Little Terns are able to nest on any of the extensive shingle beaches between Pagham Harbour in the west and Rye Harbour in the east. Pagham Harbour includes the other significant shingle feature, but is neither as extensive nor as important as Rye Harbour. Little Terns usually attempt to nest but breeding success is thought to be poor.

Sand Dunes

Sand dunes are very localised in Sussex. The three main sites are East Head at the entrance to Chichester Harbour, and the dune systems at Littlehampton West Beach and Camber. Like the shingle beaches, they tend to be heavily disturbed and of little ornithological significance. The main interest are the flocks of Sanderlings which feed on the sandy foreshore.

3. Cliffs

The Sussex coast has two distinct types of coastal cliffs. There are the 15 km of chalk cliffs between Black Rock, Brighton and Holywell, Eastbourne (which includes the famous landmarks of the Seven Sisters and Beachy Head) and the 8 km of sand and clay cliffs between Hastings and Pett. The chalk cliffs tend to be vertical with little vegetation and relatively few ledges. In contrast, the softer clay and sandstone cliffs are less steep due to the slumping and formation of undercliffs which occurs as the cliffs erode (Edgar 1979). These cliffs are subject to the most rapid rates of retreat (as at Fairlight Country Park, for example).

There has been a dramatic change in breeding seabird communities on the cliffs since the end of the 19th century. Both Razorbills and Guillemots formerly nested on the chalk cliffs, but both are now extinct as breeding species. Razorbills were not recorded breeding at Beachy Head after 1878 at the very latest, Guillemots after 1904. The reasons for the disappearance of auks from the cliffs is not known. It is part of a continuing longer term decline which appears to be affecting the whole Channel coast. The nearest remaining colony of auks is on the south side of the Isle of Wight. This colony is also in decline and only 200 Guillemots were counted in 1992 (Aspinall & Tasker 1992).

Ravens had also disappeared as a breeding species by about 1895, although a single pair nested at Seaford Head and Beachy Head between 1938 and 1945. Persecution is thought to be the cause of this extinction. Peregrines declined as a result of the effects of pesticides in the food chain and failed to nest after 1956. Fortunately Peregrines have returned as part of the national recovery after the use of the most damaging chemicals was banned or restricted.

Although a number of species have been lost, others have colonised the cliffs. Fulmars were seen on the cliffs in East Sussex in 1946 and breeding was first proved in 1976. The population has continued to expand and birds now nest on the sand and clay cliffs east of Hastings as well as on the chalk.

Kittiwakes first nested in 1976 (James 1981). Since then the numbers nesting on the cliffs at Newhaven and Seaford have increased rapidly. Over 1000 pairs now breed. Cormorants have returned as a breeding species on the sand and clay cliffs, having been absent since at least 1938.

Other cliff-nesting species noted by Edgar (1979) include Kestrel, Herring Gull, Stock Dove, Rock Pipit, Jackdaw, Starling and House Sparrow. Irregular breeders include Lesser Black-backed Gull, House Martin and Black Redstart.

Edgar (1979) noted that cliff nesting Kestrels probably declined during the 1940s and certainly did so after 1951. The distribution of Herring Gulls is more confusing. Walpole-Bond (1938) recorded "perhaps as many as 2000 couples" between Seaford and Beachy Head. This had declined to 395 pairs on the whole of the chalk cliffs by 1965. In contrast 371 pairs nested on the Hastings cliffs in 1965 compared with none there in 1935.

Edgar suggests that these population changes may be due to a change in the cliff structure with fewer suitable ledges now available. This may at least partially explain the changes which have occurred in the breeding bird communities on the cliffs. However, other factors must certainly be involved. For example, the national increase in the numbers of Fulmars has been linked to the increased availability of discards from fishing boats.

There is a serious lack of data which might explain the dramatic changes in the breeding seabird populations. This highlights a major gap in our knowledge which must be filled if we are to develop meaningful conservation measures to protect the seabirds of Sussex.

4. Open Sea

The Sussex coast does not support major concentrations of wintering divers, grebes, auks or seaduck. However, the coastal waters are very shallow and Edgar (1979) notes that the 5 fathom line only comes within 1 km of the coast off the chalk cliffs and at Fairlight. This may mean that significant numbers of birds are able to feed undetected out at sea.

Rye Bay appears to be the most significant site and supports nationally important numbers of Red-throated Divers and flocks of up to 2000 Common Scoters in winter. Small numbers of Eider are scattered along the coast and nationally important numbers of Slavonian Grebes occur off Church Norton.

Much larger numbers of divers, geese, ducks, waders, skuas, gulls and terns migrate along the Sussex coast, especially in spring. Numbers can be spectacular given the right weather conditions, including the eagerly awaited passage of Pomarine Skuas in late April and early May. An unknown proportion of these birds will undoubtedly use the coast for resting and feeding.

The conservation issues relating to the open sea are poorly understood. Over-fishing is almost certainly an issue. The use of drift nets may trap and drown birds such as auks. However, there is little evidence to confirm and quantify the scale of the problem. The only visible sign that there may be problems at sea are the all-too-familiar sight of oiled birds. Chronic oil pollution is a particular problem along the Channel coast. However, the significance of this issue in terms of its effect on overall populations is not known.

Wetlands

Chris Corrigan

The freshwater habitats of Sussex can be broadly divided into three categories; the watercourses and associated wet grasslands or grazing marshes of the floodplains and 'levels'; fens (particularly reedbeds); and the standing water of the ponds, reservoirs and gravel pits.

The wet grasslands and fens are classified as 'semi-natural habitats' because they have been heavily modified by management. The still waters are almost entirely artificial and created for water storage, as the by-product of gravel extraction, or as mill ponds, hammer ponds and ornamental lakes.

1. Wet Grasslands

The wet grasslands, or grazing marshes as they are sometimes called, are the wetland habitats associated with river valley floodplains and the 'levels' such as those at Pett and Pevensey.

This habitat can be defined as "periodically inundated pasture or meadow with ditches which maintain the water levels" (The UK Biodiversity Steering Group 1995).

Most of these grasslands are used for grazing stock, although some fields are usually reserved for hay or silage. Periods of shallow winter flooding and damp soil with saturated hollows which remain late into the spring are features which make this habitat so attractive to breeding and wintering birds. Wet grasslands are also extremely important for other forms of wildlife. The ditches are especially important for plants and invertebrates. For example, out of 160 truly aquatic plant species found in Britain, 115 (72%) occur in Sussex (Whitbread & Curson 1992). This habitat is also important for a diverse range of invertebrates, some of which are extremely rare. For example, Pevensey Levels is one of only two sites in Great Britain where the fen raft spider can be found.

Traditional management of wet grasslands involves grazing the fields in the spring once the fields are dry enough to prevent poaching of the ground by stock. Typically, animals may be introduced as late as May. This comparatively late start to grazing is important for waders, such as Lapwings and Redshanks, because earlier grazing reduces the breeding success of the birds due to trampling of the nests and eggs by the animals.

To contain animals within fields, ditch water levels are kept high so that the ditches act as 'wet fences'. In the autumn and winter, as rainfall increases, periods of heavy rain lead to shallow winter flooding creating ideal conditions for wintering wildfowl. Unfortunately, changes in agricultural policy and practice have led to more intensive management with improved drainage and greater use of fertilisers and pesticides. The scale of these changes has had damaging effects on wildlife which will be explored in more detail later in this section.

History of Wet Grasslands

As outlined above, the river valleys and levels of Sussex cannot be regarded as truly 'natural' habitats. Much of the wildlife interest of these areas is dependent upon management which has been practised for many centuries. Pevensey Levels, for example, was created by the enclosure or 'inning' of a large intertidal bay. This reclamation from the sea started in the 8th century, helped by the eastward drift of shingle along the coast (Edgar 1979). Once enclosed, the site gradually changed from saltmarsh to pasture with a field system which was very similar to that which can be found today. The combination of grassland and associated network of ditches to act as 'wet fences' provided an important wildlife resource as well as valuable farmland.

The river valley floodplains such as those of the Adur, Arun and Ouse are natural in origin, but have been heavily modified by management. The rivers would have meandered down the floodplain with occasional changes in the direction of the channels. Meanders can still be seen in the lower Cuckmere Valley but here, as elsewhere in the county, the river has been straightened and canalised to the detriment of both the wildlife and the landscape.

Importance for Birds

Wet grasslands are of most significance for breeding, wintering and migratory waders and wildfowl. Other species include Yellow Wagtails, Reed Buntings and Reed and Sedge Warblers. The loss of wet grassland and the more intensive agricultural management of what remains has reduced dramatically the bird populations of these areas. Nevertheless, significant interest remains. For example a joint RSPB and National Rivers Authority (NRA) survey of the Arun Valley in 1991 estimated that there were 77 pairs of Lapwings, 88 displaying ('drumming' and 'chipping') Snipe and 97 pairs of Redshanks. The resulting total of 262 pairs of breeding waders makes the Arun Valley one of the top ten lowland wet grassland sites for these birds in the UK. Although these figures appear substantial, there have been significant declines in both Lapwings and Yellow Wagtails since at least 1982 (Pilcher 1991). Anecdotal evidence also suggests that breeding waders in parts of the Valley, particularly Amberley Wild Brooks, have continued to decline even since 1991 (T Callaway pers. comm.).

Wet grasslands are also important for wintering birds. The Arun Valley still retains an internationally important population of Bewick's Swans. Substantial wintering wildfowl numbers are also concentrated at sites such as Pulborough Brooks RSPB reserve and Arundel Wildfowl and Wetlands Trust reserve. The value of Pulborough Brooks for birds following improved management is described in more detail in the Conservation section.

Habitat Extent

Sussex remains one of the most important counties in Great Britain for lowland wet grassland. Current estimates suggest that there are approximately

11,400 ha of wet grassland habitat in the county although this probably includes significant areas of improved grassland (Sussex Wildlife Trust 1996).

A precise figure for the extent of the habitat in the UK is not known. The UK Biodiversity Steering Group (1995) estimated that the figure may be 300,000 ha, although only a mere 10,000 ha may be good quality semi-natural habitat supporting a high diversity of native plant species. These figures highlight the declines in habitat quality which are the result largely of improved drainage and more intensive agricultural management. Nevertheless, taking the estimates of 300,000 ha for the UK and 11,400 ha for Sussex, this suggests that the county contains almost 4% of the UK's wet grassland resource.

Trends

Two factors have contributed to the loss of wet grassland in Sussex. One is direct loss of habitat by, for example, conversion to arable farming. The second factor is the reduction in the wildlife value of the remaining grassland by improved drainage and more intensive management. The latter includes earlier grazing in the spring, higher stocking densities, cutting for silage rather than hay and increased use of fertilisers and pesticides. All these factors contribute to the overall decline in habitat quality. Improved drainage resulting from canalisation and the installation of pumps means less frequent winter flooding to attract wintering wildfowl and drier conditions for breeding waders in the spring. Increased dependence on silage rather than hay means that cutting is carried out earlier, often in May, and before most of the breeding wader chicks have had chance to fledge.

Taking first the issue of direct habitat loss, fig. 5 shows the distribution of wet grassland in Sussex in 1813 and 1981 (from Whitbread & Curson 1992). The large scale losses are very clear. Much of this decline is relatively recent. For example, between the 1960s and 1980s, about 10,500 ha of wetland in Sussex (about 66% of the total) was drained (Whitbread & Curson 1992). Much of this land was turned over to intensive arable production, although some also became drier, more intensively managed pasture.

The habitat losses which have occurred in Sussex reflect the national trends. For example, Fuller (1982) recognised that "the wettest of these grasslands are amongst the most rapidly vanishing habitats in Britain". Unfortunately the declines have continued even since Fuller reviewed the status of the habitat in 1982. As an example, in the 1980s, Pevensey Levels was recognised as being internationally important for wintering waterfowl as a candidate SPA under the European Directive on the Conservation of Wild Birds. Surveys of wintering birds by the RSPB and the SOS between 1992 and 1994 revealed that the site no longer supported sufficient numbers of wintering waterfowl to merit international importance, although it still qualifies as a Ramsar site because of the botanical and invertebrate interest in the ditches.

The available evidence suggests that the declines in wet grassland breeding birds have occurred since at least the mid-1960s. For example Shrubb (1968) examined the status and distribution of Redshank (1962-67) and Snipe and Yellow Wagtail (1965-67). He concluded that a comparison with past records

41

indicated an extensive decline of all three species. Not surprisingly, he identified probable causes for the decline as "drainage of wetland pastures and increased human disturbance".

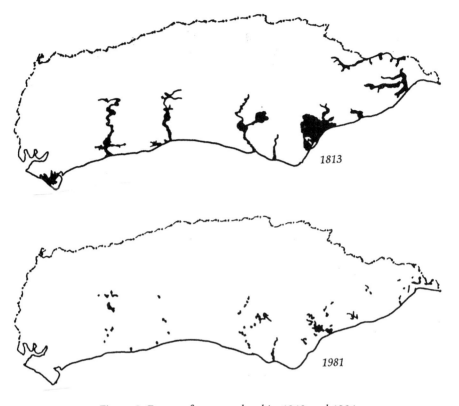

Figure 5. Extent of wet grassland in 1813 and 1981.
(redrawn from Whitbread & Curson 1992).

As indicated earlier, since Shrubb's study in the 1960s, about 66% of the wetlands of Sussex have been drained. These losses continued the trend of improved drainage and more intensive management as part of the drive to produce more food following the Second World War. As a result of this policy, in Sussex the wetlands have probably suffered more damage than any other type of habitat. Consequently a number of the sites examined by Shrubb no longer support breeding waders. For example, the Adur Levels held 3-5 pairs of Snipe and 4-15 pairs of Redshanks. There are no recent records of breeding at this site by either species.

The declines in the breeding and wintering bird populations of Pevensey Levels outlined above are a good example of the problems which have been caused by changes in management. Substantial areas of the levels are now drained by pumps which remove water faster from the system and allow water levels to be kept lower than before. Drier conditions have enabled parts of the site to be converted to arable land which is less suitable for breeding waders. In winter, the introduction of pumps has also meant that the incidence of winter flooding is reduced, to the detriment of the wintering wildfowl populations. These trends have continued right up to the present time.

The declines in breeding and wintering birds populations on Pevensey Levels make depressing reading. Sadly, these trends appear to be typical for all of the Sussex wet grasslands. It is clear that the present agricultural policy framework has not prevented continuing habitat deterioration, even on internationally important sites such as Amberley Wild Brooks. On this site the Government's rejection of a pump drainage scheme following a Public Inquiry in 1978 does not appear to have halted the decline in breeding and wintering bird interest, as described in the Conservation section.

At present, the only success stories appear to be on nature reserves such as the Sussex Wildlife Trust (SWT) Pevensey Levels reserve, the RSPB reserve at Pulborough Brooks and Stephen Rumsey's efforts on Pett Level at Icklesham. These successes show that the historic declines can be reversed. However, at present there is little evidence that such improvements have extended to areas outside nature reserves, which only occupy a tiny proportion of the overall wet grassland resource in Sussex.

To bring about improvements on a wider scale will require changes to current farming practices. This will need positive financial incentives combined with appropriate management prescriptions for environmentally sensitive farming. Some progress has already been made with the South Downs Environmentally Sensitive Area (ESA) (funded by MAFF), the Countryside Stewardship Scheme (Countryside Commission) and the Wildlife Enhancement Scheme for Pevensey Levels (English Nature). All of these schemes are relatively new and it is too early to assess fully their value for birds. However, there is no doubt that they will need to be expanded to bring about significant improvements to bird populations. As outlined in the Farmland section, this will really require a major reform of the Common Agricultural Policy, using the current budget to pay farmers to manage wetlands (and other habitats) for wildlife as well as providing subsidies to produce food.

It is clear that the loss of wet grassland, both in terms of habitat area and quality, has been one of the most damaging changes to affect birds and other wildlife since the Second World War. On the positive side, experience on nature reserves such as Pulborough Brooks has demonstrated the management techniques required to improve conditions. Schemes now exist to support farming practices which will help improve conditions outside nature reserves. Whatever schemes are adopted, one of the priorities for conserving biodiversity in Sussex must be to restore these vital wetland habitats. The deterioration of internationally important sites such as Amberley Wild Brooks and Pevensey Levels must be reversed. Great efforts are needed to ensure that healthy wetlands which are rich in wildlife are secured for future generations.

2. Fens

Fens are the second main wetland type. They cover a range of different habitats which occur in the ecological succession from wet swamp such as reedbeds to fen-carr woodland (Fuller 1982). None of these habitats occurs extensively in Sussex, although small pockets can be found in a number of places.

Reedbeds

Reedbeds are wetlands dominated by common reed with a water table which is at or above ground level for most of the year. They may include areas of open water and ditches, and wet grassland and carr woodland may be associated with them (The UK Biodiversity Steering Group 1995).

Although reedbeds support relatively few breeding bird species, the species that do occur tend to be highly specialised and dependent on the reedbed habitat. The three rare and threatened species characteristic of reedbeds are Bittern, Marsh Harrier and Bearded Tit, although Marsh Harriers also nest in other habitats including farmland. Only small numbers of Bearded Tits nest in Sussex, the other two species being absent. This reflects the lack of extensive areas of reedbed habitat in the county. However, there are large populations of commoner species such as Reed and Sedge Warblers which are able to use less extensive areas of reed, particularly along the edges of ditches and river channels.

At present, the distribution of reedbeds is limited to a small number of sites, the largest being Filsham Reedbed in Combe Haven which covers an area of approximately 13 ha. To put this in context, as a general rule a reedbed should cover at least 20 ha to support a single pair of Bitterns (RSPB 1994). However, Filsham does support important populations of the commoner breeding species such as Water Rail and Reed and Sedge Warblers.

Of perhaps greater conservation significance is the recent evidence which suggests that the Sussex reedbeds may be important migration stops for the globally-threatened Aquatic Warbler. This has been most clearly demonstrated by the Rye Bay Ringing Group at Icklesham where significant numbers of birds have been caught in recent years. The intensive ringing efforts at this site have also demonstrated that large numbers of other species such as Sand Martins, Yellow Wagtails and Sedge Warblers rely on the site for feeding and roosting.

Although Sussex does not have any extensive reedbeds at present, there may be opportunities to change this in the future. Bitterns have a precarious hold in Britain with only 20 booming males in 1995. A major conservation goal for Sussex would be to create a site which is large enough to support breeding Bitterns. This will require the combination of suitable low-lying land, a good clean water supply, a sympathetic landowner and sufficient money to fund the habitat creation. This is a daunting list but, if it can be achieved, the ornithological rewards would be great.

3. Reservoirs, Gravel Pits and Ponds

These habitats are almost all artificial in origin. Nevertheless, many support important numbers of breeding, wintering and passage birds and are among the most popular bird-watching sites in the county. The value of a reservoir or gravel pit for birds is influenced by a number of factors. These can include water depth and nutrient status, as well as external influences such as the level of recreational disturbance.

The reservoirs and gravel pits are relatively recent additions to the Sussex countryside. Most of the reservoirs have been constructed within the last 50 years (table 2). There is no doubt that this has benefited species such as wintering wildfowl and breeding Great Crested Grebes. The latter species has increased as a result of additional habitat creation (e.g. Hughes 1987a) with key sites including Chichester Gravel Pits, Weir Wood Reservoir and Bewl Water. However, the importance of the first site seems to have declined since the 1970s. This may be the result of the changes which occur as a gravel pit matures. This process was studied by Milne (1974) in Huntingdonshire who found that gravel pits had an initial flush of aquatic productivity soon after being completed. However, after this initial period the diversity and density of birds declined.

Site	Year of Construction	Area (ha)	Main Species
Ardingly	1978	70	None
Arlington	1971	63	Mallard (215), Shoveler (75)
Barcombe	1964-66 (extended 1971)	16	None
Bewl Water	1975	312	Wigeon (444), Gadwall (68), Teal (246)
Darwell	1938-40 and 1946-50	69	Mallard (210), Pochard (62)
Powdermill	1924-32	23	Teal (258)
Weir Wood	1954	114	Pochard (76)

Table 2. Sussex reservoirs.

Site	Type of Waterbody	Main Species
Arundel WWT	Nature Reserve	Teal (150), Mallard (958), Pochard (391), Tufted Duck (238)
Chichester	Gravel Pits	Pochard (243), Tufted Duck (267)
Rye Harbour	Gravel Pits	Teal (150), Shoveler (60), Pochard (281), Tufted Duck (160)
Swanbourne Lake	Artificial	Pochard (64), Tufted Duck (243)

Table 3. Major gravel pits and other water bodies.

To give an indication of the importance of each of the sites, the maximum wildfowl counts for 1993 are included in tables 2 and 3 which summarise the background information on each of the main water bodies.

These figures show that the standing waters are especially important for diving ducks, with almost all of the Pochards and Tufted Ducks occurring on these sites. Chichester Gravel Pits, Arundel WWT and Rye Harbour are the most significant sites in this respect. Not surprisingly, the importance of the lakes and gravel pits is less significant for dabbling species such as Wigeon and Teal which also occur on the coast and on wet grassland sites like Amberley Wild Brooks and Pulborough Brooks.

The area of standing water has increased significantly since the 1920s and 1930s. This is due to the expansion of reservoir construction and gravel extraction. Although some of the reservoirs and gravel pits are used for recreational activities such as sailing and fishing, and some of the pits have been filled in for waste disposal, the overall effect has been a net increase in the habitat available for birds.

This rate of habitat creation is likely to slow down dramatically. The reservoir infrastructure is largely in place and, although there have been proposals to expand Darwell Reservoir, there are no major new sites planned. The most likely future development would be the expansion of an existing site to cope with any increases in the demand for water.

Gravel extraction will continue to occur, but this is expected to decline as land-based resources are depleted and alternative sources of aggregates are developed, principally from marine-dredged gravels and 'superquarries' in Scotland and Scandinavia. Indeed current Government policy guidance aims to shift the balance in this direction, hence the recent controversial applications for aggregate dredging off Hastings and Selsey.

A problem for the future will be that as the area of habitat remains fairly static, the pressure on sites will increase as the demand for recreational use increases. In order to maintain the existing wildlife resource, this will require improved management with zoning of areas for different uses and the provision of refuge areas for birds. Apart from this, the open water habitats will probably continue to be one of the least threatened of the Sussex habitats.

Heathland

Ann Griffiths

In the Oxford English Dictionary heath is defined as "open, flat, waste tract of land, often covered with low shrubs - kind of shrub growing on such land". However, to the naturalist it is much more significant than this very basic definition suggests. A more accurate ecological definition of lowland heathland, as used by the UK Biodiversity Steering Group (1995), is a habitat "characterised by the presence of plants such as heather, dwarf gorses and cross-leaved heath and generally found below 300 m in altitude".

Heathland occurs on acid soils. In Sussex the majority of heathland occurs on the soils which overlie the Upper and Lower Greensand and the Ashdown and Tunbridge Wells Sands. In addition, small fragments remain on the acid soils south of the Downs as well as on overlying deposits in patches on the Downs themselves. This produces a unique chalk heath habitat, as at Lullington Heath National Nature Reserve (NNR).

Heathland consists of many plant associations which vary according to topography, drainage, soils and past management. These components include open heath, scrub (such as gorse, birch and willow), woodland (both broadleaved and conifer), wet heath, bog and bare sand. Maintenance of the heathland habitat is a result of management by people over at least the last

7000 years. The resulting habitat mosaic provides the food, shelter and nesting sites for a specialised range of birds including breeding Nightjar, Woodlark, Stonechat and Dartford Warbler as well as wintering Hen Harriers and Great Grey Shrikes (especially on Ashdown Forest).

In order to understand the complexities of heathland, it is necessary to understand both its origins and subsequent management.

Origins

Before human interference, heathland would have occurred in a much more natural state, but probably in smaller, more fragmented and, crucially, more widespread areas than are seen now.

The heathland communities would have occurred within the 'wildwood' which developed following the last Ice Age and on those areas where there was a suitable acid soil. Glades would have occurred in this woodland, probably created by fallen trees, or through the effects of storms, either due to wind-blow (as we saw recently in 1987 and 1990) or by fire from lightning. Subsequent maintenance of the glades by browsing animals would have created the conditions suitable for natural heathland to develop.

However, the extent of these heathland areas is open to some dispute. Tubbs (1993) suggests that the heathland may have been more extensive than previously thought. He argues that the large numbers of open ground birds, mammals, invertebrates and plants could not have survived for thousands of years in such fragmented and transient sites. This suggests that the primeval forest or 'wildwood' may have been less extensive than the pollen records suggest. Whatever their true extent, these openings were likely spots for settlements to start, particularly on the dry areas. We know from archaeological and historical evidence that early people inhabited such areas at least 7000 years ago during the Mesolithic period.

On Iping Common, for example, archaeologists have found the remains of Mesolithic flint working sites. On a nearby site, old soil profiles have been revealed during the excavations of Bronze Age burial mounds dating from approximately 2000 BC. These soils have yielded buried pollen which shows dramatic changes in the vegetation during the Mesolithic period. The pollen records indicate that there was a decline in the amount of woodland cover, which comprised mainly oak, hazel and lime with limited shrubs, to a more open landscape dominated by heathers. It is thought that these large clearings would have been maintained by the grazing of domesticated animals which would have suppressed the regeneration of trees.

The Hand of Man

From the Mesolithic and Neolithic periods onwards, use by people significantly altered the heathlands. There is considerable conjecture as to what exactly happened, but the combination of knowledge from ecologists, soil scientists, historical ecologists and archaeologists enables us to put together a picture of what might have occurred.

As attractive places for settlements, the glades were extended by clearing the adjacent scrub and woodland by cutting and burning. These areas were then used for gathering materials such as bracken. As time moved on and agricultural technology and the domestication of animals advanced, the settlements became more permanent. The open land created from the clearances provided grazing for a range of domesticated animals. Wood, scrub, gorse, heather and heather turves were used for fuel. The bracken and heather would also have been used for bedding and thatch.

Using heathland in this way replicated the natural processes of grazing and poaching by wild animals and damage caused by storms, but on a much larger scale. Exploitation by people created more open and 'maintained' heathland. The management practices became enshrined in common rights for people living either on, or close to, the heathlands.

The long term effect of this management on the land was to change the character of the soils. Under the early natural woodland regime, soils were continually enriched by falling leaves and the return of nutrients through the decay of dead wood and other plant material. On heathlands, which do not have the benefit of extensive tree cover, the return of nutrients to the soil is much reduced. On well drained soils, such as those found on the sandstones, nutrients washed through the soil until the typical 'podsol' of our present heathlands developed. This is characterised by a very thin top soil, a nutrient poor layer and then a rich mineral layer at varying depths below the surface.

The poor soil, often an almost pure white sand, is very quickly exposed when the top humus layer is eroded. The trampling of animals is one example of how this might happen. Compaction of the open sand created by the animals, and the small cliff faces that are exposed through erosion, provides an important habitat for solitary bees, wasps and burrowing beetles. It is also in this exposed sand that the reptiles characteristic of heathland such as adders, smooth snakes and common and sand lizards find the warmth they need to raise their body temperatures.

In places the mineral layer, or 'hard pan', further alters the local drainage, impeding water flow so that, over time, boggy areas develop. Digging turves, combined with the trampling of stock on such sites, produces wet areas that are important for plants including round-leaved sundew, common cotton grass, bog asphodel and marsh gentian.

The leaching of the soil combined with continued grazing of the open heathlands made recolonisation of woodland difficult. Where trees did become established, the poor soils initially only supported species such as birch on the dry areas and willow in the wet hollows.

The woodland from which the heathland was carved was also being changed in other ways. Much was cleared or managed for settlements, agriculture, forestry and industry. Although heathland was one of the first areas to be modified and exploited by people, as the population moved on to other areas, other more versatile land took on a greater importance for agriculture. Heathland became less highly valued, a stigma which still remains today. It became the common land to be shared amongst many, and indeed it had to supply the needs of many. Up until the beginning of the 20th century heathlands were very active and important places with many common rights being exercised.

During the 18th, 19th and early 20th centuries heathland would have been at its most extensive. It was a very disturbed habitat with areas of different aged heath, bare patches, bracken, sand and wet hollows.

Since the early part of this century the area of heathland has been much reduced. This is because in some cases it has now been abandoned; in others it has been taken for development, exploited for minerals, utilised for agriculture or planted for forestry. Heathland was also used for military training purposes during the two world wars, and the evidence of Canadian army trenches can still be found on many of the remaining sites.

In Sussex, many settlements such as Haywards Heath and Midhurst have been built on, or adjacent to, heathland. Mineral resources have also been extracted from heathland sites. Heathlands are found on the acid soils derived from the Greensand of the Folkestone and Hythe beds which are a valuable source of a variety of building materials. Other areas on the lighter soils of the sandstone ridges have been converted to commercial forestry plantations. The large estates such as Leonardslee have been landscaped with exotic plants (including the now extensive rhododendron), many of which were introduced during the Victorian period.

On those heathlands which continue to retain some wildlife value, management which is sympathetic to its survival is no longer part of our rural economy. Such areas have no particular economic use or value, which is a major obstacle to securing their long term survival.

All this has meant that heathland has been reduced in extent, fragmented and is becoming less able to support the wildlife groups that have adapted to it over the 7000 years since people first started to shape this environment. An example in Sussex is provided by the Curlew which no longer breeds on the county's heathlands, probably due to a reduction in habitat area and quality, as well as increased disturbance. The last 150 years have seen a greater change than in any previous period, and our wildlife is struggling to adapt.

The Last 50 Years

Fig. 6 is a dramatic illustration of heathland loss in West Sussex. Similar trends are also apparent in East Sussex and indeed throughout southeast England. Ecologists have particularly noticed the dramatic decline in extent and variety since the 1940s, when an increasing understanding of the habitat losses began to develop.

Pioneer ecologists such as Watt, and more latterly, Gimmingham and Webb, have eloquently described the ecological and man-made processes taking place. In West Sussex, Francis Rose, who has known the heathlands since the late 1940s, has recently described what is happening from a botanical perspective (Rose 1992). The invertebrate ecologists Edwards & Hodge (1993) have come to very similar conclusions. The SOS, through its monitoring work at both county and site level, has also contributed to this understanding. In particular, trends in the populations of Nightjar, Woodlark and Dartford Warbler are indicative of habitat changes. Recent data suggests that during the last ten years both the Woodlark (D Burges *pers. comm.*) and Dartford Warbler (Gibbons & Wotton 1995) have increased in numbers. However, these trends mask the problems facing the heathland habitat as a whole. In the case of the Dartford Warbler, recent increases are due to the run of mild winters, whereas for Woodlark it is due to an increase in the availability of non-heathland habitat (e.g. plantation clearfells). However, increasing heathland management is also starting to have a beneficial effect (D Burges *pers. comm.*).

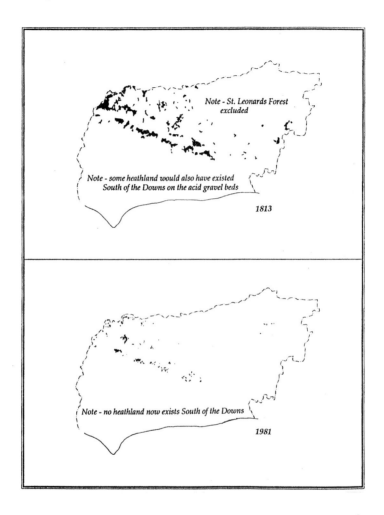

Figure 6. Extent of heathland in West Sussex in 1813 and 1991.
(courtesy of West Sussex County Council)

It is now recognised that current threats to heathland in Sussex relate much more to a lack of appropriate management than the loss of heathland to other land uses. This is neatly illustrated in the Graffham and Lavington areas of West Sussex where rhododendron dominates the roadside landscape on sites previously occupied by open heathland. On Ashdown Forest in East Sussex, birch has taken over as common grazing rights are no longer exercised. Bracken too now dominates, where before it was kept in check by cutting for use as stock bedding. Nevertheless, although lack of management is a major issue, commercial forestry, agricultural improvement, mineral extraction and development have all taken their toll.

Fortunately, greater understanding has slowed the rate of loss of heathland to other land uses. However, habitat change studies by West Sussex County Council (WSCC) have shown that heathland declined from 871 ha 1971 to 671 ha in 1981, with the losses largely accounted for by succession to woodland (WSCC 1993). This represents a loss of more than 20% of the remaining habitat within the space of a single decade. This is an alarming statistic and one which highlights the scale of the problems facing the county's heathlands.

As a result, further protection has been provided as important sites have been recognised and safeguarded from land use change through the planning system. SSSIs have been notified by English Nature and Sites of Nature Conservation Importance (SNCIs) identified by the Local Authorities and the SWT. Most recently Ashdown Forest and Woolmer Forest (a small part of which is in West Sussex) have been recognised as candidate SPAs under the European Birds Directive. The significance of this international designation is described in more detail in the Conservation section.

A few sites are also safeguarded through sympathetic ownership or management. For example, Ashdown Forest is owned by East Sussex County Council (ESCC) and Chailey Common is managed as an LNR by the same authority. In West Sussex, Iping and Stedham Common is partly owned by WSCC and the SWT and managed as an LNR with the Sussex Downs Conservation Board (SDCB). Lavington Common, amongst others, is owned by the National Trust. Ambersham Common is in private ownership but is managed under a Countryside Stewardship Scheme financed by the Countryside Commission, with guidance from English Nature. Hurston Warren, part of the West Sussex Golf Course and an SSSI, is now managed under the English Nature Wildlife Enhancement Scheme. On sites not prot- ected or managed in this way, the biggest threat is still lack of management, which continues to result in losses of this precious habitat.

Heathlands have been heavily used for many years. By chance this has replicated the effect of natural processes. Unfortunately the decline in the need for this use (for example there is no longer any need for heather turves for fuel or bracken for bedding) has meant that generally both the area and quality of heathland is declining. This is largely due to the invasion of species such as rhododendron, Scots pine, bracken (which takes over from heather and grasses in the absence of grazing) and silver birch and willow.

Implications for Wildlife

Without natural processes or management by people, species adapted to the heathland habitat are also declining. These include, for example, the silver-studded blue which is dependent on sheltered patches of young heather and the bare patches of sand favoured by ants (which are needed for the butterfly to complete its life-cycle). Sand lizards and smooth snakes which inhabit south-facing slopes with bare sand have also declined. Dartford Warblers, associated with young gorse bushes on extensive heathland areas, remain scarce despite the recent increases outlined earlier. These changes highlight the serious issues which must be addressed if heathland is to survive in the long term.

Studies of the habitats and species have shown that the lowland heathland of Sussex is of national and international, as well as local, significance. Consequently more effort is being put into heathland conservation than ever before. In other counties, notably Dorset, Suffolk, Hampshire and Surrey, work started in the late 1980s and early 1990s to establish County Heathland Projects. These have been funded by a variety of organisations, including the private sector, the Countryside Commission, English Nature and local authorities. These projects have also benefited from central government schemes such as the Manpower Services Commission. Early efforts were directed towards physical management, but now the work puts greater emphasis on developing sustainable grazing regimes. Areas such as the New Forest and the moorlands of northern England and Scotland are seen as examples to follow. It is already becoming more usual to see grazing animals on the Sussex heathlands, and Ashdown Forest is a pioneering example in this respect.

In Sussex too, opportunities are being taken to improve the conservation status of heathland. The establishment of a Heathland Forum in West Sussex has brought together ecologists, land managers and owners to exchange expertise and knowledge about heathlands. Following a recommendation from the Forum, the newly formed SDCB has now appointed a Heathland Project Officer. With a small budget he is able to initiate projects on the ground and encourage landowners to enter appropriate land management schemes. In addition, the RSPB, WSCC and the SDCB have combined to encourage schools to become involved in monitoring heathlands. The public awareness of the significance of heathland is also raised by media work, local guided walks and open days.

The Future of Heathlands in Sussex

It is widely accepted by ecologists that for heathland conservation to be 'sustainable' there must be a return to more traditional forms of management. The present grant schemes are a welcome step towards that end. However, subsidies are not the complete answer and a more exciting and potentially longer term solution will be the development of markets for heathland products. A very encouraging start has been made by promoting the use of bracken both as a mulch and a peat substitute.

The long term goal is to see our heathlands as extensive breeding and feeding areas for birds and other wildlife. An increase in bird populations would in itself be an indicator of the health of the heathland resource, which is one of the most important ecological components of the biodiversity of Sussex.

Woodland

Tony Whitbread

The 'Wildwood'

There is a strong link between the history of woodlands and their value for wildlife. Although woods appear to be constant elements in an ever-changing landscape, they are continually evolving under the influence of both natural forces and the effects of human management. The result of this is the complex habitat with associated plant and animal communities which we see today.

In the thousand years that followed the last Ice Age, most of Sussex became covered in natural forest, the so-called 'wildwood'. We can only guess at what the landscape looked like at that time but it is unlikely to have consisted of continuous dense tree cover. Perhaps 80% of Sussex might have been wooded, but this would have contained a great diversity of stages of growth and decay. The remaining 20% would have been heathlands, grasslands and marshes, largely kept open by wild herds of grazing animals.

The composition of the forest is likely to have been rather different to what it is today. On the clay lands of the Weald small-leaved lime would have been dominant, with some oak, elm and beech. On the slopes of the South Downs it would have been the large-leaved lime that was most common, while the sandy soils in the centre of Sussex would have supported a heathy forest-type of sessile oak, birch and rowan. Along the now-tamed flood plains and river valleys, long-forgotten woodland types might have occurred. Mixtures of black poplar and willows may have been the dominant trees in a forest that was forever changing as meandering rivers altered course.

Woodland History

Clearance of this 'wildwood' started during the Mesolithic period, perhaps as long ago as 7000 BC. The hunter-gatherers would have cleared fairly small areas, mainly on the heathy soils on the Greensand ridge and around Ashdown Forest, and perhaps also some of the more open woodland on the South Downs. Most openings were probably temporary as these early people moved from place to place, but the large heaths in the High Weald may date from this period.

More extensive felling occurred during the Neolithic, Bronze and Iron Ages. Much of the woodland on the Downs was removed during this period, but clearance of the heavier soils in the Weald was a slower process. Exploitation of the Wealden iron ores started during the Iron Age and this resulted in the management of woodland to provide the charcoal needed for smelting.

The iron and charcoal industry became more intensive during the Roman period. For example, the six Roman iron smelting sites that have been located in the Battle area would have needed the produce from over 9000 ha of woodland. As 36 smelting sites have been found in the Weald as a whole, large areas of woodland must have been under intensive management. A system of coppicing was probably used and sweet chestnut may have been introduced at this time.

After the Romans left Britain there was only limited expansion of secondary woodland. The Saxons continued to cultivate land which had previously been cleared but the iron industry contracted. Woodland management may have changed from coppicing to a more extensive wood pasture system.

In 1086 (Domesday), the Weald may have contained the largest concentration of woodland in England. Other parts of the southeast were less well wooded and in Sussex there was relatively little woodland outside the Weald. At this time, the coastal plain was one of the most intensively cultivated areas in the country.

Although the Wealden soils were heavy and unyielding, clearance continued between Domesday and the Black Death in 1349 in order to provide agricultural land for the growing population. Consequently, management for timber products became more important in the remaining woodlands, with a general reduction in wood pasture. This continuing loss of woodland probably only stopped with the onset of the Black Death.

In the latter part of the 14th century, as the population increased woodlands once again became very valuable as sources of charcoal for iron smelting and glass making. Both industries required a constant supply of coppice underwood. The survival of woodland in Sussex owes much to these industries which would have acquired and managed areas of coppice woodland.

During the 17th century there was a growing interest in forestry and agriculture among the gentry. The greatest expansion of woodland coincided with the decline of downland sheepwalk and heathland. The heathlands and old rabbit warrens at Ashdown Forest and in parts of West Sussex were planted with conifers, and large beech plantations were established on the West Sussex Downs.

Industries using wood products declined during the 19th century. Consequently timber production replaced coppice wood production in importance, and the purchase of woods for amenity and landscape value increased. However, large areas of actively worked coppice have been retained in southeast England. In particular sweet chestnut coppice in East Sussex has remained in production, one of the few areas in Britain where this has happened. In parallel, high forest management which aims to produce large trees has become progressively more important.

The history of woodland management in Sussex explains the present distribution of ancient woodland. The fertile, easily worked land of the coastal plain and river valleys now have little ancient woodland, while the poorer, wetter areas of the Low Weald have retained considerable woodland cover. The Downs and parts of the Greensand ridge and High Weald were also cleared early on, although the regeneration of recent woodland on previously cleared sites (secondary woodland) now complicates the picture for the Greensand and High Weald.

Management has also altered the species composition of the woods. The small-leaved lime of the 'wildwood' has been replaced by species which were preferred for coppicing, such as hornbeam and sweet chestnut. In other places the complex mixtures which might have been found in the 'wildwood', or which resulted from traditional management, have gradually been replaced by more simple stands of beech or conifers following a change to plantation forestry.

Woodland Management

Woodland management has a very long history. Over time three broad categories of traditional woodland management have evolved. These are:

i) Wood pasture

This is a mixture of trees and grazing land. The land is grazed by livestock between trees which are cropped at head height (pollarded) to provide wood for fuel.

ii) Coppice-with-standards

This has two elements. The shrubs are cut at ground level (coppiced) on a short rotation which is usually 7-20 years. The standards, or timber trees, are cut on a longer rotation (usually over 60 years) to provide timber for uses such as house building. The woodlands are usually arranged so that a different section or compartment is cut every year, thereby creating a range of stages of regrowth.

iii) High forest

This is a more recent form of management where the timber trees are favoured. Trees are grown fairly close together and compartments are clear-felled on a rotation of over 70 years for broadleaved trees, less (perhaps 50 years) for conifers.

There is a widespread understanding that sensitive management is good for wildlife. Well designed management will create a great diversity of stages of growth and regrowth throughout a wood. Without this management, a small wood is likely to develop towards a fairly uniform structure, probably a simple layer of canopy trees over fairly poor, overshadowed shrub and ground flora layers. Management creates diversity which can be exploited by many more plants and animals.

But why should this be the case? It implies that nature needs to be carefully controlled in order to stay healthy. How can this be true when in the past ecological processes have always been able to function perfectly well without human intervention? To answer this we need to look back at the likely effect of human intervention on the early 'wildwood'.

There were, arguably, two main elements to human influence on the 'wildwood'. Firstly, the 'wildwood' was fragmented as the early agriculturalists cleared the forest to make way for farmland. Gradually the landscape changed from being a sea of forest with islands of agriculture more towards a sea of agriculture with small pockets of woodland. The second effect was that as woodlands became relatively scarce, their value increased for industry and fuel. Consequently there was a change of emphasis from simple exploitation of the 'wildwood' towards conservation and management of the remaining areas. Thus the 'wildwood' became fragmented as the patches of woodland became increasingly isolated. At the same time these patches were brought into some form of active woodland management.

In practice, the cycle of disturbance due to natural processes on a large scale (such as wind damage and disturbance by large herbivores), was replaced by an imposed cycle of disturbance through management. This produced smaller scale effects in smaller woodland relicts. If a wood is unnaturally restricted by fragmentation and isolation then natural processes are no longer able to maintain the variety which was once present in the 'wildwood'. Consequently an imposed cycle of disturbance is needed to re-establish this variety.

Simple neglect of isolated woods does not result in a natural woodland and is unlikely to produce a rich and diverse habitat. The key to conserving woodland biodiversity is to maintain or mimic the natural processes which give rise to the characteristic habitats and species. This would either involve setting aside large areas of land and allowing a natural cycle of disturbance, or imposing or encouraging disturbance by management.

Woodland Today

Woodland today covers about 16% of Sussex. This is well above the national average, which for England is about 9%. Ancient woodland (that is, woodland sites thought to be over 400 years old) which still consists essentially of native trees which are not obviously planted (i.e. semi-natural) covers about 29,300 ha of Sussex. This is about 6% of the land surface and is significantly higher than the national average which is less than 2%.

The overall woodland area has probably increased over the last few decades - the result of trees and shrubs colonising abandoned grassland, and because of tree planting. However, about 56% of the ancient semi-natural woodland has been lost since the 1920s. Only about 7% has been grubbed out entirely, mainly for agriculture, the rest has been converted to plantations. Though reduced in their species diversity, replanted ancient woods may still retain a high conservation value, particularly if the edges of rides are allowed to develop and the use of herbicides is discontinued.

The data outlining changes in woodland cover are difficult to interpret. The Forestry Commission carried out surveys of different woodland types in 1947, 1965-67 and 1980. Unfortunately different methods were used in each case so direct comparisons are difficult to make. Edgar (1979) attempted to compare the data for 1947 and 1965-67. This comparison contains a number of errors which are linked to the differences in survey methods. A more recent analysis by the Forestry Authority (A Betts *pers. comm.*) has compared the surveys of 1947 and 1980 which used the most comparable methods. Even so, problems still exist. For example, in 1947 all woods over 5 acres (2 ha) were surveyed whereas in 1980 all woods over 0.25 ha were included. There are also slight differences in the definition of each woodland category. The comparative figures are set out below (table 4).

Forest type		Area (ha)	
		1947	1980
High Forest	mainly conifer	4900	15,523
	mainly broadleaved	14,889	29,442
Coppice-with-standards		20,860	2992
Simple coppice		7428	5864
Scrub		3954	7531
Devastated		2783	-
Felled		3351	1216
Total		58,165	62,568

Table 4. Area of different woodland categories in 1947 and 1980.

The table illustrates some of the most significant changes which have taken place. For example, there has been an obvious increase in the area of broadleaved high forest. This is due mainly to conversion from scrub and coppice-with-standards as a result of reduced management, particularly coppicing. Without regular cutting much of the coppice has matured and developed into high forest. The only other major difference is the 'devastated' woodland found in 1947 which was woodland left in a very poor state following the Second World War. Apart from these major differences, detailed trends are difficult to determine because of the problems with the survey methods outlined above.

Types of Woodland

The ancient woodlands of Sussex can be divided into three basic types; those on the clays of the Weald; those on the heathy soils in the central High Weald and along the Greensand ridge; and those of the Downs. In addition there are some fine examples of well-managed planted woods and several very interesting wood-pasture or parkland woods.

Wealden woods

Oak-hazel woodland is the main woodland type of the Weald. Here oak forms a canopy over a coppice layer of hazel and other shrubs. The large Nightingale population in Sussex particularly favours hazel where it is still managed as coppice woodland (Edgar 1979). Uncommon trees such as wild service tree and, very occasionally, small-leaved lime can also be found in these woods. There are, however, several variants of this community which, though they look different, are still essentially the same habitat type.

In many woodlands hornbeam forms a dense shrub layer, particularly on the heavier soils. Often the coppice has been left unmanaged for several decades so the old coppice layer now often merges with the oak canopy layer. Oak-hornbeam woods are an interesting woodland type. They are characteristic of southeast England and there are a number of excellent examples in Sussex.

In the east, especially on the sandier soils, sweet chestnut coppice becomes very common. This is often well-managed with a diverse structure of trees and shrubs at different stages of growth. This creates conditions which are suitable for a wide range of species including breeding Nightjars. During the 1991

57

1991 national Nightjar survey 19 out of a total of 145 territories in Sussex (i.e. 13%) were located in this habitat (Halls 1993).

Wealden woods contain a ground flora which is characteristic of a nutrient poor clay soil. Impressive carpets of bluebells and wood anemones occur alongside colonies of lesser celandine, red campion and greater stitchwort.

Within the Weald are a few 'near-natural' high forests. These have often been left unmanaged for long periods, and prior to neglect they were often well-wooded commons. Consequently they may not have received the same degree of management pressure as other woodland types. Examples are found on the SWT reserves at Ebernoe Common and The Mens. These have a real feeling of the 'wildwood' about them. Even though the species composition may be different to the original 'wildwood', the patchwork of trees and shrubs at various stages of growth and decay is more a function of natural processes than of human management.

Heathy woods

The area around Ashdown Forest in the High Weald and the Greensand ridge in central and west Sussex support a much more heathy woodland type. Sessile oak and birch are the main trees, often forming a varied canopy layer rather than the more regular tree and coppice structure of Wealden woods. Other typical species include alder, alder buckthorn and rowan.

The ground flora is usually dominated by bracken and wavy hair grass and can be quite poor in terms of flowering plants. However, heathers can be fairly abundant in places, adding structure and diversity to the habitat. The more humid sites are characterised by expanses of bilberry with patches of buckler fern, giving the wood the feel of a western oakwood.

The ghyll (or gill) woods of the High Weald are particularly rare and interesting places. These are well-wooded, steep-sided stream valleys, occasionally with sandstone rock outcrops. They are found in unmanaged belts of woodland often hidden amongst larger woods. These provide a stable moist microclimate which favours the growth of various ferns, liverworts and mosses. Some of these are characteristic of an oceanic microclimate more typical of the western seaboard of Britain. In the south east they represent a relict flora from the Atlantic period of over 5000 years ago.

The Woodland Survey carried out between 1963 and 1974 (Edgar 1979) found that these woods support a greater diversity of bird species (although often with lower overall numbers) than any of the other woodlands found in Sussex. In particular the small populations of Redstarts and Wood Warblers are almost entirely dependent on this woodland type.

Woods of the South Downs

In general, most of the downland woods are found west of the River Adur. Woods on the more gentle south-facing slopes of the South Downs often consist largely of oak and hazel with some hornbeam, ash and chestnut, as on the Weald. There are also lime-loving plants such as maple and whitebeam because of the chalk. These woods are sometimes even richer in plant species than those on the Weald. Carpets of bluebells and wood anemones can be very extensive, along with other ancient woodland plants such as butcher's broom, sweet woodruff, nettle-leaved bellflower and wood spurge. The lichens growing on the bark of trees can be very diverse, particularly in more sheltered locations. The moss and liverwort ground flora is often interesting in that the disturbed, more acidic soil surface supports species not normally associated with chalk areas.

In some locations dense yew woods can be found. Many of these have developed in the last few centuries from old chalk grassland or juniper scrub, but some are of considerable antiquity. These yew woods are very uncommon on a European scale, so the examples on the Sussex Downs are worthy of special consideration. The associated flora and fauna is often sparse. The best example of such a yew wood is at Kingley Vale NNR, northwest of Chichester. Here an ancient grove of giant yew trees occupies the floor of a valley, with a more extensive yew wood, probably dating from the 19th century, on the slopes above.

Woods on the steeper north-facing slopes are different to those on the southern slopes. They have generally developed on chalk soils and tend to be particularly favoured by species which prefer lime-rich soils. Although ancient in origin, most of these woods have been heavily managed. They often consist of a mixture of planted beech with naturally regenerated ash, oak, maple, whitebeam, yew and a range of shrubs. The ground flora can be very rich. A carpet of dog's mercury is characteristic, but often mixed with a range of other plants.

The beech plantations do not hold large bird populations. This is at least partly because they lack sufficient old and dead wood to support hole nesting species such as tits and woodpeckers so they tend to be relatively species-poor.

On the steeper more unstable slopes, the predominantly beech-ash woods tend to give way to a mixed woodland where yew is more common. Beech is particularly sensitive to windthrow and disturbance, whereas yew is better able to retain a roothold on the shallow soils, and develops a dense canopy shading out competitors.

Within the last ten years a previously overlooked type of ancient woodland has been identified towards the base of the scarp slope of the Downs. This contains a few individuals of the rare large-leaved lime. This tree never seems to occur in even long-established secondary woods further up the scarp slope, but is always restricted to ancient sites. Furthermore, it occurs as large coppice stools that may be extremely old, mixed with wych elm, maple, hazel and whitebeam.

The woods with large-leaved lime are also interesting in a European context. Some contain southern species such as fly honeysuckle, recalling the limestone woodlands in central France. On the other hand, the damp, moss-rich flora gives the woods a similar character to the large-leaved lime woods of the Derbyshire limestone. Could these woods, therefore, be a 'link' between large-leaved lime woods in central and western Britain and those of the continent? There is no firm evidence to support such a theory, although this may simply be because more research is required.

Wood-pasture

In addition to the ancient woods which have been managed as woodland for centuries, Sussex has some fine examples of wood-pasture. These remain in the Sussex Weald in Mediaeval parks and old Royal Forests. Classic examples are to be found in the parks at Eridge, Heathfield and Parham. The main features of interest are the ancient trees which survive in these areas. These are often far older than trees found in other ancient woods and can be many centuries old. There is evidence that these old parks might originally have been created from areas of original 'wildwood'. Consequently the sites, and particularly their ancient trees, may have direct links with Britain's prehistoric forest.

Old parks and forests are of immense conservation value, and Britain has some of the best examples in Europe. The trees are of value to a range of organisms which rely on old dead wood such as lichens, mosses, fungi and invertebrates. Also, the ancient trees tend to be hollow and misshapen and have many holes and crevices used by bats and birds, a feature often missing in managed woods.

Recent woodland

Though ancient woods are generally of greater value to nature conservation than more recent woods, new sites can add a great deal of ecological value to the landscape.

New woods form by natural regeneration in areas where grazing ceases, or as a result of planting. Where the habitat prior to woodland growth is of high conservation value, the growth of a new wood can be a considerable conservation loss. Examples are old downland or heathland where trees are planted or left to regenerate. However, new woods can be created in a range of situations and may be ecologically beneficial. Although they are unlikely to acquire the same range of organisms as older sites, their structure and location can improve the populations of other species. A particularly important group in this respect are birds. Some appear to prefer ancient woods, but it is the structure of the site due to the layering of vegetation and presence of many micro-habitats which attracts these species. These features are often re-creatable (often by accident) in new woods. Thus species like woodpeckers, Nightingale and a range of warblers may be frequent in ancient woods but could move to new habitat should the appropriate conditions appear. The same process takes a great deal longer (perhaps centuries) with some of the more exacting plants and invertebrates. These processes are clearly illustrated by the changes which have followed the extensive planting of conifers mainly on the lighter soils of former heathland sites and the Downs.

In the early stages of growth, or following clearance and restocking, these sites are important particularly for Nightjars and the increasing population of Woodlarks. For example, the BTO and RSPB Nightjar survey of 1991 found that 39 of the 145 territories (27%) in Sussex were in plantations (Halls 1993).

Other species to benefit include Woodcock, Crossbill, Redpoll and Tree Pipit. Grasshopper Warblers formerly used plantations (Edgar 1979), but the total Sussex population has now dwindled to less than ten pairs.

Conifer plantations can therefore support important populations of a limited number of bird species. However, for the two most important species, Nightjar and Woodlark, it is the structure rather than the type of tree which is the critical factor. Therefore where there are opportunities to re-create heathland from conifer plantations, this is of overall ecological benefit even if it leads to a reduction in the total woodland cover.

The Future

There is no reason why Sussex should not remain a well-wooded county. The need to conserve woodlands for landscape, amenity, economic and nature conservation reasons is widely accepted. However, the proportion of different woodland types will continue to change in response to the economics of different forms of management. For example, at the moment there is little evidence of a recovery in the market for coppice.

If the woodlands of Sussex are to survive as a healthy and productive environment, planning policies and woodland grant schemes must be directed at protecting and enhancing this valuable resource for future generations.

Downland and Scrub

Chris Corrigan

Although these two habitats support very different bird communities, they are closely linked in a wider ecological sense. Open downland is maintained by grazing. If grazing is removed or reduced then the grassland will be invaded by scrub and eventually turn into mature woodland. This provides an excellent demonstration of ecological succession in action.

1. Downland

The grassland of the South Downs is a type of calcareous grassland which has developed on the shallow, lime-rich soils which overlie the chalk. This habitat is particularly renowned for supporting a wealth of rare plants and invertebrates, particularly butterflies.

At present there are an estimated 2650 ha of unimproved chalk grassland on the South Downs in Sussex (SWT 1996). However, the downlands of Sussex, in common with chalk grassland throughout the country, have undergone enormous changes. There are no comprehensive data detailing the rates of habitat loss which have occurred, although it has been estimated that 850 ha or 25% of the chalk grassland in Sussex was lost between 1966 and 1980. Of course, this figure does not provide the full picture because the most significant changes actually took place in the decade following the Second World War (Leverton 1994). For many centuries before this the management of the Downs hardly changed. Leverton identified the 1947 Agriculture Act as a key turning point. This provided "lucrative grants for the ploughing of old grassland, plus high annual acreage payments for growing barley". These incentives precipitated large scale ploughing of the downland. Further losses occurred as a result of a second phase of arable conversion which took place during the 1960s and 1970s caused by a world shortage of grain (Leverton 1994).

The present day image of chalk downland is one of colourful flowers and large populations of butterflies, particularly species such as the Adonis and chalkhill blues. However, such scenes would not have been typical of the traditional sheepwalk described by Hudson (1900) who noted how the River Adur appeared to form the boundary between the "great naked hills" of the east and the "wooded and partially cultivated Downs" of the west. This divide is still apparent today with generally more extensive areas of woodland on the western Downs.

There appear to have been three different types of land use on the Downs in the 19th and early 20th centuries. The bulk of the area would have been the tightly grazed sheepwalk. This would not have supported the rich diversity of plants and insects which we associate with downland today. The conditions of the sheepwalk were probably recreated in an experiment with intensive summer grazing at Castle Hill NNR in 1980. This resulted in a crash in the population of blue butterflies and the elimination of most of the flower spikes of plants such as orchids.

The key factor influencing the bird communities on the sheepwalk was the vegetation structure. Venables (1939) found that Stone Curlews, Lapwings, Woodlarks and Wheatears occurred on the tightly grazed turf. In contrast, Skylarks and Meadow Pipits were associated with areas of longer grass where grazing pressure was less intense or the quality of grazing was poor. The loss of short chalk grassland is probably one of the reasons why Stone Curlews, Woodlarks and Wheatears no longer breed on the Downs. Interestingly, some species disappeared even before the most recent habitat changes. Great Bustards were scarce even when Gilbert White was writing in the 1700s and appear to have become extinct in the 1820s (Walpole-Bond). The Stone Curlew may have become temporarily extinct at the turn of the present century (Hudson 1900), although this is disputed by Walpole-Bond.

As well as the sheepwalk, there may also have been some arable fields on the lower slopes of the Downs (Leverton 1994). Wheat was also periodically grown on the summits and high slopes of the Downs when prices became unusually high (Hudson mentions 1800 and around 1880). This provided areas called 'barrens' where the destruction of the turf as a result of cultivation left a thin eroded soil with exposed flints and little vegetation. These areas, which may have been 10-15 ha in extent, persisted for up to 25 years. These would have formed ideal habitats for the Stone Curlews and Wheatears, which probably used these areas for nesting in preference to the sheepwalk.

The agricultural changes following the Second World War altered the situation dramatically. The problems caused by increased arable farming were exacerbated by the outbreak of myxomatosis in 1954. Grazing rabbits play an important role by preventing scrub seedlings from becoming established and, with reduced rabbit grazing, scrub quickly invaded the open turf.

2. Scrub

Scrub is not a uniform habitat type. It varies according to factors such as species composition, openness and height. In general the older the scrub the taller and less open it becomes (Fuller 1982). The vegetation structure is also affected by external factors such as soil type and degree of exposure.

Leverton (1994) described the different types of scrub which occurs at a number of sites. The simplest type is found, for example, on the downland which includes Castle Hill NNR. It consists of gorse, hawthorn, elder, bramble and wild raspberry.

At the other end of the spectrum, Leverton identified sites such as Ashcombe Bottom. This site contains a much greater variety of scrub species including dogwood, wayfaring tree, spindle, sloe, wild privet, buckthorn and even sallow in the damper hollows. Leverton attributes the greater species diversity at the latter site to the deeper soils and sheltered south-facing dry valley system.

All forms of scrub represent transition habitats between open grassland and mature woodland. Indeed Leverton found oak saplings, ash, silver birch and hazel at Moulsecoomb Wild Park, indicating the onset of woodland development.

Breeding Birds in Scrub

The composition of the bird communities changes as the habitat moves from open grassland to scrub and eventually to woodland.

Both Fuller (1982) and Leverton (1994) describe these changes in more detail. In very general terms, Skylarks and Meadow Pipits dominate the open grassland. As the succession moves through the open canopy scrub stages, species such as Linnet and Yellowhammer take over. As the canopy of the scrub closes, and the ground vegetation is shaded out, then other species such as Song Thrush and Chaffinch move in.

As species composition varies during the successional process, so too does the density and diversity of the bird community. Fuller (1982) found that both the number of species and the number of pairs of birds increased as an area changes from open grassland to closed canopy scrub. However, Leverton (1994) suggests that this increase is likely to be reversed once succession has reached a certain stage (which he describes as "over-mature scrub"). At this point the density and diversity of bird species may decline. This is recognised by Fuller who draws on the work by Williamson & Williamson (1973). This study examined the changes in the bird community at Kingley Vale NNR as the habitat changed from open chalk scrub with yew and oak stands to a mature closed yew wood. In this example, the initial open chalk scrub supported 26 species of bird whereas the mature closed yew wood supported only 20 species.

As in many aspects of ecology, there are no hard and fast rules which determine how a bird community will change at any given site. If the climax woodland is dominated by species such as beech or yew which provide relatively poor habitats for breeding birds, then the final woodland is likely to have a less diverse and smaller overall bird population compared with earlier scrub stages. However, as a general rule, the evidence does suggest that total numbers and diversity of birds will increase as the scrub develops. Where the scrub is most diverse and varied, bird densities can be extremely high. As an example, at Ashcombe Bottom, Leverton found approximately 25 pairs of Lesser Whitethroats and 10-15 pairs of Garden Warblers in 100 ha of scrub, and 10-16 singing male Nightingales in an area of 80 ha.

Scrub contains a high proportion of berry bearing shrubs such as hawthorn, yew and bramble. Williamson (1978) described how this resource was exploited by thrushes at Kingley Vale. Mistle Thrushes were the first species to start feeding on the berries and began to form flocks as early as mid-July. By October these are joined by large flocks of Blackbirds and Song Thrushes, and also Redwings and Fieldfares from the continent.

As well as providing food, scrub also provides safe roost sites for a wide range of species such as Woodpigeons, thrushes, finches and buntings.

Downland scrub can also be a refuge for migrating birds, particularly in autumn when sites such as Cissbury Ring and Beachy Head can support large numbers of Redstarts, Whinchats, warblers and flycatchers, along with more unusual species such as Wrynecks and Firecrests. On the more open fields of the Downs different species can be found including Wheatears and Ring Ouzels as well as more unusual species such as Dotterel, which occur almost annually in the Balsdean area.

Downland and Scrub Conservation

As outlined above, scrub supports an interesting and constantly changing bird community. However, in overall ecological terms, the replacement of chalk grassland by scrub is a negative change (The UK Biodiversity Steering Group 1995). Priority must be given to retaining chalk grassland where it is rich in plants and invertebrates. However, in certain circumstances chalk grassland may not be the optimum habitat. For example, the yew woods of the western Downs are some of the best examples of this habitat in Europe. In other cases such as the north facing slopes which plants and invertebrates find less favourable, then scrub may be a richer and more important habitat.

Maintaining open grassland and restraining the spread of scrub requires intensive management. Grants through the ESA scheme of MAFF are now available to help address these issues. These are discussed further in the Conservation and Farmland sections.

Farmland

Sarah McKenzie

Farmland is a broad term encompassing a mosaic of habitats. As already described, human activity has exerted an increasing influence on the landscape and wildlife of Sussex since Mesolithic times. The change from hunter-gatherers to settled agricultural communities probably began at least 7000 years ago with localised clearance of woodland. Since that time the relationship between humans and the Sussex avifauna has been increasingly interlinked, often with mixed results. Modern agriculture is frequently blamed for the decline in many of our farmland birds, but even in medieval times the need for food resulted in the exploitation of all available land in Sussex (Shrubb 1982). Tittensor (1981) demonstrated that in the Chilgrove Valley

Rye Harbour in early May

Rowlands Wood, a RSPB woodland reserve

north of Chichester, over 50% of a 30 km² site was under arable production in the medieval period.

The essence of good farmland habitat for birds is the mosaic or patchiness that is created. The basic unit of a lowland farming system is the field, which can vary greatly in size and use. Boundaries are equally variable; hedges, woods, treelines, broader woodland strips (or 'shaws' as they are referred to in the Weald), earth banks, ditches, streams, rivers, fences, stone walls or tracks. This multitude of different habitats allows many bird species to occur together and exploit the range of food supplies available. 'Traditional' farming methods contributed to this food supply by following practices which are considered to be inefficient by today's standards.

Lack (1992) identified 55 bird species found on farmland in the breeding season, 12 of which are summer visitors and the remaining 43 resident. Six additional species occur as winter visitors, making a total of 61 species over the year that utilise farmland. Lack is describing the national situation, but it is interesting to note that all the species he identified as being "common birds in British farmland" (tables 5 and 6) are found in Sussex.

Fields	Hedges & other boundaries	Hedges & woods	Woods & scrub	Ponds & streams	Near farm buildings
Lapwing	Kestrel	Wood Pigeon	Pheasant	Mallard	Collard Dove
Skylark	Red-legged	Wren	Stock Dove	Moorhen	Swallow *
Yellow Wagtail *	Partridge	Dunnock	Turtle Dove *	Pied Wagtail	Starling
	Grey Partridge	Robin	Cuckoo *	Sedge Warbler *	House Sparrow
	Little Owl	Blackbird	Green	Reed Bunting	
	Lesser	Song Thrush	Woodpecker		
	Whitethroat *	Mistle Thrush	Great Spotted		
	Goldfinch	Blackcap *	Woodpecker		
	Corn Bunting	Whitethroat *	Garden Warbler *		
		Willow Warbler *	Chiffchaff*		
		Long-tailed Tit	Goldcrest		
		Blue Tit	Spotted		
		Great Tit	Flycatcher *		
		Magpie	Coal Tit		
		Carrion Crow	Treecreeper		
		Tree Sparrow	Jay		
		Chaffinch	Rook		
		Greenfinch	Jackdaw		
		Linnet	Bullfinch		
		Yellowhammer			

* denotes summer visitors

Table 5. The common birds in British farmland (breeding season).
(reproduced from Lack (1992) - Crown Copyright)

Feeding mainly in fields	Feeding in fields and hedges
Golden Plover	Fieldfare
Snipe	Redwing
Black-headed Gull	
Meadow Pipit	

Table 6. The common birds in British farmland (winter).
(reproduced from Lack (1992) - Crown Copyright)

65

These lists are not exhaustive and further species either breed or winter on farmland to a greater or lesser extent. For example, the Meadow Pipit, a greatly under-recorded species, breeds on the South Downs, favouring unimproved permanent pasture. Work done recently by the Game Conservancy Trust (A Wakeham-Dawson *pers.comm.*) has revealed a number of singing males on the Downs above Brighton and Worthing. Reed Warblers often breed in the reeds which grow along ditches and drainage channels in the river valleys such as the Arun, and on Pevensey Levels.

	1939	1957	1963	1967	1979	1983	1987	1993
Cereals	24,644	59,512	58,577	75,335	74,917	76,378	74,496	47,028
Temporary Leys	9,478	50,458	59,990	47,465	37,628	36,748	31,542	23,428
Other crops	20,398	24,985	17,721	15,253	14,987	16,140	19,893	28,342
Total Arable	54,520	134,955	136,288	138,053	127,532	129,266	125,931	99,798
Permanent Pasture	160,304	96,249	96,736	93,817	0*	0	0	0
Rough Grazings	34,113	17,720	11,493	10,556	0	0	0	0
Total Grassland	197,417	113,969	108,229	104,373	89,839	87,697	86,942	98,333
Set-aside								15,668
Total Agricultural Area	251,937	248,924	244,517	242,426	217,371	216,963	212,873	213,799

(Adapted from MAFF June Agricultural Cenus figures)
* Because of changes in the method of collecting data, permanent grassland and rough grazings are not given separately

Table 7. Areas of arable and grassland in Sussex. (Crown Copyright)

Of the total land area in Sussex, about 80% is under agriculture, forestry or other woodland. This clearly has a major influence on the habitats available for birds. The total agricultural area in Sussex remained fairly constant until the late 1960s (table 7) after which there was a 10% decrease, mainly as a result of urban development. The geology of the county influences the distribution of arable crops, with approximately half occurring along the Downs and on the coastal plain. Grassland is distributed in large blocks in the river valleys and on the levels, together with a thin strip running along the scarp slope of the Downs, which has proved too steep to plough. The Weald maintains its more traditional mix of arable and grassland, interspersed with woodland, with a significant area of arable on the Greensand belt in the Low Weald. Overall the distribution reflects the quality of the soils, with grassland predominating on heavier clays and damp low-lying areas, while arable crops prosper on lighter free-draining soils.

A large proportion of the birds listed in tables 5 and 6 are in decline, mainly through changes in habitat. This can be attributed to the intensification of farming practices and changes in the types of crops. The most significant developments over the last 50 years have been increased mechanisation through technical innovation, development of new plant varieties and the use of chemicals.

Table 7 shows the changes in agricultural areas in Sussex since the start of the Second World War. The most obvious and dramatic change is in the balance between arable and grassland, as illustrated in fig. 7. In 1939 there were nearly 200,000 ha of grassland, of which 82% was permanent pasture. In contrast there was only 54,520 ha of arable land at this time. By 1957 the area of arable had increased by nearly 150%, while total grassland decreased by 42% to 113,969 ha. Within this total grassland figure is concealed an even more dramatic decrease, that of rough grazings or unimproved pasture that had virtually halved over the same time period. This is a major factor contributing to the decline in the population of Barn Owls since the 1940s. The decrease in available nesting sites through loss of traditional farm buildings has also been a factor.

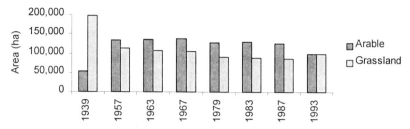

Figure 7. Comparison of areas of arable and grassland in Sussex, 1939 - 93.

The use of chemicals such as organochlorines (especially aldrin and dieldrin) has also had a marked effect on breeding success and survival rate. Since these have been withdrawn from use, there has been a decrease in the levels of residues of these chemicals found in Barn Owl corpses (Newton, Wyllie & Asher 1991). This trend is also well known in raptors such as the Sparrowhawk and Peregrine, although the latter species has made a slower comeback in Sussex than almost anywhere else in England. Modern molluscicides, used extensively to protect certain crops, may be contributing to the decline of Song Thrushes. The livestock anti-worm treatment Ivermectin kills non-target invertebrates in dung, thus depriving a number of insectivorous species such as Lapwings, Golden Plovers, Mistle Thrushes and Blackbirds of a valuable food source.

Since 1939 changes in the ratio of grassland to arable have affected the whole county, but these effects have been particularly marked on the Downs. In a relatively short time large areas of grassland were ploughed up and sown with arable crops. Initially this was to support the war effort then subsequently, with Government encouragement, to increase the amount of home grown food. Such major shifts in agricultural policy have had a considerable impact on the habitat.

Sheep numbers had been declining from 1926. This trend continued until the mid-1950s when the introduction of myxomatosis decimated rabbit populations. This combined reduction in grazing pressure resulted in a marked change in character of the remaining grassland. Coarse grasses dominated and scrub encroachment followed, contributing to the decline of breeding Wheatears and Stone Curlews. These changes are described in more detail in the Downland and Scrub section.

Some species have taken advantage of changing farming practices and, although the Skylark has undergone a marked decline nationally in recent years (New Atlas), it is still commonplace in Sussex. The South Downs is a particular stronghold where it may have taken advantage of the increased number of cereal fields. However, it remains to be seen whether the Skylark's current status and distribution can be sustained in the longer term.

Changes in cropping pattern (from spring sown to predominantly autumn sown cereals) has had a marked effect on winter finch and bunting flocks and has contributed to the extinction of the Cirl Bunting as a breeding bird in Sussex. Changes in farming practice, perhaps coupled with climatic changes and the spread of urban development in former traditional breeding sites, have resulted in the sad disappearance of this colourful species from the county.

Linnet and Corn Bunting numbers have also decreased and large winter flocks of finches and buntings are much reduced. Long-term studies by the Game Conservancy Trust on a 62 km² site in Sussex, attribute the decline of both the Corn Bunting and Grey Partridge to a shift away from traditional ley farming. Ley farming comprises spring cereals and rotational grass. This has been replaced by intensive winter cereal production with limited rotational grass. This change has drastically reduced the food sources for the chicks of both species, mainly sawfly larvae and Lepidopteran caterpillars (Game Conservancy Trust 1995).

Lapwings have also suffered with the switch to autumn sown cereals. Work done by Shrubb & Lack (1991) showed that Lapwings prefer spring sown to autumn sown crops and tend to avoid leys and improved grassland in favour of unimproved pasture. This study, and the work of Galbraith (1988), also revealed additional complexities which may influence the choice of nest sites. The close proximity of spring sown crops to grass fields seems important as the birds prefer to nest in the former but raise chicks in the latter. Thus the most suitable habitat would seem to be a small mosaic of grass and spring sown cereals, but this is now increasingly rare.

Future for Farmland Birds

Shrubb (1982) was rather pessimistic foretelling of "further ecological impoverishment" caused by the use of "increasingly sophisticated herbicides". The net result, he feared, would be greater numbers of a few opportunistic species with a continuing reduction in species diversity. To some extent his fears are well grounded, but there are signs of increasing awareness amongst farmers, land owners and the general public of the consequences of such policies. Public opinion, coupled with market forces, have combined to bring about substantial changes in Government policy, both at national and European level.

A number of support schemes have been introduced which encourage reduced inputs to farming, leading to an easing of pressure on habitats and species. The ESA scheme is one example of such an initiative. Farmers receive payments from MAFF if they follow management regimes considered beneficial to the environment. The South Downs ESA, launched in 1987 covers almost 62,000 ha of downland in Sussex (it extends a little way into Hampshire). Within this area, which includes a number of different land use types, approximately 5720 ha of arable have been reverted to permanent grass and to date, 45 ha are managed as conservation headlands. This scheme, together with the introduction of compulsory set-aside in 1992, has helped redress the balance between the total arable and total grassland areas in the county. By 1993 there were 98,333 ha of grassland, compared with a low of 87,697 ha in 1983 and a post-war high of 113,969 ha in 1957 (table 7). However, it is not yet clear whether these changes have benefited farmland birds.

Other Government schemes such as Countryside Stewardship are encouraging sensitive management of key habitats by providing grant aid for particular work. Although such initiatives influence only a small proportion of agricultural land in Sussex, a process has been started which is gathering momentum and could have significant benefits in the long term.

New developments are also occurring. In 1994 MAFF introduced the Habitat Scheme which "encourages farmers to create, protect or enhance a range of wildlife habitats by managing land in an environmentally beneficial way" (MAFF 1994). The scheme targets former set-aside land, water fringes and saltmarsh, but so far only set-aside has been eligible in Sussex. As the scheme runs for 20 years on set-aside land, there is enormous potential for significant habitat creation and enhancement. It is early days as yet but the uptake to date in Sussex is just over 300 ha (out of a national total of approximately 4000 ha). Market forces will be the deciding factor in most cases, but the increased cost of agricultural chemicals, plus a greater understanding of the consequences of their use has meant that attitudes in the farming community are changing. The Sussex farmland avifauna is still under enormous pressure and such schemes only tackle a small part of the problem. However, there may be grounds for a little cautious optimism.

The Urban Environment

Chris Corrigan

Archaeological evidence suggests that people have lived in Sussex for over 500,000 years (WSCC 1993). This represents the earliest part of the Old Stone (Palaeolithic) Age, a warm period before the last Ice Age. Although no human remains have ever been found, the discovery of large flint tools at Eartham Quarry in West Sussex suggests that these first people were hunter-gatherers.

The onset of the last Ice Age forced the inhabitants to move further south and it was not until conditions improved, perhaps 7000-9000 years ago, that people returned to live in Sussex. Since then, the urban fabric of Sussex has steadily developed, with particularly rapid changes this century.

These changes have lead to an ever expanding urban area which has resulted in considerable losses of ecologically important habitats such as woodland, wetlands and unimproved grasslands. Thus the main significance of the urban environment is the habitat loss associated with its expansion rather than any intrinsic nature conservation value of its own.

Population Trends

Although Sussex is still very much a rural county, there has been a dramatic expansion of the towns, villages and associated infrastructure, notably roads, over the last 150 years. The current population estimate, based on the 1991 census, is 1,378,000 (Office of Population Censuses and Surveys 1992, 1993). This means that the population is now two and a half times greater than it was in 1891 when only 547,600 people lived in the county.

The population trends are illustrated in fig. 8. This shows the different growth rates in the two halves of the county, with the West Sussex population increasing at a much greater rate. This is largely attributable to growth after the Second World War, much of which has occurred in and around Crawley. As a result, the population of West Sussex has increased by more than 80% since 1951 (WSCC 1993).

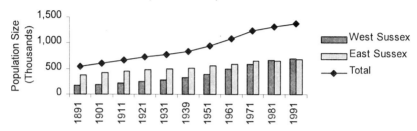

Figure 8. Population trends in East and West Sussex, 1891 - 1991.
(Crown Copyright)

Added to the problem of population growth is the trend towards smaller household sizes. Various factors contribute to this such as increasing divorce rates, people living longer and young people setting up home earlier in their lives, but the significance for the environment is the resulting increased demand for housing. Projections by the Department of the Environment indicate that these trends will continue with, for example, a rapid increase in the number of one person households. Therefore house building is likely to remain the biggest consumer of land and stimulate many of the demands for other development.

Settlement Pattern

As most people live in urban areas the predominantly rural character of the county has been maintained. In East Sussex for example, over 85% of the population live in towns of over 5000 people.

The urban areas of Sussex are largely concentrated in the densely populated coastal strip. There are few gaps between Bognor Regis in the west and Seaford in the east. Other coastal development is centred around Eastbourne and Hastings and Bexhill. Many of these larger towns developed as seaside resorts, although Shoreham-by-Sea has been a port since Roman times. Further inland are other towns such as Haywards Heath and Burgess Hill which expanded with the opening of the Brighton to London railway line in 1841. More recently Crawley has grown as one of the post-war new towns located close to Gatwick Airport (WSCC 1993).

Ornithological Importance

Unlike most semi-natural habitats, the urban environment is not under threat. Indeed, its continued expansion is one of the major causes of damage to some of the most important sites, species and habitats in Sussex.

Urban areas are relatively species poor. The birds which are found there tend to be the most adaptable and successful and not of high conservation priority. Nevertheless, for birds, living in an urban area can offer a number of advantages. First of all the buildings themselves can provide ideal nest sites. For some species such as Swifts, House Martins and House Sparrows, most of the Sussex population nests in or on buildings. Towns and villages can offer some shelter from the elements so some species, notably Starlings, will come into towns to roost, often even in town centres such as Brighton. Finally, garden birds such as Blue Tits and Greenfinches and less familiar species such as Siskin and wintering Blackcaps have learned to take advantage of the food put out for them in winter. Other species, including Herring Gull and Feral Pigeon, have taken advantage of waste and refuse.

Although overall urban habitats are not significant for birds, there are two notable exceptions in Sussex. The first is the small population of breeding and wintering Black Redstarts. Although breeding is not recorded every year, Sussex was the first county in Britain to record breeding in 1923 (Batten *et al* 1990). With a national population estimated at between 80 and 120 pairs (New Atlas), Sussex remains a significant county for the species in Britain. This is perhaps not surprising in view of the proximity of Sussex to the continent. The combination of location and the relatively mild winters also explains why there are small but significant numbers of wintering Black Redstarts.

Of greater conservation significance is the large population of breeding Herring Gulls in the coastal towns. Breeding in Hastings and St Leonards was first noted in the 1950s and reached Brighton and Hove and Worthing in the 1970s. This increase contrasts with a national decline of almost 50% between 1969 and 1987. No accurate population estimate is available for Sussex, but there is little doubt that the urban breeding population is now of national significance, particularly in the context of an overall national population decline.

Other typical urban species are of less conservation importance. Nevertheless it is worth pointing out that both the Starling and House Sparrow have undergone significant national declines during the last 20-30 years (New Atlas). There is no reason to doubt that similar trends have not occurred in Sussex. The reasons for these declines are not entirely clear, although changes in agricultural practices may be playing a part as with other more typical farmland species such as the Skylark. Further research is still needed to clarify this issue.

In the future the main conservation challenge relating to the urban environment will be to check its current rate of expansion. This is essential to prevent further losses of important woodlands, wetlands and heathlands to still more roads, houses and other development. There is no doubt that the rates of urban expansion since the Second World War cannot continue without major impacts on the environment.

Conservation

Robert D M Edgar

History

The SOS became involved in conservation from its inception in 1962. Early action involved the preparation of a joint report with the Sussex Naturalist's Trust (now the SWT), detailing the scientific importance of Pagham Harbour. This was instrumental in leading to the declaration (in 1964) of an LNR, the first in Sussex and one of the earliest in Britain. A less successful campaign in the previous year involved an attempt to prevent a yacht marina being built at Manhood End, near Chichester, then an important site for feeding and roosting waders. This area, Chichester Marina, now accommodates 1300 boats. These are early examples of co-operative conservation efforts, although individuals were involved in bird conservation in the county much earlier. Indeed, Sussex has a long and distinguished history of involvement in the nature conservation movement.

The pioneering work of E C Arnold, who was headmaster of Eastbourne College, has been outlined in the first chapter of this book. Arnold in his book *Bird Reserves* (1940) wrote that people should follow his example and purchase land for "preserving bird haunts". He records that his friends thought little of his idea of spending £100 on acquiring a small pond and adjacent land in about 1911 in Eastbourne (now surrounded by buildings and part scheduled for development). He wrote "I was scoffed at by all my friends when I effected this purchase". However, through judicious management, he achieved his aim of attracting breeding Marsh Warblers. He also recorded small crakes in four years at his pond. (Arnold was certain these were Little or Baillon's Crakes but did not believe they could be distinguished other than in the hand). He acquired land at three other sites in the county; 12 ha of woodland at Polegate; 1.6 ha at Rockhouse Fen, Pevensey Levels and 36 ha of pasture with some bog at 'West Dene Brooklands' (part of which is now known as Charleston Reedbed) in the Cuckmere Valley. The last two reserves still exist, the former within the Pevensey Levels NNR and the latter now owned by Eastbourne College and managed by the SOS. Sadly his name and efforts are now largely forgotten in Sussex. Despite his concern for both birds and their habitats he clearly supported bird trapping "as it may quite well bring interest and happiness into an otherwise sordid home"!

Although concern for the Sussex landscape has a long history (the Society of Sussex Downsmen, was founded in 1926), organised involvement in nature conservation in the county stems from the early 1960s. The SWT, which now has 9500 members, was founded in 1961, the year before the SOS.

The Nature Conservancy (now called English Nature), the Government's adviser on nature conservation, was active even earlier and established the first NNR in the county in 1952, at Kingley Vale north of Chichester. This reserve, one of the earliest in Britain, was established to conserve the finest yew woods in Europe (and is now a well known site for Golden Pheasants). Here, and at Lullington Heath NNR declared in 1954, two of the longest running Common Birds Census plots have been monitored, commencing in 1963 and 1964 respectively. Some of the results of these appear in Bowley (1994), Williamson & Williamson (1973) and Williamson (1978).

The RSPB opened a southeast England regional office in Portslade in 1974, before moving to Shoreham-by-Sea. By March 1994 it had a membership of approximately 31,000 in Sussex (comprising 28,000 full members and 3000 members of the Young Ornithologist's Club) which illustrates the strength of feeling in the county for birds in particular and wildlife in general.

Site Protection

A large area of land in Sussex has been designated for its special significance to wildlife. The county is fortunate to have a series of wildlife habitats which are of international importance. The most important for birds have been classified (or formally proposed) as Special Protection Areas (SPAs) under the European Directive on the Conservation of Wild Birds. These are Chichester Harbour, Pagham Harbour, Ashdown Forest and Dungeness (Kent) to Pett Levels.

Wetlands of international importance are also listed under the Ramsar convention. In Sussex, formally listed sites include Chichester and Pagham Harbours while Dungeness to Pett Levels, Pevensey Levels and Amberley Wild Brooks are potential Ramsar sites.

There are also five candidate Special Areas for Conservation (SAC) sites in the county, designated under the European Habitats Directive. Three are of special interest for birds; Ebernoe Common, The Mens and Kingley Vale. There are two more possible sites, both of which include large areas of Sussex. These are the Solent and the Isle of Wight (which includes Chichester Harbour) and Dungeness (which includes Rye Harbour).

All of the above sites (except the marine areas of some SACs) have already been notified as SSSIs under the Wildlife and Countryside Act 1981, of which there are 131 covering approximately 23,000 ha or 6% of the county. At least 50 of these (and the majority in area) have special value for birds and include all the major coastal and freshwater wetlands and heathlands.

A non-statutory designation, introduced by the local authorities is the Site of Nature Conservation Interest (SNCI) which is of significance in a county context. There are 220 in West Sussex, covering approximately 8000 ha. East Sussex is in the process of surveying and identifying sites.

Despite this apparent plethora of designations in the countryside, they do not ensure complete protection against threats of development from housing, roads or inappropriate management (either too much or too little being equally damaging). A 'cause celebre' was Amberley Wild Brooks, a lowland wet grassland SSSI well known for its breeding waders and wintering wildfowl. It was threatened by a pump drainage scheme proposed by the Southern Water Authority in 1978. This aroused intense opposition. Consequently MAFF, to whom an application for grant aid had been made, held a public inquiry, the first one ever for a drainage scheme. Evidence was presented by all the major conservation bodies with the result that the Secretary of State did not approve the grant and the scheme was abandoned. He did, however, recommend that "minor improvements to the drainage" be made. It is now clear that these improvements have lessened the value of the area for breeding and wintering waterfowl by reducing both ditch water levels and the frequency of winter flooding. Important discussions are currently taking place between the NRA (now the Environment Agency), the conservation bodies and the agricultural community to develop a management scheme which will restore the importance of the Wild Brooks for birds.

Nature Reserves and Management

The direct management of sites by conservation organisations is the most effective but also the most expensive way of achieving habitat conservation. Unfortunately, for very mobile species such as birds, this has particular problems as only parts of their life cycle may be spent at these sites.

There are five NNRs covering 363 ha in Sussex. Three of these are of interest for birds (Pevensey Levels, Lullington Heath and Kingley Vale). The first is a lowland wet grassland site, the second consists of downland scrub and chalk heath (an exceedingly rare vegetation type), and the third is a mosaic of yew woodland and chalk downland.

As mentioned earlier, the SOS played an important role in the establishment of Pagham Harbour as the first LNR in Sussex. There are now 26 LNRs in the county, totalling some 2500 ha. Important bird habitats include heathland (Iping and Chailey Commons and Old Lodge at Nutley); reservoirs and large lakes (Burton Mill Pond, Arlington and Weir Wood Reservoirs); wetlands (Filsham Reedbed) and coastal sites (Nutbourne Marshes, Pilsey Island, Pagham and Rye Harbours).

The voluntary conservation bodies manage many sites within the county, some of international importance. The SWT has 37 reserves totalling over 1000 ha, of which at least 15 are of special bird interest (including reserves at Amberley Wild Brooks, Bewl Water, Filsham Reedbed, Stedham Common and Waltham Brooks). The SOS has assisted in the purchase of a number of prime bird habitats by the SWT, most notably at Pevensey Levels, Ferry Field at Sidlesham (part of Pagham Harbour LNR) and Castle Water at Rye Harbour (now also an LNR).

The RSPB has four reserves in Sussex covering 335 ha. These are the Adur Estuary (intertidal mudflats and saltmarsh), Fore Wood (ancient semi-natural woodland), Pilsey Island (a shingle island and saltmarsh within Chichester Harbour) and Pulborough Brooks (lowland wet grassland). This latter reserve covers 171 ha and is a good example of what can be achieved by intensive habitat management. Since acquiring the site in 1989, the RSPB has been progressively restoring the hydrological regime on 121 ha of floodplain and reintroduced low intensity grazing and mowing. The carefully controlled water levels have had a dramatic effect on breeding wader and waterfowl numbers (fig. 9). Teal, Shoveler and Garganey have all become established as breeding species as a result of reserve management. Up to 80 ha are flooded in winter and in January 1995 there were 24,500 waterfowl on the reserve, which exceeds the figure needed for a site to be internationally important. A number of species, including Wigeon, Teal and Pintail now occur in even larger numbers than before drainage works were undertaken in the Arun Valley in the 1960s.

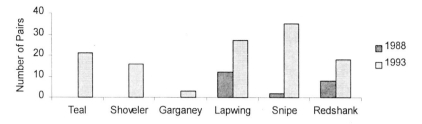

Figure 9. Numbers of breeding ducks and waders at Pulborough Brooks RSPB nature reserve before (1988) and after (1993) the retention of high ditch levels and construction of permanent pools.

(Reproduced from Self et al 1994)

This reserve is extremely popular with visitors and 85,000 were attracted in the reserve's first full year after its official opening in 1993.

Other reserves of voluntary bodies include one of the largest inland reedbeds in Sussex at Arundel WWT. Together with the holdings of the Woodland Trust and various smaller charities, this makes for a sizeable area of land under direct conservation management.

The pioneering spirit of E C Arnold lives on through other individual efforts to manage land specifically as bird reserves. These are mostly carried out on a modest scale, but one of the more imaginative initiatives is that of Stephen Rumsey. On his farm at Icklesham he has progressively converted 20 ha into open water, reedbed and sallow scrub habitats since the mid 1980s.

Outside nature reserves, a large area of Sussex is managed with nature conservation as one of the objectives, alongside other management aims. A good example is the South Downs ESA (designated in 1987) as well as some sizeable areas of local authority public amenity land.

The SOS is also involved in conservation management work in the field. Through the Conservation Field Officer and work parties, up to 450 man days of labour are completed per year at more than 25 sites of importance to birds (A Griffiths *pers. comm.*). Particularly notable is the management of one of the gravel pits at Chichester with its tern rafts, where the colony of Common Terns reached 18 pairs in 1993. Another success story is the lowering of water levels by pumping out one of the coastal pools at Pett Level to provide exposed mud. This has taken place each autumn since 1976, much to the delight of both passage waders and bird-watchers.

Surveys

The conservation of birds and their habitats must be based on sound science. It is here that perhaps the Society's greatest contribution to conservation lies. The prodigious, well managed and easily accessed database, compiled from the reports of members and the regular and wide ranging species and site surveys, is a powerful tool in the conservation of Sussex wildlife.

The Society commenced co-ordinated wader counts within the western Harbours and along the Sussex coastline in 1964, five years before the pilot survey of the national Birds of Estuaries Enquiry (now part of the Wetland Birds Survey or WeBS). Other national surveys in which the Society has participated have included the Breeding and Wintering Bird Atlases, surveys such as Breeding Waders of Wet Meadows (1982 and 1989), birds of Winter Farmland Hedgerows (1988-89), the Common Birds Census and numerous national single species and species group surveys. Of at least equal importance have been the countywide surveys, too numerous to list in detail. The Cirl Bunting (1972-73) and Stone Curlew (1962-64) surveys are particularly poignant since both species are now extinct as breeding species in Sussex. Unless there is a marked improvement in the status of the Grasshopper Warbler, the surveys of 1977-80 and 1995 may also chart the decline of a species to extinction.

Among the most useful surveys from a nature conservation point of view have been those of wetland birds. These include the surveys of birds of lowland wet grasslands (e.g. Redshank, Snipe and Yellow Wagtail, with five surveys between 1962 and 1989) and the particularly comprehensive survey of Reed and Sedge Warblers (1986-87). This work has revealed the importance of the Sussex river valleys and coastal grazing marshes in a national context.

However, species surveys can only provide a limited amount of information about individual sites, and it is often at the site level that local conservation battles are fought. Here the advantages of a computerised database have become clearly evident. In addition, to increase our knowledge of little frequented sites, the SOS has organised the Margaret Millner Memorial Award. This is funded by Margaret's family in memory of her enthusiastic support for bird conservation. The Award is given for reports which further our knowledge of sites, so aiding their protection.

Species Priorities

No species can exist in isolation. There is no doubt that the conservation of habitats is the most effective way of protecting species. The very mobility of birds makes their conservation particularly difficult, especially in the case of long distance migrants. However, there are particular species or groups of species that require special attention. Those of highest priority are the 117 Red Data Birds (Batten *et al* 1990). The complex qualification criteria for the Red Data list relate to the international significance of our populations, scarcity, vulnerability and/or declines in recent times. Sussex supports a number of these species for at least part of their life-cycles. No less than 48 Red Data Birds that breed or winter regularly in the county (table 8) have been identified by English Nature as 'High Priority' (Brown & Grice 1993). The Lapwing is included as an additional species in the table as recent evidence of population declines has shown it to be eligible.

The majority of the 48 species for which Sussex is particularly important are wetland species. The Red Data list is currently being revised and declining species of agricultural habitats are likely to become an increasing priority in the future.

Red-throated Diver	Oystercatcher
Black-throated Diver	Ringed Plover
Great Northern Diver	Golden Plover
Black-necked Grebe	Grey Plover
Gannet	Lapwing
Bewick's Swan	Knot
Dark-bellied Brent Goose	Sanderling
Shelduck	Dunlin
Wigeon	Ruff
Gadwall	Black-tailed Godwit
Teal	Bar-tailed Godwit
Pintail	Curlew
Garganey	Redshank
Shoveler	Turnstone
Pochard	Sandwich Tern
Scaup	Little Tern
Long-tailed Duck	Guillemot
Common Scoter	Razorbill
Velvet Scoter	Barn Owl
Hen Harrier	Nightjar
Goshawk	Woodlark
Merlin	Cetti's Warbler
Peregrine	Dartford Warbler
Quail	Bearded Tit
Grey Partridge	

Table 8. 'High Priority' British species that breed or winter regularly in Sussex.

(Adapted from Brown & Grice 1993)

English Nature has examined the conservation status of all our birds in their international context (Brown & Grice 1993). A number of bird species occur in Britain at or near the normal northern or southern edge of their western Palaearctic range. Those that occur regularly in Sussex are listed in table 9.

Breeding Range		Wintering Range	
Northern Edge	Southern Edge	Northern Edge	Southern Edge
Kingfisher	Fulmar	Black-necked Grebe	Long-tailed Duck
Cetti's Warbler	Kittiwake	Little Egret	Glaucous Gull
Dartford Warbler		Green Sandpiper	
Nightingale		Ruff	
Bearded Tit		Black-tailed Godwit	
		Mediterranean Gull	
		Kingfisher	
		Cetti's Warbler	
		Blackcap	
		Dartford Warbler	
		Firecrest	
		Black Redstart	
		Bearded Tit	

Table 9. Species at or near the edge of their range in the Western Palaearctic which breed or winter regularly in Sussex.

(Adapted from Brown & Grice 1993)

Most of these species are wintering birds at the northern edge of their range, a reflection of our very mild winters. Species at or near the edge of their range can be of particular conservation significance as indicators of environmental change.

Britain supports a number of species in internationally important numbers and those occurring in the county are listed in table 10.

Breeding	Wintering	
Peregrine	Red-throated Diver	Ringed Plover
Sandwich Tern	Black-throated Diver	Golden Plover
Little Tern	Great Northern Diver	Grey Plover
	Bewick's Swan	Lapwing
	Dark-bellied Brent Goose	Knot
	Shelduck	Sanderling
	Wigeon	Dunlin
	Gadwall	Bar-tailed Godwit
	Teal	Curlew
	Pintail	Redshank
	Pochard	Turnstone
	Oystercatcher	

Table 10. Species with internationally important populations in Britain which occur regularly in Sussex.

(Adapted from Brown & Grice 1993)

There is a preponderance of wetland wintering species which highlights the importance of our freshwater and estuarine habitats. A number of species breeding in this country are rare (less than 300 pairs), occur at only a few sites, or have shown marked declines (50% or more) over the last 25 years. Sussex has an important part to play in maintaining the populations of a number of these vulnerable species which are listed in table 11.

Rare	Local	Declining
Garganey	Sandwich Tern	Grey Partridge
Pochard	Little Tern	Lapwing
Goshawk	Dartford Warbler*	
Quail	Bearded Tit	
Woodlark		
Black Redstart		
Cetti's Warbler		
Dartford Warbler *		

* qualifies in two categories

Table 11. Rare, local or declining breeding birds of Britain that breed regularly in Sussex.

(Adapted from Brown & Grice 1993)

The fortunes of various species are described throughout the pages of this book. There have been both gains and losses, the latter mainly amongst the more specialised species. Some, such as the Great Bustard and Great Auk (fossil remains of the latter have been found near Chichester), will never return. Sadly, persecution (both direct and indirect) is still a significant factor, mainly as far as raptors are concerned. Three Red Kites have been found poisoned (two in 1979, one in 1980) and there are regular reports of Buzzards being shot. Indeed it seems likely that persecution must be the only reason for the latter species not becoming widely re-established when there appears to be so much ideal habitat. On the other hand, the Peregrine has now returned to Sussex (one of the last areas in the country where this has happened) and there is no reason why some other species should not do the same.

Habitat Priorities

Despite having a rapidly increasing human population and one of the most built-up coastlines in Europe, Sussex is mainly a rural county with some prime bird habitats. The preceding habitat accounts have highlighted a number of the most significant threats, including:

- the loss and fragmentation of lowland heathland to development, afforestation and lack of management.

- increased recreational disturbance of intertidal areas and the ongoing and future losses due to sea-level rise as a result of fixed sea-defence lines.
- the loss of wetlands due to improved drainage.

- the declines in farmland birds linked to agricultural intensification, particularly since the Second World War.

These represent the key issues and challenges for the future. Such a catalogue of problems presents a bleak picture of bird habitats in Sussex. Nevertheless many important sites and habitats remain. The sites which are left must be protected but conservation efforts must extend beyond protection and address the issue of site enhancement and creation.

The Future

What of the future? What is our ornithological vision for Sussex in the next century? Targets for conservation are being developed by the conservation bodies but the problems facing certain species lie outside the county. At present there is nothing to indicate that the numbers of summer visitors such as Turtle Doves, Sand Martins, Redstarts, Grasshopper Warblers and Spotted Flycatchers will not continue to decline. However much we conserve their breeding habitats, these birds also depend on conditions in their wintering areas and the countries through which they migrate.

Other species such as the Black Grouse, a breeding bird in the 18th century, will surely never return. On the other hand the Peregrine and Cormorant are now re-established. The latter has also increased greatly inland as a non-breeder, causing considerable conflict with fishermen. Further changes can be expected. For example, the Little Egret could well become a breeding bird in the county, something which could not have been contemplated only a few years ago.

The agricultural system is now less sympathetic to breeding and wintering birds. Programmes such as Set-aside, Countryside Stewardship and ESAs may help to redress the balance. The Song Thrush is showing a significant decline, perhaps at least partly due to chemicals in gardens, places that have been seen as great havens for wildlife. We have lost some important areas through development pressure including the wetlands of Newhaven Tide Mills and the Crumbles (the latter to another yacht marina) and the road building programme has sliced through many other areas of the county. On the other hand there is now more land in direct conservation management than ever before. It seems possible that specialised species inhabiting wetlands and heathlands may have a better short-term future than those birds which have been generally regarded as 'common' and inhabit the wider countryside.

People are showing much greater concern for their environment and its wildlife. The conservation societies have managed to maintain an increasing membership through a difficult financial period and people are visiting the countryside more often. Nationally more than 70% of households own a motor-car and in West Sussex the figure is over 75%. As a consequence there has been a 54% increase in traffic between 1980 and 1993. At least 45% of all journeys are made for leisure purposes and 70% of the English population visited the countryside at least once in 1990. Although welcome, this level of interest associated with increased leisure time inevitably brings its own pressures. A more subtle consequence is that people tend to expect the landscape to conform to their preconceived ideas. This may not necessarily equate to what is best for wildlife. As an example, the commonly held perception of a properly managed downland landscape consists of unlimited species-rich chalk grassland with clouds of blue butterflies. As already described, this situation probably only existed for a short time and it is not particularly good for birds. Areas of young scrub for nesting, food and shelter (especially for migrants) along with autumn stubbles can support both a greater number of birds and a greater diversity of species (Leverton 1994, Shrubb 1982).

Increased access to the countryside can also lead to much greater general disturbance. It is unlikely that the more sensitive species that require large undisturbed territories such as the Montagu's Harrier, Stone Curlew and Curlew could breed again, except possibly in very small numbers. There is thus a serious dilemma between public aspirations and wildlife conservation. This is nowhere clearer than at large water bodies where there is pressure for water sports on the one hand and bird conservation on the other.

Local ornithology has an important part to play in nature conservation in Sussex and the SOS has demonstrated this through its survey programme and database, its grant aid to nature reserve purchase and its respected profile in the conservation movement.

Balsdean, near Rottingdean

The South Downs above Brighton

Systematic List of the Birds of Sussex

Introduction

The following species accounts have been written by a large team of 37 authors with inevitable variations in style and presentation. Every attempt has been made to ensure that they provide a concise, yet accurate, picture of the occurrence of each species in the county. While endeavouring to maintain each author's individual style, it has been necessary to alter and edit some accounts to ensure a reasonable degree of uniformity. Each author has been duly acknowledged at the end of each species account; in a few instances the final version has resulted from the joint efforts of more than one author.

The main sources of information have been the *Sussex Bird Report*, published annually by the Sussex Ornithological Society since 1962, and the previous county avifaunas (detailed below). For a number of species, particularly the scarcer ones, the archived files held by the Society have been researched and, as a result, several previously unpublished records are included in the text. Other sources of information include the results of the Sussex Tetrad Atlas, a wide variety of species and habitat surveys, censuses of breeding birds in defined areas and the monthly wildfowl and wader counts. A variety of other ornithological activities have affected the availability of data for this publication, some of which are considered in more detail later in the chapter.

The accounts review the status of each species in Sussex, but also put these in a wider context, both nationally and by comparison with neighbouring counties. Statements made in the text are either supported by individual records or by analysis of the records available. For each breeding species, the text includes an estimate of the county population based either on actual surveys of that species or by combining the results of the Tetrad Atlas Survey with Common Bird Censuses and other surveys of breeding birds in defined areas.

Area & period covered

Under local government reorganisation in 1974, the former county of Sussex was divided into the two counties of East Sussex and West Sussex. There were few border changes compared with those in some other counties, with West Sussex gaining a portion of south Surrey together with part of the former administrative area of East Sussex. A small area of East Sussex was lost to Kent. Records included in this publication are either for the former county of Sussex (pre-1974) or for the modern counties of East Sussex and West Sussex. The estuary counts for Chichester Harbour cover the whole area which includes a small part of Hampshire. The localities mentioned in the text are as precise as possible, especially for rare and scarce species. Where the location is obscure, it has been supplemented with the name of the nearest town or well known locality (e.g. Shooter's Bottom, Beachy Head). Where a locality mentioned in the text has not been identified as being in East or West Sussex the grid reference, which is given in the Gazetteer on pages 563-570, will confirm the location. The texts for species which are fairly common to abundant in the county include records up to the end of 1993, whereas those for rare and scarce species cover the period up until the end of 1994. Although this publication concentrates on the period since the formation of the Sussex Ornithological Society in 1962, historical information is included for some species.

Explanation of Status Terms

Preceding each species account, there is a brief description of its status in the county. The terms and numerical ranges used are the same as those in Clark & Eyre (1993) except for the addition of a "very rare" category and the use of "fairly common" and "very common" rather than "moderately common" and "numerous":

	Breeding pairs	Winter / Passage
Very rare		1-10 records in total
Rare	less than annual	less than annual
Very scarce	1-10 per year	1-20 per year
Scarce	11-100	21-200
Fairly common	101-1000	201-2000
Common	1001-5000	2001-10,000
Very common	5001-30,000	10,001-60,000
Abundant	30,000+	60,000+

The definitions for rare, very scarce and scarce are intended to be average figures for the 33-year period from 1962 to 1994. Puffin, for example, is defined as very scarce as about 59 were recorded between 1962 and 1994 whereas Long-tailed Skua is defined as rare as just 11 were recorded in the same period. The headings in the left hand column of the table are linked in the text to terms such as vagrant, passage migrant, partial migrant, winter visitor and summer visitor, as appropriate. The following definitions are taken from Campbell & Lack (1985):

Vagrant: A wanderer outside the normal migration range of the species or sub-species.

Partial Migrant: Term applied to a species in which, in a given breeding area, some individuals are migratory while others are not, e.g. Song Thrush.

Passage Migrant: Term applied to birds that pass through an area on migration without remaining throughout either the summer or the winter.

Visitor: Present in an area only at certain times of the year, being applied to a species, subspecies, population or individual bird as the context requires. Thus there are 'summer visitors', 'winter visitors', 'visitors on migration' and 'occasional visitors'; but these terms indicate merely local status and are meaningless except in relation to a stated area, a summer visitor in one place being necessarily a winter visitor somewhere else.

Resident: Remaining throughout the year in the area under reference, the term being applied to a species, subspecies, population or individual bird as the context requires.

Records of Rare and Scarce Species

des Forges & Harber's *A Guide to the Birds of Sussex* (1963) is the standard reference for records of rare and scarce species in Sussex prior to 1962. More recent records are to be found in the *Sussex Bird Report* (1962-94) while rarities are also listed in the annual *British Birds* Rarities Reports. For the most recent complete listing of all the species recorded in the county, and its derivation, see Fairbank (1990, 1991a & 1992).

des Forges & Harber did not list individual records for the rare species which had occurred in the county on more than ten occasions up to 1961. Unfortunately, Harber's working papers detailing the records that were included in *A Guide to the Birds of Sussex* were not left in the Sussex Ornithological Society's files and were lost following his death (G des Forges *pers. comm.*). Individual records have been extracted from Walpole-Bond's *History of Sussex Birds* (1938), the *South Eastern Bird Report* (1939-47) and from the *Sussex Bird Report* (1948-61) in an attempted reconciliation with the summaries in des Forges & Harber. Some of the early published records were, however, not acceptable to, and subsequently omitted by, des Forges & Harber as part of their comprehensive review of all county records. As a result, it has not been possible to determine, for some species, exactly which records were excluded or whether any additional records were found. Reference is made in the relevant species accounts to untraced records.

While des Forges & Harber's review of records was very wide ranging, a few records that were acceptable to them seem decidedly suspect now (e.g. those of Ivory Gulls). These have been included, with caveats where deemed appropriate. The *British Birds Rarities Committee* is currently in the process of reviewing a number of 'contentious' records of post-1958 rarities, details of which can be found in the relevant species accounts. All but one of the eight records for which this review has been completed are now considered to be inadequately documented.

Records have been extensively researched where it was felt insufficient detail had been published in des Forges & Harber or the *Sussex Bird Report*, e.g. the age or sex of a bird, precise location, duration of stay and direction of flight. This has involved examination of the original record submissions that remain in the Society's files and correspondence with the Secretary of the *British Birds Rarities Committee* and individual observers. In addition, visits were made to the Bognor Local History Museum (only to discover that the specimens lodged there had been 'lost' some 15 years ago) and to the Booth Museum of Natural History in Brighton, where reference was made to the collection's database. Other sources of information included Arnold's *Birds of Eastbourne* (1936) and Walpole-Bond (1938), as well as the monthly journals *British Birds* and the more recent *Birding World* (both of which contain some excellent photographs of Sussex rarities).

All accepted records up to the end of 1994 have been included in the text and also two records of very rare vagrants for 1995.

The species accounts generally fall into three sections. The first is a summary of records up to the end of 1961, although greater detail is given in relation to some old records where it is felt warranted. The main body of each species account is either a detailed list or an analysis of records for the period

1962-94, which is followed by a brief summary of the species' British status and world distribution, in an attempt to put the Sussex records in context. Species for which all the county records are no longer considered acceptable or are most likely to be of captive origin are included in the main body of the text but with appropriate caveats. Least Tern, potentially a first for the Western Palearctic and currently undergoing assessment by the *British Ornithologists' Union Records Committee (BOURC)*, is also included in the main text. *Richard Fairbank*

Nomenclature and Sequence

The English names, scientific names and sequence used follow the *British Birds' List of Birds of the Western Palearctic* (1984). All species that have occurred in Sussex in a wild or feral state, including those which have recently been deleted from the county list after review, are included in the systematic list. Details of Category D species and other escapes and exotics recorded in the county are given in appendix one.

Tables and Figures

The histograms, all produced using Microsoft Excel software, are mainly used to depict the patterns of occurrence of scarcer species. In most cases, they show the total number of birds recorded annually in the period from 1962 to 1994 or in each winter from 1961/62 to 1993/94. Some histograms are also included which show the total number of birds recorded by month or 10-day period, while others show the 'rate' of coastal passage, i.e. the total number of individuals recorded divided by the number of hours of observation.

The text is liberally augmented with tables to show the results of analysis more clearly. All the tables are referred to in the text and, in general, only the larger tables, mainly involving wader and wildfowl counts, have been numbered. For many species, the text includes a table of the cumulative monthly totals. Unless otherwise stated, birds are included for all the months they were present, not just the month in which they arrived.

For those species monitored by the Birds of Estuaries Enquiry (BoEE) and the National Wildfowl Counts, the available counts are tabulated in two ways. Firstly the counts for the 25 winters from 1969/70 to 1993/94 are divided into five periods covering five winters each, i.e. 1969/70 to 1973/74, 1974/75 to 1978/79 etc. For each of these periods, the mean of the maximum count recorded in each winter is shown together with the peak count made during the 25 years. Secondly the monthly maximum and minimum counts together with the mean count for the 20 year period 1974/75 to 1993/94 is presented; these data represent a summation of all the counts in each month in Sussex. Examples of these tables, with accompanying notes, are shown below.

	69-74[1]	74-79	79-84	84-89	89-94	Peak counts	
Pevensey Levels	800*[2]	2483**[3]	1306	913*	190**	5300, Feb.1977	
Pett Level	[4]	420	575	81	44	1000, Dec.1978	

	Sep	Oct	Nov	Dec	Jan	Feb	Mar
Maximum[5]	766	1449	3781	4133	3651	5823	2701
Mean[6]	202	409	1163	1587	1757	1507	710
Minimum[7]	1	1	37	188	5	26	0

Notes:

1   This shows the five winters covered, i.e. 1969/70-73/74.
2   * Mean derived from counts for three or four winters, not five.
3   ** Mean derived from counts for one or two winters only, not five.
4   No counts available
5   Maximum county total in each month.
6   Mean county total in each month.
7   Minimum county total in each month.

General records and contributors

In compiling the Systematic List, extensive use has been made of the records submitted to the Sussex Ornithological Society. For a number of species, these have indicated that there has been a change in status in the period under review. Often this can be attributed to increased observer coverage. However, despite the huge growth in the popularity of birdwatching over the last 20 years, the number of contributors to the *Sussex Bird Report* has remained remarkably constant over the same period.

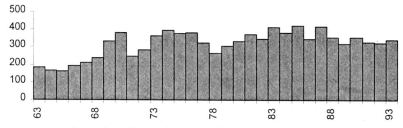

Annual number of contributors to the Sussex Bird Report, 1963-93

More important to the production of an avifauna is a balanced spread of records. The following map plots, by tetrad, the distribution of over 90,000 computerised general records for the period 1976-93.

The map shows the expected bias to coastal areas, the Downs, the river valleys, the commons in West Sussex and Ashdown Forest. Conversely there are large areas of the county, particularly in the Weald, which are poorly represented and there remain 11 tetrads for which there are no records.

Society Surveys

The species accounts include, where available, the results of relevant surveys that have been carried out in the county, details of which are given in the following tables:

Annual counts:
- Heronries
- National Wildfowl Counts
- Birds of Estuaries Enquiry

General surveys:

Survey of Sussex Woodland Birds	1963-67 (SOS)
Sussex/Hampshire migration watches	1963-64
The Atlas of Breeding Birds in Britain and Ireland	1968-72 (BTO)
The Atlas of Wintering Birds in Britain and Ireland	1981-84 (BTO)
Farmland: Winter Hedgerow Survey	1988-89 (BTO)
The New Atlas of Breeding Birds in Britain and Ireland	1988-91 (BTO)
The Sussex Tetrad Atlas	1988-92 (SOS)

Species Surveys:

Species	Type	Year(s)	Species	Type	Year(s)
Little Grebe	B	1985	Black-headed Gull	B	1973 (BTO)
Great Crested Grebe	B	1962-64	Tawny Owl	C	1989 (BTO)
	B	1975 (BTO)	Nightjar	B	1967-69
	B	1985		B	1977
Cormorant	R	1985 (BTO)		B	1981 & 1991-92
Wildfowl	B	1983			(BTO/RSPB)
	C	1984	Sand Martin	B	1985-86
Mute Swan	B	1978/83/90	Yellow Wagtail	B	1965-66
	B	1983 (BTO/WWT)		B	1980-81
	C	1990	Grey Wagtail	B	1993-94
Canada Goose	C	1991-92 (WWT)	Nightingale	B	1974-76
Greylag Goose	C	1991-92 (WWT)		B	1980 (BTO)
Shelduck	B	1992 (WWT)	Black Redstart	B	1977 (BTO)
Kestrel	B	1965-66	Redstart	B	1982
Peregrine	B	1991 (BTO)		B	1984 (BTO)
Quail	B	1989-90 (BTO)	Stonechat	B	1962-64
Water Rail	B	1962-65	Wheatear	B	1962-64
Stone Curlew	B	1962-64	Grasshopper Warbler	B	1977-80
		1991 (RSPB)	Marsh Warbler	B	1991 (BTO)
Waders of Wet	B	1982 (BTO)	Reed Warbler	B	1974-76*
Meadows	B	1989 (BTO)		B	1986-87
Little Ringed Plover	B	1973 (BTO)	Sedge Warbler	B	1986-87
Ringed Plover	B	1973 (BTO)	Blackcap	W	1978/79 (BTO)
	B	1984	Wood Warbler	B	1982
Golden Plover	C	1977-78		B	1984 (BTO)
Lapwing	B	1984	Rook	B	1972-74
	B	1987 (BTO)		B	1975-80 (BTO)
Snipe	B	1965-66	Redpoll	B	1975-80
	B	1980-81	Cirl Bunting	B	1972-73
Redshank	B	1962-65	Yellowhammer	B	1993 (BTO)
	B	1980-81	Reed Bunting	B	1993 (BTO)
Gulls	R	1977-79	Corn Bunting	B	1977-80
	R	1983 (BTO)		W	1992-93 (BTO)
	B	1983-84		B	1993 (BTO)
	R	1993 (BTO)		B	1993-94 (SOS)

*   West Sussex only
Key   B = Breeding; C = Census; R = Roosts; W = Winter survey

In addition to the surveys listed above, there have also been a number of censuses of the breeding birds of specific sites or habitats. Details of those referred to in the text are included in the following table:

Type of survey	Year(s)	Reference
Farmland bird communities of Brinsbury Estate	1980	Prater (1982)
Woodland bird communities of the West Sussex Weald	1982	Bealey & Sutherland (1983)
Farmland bird communities at Plumpton	1982	Prater (1983b)
Breeding and wintering populations of wetland birds on Pevensey Levels	1986-87	Hitchings (1988)
Breeding waders of the Arun Valley	1991	Corrigan (1993)
Downland bird communities around Brighton and Lewes	1964-89	Leverton (1994)
Downland bird communities at Lullington Heath NNR	1964-88	Bowley (1994)

The Sussex Tetrad Atlas

This survey, covering the years from 1988 to 1992, was organised by Val Bentley (West Sussex) and Mike Scott-Ham (East Sussex) with advice from the Society's Scientific Committee and considerable help from the network of 10-km square stewards. All observers who helped with the fieldwork for this survey, the aim of which was to map the distribution of all breeding species in the county on a tetrad basis, were acknowledged in the *Sussex Bird Report* (1992). The results have not been published separately but are incorporated in this book.

The fieldwork for the Sussex Tetrad Atlas coincided with that for BTO New Atlas of Breeding Birds; hence the methodology employed was the same as that used nationally. Unsure about the likely response from the membership, the Society delayed making a full commitment to a tetrad survey until the results of the 1988 fieldwork for the New Atlas were known. A requirement of the fieldwork for the New Atlas was that observers should spend two hours in each tetrad, split into two one-hour visits. Once the decision had been made to proceed with the Sussex Tetrad Atlas, observers were asked to spend extra time in each tetrad in an attempt to find additional species. Despite these extra visits, it was felt that the fieldwork that had been carried out did not truly represent the occurrence of some of the scarcer and more difficult species. It was therefore decided to augment the mapped data with general records submitted to the Society. Although this made little difference to the maps for many species, the effect of including these general records can be gleaned from the number of medium-sized dots on the maps, representing 'probable' breeding. The general breeding records were computed using three categories: 'Possible Breeding', 'Probable Breeding' and 'Confirmed Breeding' whereas those gathered by the fieldwork for the New Atlas were divided into two categories: 'Seen' and 'Breeding'.

Six 10-km squares, which formed part of the 'Key Square Survey' for the New Atlas, were surveyed more thoroughly than the other 10-km squares in the county. The additional fieldwork in these squares is reflected in the larger proportion of species found 'breeding' compared with neighbouring areas. The 10-km squares selected for this survey were as follows:

SU80	Chichester	TQ40	lower Ouse
TQ10	Worthing	TQ43	Ashdown Forest
TQ13	Horsham	TQ70	Bexhill

A total of 1014 tetrads in the county was visited at least once during the period 1988-92. Most, however, were visited at least twice to comply with the fieldwork requirements for the New Atlas and a significant number would have been more thoroughly surveyed. About 14% of these tetrads are incomplete 2km x 2km squares in that portions of them fall within the bordering counties of Hampshire, Surrey and Kent or within the sea. The following tetrads, of which only TQ24K contains more than a very small portion of Sussex, were not surveyed:

SU70K	SU71F	SU71P	SU72R	SU72S	SU72Y	SZ89G	SZ89R
SU83A	SZ99D	SZ99U	SU93G	SU93W	TQ13I	TQ24F	TQ24K
TQ34A	TV49E	TV49J	TV49U	TQ44F	TQ44Q	TQ44V	TV59H
	TQ54A	TQ53P	TV69J	TQ91Y	TQ92W		

In all, a total of 48,966 records was computed, of which 33,222 were for confirmed breeding and the remainder for possible breeding. A total of 164 species was recorded during the survey but at least 17 of these were most unlikely to have been breeding. The average of 45 species per tetrad compares with 56 in Hampshire (Clark & Eyre 1993) and 40 in Kent (Taylor, Davenport & Flegg 1981). The following map shows the number of species recorded in each tetrad.

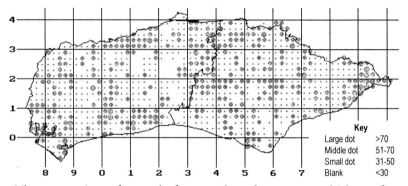

Key
Large dot   >70
Middle dot   51-70
Small dot   31-50
Blank   <30

The proportion of records from each 10-km square which confirmed breeding varied from 94%, in the small Sussex portion of SU72, to 45% in TQ20. In three 10-km squares, TQ00 (Arundel), TQ40 (lower Ouse) and TQ81 (Hastings), over 90 species were confirmed breeding although the average was 70 species per 10-km square. The following map, which uses the same scale as that above, shows the number of species confirmed breeding in each tetrad. The apparent diversity of species in some tetrads partly reflects the effort made by some observers to obtain evidence of confirmed breeding.

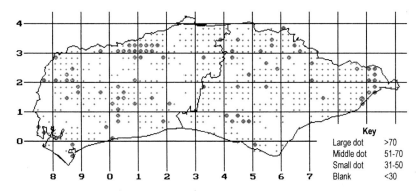

Key

Large dot	>70
Middle dot	51-70
Small dot	31-50
Blank	<30

Maps

All the distribution maps have been produced using the mapping programme DMAP written by Alan Morton. In all, except those in this introductory section, the three dot sizes represent the degree of a certainty of the species' breeding within a tetrad. For most species, only the records for the years covered by the Atlas Survey (1988-92) are plotted. For several species, however, where earlier records are both available and add to the value of the text, these are also plotted (as open symbols). For Pochard, Shoveler, Woodcock and Tree Sparrow, these records extend back to the 1960s, but for other species the open symbols represent their occurrence in a tetrad during the years 1976-87. In all instances, the Atlas Survey records represented by solid dots take precedence over the earlier records. For all species, except Grey Wagtail and Corn Bunting, for which more recent survey data are available, the solid dots represent records for the period 1988-92. The numbers shown in the inset box on each map indicate the number of registrations in the three breeding categories during the period 1988-92. Maps have not been produced for the species which are found in most of the county's tetrads nor for those for which there were very few registrations. All the maps show the actual registrations; in no cases was it considered necessary to move the position of dots for security reasons.

Sea-watching

The Sussex coast is about 140 km in length excluding the convolutions of the shoreline. It is not surprising, therefore, that many of the records received by the Sussex Ornithological Society are of birds moving along, arriving or departing from the coast. Whereas the systematic list includes details of particularly large or significant movements, the aim of this introductory section is to place these sea-watching records in context.

With the exception of D D Harber's observations at Langney Point from the late 1940s, little systematic sea-watching was carried out in the county until 1959, when a small group of observers realised the potential of Selsey Bill, and began a programme of almost complete coverage during spring and autumn, which lasted until 1965 (Mitchell 1991). At Beachy Head spring sea-watches have taken place annually since 1960, at first mainly at weekends, but then on a more intensive basis from 1972 onwards (Cooper 1976a). Casual observations at Selsey Bill during the 1970s gave way to a further co-ordinated effort at the end of the decade culminating in the publication of a series of annual bird reports (Janman & Mitchell 1979-83). A further development in late 1970s and early 1980s was the commencement of regular watching away from Beachy Head and Selsey Bill, initially at Worthing and then at Brighton Marina. Records from the latter sites have been published in the annual reports of the Shoreham District Ornithological Society (1978-94) and summarised by Newnham (1988). Sea-watching continues to this day at all the above sites and also at Hove, Newhaven Harbour, Seaford and Bexhill. The number of hours of observation at each of the main sites in spring (March-May) between 1972 and 1993 is shown in the following table:

	Selsey Bill	Worthing	Brighton Marina	Newhaven	Seaford	Beachy Head
1972	?					243
1973	?					259
1974	?					199
1975	?					211
1976	?	40				>209
1977	?					229*
1978	?	71				198*
1979	392	96				170*
1980	191	108				>144
1981	453	346	>109			>86
1982	466	357	184			165
1983	471	352	284			111
1984	282	366	487			162
1985	227	454	88			102
1986	233	388	68		98	88
1987	208	231	?		103	56
1988	208	345	45		284	48
1989	401	371	55		412	72
1990	421	305	53	84	453	111
1991	443	226	?	31	547	87
1992	525	204	?	130	337	50
1993	463	301	?	?	520	?
Total	5384	4561	1373	245	2754	3000

* indicates a minimum total derived from the number of hours watched on selected days

? total number of hours sea-watching not known

The south facing coast of Sussex is best watched in spring when large numbers of migrants pass up-Channel heading for their breeding grounds further north. Although the spring is the most intensively watched period, autumn and winter can also be productive, the former in strong on-shore winds and the latter in hard weather. Most sea-watching in autumn and winter has been at Selsey Bill and Worthing but also increasingly at Seaford. Although not regularly watched, some of the best autumn movements have been recorded at Langney Point.

Several of the species accounts give the monthly totals of birds recorded flying east or west or, alternatively, the rate of passage in birds per hour in successive 10-day periods at Worthing. Records for this site have been used as they provide the longest uninterrupted run of data for each month. The number of hours spent sea-watching per month at Worthing between 1978 and 1993 is shown in the following table:

Jan	Feb	Mar	Apr	May	Jun	Jul	Aug	Sep	Oct	Nov	Dec
248	214	632	1898	1990	180	128	330	384	421	310	310

Ringing

Leverton (1987), in his excellent appraisal of 25 years of ringing in Sussex, noted that the number of birds caught annually in the county during the period 1962-87 had remained fairly constant, fluctuating about the 20,000 mark. He also mentioned "a most exciting experiment combining farming and the creation of new habitat for birds" at Elms Farm, Icklesham, the main ringing site for the Rye Bay Ringing Group. Little was it then realised how this "experiment" would result in a dramatic rise in the county's ringing totals.

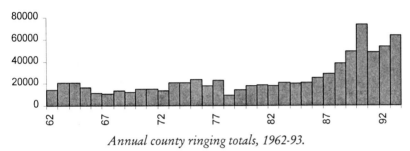

Annual county ringing totals, 1962-93.

Just as the 18th and 19th century bird trappers caught new species for Sussex, and in a number of instances for Britain, so modern day ringers have caught new species for the county. Of the 23 additions to the Sussex List between 1980 and 1994, four were found in ringer's mist-nets (Fairbank 1995), including three at Icklesham in the 1990s. Ringing has also accounted for many of the records of skulking species such as Spotted Crakes, Bluethroats and Aquatic Warblers.

Leverton also referred to a number of detailed ringing studies in the county, some of which have been carried out over many years. Those published include studies of Canada Geese at Petworth Park (Hughes & Watson 1986), wintering gulls in the Worthing area (Newnham 1986b), Sand Martins at Chichester Gravel Pits (Mead, Boddy & Watson 1964, Mead & Harrison 1979), passage and wintering thrushes at Ashcombe (Leverton 1986), warbler migration at Beachy Head (Cooper 1975, Edgar 1986) and Siskins at East Grinstead (Cooper 1985, 1987).

The systematic list contains details of the more significant movements which have been revealed by ringing. Some of these refer to birds which were controlled (i.e. caught at a different site to where they were originally ringed) whereas others were of birds which were recovered (i.e. reported, often dead, by members of the public). The term retrap is used to indicate a bird that was ringed and subsequently recaptured at the same site.

Standard References and Abbreviations used

Several references have been regularly used throughout the text and are abbreviated as follows:-

BWP	Cramp, S (Ed) 1977, 1980, 1983, 1985, 1988, 1992, 1993, 1994a, 1994b. *The Handbook of Birds of Europe, The Middle East and North Africa: The Birds of the Western Palearctic.* Vols 1-9. Oxford University Press. Oxford
des Forges & Harber	des Forges, G and Harber, DD 1963. *A Guide to the Birds of Sussex.* Oliver and Boyd. Edinburgh and London.
New Atlas	Gibbons, DW, Reid, JB and Chapman, RA 1993. *The New Atlas of Breeding Birds in Britain and Ireland:1988-91.* Poyser. London.
Winter Atlas	Lack, P 1986. *The Atlas of Wintering Birds in Britain and Ireland.* Poyser. Calton
68-72 BTO Atlas	Sharrock, JTR 1976. *The Atlas of Breeding Birds in Britain and Ireland.* British Trust for Ornithology, Tring.
Shrubb	Shrubb, M 1979. *The Birds of Sussex: Their Present Status.* Phillimore. Chichester.
Walpole-Bond	Walpole-Bond, J. 1938. *A History of Sussex Birds* (3 volumes). Witherby London.

Other abbreviations used in the texts are as follows:-

Atlas Survey	Sussex Ornithological Society Tetrad Atlas 1988-92.
BoEE	Birds of Estuaries Enquiry
BoMNH	Booth Museum of Natural History
BBRC	*British Birds Rarities Committee*
BOURC	*British Ornithologists' Union Records Committee*
BTO	British Trust for Ornithology
CBC	Common Birds Census
LNR	Local Nature Reserve
NNR	National Nature Reserve
RSPB	Royal Society for the Protection of Birds
SOC	Scottish Ornithologists' Club
SOS	Sussex Ornithological Society
SPA	Area for Special Protection of Birds
SSSI	Site of Special Scientific Interest
SWT	Sussex Wildlife Trust
WAGBI	Wildfowlers' Association of Great Britain and Ireland
WeBS	Wetland Bird Survey
WWT	Wildfowl and Wetlands Trust
m	metre
ha	hectare
km	kilometre
km²	square kilometre
tetrad	2 km x 2 km square of the British National Grid
10-km square	10 km x10 km square of the British National Grid

Paul James & John Newnham

92

Red-throated Diver

Gavia stellata

Status:- A fairly common winter visitor and passage migrant.

The Red-throated Diver is by far the most frequently recorded diver off the Sussex coast. It has been seen in every month of the year, although it is rare in June, July and August.

The earliest recorded in autumn were singles off Church Norton on 27 July 1978 and Selsey Bill from 31 July to 1 August 1982, five that flew west off Pett on 27 July 1984 and four that flew east off Atherington on 10 August 1992. In other years between 1962 and 1993, arrival dates varied between 16 August and 15 November, with the average 4 October. Few are recorded in September or October, the maximum totals for these months being just three and 21 respectively. A more general influx is apparent in November-December although a record of 85 flying west off Selsey Bill on 24 November 1992 suggests that some of these birds may be on passage. In mid-winter, the largest concentrations occur in Rye Bay, with counts of 100 or more as follows: 423 on 3 February 1985, 200 on 7 February 1965, 150-200 on 4 March 1979, 169 on 24 January 1982, up to 150 between 11 and 15 January 1986 and 130 in the early months of 1989. Elsewhere, counts of 20 or more are unusual, although up to 55 were recorded off Goring in January 1982 and 52 off Bexhill on 29 December 1985. Sites that regularly hold 50 or more birds are considered to be of national importance for this species (Waters & Cranswick 1993).

Spring passage usually starts in early March and continues until the end of May. The number of birds involved is difficult to assess as some divers, especially those seen in flight far out to sea, are not specifically identified. At Selsey Bill, about 10% of all divers recorded in spring between 1980 and 1992 were positively identified as this species, compared with 12% of those at Worthing. These figures may, however, be rather misleading given that the majority of divers recorded in March and early April are thought to be Red-throated. Singles off Pett on 1 June 1978 and flying east at Worthing on 1 June 1984 and at Selsey Bill on 5 June 1991 are the latest to be recorded in recent years.

Although most Red-throated Divers occur on the open sea, birds may also be seen on gravel pits and lagoons close to the coast. Of 57 recorded further inland between 1962 and 1993, 18 were at Arlington Reservoir, 11 at Chichester Gravel Pits and 10 at Bewl Water. Others occurred at Weir Wood Reservoir (7), Darwell Reservoir (4), Barcombe Reservoir (2) and singles at Ashburnham Place, Pond Lye, Wannock and on the River Arun at Arundel and Coldwaltham. Most stayed for short periods only, but exceptions have included singles at Chichester Gravel Pits from 22 January to 10 February 1971, at Arlington Reservoir from 9 April to 8 May 1971, 4 January to 1 March 1978 and 15 January to 7 February 1989 and at Weir Wood Reservoir for three weeks from 20 November 1993. Two were present at Bewl Water from 19 February to 13 March 1983. The Wannock individual was found in a garden after a period of severe gales on 16 January 1974 while another unusual record concerned an immature found "walking the streets" of Shoreham-by-Sea on 15 April 1986.

One ringed as a chick on North Mainland, Shetland on 4 August 1979 was found freshly dead off Seaford, 1096 km south, on 21 January 1981.

Tony J Wilson

Black-throated Diver   *Gavia arctica*
Status:- A scarce winter visitor and passage migrant.

The Black-throated Diver is an annual visitor to Sussex, occurring most often during the winter months and on passage in spring. Although the records suggest an increase in the last 20 years, this is likely to be due to the growth in sea-watching over this period and to a greater awareness of the relevant identification criteria.

By far the earliest in autumn was one off Selsey Bill on 3 August 1969. There are just five county records for September while prior to 1977 only two had occurred in October. Between 1977 and 1993 there were records for this month in 12 years, including four in 1983 and an exceptional 15 in 1991.

The first wintering birds usually arrive in November but totals for this month and December rarely reach double figures. There were, however, unusual numbers in late 1991 when 26 were seen in November and 19 in December, including three off Brighton on 10 November and totals of ten flying east and 14 west off Selsey Bill during the period. Most are normally recorded in January, including totals of 24 in 1982 and 23 in 1986, or occasionally February. The species may be found anywhere along the coast, although it is most frequently observed off Selsey Bill, between Goring and Brighton, between Bexhill and Hastings, and in Rye Bay. Most are singles although up to three are regularly recorded. The largest concentrations since 1962 were 13 in Rye Bay on 11 February 1967 and 11 January 1977 while at Selsey Bill, a total of 13 flew east on 3 January 1982. It is likely, however, that larger numbers are present in winter, as many of the divers recorded in the county are not specifically identified.

Wintering birds disperse quickly by early March and most are then seen moving up-Channel. Passage occurs between March and late May with a peak between mid-April and mid-May. Between 1968 and 1993 the average spring totals at Selsey Bill and Beachy Head were 19 and 36 respectively, representing about 12% of the total number of divers recorded at these sites. This figure may, however, be misleading as many of the birds observed in late April and May are thought to be of this species. For example, of 102 divers that passed Beachy Head on 5 May 1971, 90% were considered to be Black-throated. A party of seven was seen resting on the sea off Beachy Head during poor weather on 6 May 1977, although it is generally unusual for birds to linger at this time of the year. The maximum number recorded in any one spring was 150 at Beachy Head in 1973. Of seven June records for the county, the latest were at Rye Harbour from 11 to 17 June 1988 and off Selsey Bill on 19 June 1982. There are no records for July.

Inland, a total of 35 was recorded between 1962 and 1993. The majority were at Bewl Water (21) with much smaller numbers at Arlington Reservoir, Chichester Gravel Pits and Weir Wood Reservoir (3 each), Barcombe Reservoir (2) and Darwell Reservoir, Newells Pond and Powdermill Reservoir (1 each). Most were singles although, at Bewl Water, there were two on 13 February 1983 and from 16 to 30 December 1980, and three there from 31 December 1980 until 20 January 1981. Sightings have normally been during the winter but spring birds are occasionally seen, notably one in summer plumage at Bewl Water on 15 May 1979 and another there from 5 to 11 May 1985.   *Tony J Wilson*

Great Northern Diver   *Gavia immer*

Status:- A very scarce winter visitor and spring passage migrant.

The Great Northern Diver is an annual visitor to Sussex, occurring most frequently in mid-winter or on spring passage. The cumulative monthly totals for the periods 1962-76 and 1977-94, shown below, suggest a slight increase in recent years although this may be due to increased observer activity and greater awareness of the relevant identification features.

	Oct	Nov	Dec	Jan	Feb	Mar	Apr	May	Jun
1962-76	5	7	13	13	8	9	18	6	1
1977-94	7	22	20	23	12	15	36	28	-
Total	12	29	33	36	20	24	54	34	1

The earliest recorded in autumn were off Langney Point on 9 October 1981 and Church Norton on 10 October 1990. Wintering birds have usually arrived by mid-November although away from the extreme west of the county they rarely remain for any length of time. Chichester Harbour and off Church Norton are the most favoured localities, accounting for two-thirds of the winter records since 1976 although, even here, some duplication is likely as it is suspected that birds move between sites. Most are seen singly although there have been nine records of two together in the last 15 years, all in the vicinity of the western harbours, except for two off Atherington on 15 December 1990. Unusually, two remained off Church Norton from 15 January to 8 April 1978 and three were seen together in Chichester Harbour on 10 and 16 December 1986. Away from the western harbours, the species is only regularly recorded in winter at Langney Point, where there have been seven since 1976.

Spring passage has been noted between 1 March (1987, Beachy Head) and 21 June (1970, Selsey Bill). Most birds are observed flying up-Channel although there have been occasional records of birds flying west and also lingering offshore. Of those recorded in the period 1977-94, the majority were off Selsey Bill (28), Worthing (19) and Beachy Head (19). Spring totals in this period varied between none in 1977 and 1978 to ten in 1985 and 1988. The maximum reported on any one day was six that flew east off Worthing on 30 April 1988.

The only inland records since 1962 were of singles at Arlington Reservoir from 5 February to 11 May 1972 (when found dead) and from 16 December 1974 to 1 March 1975, at Bewl Water from 23 October to 8 November 1991 and at Darwell Reservoir on 3 December 1994. *Tony J Wilson*

Divers *Gavia species*

A large proportion of the divers recorded off the Sussex coast are not identified, mainly due to the difficulties of distinguishing the species in flight. It is generally considered that most of those observed in winter and early spring are Red-throated and that Black-throated is the most common species during late April and May.

Large movements in the early part of the year are sometimes associated with hard weather but it is likely that spring passage may start as early as the beginning of February, given that totals of 129 and 289 flew east at Seaford on 1 and 22 February 1987 respectively. Notable easterly movements later in the spring have included 234 off Brighton Marina on 23 March 1984 and 167 off Seaford on 5 April 1987, while at Beachy Head there were 169 on 8 April 1979 and 102 on the late date of 5 May 1971. The number of divers recorded passing up-Channel in spring has increased significantly in recent years. At Seaford, for example, the totals for the years 1991, 1992 and 1993 were 844, 1280 and 1050 respectively, far exceeding the previous highest total of 641 at Beachy Head in 1979.

Large movements are not often recorded in the latter part of the year although this may merely reflect a lack of observer coverage at this time. At Worthing totals of 171 flew east and 216 west in December 1981, while at Selsey Bill 72 flew east and 308 west between October and December 1992, including 127 west on 19 December. A total of 403 flew east at Seaford during the same period. *Tony J Wilson*

Little Grebe *Tachybaptus ruficollis*

Status:- A scarce resident, passage migrant and winter visitor.

The Little Grebe is an inconspicuous species often nesting on small waters, usually with dense marginal vegetation. It is secretive and easy to overlook during the breeding season and, consequently, it may be under-recorded. Breeding in Sussex takes place between March and October (Hughes 1989) and in this period the species is more likely to be detected by its whinnying call than by sight.

Walpole-Bond stated that in his recollection the Little Grebe had always been a scarce breeding species in Sussex, and des Forges & Harber were of the opinion that since the 1939-45 war its status had not changed. Shrubb considered that between 1970 and 1976 there were probably less than 100 pairs in the county and among a list of the more important breeding sites he cited Rye Harbour with 4-10 pairs and Chichester Gravel Pits with 3-6 pairs as having the largest numbers.

Similar results were obtained from a survey in 1985, with the addition of Forest Mere, close to the Hampshire border, where there were probably four nesting pairs. Hughes (1989), reporting the results of that survey, listed 28 sites where adult Little Grebes were present in the spring, with a total of probably less than 40 pairs nesting. 1985, however, was a poor year with the census coinciding with a population low following a series of moderately severe winters; Hughes suggested that a figure of 60-65 pairs could be regarded as about average.

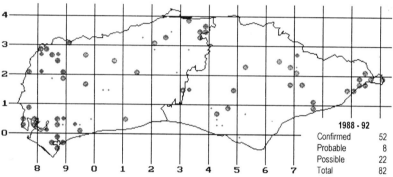

	1988 - 92	
	Confirmed	52
	Probable	8
	Possible	22
	Total	82

Based on the records submitted, and therefore probably minimum figures, 42 pairs bred at 26 sites in 1990 and 29-31 pairs at 18 sites in 1991. Records of just 14-15 pairs at nine sites were submitted in 1992, but it is considered that these represent significant under-recording. The situation is further confused as nesting may not occur at each site every year. Nationally, there was a 6.6% reduction in the number of pairs breeding, or present but without evidence of breeding, between the 1968-72 and 1988-91 BTO Atlas surveys (New Atlas).

Distribution and numbers outside the breeding season in the years 1966-89 were reviewed by Hughes (1991a). He included in this review the position in autumn, defined as August to October, given that young from early broods and some failed pairs may disperse from their sites in July. In late summer and autumn, many birds move from their breeding sites to other, often larger, inland waters. For example, totals of 25 were recorded at Darwell Reservoir in October 1967 and at Weir Wood Reservoir in October 1970. Others, however, may disperse directly to the vicinity of the coast. As winter approaches, a marked coastal distribution becomes apparent, concentrated in the harbours and estuaries, on tidal reaches of the main rivers, in the dykes and ditches of the levels and on other undisturbed waters within 10 km of the coast. Ninety percent of the winter population in Sussex was found in coastal areas during a survey in the winter of 1985/86. A coastal distribution is more evident around the south coast of England than elsewhere (Winter Atlas).

Numbers fluctuate from year to year; in January 1984 counts at 172 sites produced 96 birds, whereas in November 1985, 190 birds were counted at 101 sites. Maximum winter numbers at some important localities in the years reported on by Hughes were 101 in Chichester Harbour in both January and November 1976, 62 in the lower Cuckmere Valley in February 1975, 56 at Rye Harbour in November 1983 and 45 at Newhaven Harbour and Tide Mills in November 1968. Since 1989, 41 were recorded in Chichester Harbour in January 1990 and 43 there, and in the lower Cuckmere, in December 1990. A total of 53 birds was counted in Chichester Harbour in November 1991.

There is little clear evidence of large influxes of birds from outside the county, as described by Walpole-Bond. Nevertheless there is ringing evidence that continental birds move into southeast England and these probably replace local birds which have moved on westwards (Winter Atlas). Passage is suggested by the presence of parties of 44 and 18 at Pett Pools on 1 April and 5 April 1981, a locality not used regularly during the winter.   *Mike Mason*

Great Crested Grebe   *Podiceps cristatus*

Status:- A fairly common resident, passage migrant and winter visitor.

The Great Crested Grebe breeds at suitable inland locations over much of Sussex, but in winter is also found, occasionally in considerable numbers, on the coast.

Shrubb felt that there had been little recent apparent change in status but that the increase in resident population noted by des Forges & Harber had probably continued. He showed that between 1962 and 1975 there were 18 sites which held breeding Great Crested Grebes regularly and another five which were probably occupied more often than not. In 1975 most birds were, by a substantial margin, to be found at Chichester Gravel Pits and at Weir Wood Reservoir. Hughes (1987a) in reviewing the changes in breeding status since 1962 was able to draw on the results of a census conducted on 1-2 June 1985 which covered 92% of the potential sites in the county and which found

179 birds. A further 11 birds were located at non-breeding sites or in coastal waters.

The distribution of breeding sites revealed by the 1985 census was primarily an inland one, but near the coast birds were found in Pagham and Chichester Harbours and at Littlehampton in the west of the county, while in the east there were breeding sites at the Crumbles, Pett Pools and Rye Harbour. A further census in May 1990, reported in the *Sussex Bird Report* for that year, produced a total of 225 adults at 27 sites. The figures from Hughes and the 1990 survey suggest that the increase in population noted by des Forges & Harber and by Shrubb had continued. The Atlas map shows confirmed breeding in 19 10-km squares in at least one of the years during 1988-92.

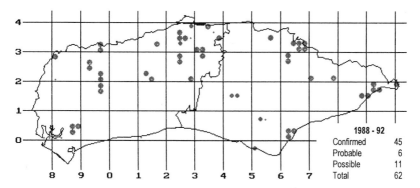

	1988 - 92
Confirmed	45
Probable	6
Possible	11
Total	62

Breeding may commence as early as February with eggs having been found, in 1967, as early as 20th; indeed Simmons (1974) stated that Great Crested Grebes will breed at almost any time of the year if conditions are satisfactory. Breeding success may be patchy; in the 1990 survey, 48 birds were present at Bewl Water but no young were raised whereas the following year at the same site 15 pairs raised 17 young from seven successful nests. A similar situation arose at Weir Wood Reservoir where only six young were reared in 1990 while in 1991, 69 young, in 28 broods, were hatched and at least half were known to have survived (Mortlock 1992). Fluctuating water levels, and weather conditions may be the cause of varying breeding success on the reservoirs.

Walpole-Bond stated that the species rarely wintered inland. However des Forges & Harber recorded small numbers doing so regularly by 1961. Post-breeding dispersal is evident by mid to late July and while many birds move to the coast, there are now many more records of inland wintering. Totals of 140 at Weir Wood Reservoir on 9 November 1991 and 112 in November 1992 appear to be the largest numbers reported inland, but all the reservoirs have supported significant numbers in recent winters. Sites regularly holding 100 or more birds are considered to be of national importance for the species (Waters & Cranswick 1993). Numbers on the coast rarely exceed 50 at any one locality except in severe weather, when continental birds may be forced westwards by freezing conditions in their usual wintering areas. Large parties recorded offshore include 500 in Rye Bay on 20 February 1949, 450 between Hove and Saltdean on 18 February 1987, 330 off Pett Level on 19 February 1992 and *ca.* 200 there on 1 December 1990. Most coastal wintering birds depart by mid-March but a small passage in April and May is evident from occasional sightings of birds offshore or moving past the main sea-watching localities.

An interesting ringing recovery involved a bird ringed in Sussex on 23 March 1985, after being cleaned of oil. It survived until 15 August 1988 when it was killed in a trap set for muskrats in southern Holland.   *Mike Mason*

Red-necked Grebe   *Podiceps grisegena*

Status:- A scarce winter visitor and passage migrant.

The Red-necked Grebe has occurred every winter except 1972/73 in Sussex (fig. 1) although the number of birds recorded is affected by the incidence of severe weather during the winter months.

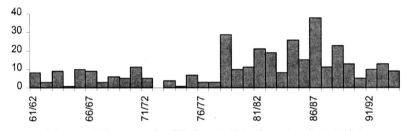

Figure 1. Winter totals of Red-necked Grebes, 1961/62 - 93/94.

Even allowing for a large upsurge in observer activity, it is clear that there has been a significant increase in recent years, which has also been apparent in Hampshire (Clark & Eyre 1993). des Forges & Harber recorded only 40 during 1950-60 and Shrubb noted a total of about 83 between 1961 and 1976, with between one and 12 birds recorded annually, whereas in the following 18 years to 1994, about 283 were recorded. Totals in the latter period varied between three and 38 per year, the average being 16, a figure greater than any annual total for 1962-76.

There are old records for 3 August (1872, off Brighton) and 13 August (1866, Chichester Harbour) but the earliest recorded during 1962-94 was at Camber on 19 August 1964. The average arrival date in this period was 4 October, although if only the last fifteen years are considered, the average moves to 13 September, indicating a trend towards earlier arrival. In recent years there has been a marked passage in October as shown by the cumulative monthly totals below.

	Jul	Aug	Sep	Oct	Nov	Dec	Jan	Feb	Mar	Apr	May	Jun
1962-76	-	3	4	14	11	15	20	10	8	5	2	-
1977-94	-	5	41	73	40	36	79	80	46	28	10	1
Total	-	8	45	87	51	51	99	90	54	33	12	1

Prior to 1977, the number of birds recorded in October was about the same as in December but the total for October for 1977-94 was double that for December. The largest numbers in autumn are usually recorded at Church Norton where there were up to seven in October 1981 and 1982 and six in 1980. These birds usually move on but smaller numbers may be recorded both here and in Chichester Harbour during the winter months. Cold weather in January and February may produce an influx of the species into the county. Such was the case in 1979, when 27 were recorded between January and March, and in 1987, when there were 28 in January-February. During influxes such as these, birds may be widely scattered at both coastal and inland localities, although movement between sites make it difficult to assess accurately the number of individuals involved. It is unusual to find more than three together although there were four at Rye Harbour on 3 February 1979, up to seven at Bewl Water in January 1987 and, most unusually, ten off Bexhill on 1 February 1985. Birds often remain into March but most have left by the end of the month.

Since the mid-1970s, there has been an increase in the number of birds recorded on spring passage. Although singles have been noted as late as 16 May at Littlehampton in 1983 and Worthing in 1993, the records indicate that April is the main month for passage. Most of those recorded in spring are single birds on one day only, although regular sightings of one off Seaford and Birling Gap between 14 April and 14 May 1988 probably involved the same individual. One at Church Norton on 19 June 1988 is the only county record for the month and there have been none in July.

Between 1962 and 1994, a total of about 40 was recorded inland; at Bewl Water (19), Arlington Reservoir (7), Weir Wood Reservoir (4), Chichester Gravel Pits and Darwell Reservoir (3 each) and Arundel, Barcombe Reservoir, Bramber and Southease (1 each). Although most were single birds, five at Bewl Water on 18 January 1987 increased to seven on 24 January, two remaining to 15 March and one to 21 April. The cumulative monthly totals of inland records for 1962-94 shown below confirm that most were recorded in the winter months.

Sep	Oct	Nov	Dec	Jan	Feb	Mar	Apr
3	9	6	11	19	11	8	1

Tony J Wilson

Slavonian Grebe   *Podiceps auritus*

Status:- A scarce winter visitor and passage migrant.

The Slavonian Grebe is the most frequently encountered of the non-breeding grebes. des Forges & Harber referred to averages of 15 birds per year prior to 1961 and Shrubb to over 55 per year between 1967 and 1976. More recently, numbers have stabilised at about 50-60 per year.

The earliest recorded in autumn were singles at Thorney Island on 15 July 1971, off Worthing on 5 August 1986 and off Church Norton two days later, and at the Crumbles on 27 August 1990. In other years between 1962 and 1993, arrival dates for autumn birds varied between 4 September and 20 November, with the average 5 October. Thereafter, numbers build up slowly, reaching a peak in mid-November which is then maintained until late February, when a gradual dispersal takes place.

During the winter months, the species is mainly found in Chichester Harbour and off Church Norton, where the average winter maxima during 1977-93 have been eight and 25 respectively. Much larger numbers have been recorded at the latter site on a number of occasions including 50 on 11 December 1971, 51 on 10 November 1981 and 52 on 10 December 1989. Totals of this size represent up to 12.5% of the British wintering population (Winter Atlas), demonstrating the importance of this site for the species. Away from the main localities, it is unusual to record in excess of three birds; exceptions have included 12 off Worthing on 20 January 1990, nine off Bexhill on 16 February 1993, eight off Lancing on 28 January 1987 and six off Atherington on 15 December 1990. In contrast to both Red-necked and Black-necked Grebe, no large influxes during harsh weather have been recorded although it is usual for there to be slightly fewer at the two regular sites and more elsewhere, suggesting a general dispersal from the west of the county. For example, during the cold winter of 1978/79, birds were seen at 16 sites, five of which were inland, although at Church Norton the maximum count was only nine.

Singles or small parties may be recorded at the main sea-watching localities between late March and mid-May. A total of 24 was reported in 1989 although the spring average during 1976-92 was about nine. There is an easterly bias to the records and it is not unusual for the same parties to be observed, first off Seaford and later off Birling Gap, as they drift east. One such flock of 11 on 20 April 1992 is the largest to be recorded on spring passage in Sussex, exceeding that of nine off Rye Harbour on 1 May 1978. There are four records for late May-June as follows:

1970: One at Chichester Gravel Pits from 17 May to 13 June and again in Chichester Harbour on 19 July.
1982: One at Weir Wood Reservoir from 13 to 28 June.
1991: One at Cuckmere Haven on 25 May which flew inland.
       One at Church Norton from 20 June to 11 July.

Between 1962 and 1993, about 78 were recorded inland, at Weir Wood Reservoir (17), Chichester Gravel Pits (17), Arlington Reservoir (15), Bewl Water (11), Barcombe Reservoir (8), Ardingly Reservoir (3), Amberley and Darwell Reservoir (2 each) and Billingshurst, Horsted Keynes and the River Ouse at Lewes (1 each). Most occurred during the winter months as shown by the cumulative monthly totals for 1962-93 below.

Jul	Aug	Sep	Oct	Nov	Dec	Jan	Feb	Mar	Apr	May	Jun
1	-	1	7	10	13	24	21	8	-	1	2

Although most were single birds, two were seen together on nine occasions and three at Bewl Water on 30 January 1982. Few stayed more than a week although one was present at Weir Wood Reservoir from 27 January to 29 April 1973. The most unusual records involved a bird picked up in the centre of Billingshurst in January 1985, which was subsequently taken into care, and a pair at Weir Wood Reservoir from 20 October to 25 November 1993 that was seen displaying and heard calling.   *Tony J Wilson*

Black-necked Grebe   *Podiceps nigricollis*

Status:- A very scarce winter visitor and passage migrant.

The status of the Black-necked Grebe in Sussex has changed in recent years. des Forges & Harber stated that it "appeared to occur about as frequently as the Slavonian" whereas Shrubb noted a steady decline from an average of 16.8 birds per year during 1952-56 to just 6.5 per year between 1972-76. Since 1976, the average has been ten per year although more are now recorded in spring than in the winter months. This trend is shown by the cumulative monthly totals for 1962-76 and 1977-94 below.

	Jul	Aug	Sep	Oct	Nov	Dec	Jan	Feb	Mar	Apr	May	Jun
1962-76	-	8	17	15	11	18	24	22	8	11	3	1
1977-94	1	18	20	17	16	18	27	13	20	40	7	1
Total	1	26	37	32	27	36	51	35	28	51	10	2

The first returning birds are typically recorded in August although singles were recorded at Rye Harbour as early as 21 June 1964 and 16 July 1988. Passage continues throughout September and October, months in which birds have been recorded at a number of coastal and inland localities. Certain sites, however, are particularly favoured and these have included the Crumbles, Pagham Harbour, Rye Harbour and Weir Wood Reservoir.

The first wintering birds typically arrive in November. No more than four have occurred in any winter since 1976/77, except in 1978/79 and 1986/87 when totals of 8-10 and eight were recorded, the majority of which were noted following the onset of severe weather in early 1979 and 1987. des Forges & Harber stated that "most records were for Chichester and Pagham Harbours". Although birds may still be recorded at these localities during the winter months, the parties of 10-15, previously reported there, no longer occur. It is possible, however, that those in Chichester Harbour have simply changed wintering site to Langstone Harbour, Hampshire where concentrations of 30-40 regularly occur (Clark & Eyre 1993). Departure of wintering birds is evident as early as February. In 1979 and 1987, for example, there was a decrease from six in January to one and two in February respectively.

Spring passage has been noted between early March and early June, although most birds have occurred in the first half of April. The species is more frequently observed at coastal sites than inland, especially off Worthing, where 25 have been recorded since 1978, including parties of three on 12 April 1980, 2 April 1988 and 21 April 1994, five on 14 April 1986 and a late single on 6 June 1991.

Although the Black-necked Grebe has never been proved to breed in Sussex, a pair was recorded at Tilgate Park Lake on 6 March 1977 while in April 1993 nest building was observed at Rye Harbour.

Between 1962 and 1994 about 56 were recorded inland at Chichester Gravel Pits (25), Weir Wood Reservoir (14), Arlington Reservoir (6), Bewl Water (3), Barcombe Reservoir, Darwell Reservoir and Tilgate Park Lake (2 each) and Amberley Wild Brooks and Heathfield (1 each). As the cumulative monthly totals show, most inland birds were recorded in the autumn.

Aug	Sep	Oct	Nov	Dec	Jan	Feb	Mar	Apr	May
11	16	9	6	4	7	2	4	1	2

At Chichester Gravel Pits, there were three on 27-28 September 1979 but all other inland records have been of ones and twos. The most unusual occurrence concerned one found in a road near Heathfield during foggy conditions on 29 September 1986. The bird was released on a small pond and had gone by the following day. *Tony J Wilson*

Black-browed Albatross *Diomedea melanophris*

Status:- One record, no longer considered to be acceptable.

A record of one flying north off Sandy Point into Chichester Harbour on 10 May 1974 has recently been reviewed and is considered to be inadequately documented (Rogers *et al* 1995). One at sea about 54 km southeast of Newhaven on 17 October 1993 is hardly an adequate substitute, being approximately in mid-Channel. It is the only record for southeast England.

There were 25 records of this regal southern seabird in the British Isles during 1962-94. It breeds on islands in the southern oceans and disperses north to the Tropic of Capricorn and very occasionally beyond. *Richard Fairbank*

Fulmar *Fulmarus glacialis*

Status:- A fairly common breeding species and passage migrant, resident on coastal cliffs from November to September.

The Atlas map shows the Fulmar to be well-established on the chalk cliffs between Brighton and Beachy Head and on the sand and clay cliffs east of Hastings to Cliff End, Pett. Birds were seen on the chalk cliffs as early as 1946 (C M James *pers. comm.*) but despite a considerable increase in numbers since five pairs were first located at Beachy Head in 1965, breeding was not proved until 1976. Neither type of cliff formation provides ledges of any size or permanence and it is significant, perhaps, that breeding was first proved at Newhaven where some pairs occupy holes in the cliff-face, rather than ledges.

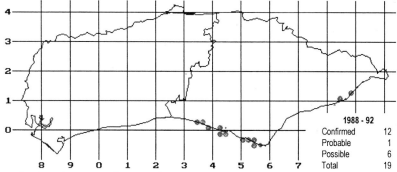

1988 - 92	
Confirmed	12
Probable	1
Possible	6
Total	19

The breeding population of Fulmars in Sussex almost quadrupled between 1969, when 30 occupied sites were located for Operation Seafarer (Cramp, Bourne & Saunders 1974), and 1983-84, when an SOS survey located a total of 106 sites (Prater 1985). A further survey in 1985-1987, organised by the Seabird Group, found 116 occupied sites (Lloyd, Tasker & Partridge 1991). Since then, counts have been far from complete, but the presence in 1992 of 58 occupied sites between Hastings and Pett and 26 sites at Newhaven suggests that the population may still be increasing. A number of explanations have been given for the increase in Fulmars in the North Atlantic. Fisher (1952) linked the expansion to the availability of offal, first from Arctic whaling, and then from trawlers. Wynne-Edwards (1962) argued that a special genotype must have arisen in the population in Iceland, allowing the species to break away from nesting in dense, but widely separated colonies.

Birds are present on the cliffs from late November to mid-September but it is not until March and onwards that significant numbers are recorded passing along the coast. Regular sea-watching at Brighton Marina, Selsey Bill and Worthing has revealed that Fulmars pass both up and down-Channel in spring although most recorded at Brighton are moving eastward whereas the majority off Selsey are moving westward. Worthing, placed more centrally, shows a more even distribution of passage in both directions. The significance of these movements is unclear although Newnham (1987) suggested that this variation may be attributable to birds returning to the nearest nesting cliffs.

The largest movements recorded in Sussex have been in April and May, with 82 flying east and 48 west off Worthing on 4 May 1986, 131 east off Seaford on 2 April 1989 and 135 east off Brighton Marina on 16 April 1989. In autumn, passage is heaviest in August but very few are recorded thereafter, particularly in late October and November.

A total of ten has been recorded inland since one was seen over Arundel WWT on 29 May 1978. These have been at Lewes (2) and Arlington Reservoir, Beddingham, Ditchling Beacon, Mill Hill, Mount Caburn, Stoughton, Washington and Weir Wood Reservoir (1 each). The records for the Lewes area are of particular interest given that these birds may have been prospecting quarries in the Ouse Valley.

The increase in the Fulmar in Sussex has coincided with the appearance of a number of birds showing the characteristics of the dark morph, colloquially known as 'Blue Fulmar'. There have been six records for the county: at Beachy Head on 5 May 1985, Birling Gap on 19-20 April 1984 and 17 April 1987, off Selsey Bill on 16 May 1987, at Newhaven on 6-7 May 1992 and off Beachy Head on 28 March 1994.

A Fulmar ringed at Inchkeith in the Firth of Forth on 13 August 1975 was found dead at Ovingdean on 18 May 1983, as was a bird at Rye Harbour on 25 January 1983 that had been ringed on Fair Isle on 23 July 1982. Another found dead at an unspecified locality in the county on 29 January 1969 had been ringed in South Leinster, Ireland, on 4 June 1967. *Paul James*

Bulwer's Petrel *Bulweria bulwerii*

Status:- One old record, no longer considered to be acceptable.

A male reported to have been picked up dead near Beachy Head on 3 February 1903 is in the Booth Museum (BoMNH 204820). It is no longer regarded as being acceptable due to its close proximity to the 'Hastings Rarities' (Bourne 1967, Snow 1971). *Richard Fairbank*

Cory's Shearwater *Calonectris diomedea*

Status:- A rare vagrant (14 records involving 17 individuals).

Three were recorded before 1962 (des Forges & Harber): one at sea from the Dieppe to Newhaven ferry a few miles off Newhaven on 21 September 1936 (White 1936) and singles flying east past Langney Point on 15 October 1948 (*SxBR* 1: 18, Harber 1949) and 19 November 1950 (*SxBR* 3: 17, Harber 1951a).

Since the beginning of 1962 there have been 11 records involving 14 individuals:

1977: One in Rye Bay on 4 April.
1978: One in Rye Bay on 13 April.
       One in Rye Bay on 5 May.
1979: One flying west past Hove on 12 April.
1981: One flying west past Worthing on 3 May.
1984: One flew towards Brighton Marina on 3 May landing 250 m offshore before departing east.
1985: One flying west past Selsey Bill on 2 August.
       Two flying west past Pett Level on 5 August.
1987: One flying east past Selsey Bill on 6 June.
       Two flying west past Cow Gap, Beachy Head on 18 October, presumably relocating in the wake of the great storm.
1993: Two flying west past Selsey Bill on 11 August.

No clear pattern emerges as there are records in all months between April and November with the exception of July, although with three records each, April, May and August have a slight edge. Three of the last five records have come from Selsey Bill.

Despite in excess of 1000 individuals recorded off the British Isles in some recent years (Evans 1993a), this remains a very rare species in southeast England. Just one has been seen in Hampshire (Clark & Eyre 1993), although there have been 31 in Kent, all but two since 1962 (J Cantello & T Hodge *in litt.*). It breeds in the Mediterranean and off northwest Africa, dispersing into the North Atlantic and wintering off South Africa.   *Richard Fairbank*

Great Shearwater   *Puffinus gravis*

Status:- A very rare vagrant (one record).

The remains of one were found at Rye Harbour on 27 November 1938, six days after another, thought to have been dead for at least a week, had been found at Dungeness, Kent (Joy 1939).

This is the only record following the recent withdrawal, much to the credit of the observer concerned, of a previously published record of one flying west past Langney Point on 4 June 1956.

Variable numbers of this impressive Atlantic shearwater are recorded off the British Isles each year, for example, 1693 in 1991 but only 27 in 1992 (Evans 1993a). Breeding at three main sites in the South Atlantic, it migrates clockwise around the north Atlantic from June to October, most being in the northeast Atlantic during August and September (BWP). There are no records from Hampshire and only seven from Kent, of which only three have been since 1962 (J Cantello & T Hodge *in litt.*).   *Richard Fairbank*

Sooty Shearwater   *Puffinus griseus*

Status:- A very scarce autumn visitor.

Until 1961 des Forges & Harber recorded a total of four, the first of which was found dead at Seaford Head on 7 June 1850. Since then, there have been records in 25 years totalling 215 birds, all in the period 14 July (1968, Selsey Bill) to 24 December (1989, Hastings), except for one observed from a fishing boat 8 km off Brighton on 1 February 1989. Most have been off Langney Point and Selsey Bill, flying west on days with strong onshore winds and frontal rain.

No more than seven have been seen in any one year, except in 1987 when the unprecedented total of 164 was recorded. Of these, 160 flew west in four hours off Langney Point on 9 October. The movement was also observed at Dungeness, Kent where 406 were recorded on this date (Davenport 1989).

The cumulative monthly totals of all records for the county up to the end of 1994 are shown below:

Jun	Jul	Aug	Sep	Oct	Nov	Dec	Jan	Feb
1	3	10	26	171	5	2	-	1

Sooty Shearwaters breed in the sub-Antarctic and then migrate rapidly across equatorial seas to winter in the North Atlantic and North Pacific (BWP).   *Paul James*

Manx Shearwater   *Puffinus puffinus*

Status:- A scarce spring and autumn passage migrant.

Manx Shearwaters occur annually in Sussex, although numbers may vary considerably from year to year. They are most frequent in spring and autumn but have been recorded in every month except January (although one was found long dead at Brighton Marina on 11 January 1986). The extreme dates are 5 February (1989, Newhaven) and 28 December (1990, Worthing).

There were no March records before 1977, but between then and 1984 a total of eight was recorded in that month in five different years. Of these, one flying west off Selsey Bill on 14 March 1979 was the earliest. Since 1984, however, there have been no March records and in some years birds have not appeared until May, when the largest spring movements normally occur. Summer records are not unusual (e.g. 16 flying east off Selsey Bill on 24 June 1979) and autumn movements may occur at any time from August onwards, but especially in September and October. There was only one November record before 1962 (des Forges & Harber) and only one other to 1976 (Shrubb) but more recently there have been records in this month in four years, including an exceptional movement of 29 flying west off Ferring on 20 November 1980.

The largest movements observed in Sussex have been in May and October. At Beachy Head, 81 flew east and three west on 28 May 1972 while in 1975 there were 64 east on 8 May and a further 126 east the following day. Unprecedented numbers occurred in May 1983 following the displacement of a large number of birds into the eastern part of the Channel. At Portland, Dorset, *ca.* 1600 flew east on 1 May and the following morning many were observed from the Sussex coast returning down-Channel as weather conditions improved (Newnham 1984). Totals included 159 off Beachy Head, 82 off Worthing and 177 off Selsey Bill, all flying west. On other days a further 66 were recorded, bringing the total for spring 1983 to a minimum of 233 or possibly as many as 495. Another large movement on 22 May 1984 was unusual in that birds were recorded passing both up and down-Channel. At Worthing 91 flew east and 47 west, while counts for other sites included 25 east off Brighton, 80 east and six west off Hove, 36 east and two west off Lancing, 47 west off Church Norton and 21 east and 11 west off Selsey Bill. The movements in 1983 and 1984 both occurred in cyclonic weather conditions with strong onshore winds and the records probably involve significant duplications.

The largest numbers recorded in autumn were in October 1987. Frontal rain and winds veering from southwest to south-southeast on 9 October produced totals of 40 at Langney Point and 13 at Worthing, all flying west. This passage was also observed at Dungeness, Kent where a total of 241 was recorded (Davenport 1989). A further movement on 18 October, two days after the great storm, comprised 24 at Selsey Bill and 15 at Beachy Head, again all flying west.

The only recent inland record was of one found exhausted at Moorhead Farm between Horsham and Crawley on 15 September 1980. It was released the following day at Warnham Mill Pond.   *Paul James*

Mediterranean Shearwater

Puffinus yelkouan

Status:- A rare vagrant (42 records involving 61 birds).

Following singles off Langney Point on 26 August (Alder, Harber & James 1952) and 24 November 1951 (Harber 1953), a further 18 were recorded up until the end of 1961. Of these, ten were in 1960 including a total of eight that flew west off Selsey Bill on 21 June. Since then, there have been records in 16 years totalling 41 birds (fig. 2), at Selsey Bill (20), Worthing (9), Beachy Head (6), Langney Point (2) and Brighton, Goring, Pagham Harbour and Seaford (1 each).

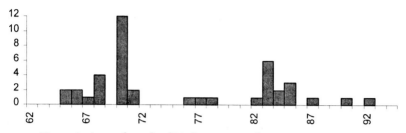

Figure 2. Annual totals of Mediterranean Shearwaters, 1962 - 94.

The cumulative monthly totals for the periods 1951-61 and 1962-94 are shown below.

	Apr	May	Jun	Jul	Aug	Sep	Oct	Nov
1951-61	-	2	8	2	2	3	2	1
1962-94	3	3	1	8	14	11	1	-
Total	3	5	9	10	16	14	3	1

The extreme dates were 13 April 1983 at Beachy Head and 24 November 1951 at Langney Point. All records since 1962 have been of 1-3 birds, except for a party of nine off Selsey Bill on 16 August 1970.

Formerly called Balearic Shearwater, it has now been given full species status following its 'split' from Manx Shearwater (*BOURC* 1992). *Paul James*

Audubon's Shearwater

Puffinus lherminieri

Status:- One old record, no longer considered acceptable.

One found being attacked by gulls in Bexhill on 7 January 1936 was taken into care but died shortly afterwards (Harrison 1936). The only British record of this small tropical shearwater, it is no longer considered acceptable, in part, at least, due to its indirect association with the 'Hastings Rarities' (*BOURC* 1978, Bourne 1988). *Richard Fairbank*

Storm Petrel

Hydrobates pelagicus

Status:- A rare vagrant, mainly in autumn after severe gales.

Walpole-Bond referred to innumerable reports for both spring and autumn, but des Forges & Harber recorded only 19 between 1946 and 1960. This apparent decline has continued, despite the increase in sea-watching, with just 13 records during 1962-94:

1967:   One flying west past Selsey Bill on 29 October.
1969:   One off Bexhill on 16 October.
1971:   One found dead at an unspecified locality on 27 September had been ringed in Pembrokeshire on 30 June 1969.
1976:   One flying west past Selsey Bill on 15 October.
1980:   One flying west past Shoreham Beach on 4 September.
1983:   One flying west past Brighton Marina on 17 October.
        One picked up exhausted on the beach at St Leonards on 30 November.
1987:   One picked up exhausted in a garden at Ferring on 16 October was kept overnight and released the following morning.
1988:   One found dead at Beachy Head on 4 April.
        One flying west past Galley Hill, Bexhill on 9 October.
        One found dead under power lines at Birling Gap on 16 October.
1991:   An oiled bird found on a boat, recently arrived from Cornwall, at Littlehampton Marina on 3 September.
1994:   One seen from a fishing boat, 10 km off Brighton, on 6 July

The cumulative monthly totals for the periods 1946-61 and 1962-94 are shown below:

	Apr	May	Jun	Jul	Aug	Sep	Oct	Nov	Dec
1946-61	1	1	2	-	-	-	1	13	1
1962-94	1	-	-	1	-	3	8	1	-
Total	2	1	2	1	-	3	9	14	1

There are old reports for all other months except for August and of storm-driven birds found inland.   *Paul James*

Leach's Petrel   *Oceanodroma leucorhoa*

Status:- A rare vagrant in autumn and winter, usually appearing after gales.

Until 1961 des Forges & Harber recorded a total of about 75 birds, of which 60 were up to 1938. Since then, there have been records in eight years totalling 51 individuals as follows:

1964:   One off Langney Point on 31 December.
1966:   One picked up exhausted at Saltdean on 19 October was taken into care and released three days later.
1982:   One at sea 1 km off Brighton on 12 September.
        One at Bewl Water on 23 September.
1986:   One found dead at Bexhill on 10 September had struck the window of the De La Warr Pavilion.
1987:   One found dying at Westfield on 16 October.
        One flying west at Brighton Marina on 17 October.
        One flying west at Church Norton on 17 October.
1989:   One at the mouth of the River Arun at Littlehampton on 24 December.
        A total of 31 flying east at Birling Gap during the morning of 25 December.
        Seven off Brighton Marina during the afternoon of 25 December.
1991:   One on the River Adur at Shoreham-by-Sea on 2 January.
        One flying west at Langney Point on 28 September.
1992:   One at sea 10 km off Brighton Marina on 13 September.
        One at Rock-a-Nore, Hastings on 9 November.

The unprecedented county total of 39 in 1989 was the largest ever, far exceeding the four recorded in the 'wreck' of 1952 (des Forges & Harber).

The cumulative monthly totals of all records for the periods 1948-61 and 1962-94 are shown below:

	Sep	Oct	Nov	Dec	Jan
1946-61	3	5	5	-	-
1962-93	5	6	1	41	1
Total	8	11	6	41	1

The extreme dates during 1962-94 were 10 September and 2 January. Additionally, there is one old record for May (1895, Shoreham-by-Sea).

Paul James

Gannet *Morus bassanus*

Status:- A fairly common passage migrant and non-breeding summer visitor; once scarce but now increasingly numerous in winter.

Gannets occur in Sussex in every month of the year, but the largest numbers are recorded between March and May and August and October.

Given that the assembly of adults at most British gannetries is from early January (BWP), it is likely that many of the Gannets observed passing up-Channel in spring are non-breeders. Newnham (1987) suggested that these birds may attend the North Sea colonies before being sufficiently mature to breed. He also suggested that some of the westward movements observed in spring may involve birds on fishing expeditions from Alderney and Brittany, as Gannets may travel up to 400 miles to feed (BWP). The largest movements so far recorded in spring were of 794 that flew east at Splash Point, Seaford between 10 and 18 May 1983 and 688 that did likewise between 13 and 18 May 1993. The former movement included 213 on 14 May, this being the highest day total for the county in spring.

In the summer months, feeding parties of 100 or more may be seen offshore. Again these may have originated from the nearest breeding colonies but they may also comprise non-breeding birds, thought to be summering in the English Channel.

In autumn, large numbers may be recorded, particularly on days with strong onshore winds. Such movements have included 800 flying west off Beachy Head on 18 September 1976, 339 west off Selsey Bill on 29 September

1990, 309 west off Worthing on 8 October 1989 and 262 east off Selsey on 8 September 1993.

Shrubb referred to Gannets as scarce or rare from December to March. However, in recent years there has been a marked increase as shown by movements, at Seaford of 167 east on 21 February 1991 and 111 east on 6 March 1988, and at Beachy Head of 115 east on 26 February 1978. At Brighton Marina 100 flew east on 27 December 1981.

Birds are occasionally found inland, the most noteworthy of which in recent years were singles at Bewl Water on 8 August 1980 and Weir Wood Reservoir on 25 October 1991.

Of the 19 Gannets ringed outside the county and recovered in Sussex, 14 originated from Scotland, three from Wales and two from Alderney, Channel Islands. *Paul James*

Cormorant *Phalacrocorax carbo*

Status:- A scarce breeder and common winter visitor.

Cormorants have recently started breeding on the Sussex coast after a gap of some 50 years. The population of non-breeding and wintering birds is increasing steadily, both on the coast and inland. Walpole-Bond found references to nesting at Seaford Head in the 19th century but seemed not convinced of their accuracy. There was none there from 1904 but he knew of 1-3 pairs in some years in the Belle Tout to Beachy Head area. Searches of the Sussex coast proved negative in 1957, 1965, 1969 and 1983-84 (Prater 1985). Then in 1985 a pair hatched two young on the cliffs near Fairlight, a regular roosting site, and the following year four pairs nested and produced three young. The next count, in 1992, was of 28 nests, most of them containing young. Two sub-adults showed nest building activity at Rye Harbour in 1986 and several adults built rudimentary nests there in 1988 while in 1991 one pair attended a nest.

Cormorants are present throughout Sussex in all months of the year, the considerable non-breeding population being swelled in the autumn by birds dispersing from colonies in other parts of Britain (Winter Atlas). Many feed close inshore along the coast, but numbers there have not been properly assessed. Up to 200 may be seen in Pagham Harbour and at Rye Harbour, and gatherings on Bognor Pier may approach 200 at times. Cormorants also feed along our rivers, in lakes and reservoirs and in ponds, in one case, Mallydams Wood, as small as just over half an acre (Hughes 1982). When fishing they do so individually, but in Chichester, Pagham and Rye Harbours and at the larger reservoirs they gather in large groups on secluded banks or islands to dry their wings and loaf. They are regular at Weir Wood Reservoir and Bewl Water, respectively 32 and 25 km from the coast.

Communal roosting at night is usual, and some of the roosts are long established and well known. The word roost is often used for daytime resting or loafing gatherings, but known nocturnal roosts in recent use are listed as follows from west to east:

Chichester Cathedral

Up to eight birds roosted on Chichester Cathedral in August 1973 and on a few occasions in autumn 1974 (Hughes 1975).

Chichester Gravel Pits

At Chichester Gravel Pits birds fishing the lakes during the day are joined at sunset by parties flying in from Pagham Harbour. On occasion they are joined by some of the birds which collect by day on Bognor Pier (Knight & Cox 1996) and possibly by some from Chichester Harbour. During summer and early autumn they roost on pylons and power wires over the Trout Lakes, and during winter on trees on the islands in Ivy Lake. Counts of over 100 are common and are sometimes of 200 or more, as in March 1993 when 295 were present.

South Stoke

A tree roost was first noticed along the bank of the Arun near South Stoke in 1950, and ca. 30 birds were counted there in 1956 and 53 in January 1962. In March 1970, 103 birds flew towards this roost and in December 1980 there were 140-150 there. On 16 February 1986, 200 Cormorants roosted and on 26 January 1993, there were 307. It has become apparent that some or all of the birds collecting on Bognor Pier during the day regularly fly along the coast and up the River Arun to roost at South Stoke, a flight of some 15 km.

Southwick and Adur Levels

In the 1960s Cormorants roosted on pylons on the coast at Southwick, but in 1972 there were 29 recorded on pylons on the Adur Levels between King's Barn and Wyckham Farms, north of Upper Beeding and 8 km inland. This roost has been in continuous use since, recently in all months of the year, with a peak count of 188 in October 1994.

Ardingly Reservoir

In mid-Sussex there is a tree roost at Ardingly Reservoir, 25 km inland. Here birds fly in from the east to join those at the reservoir during the day, probably from Weir Wood Reservoir. Four birds were recorded roosting there in January 1980 and 26 in February 1984, since when the numbers have built up so that now winter counts of between 40 and 50 are usual.

Newhaven Cliffs

There are occasional reports of roosting on the cliffs between Brighton and Newhaven, the highest count being 26 in February 1984. This habit may be more regular than the few reports received suggest.

Ouse Valley

Pylons are used in the Ouse Valley near Lewes, and in 1986 this roost was occupied in every month of the year, numbers ranging from two in June to 24 in December.

Pevensey Levels

There are occasional reports of a small pylon roost on Pevensey Levels.

Fairlight

The cliff roost between Hastings and Fairlight is in regular use but is not often counted. It is used by birds spending the day at Rye Harbour and in Rye

Bay, and is the site at which birds returned to nest in 1985. The highest count was 95 in October 1980.

The Sussex population of Cormorants has clearly increased greatly during recent years, but past numbers are difficult to estimate with any certainty from the few counts available. In 1947, 50 were reported on the cliffs at Seaford Head and in 1948 between one and seven were noted at Rye Harbour between January and March and again between September and December. On 31 October of that year, 96 were seen at Thorney Island. In 1953 there were some 200 in Chichester Harbour at the end of the year, and in 1954 120 at Rye Harbour in February, but these may have been exceptional peak counts. The Warden's Report for Pagham Harbour LNR for 1978 mentions "Regularly over ten in the Harbour during the winter, with 30 on Tern Island on 2 December", whereas that for 1993 records significant numbers throughout the year as shown by the following table of monthly maxima at this locality.

Jan	Feb	Mar	Apr	May	Jun	Jul	Aug	Sep	Oct	Nov	Dec
105	50	89	100	157	81	178	176	199	159	189	40

A similar increase is apparent at Rye Harbour, where counts in excess of 100 are frequent, but mainly between June and September. Reporting the Sussex results of a national census in the winter 1985/86, Watson (1987) suggested a minimum of 400 birds and a maximum of 600 wintering. However during the winters of 1992/93, 1993/94 and 1994/95 simultaneous counts of the roosts at Chichester Gravel Pits and at South Stoke regularly gave a total of over 200 and twice of over 300 for these sites alone, and a county total of over 1000 is suggested (Knight & Cox 1996).

Ringing has shown that many of the Cormorants in Sussex come from colonies in Scotland, northern England, Ireland and Wales. There have been two Sussex recoveries of birds ringed in the Channel Islands. This mainly represents dispersal from the colonies of juvenile birds, but a colour ringed individual hatched in the Netherlands and seen in the Pagham area in 1990, 1993 and 1994 indicates a degree of winter site fidelity notwithstanding a sighting near Arcachan, France in 1992. Five colour-ringed birds hatched in colonies in Denmark have been seen at Rye Harbour.   *Barrie Watson*

Shag   *Phalacrocorax aristotelis*

Status:- A scarce winter visitor and passage migrant.

The Shag has only been recorded regularly in Sussex since 1950. Between 1950 and 1976 from one to about 30 were seen annually, except in 1960 when there were about 160, mainly in the spring (Shrubb). There were only five inland records for this period, totalling 13 birds, including a party of six at Weir Wood Reservoir on 18 March 1962.

The monthly totals for the periods 1950-61, 1962-76 and 1977-93, which confirm that there has been an increase in the number of Shags recorded in the county, are shown below.

	Jan	Feb	Mar	Apr	May	Jun	Jul	Aug	Sep	Oct	Nov	Dec
1950-61	26	29	123	76	58	41	27	11	6	8	18	11
1962-76	15	17	27	42	49	7	8	23	23	17	25	23
1977-93	108	96	98	104	139	21	24	36	68	101	86	97
Total	149	142	248	222	246	69	59	70	97	126	129	131

In autumn, most appear following gales, for example, 13 off Selsey Bill on 22 October 1989 and up to seven there in September 1992.

Between November and April, the species is most frequent at Brighton Marina where the maximum counts have been 16 on 16 January 1985 and 15 in April 1988. Occasional large gatherings may be recorded elsewhere, including seven in Newhaven Harbour on 5 March 1988 and 15 in Shoreham Harbour on 16 March 1988, although the close proximity of these sites to Brighton suggests that some duplication is likely.

Small numbers of Shags are now frequently recorded at the main sea-watching localities in spring. A total of 12 off Splash Point, Seaford on 14 May 1993 was noteworthy, as were 13 at Brighton Marina on 3 July 1991, a month in which the species is normally very scarce.

During 1977-93, there were records of inland birds in ten years. Most were at Bewl Water (24) and Weir Wood Reservoir (17) but, unusually, two were at Lindfield Pond from 15 March to 6 July 1988 and from 7 to 12 January 1991, one remaining until 26 January. Other records were for Lewes and Barcombe Reservoir (2 each) and Ardingly Reservoir, Arlington Reservoir and Combe Haven (1 each). The cumulative monthly totals of all inland records for the county are shown below.

Jan	Feb	Mar	Apr	May	Jun	Jul	Aug	Sep	Oct	Nov	Dec
23	8	19	3	2	3	2	1	3	9	4	4

Of 45 Shags ringed outside Sussex and recovered within the county, 19 had been ringed in Scotland, 19 in northern England, three in the Channel Islands, two in Wales and singles in Ireland and southern England. One ringed on the Isle of May on 18 July 1979 was found dead at Bewl Water, 599 km SSE, on 4 March 1982.   *Paul James*

Bittern   *Botaurus stellaris*

Status:- A very scarce winter visitor.

The Bittern is of almost annual occurrence in Sussex, having been recorded in 30 of the 33 years during 1962-94. It is essentially a winter visitor, although numbers vary depending on the severity of the weather. From 1961/62 to 1977/78 an average of about three per winter was recorded. However, between 1978/79 and 1986/87, when there was a series of harsh winters, this increased to almost seven (fig. 3). In the hard winter of 1978/79, a record 189 Bitterns were recorded in Britain (Bibby 1981), and this was reflected in the correspondingly high total for Sussex. Unfortunately, several of these were found either dead or exhausted.

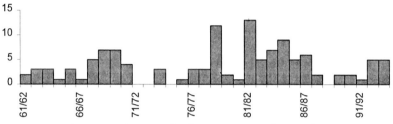

Figure 3. Winter totals of Bitterns, 1961/62 - 93/94.

The cumulative monthly totals for the period 1962-94 shown below confirm that most Bitterns have been recorded during December to February, their arrival often coinciding with the onset of severe weather. Few are seen after mid-March but there were singles on Pevensey Levels on 10 April 1966, at Rye Harbour from 13 to 15 April 1970 and at Filsham Reedbed from 9 to 24 April 1988.

Jul	Aug	Sep	Oct	Nov	Dec	Jan	Feb	Mar	Apr	May	Jun
1	1	2	-	11	32	67	35	23	7	-	2

Although Bitterns have bred in Kent, there is no suggestion that they have ever done so in Sussex. There have, however, been occasional records for the summer months, the most recent of which were at Pett Level on 23 June 1970, Weir Wood Reservoir on 4 July 1977, Chichester Gravel Pits on 13 June 1982 and at Icklesham on 26 August 1989, the latter probably that seen at Pett Pools a week later. There are no May records and the most recent for October was in 1957 at Pagham Lagoon.

Locality	No. of winters in which recorded	Range of winters in which recorded	Total no. of birds
Chichester Gravel Pits	13	1963-93	15
Rye Harbour	13	1968-94	13
Arundel WWT	9	1978-87	9
Filsham	7	1971-88	9
Weir Wood Reservoir	7	1967-93	7
Pett Level	6	1975-94	6

Table 1. Totals of Bitterns at principal localities, 1961/62 - 93/94.

In view of their secretive nature, it is likely that Bitterns are under-recorded in the county. Of the *ca.* 126 reported during 1962-94, most were seen in reedbeds or in relatively small areas of reeds in dykes, gravel pits and reservoirs (table 1).

Bitterns have also been recorded at sites with few if any reeds, such as the Crumbles, where there were singles on 13 January 1979, 12 January 1985 and 3 March 1985, and Newhaven Tide Mills, where there was one on 11 January 1982.

Unusual records were those of singles seen flying over the Downs at No Man's Land, near Sompting, on 7 November 1986 and over the A26 near Eridge on 3 March 1991. *Richard Kelly*

American Bittern *Botaurus lentiginosus*

Status:- A very rare vagrant (three very old records, all in late autumn).

Three were recorded well before 1962 (des Forges & Harber): one shot on Pevensey Levels on 26 November 1867, one obtained at Amberley Wild Brooks on 30 November 1883 and a female caught alive in a chicken run at Upper Cottage, Hollingbury Park, Brighton on 24 October 1909 (Langton 1909). The latter two are in the Booth Museum (BoMNH 204081 and 204082 respectively).

This enigmatic bittern has become less frequent in the British Isles with only ten of the 60 recorded up to 1994 being since the beginning of 1962. It breeds across North America and winters south to Central America.
Richard Fairbank

Little Bittern *Ixobrychus minutus*

Status:- A rare vagrant (29 individuals recorded).

Prior to 1962 there were about 17 records, those dated being in March, April (2), May (5), August (2), September and October (2) (des Forges & Harber), although one record, for May, has not been traced. The earliest was shot at Carter's Farm, near Pett on 15 March 1947 and the latest was obtained at Grand Parade, Eastbourne on 31 October 1888. A male which flew into a window in Hartington Road, Brighton in April 1937 is in the Booth Museum (BoMNH 207305) as is a juvenile male caught in a stable in Hove on 3 September 1894 (BoMNH 207542).

Twelve individuals have been recorded since the beginning of 1962:

1964: A male at Chichester Gravel Pits from 29 May to 2 June.
1966: A male at Steyning Mill Pond from 30 April to 5 May.
1967: A male at Ivy Lake, Chichester from 22 to 28 July.
1969: A male at Chichester Gravel Pits on 8 June.
1971: A male by the River Adur, near Shipley Church, from 23 April to 2 May.
       A male at Pagham Harbour North Wall on 9 May.
1977: A male found dead at Birling Gap on 30 April appeared to have caught itself on a wire fence a day or two previously.
       A juvenile at Ternery Pool, Rye Harbour from 19 to 27 August, with two juveniles seen on 23 August.
1986: A female at Shoreham Sanctuary, below Mill Hill on 1-2 June.
1987: A male at Ivy Lake, Chichester from 10 to 15 May.
1988: A male picked up exhausted on the A259 at Hove Lagoon on the morning of 30 March was released later that day at Oreham Common where it remained until 12 April (Sadler 1988, *Brit. Birds* 81: plates 206 and 207).

Since 1962 most records have been in spring, with one in late March and eight between 23 April and 8 June. Four have been seen at Chichester Gravel Pits and two (together) at Rye Harbour. Over half the records relate to individuals present for at least five days.

There were over 150 records of this engaging species in the British Isles during 1962-94 and it has bred once for certain, in Yorkshire in 1984, although it is perhaps now declining as a vagrant as its range in Europe contracts (Rogers *et al* 1994). It breeds across Europe to western Asia and in Africa where European birds winter. There are also isolated populations south of the Himalayas and in Australia. *Richard Fairbank*

Night Heron *Nycticorax nycticorax*

Status:- A rare, mainly spring, vagrant (26 individuals recorded).

Before 1962 there were seven records (des Forges & Harber): six between 1816 and 1895 (one undated, one shot 'prior to' 13 May, one in autumn, two in September and one in November) and one in 1954. The last, a juvenile in an alder hedge near Lancing College on 12 December, was possibly an escape from captivity.

About 19 individuals have been recorded since the beginning of 1962, all but four since 1987 (when five were seen):

1969: A juvenile picked up at Rye Harbour on 29 September died shortly afterwards.
1970: A sub-adult at Sidlesham Ferry on 27 May.
1975: An adult at Rye Harbour from 2 to 4 September.
1983: An adult at Slinfold on 21 April.
1987: A first-year and a second-year in the lower Cuckmere Valley on 4 May, the latter remaining to 6 May.
An adult and a probable adult at Chichester Gravel Pits on the evening of 5 May.
A first-year, possibly the Cuckmere individual, near Chalvington on three dates between 24 May and 7 June.
1988: An adult at Woods Mill on 6 May.
1989: An adult near Piddinghoe from 30 April to 3 May.
1990: An adult at Littlehampton Golf Course on 15-16 April when it departed east.
An adult on the Long and Narrow Pits at Rye Harbour from 27 April to 1 May, with a second adult on 2 May and an adult on 23 June (possibly one of the individuals seen in May).
1992: An adult at Pulborough Brooks on 8 April.
1993: An adult on an island at Castle Water, Rye Harbour on 10 September.
1994: An adult at the western end of Thorney Great Deep on the evening of 19 April.
A juvenile at Chilver Bridge Farm, Arlington on 23 December.

The increase in records since the mid-1980s is very pronounced (fig. 4), possibly reflecting the increasing breeding population in France (Tucker & Heath 1994).

Since 1962 individuals have been found in April (6), May (8), June, September (3) and December, although it is possible that all but two of those recorded since 1983 had arrived during the period 8 April to 6 May. This is in complete contrast with earlier records, most of which were in autumn.

Six have been recorded at Rye Harbour since 1962 with two at both the lower Cuckmere Valley and Chichester Gravel Pits and singles at Arlington,

Chalvington, Littlehampton, Pagham Harbour, Piddinghoe, Pulborough, Slindon, Thorney Island and Woods Mill.

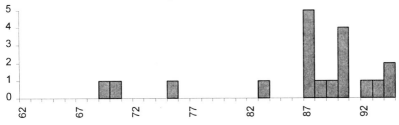

Figure 4. Annual totals of Night Herons, 1962 - 94.

There were nearly 350 records of this almost cosmopolitan species in the British Isles during 1962-94. The European populations winter in sub-Saharan Africa.   *Richard Fairbank*

Squacco Heron   *Ardeola ralloides*

Status:- A very rare vagrant (four records).

Three were recorded before 1962 (des Forges & Harber). One, shot at Warnham Mill Pond on the hottest day of summer 1849, was also described 'with assurance' as the first British record of Little Egret (Walpole-Bond)! One was found shot between Henfield and Steyning on about 30 September 1934 and used as a scarecrow before being 'discovered' and converted into a specimen, now in the Booth Museum (BoMNH 204054), and one was, rather surprisingly, seen in trees adjoining Manor Road, Brighton from 13:00 hrs to dusk on 29 April 1951 (Dawson 1952).

One at Holme Farm, Mannings Heath from 16 to 19 June 1982 is the only recent record.

There were 35 records of this subtly-plumaged heron in the British Isles during 1962-94. It breeds from Iberia to southwest Asia and in Africa, where European birds winter.   *Richard Fairbank*

Cattle Egret   *Bubulcus ibis*

Status:- A very rare vagrant (three spring records involving six individuals).

First recorded in 1962, when five were seen; there has been one since.

1962: Four in fields north of Pagham Harbour on 27 April with one being seen on
       29 April (Marr, Phillips & Sheldon 1963).
       One with cattle in water meadows at Lancing on 28 April was possibly one of
       the 'four'.
1986: One in fields adjacent to Pagham Harbour North Wall from 30 April to
       14 May.

In addition to the above, one at Ford from 14 to 20 December 1964, when it was captured by hand in a weak condition, and one on the Kent/Sussex border near Wittersham from 8 to 15 August 1974 were considered to be escapes. The main factors against the Ford individual were the unlikely time of year and its exceptional tameness. Had it been in more recent times the date would probably not have been detrimental as, for example, 13 of the 14 recorded in Britain during 1980-85 were in winter (Rogers *et al* 1986).

Prior to the 1962 occurrences in Sussex, there had only been two records of this opportunist heron in the British Isles, although by the end of 1994 the total stood at 75. It breeds across Europe, Asia, Africa and Australia and colonised the Americas earlier this century. European birds winter south to northwest Africa. *Richard Fairbank*

Little Egret *Egretta garzetta*

Status:- Formerly rare but now a scarce and increasing passage migrant and winter visitor.

Following the first at Manhood End on 10 June 1952 and in nearby Chichester Harbour from 2 July to 1 September 1952, a further four were recorded up to 1961 and then 23 during 1962-88 (fig. 5).

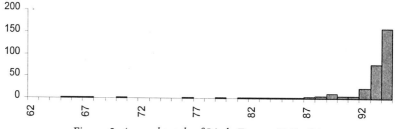

Figure 5. Annual totals of Little Egrets, 1962 - 94.

All records up until the end of 1988 were of single birds, except for two at Cuckmere Haven from 6 to 9 May 1988, and apart from those at Weir Wood Reservoir on 8-9 May 1982, Chichester Gravel Pits on 23 August 1986 and Waltham Brooks on 7-8 May 1988, all were at coastal localities. The earliest was at Rye Harbour on 18 April 1985 and the latest at West Wittering from 4 to 20 September 1987.

In 1989, two were recorded at Pagham Harbour from 16 to 26 July, after which there was an unprecedented influx into southern England. These birds were thought to have originated from Brittany where a post-breeding dispersal, mainly of juveniles, has been regular since about 1980 (Combridge & Parr 1992). Most were recorded in Chichester Harbour, especially at Dell Quay, where there was an increase from three on 29 August to five on 4 September and six on 30 September 1989. Up to three were recorded at this locality in October and two at Pilsey Island on 29th. One remained in Chichester Harbour until 9 April 1990, this being the first incidence of wintering by this species in the county.

In each subsequent autumn, the number of Little Egrets has increased, most notably at Thorney Deeps which is now the main roosting site in Sussex (table 2). Two were recorded at this locality from 12 December 1991 to 23 April 1992, 12 from 29 to 31 August 1992, 13 from 5 March to 2 April 1993,

57 from 30 August to 7 September 1993 and a staggering 98 on 25 August 1994.

	Jan	Feb	Mar	Apr	May	Jun	Jul	Aug	Sep	Oct	Nov	Dec
1991	2	1	-	-	-	-	-	1	-	1	-	2
1992	2	2	2	2	1	-	5	12	11	7	7	11
1993	11	12	13	13	3	6	17	57	57	32	37	27
1994	32	36	33	28	8	8	24	98	94	88	82	77

Table 2. Monthly maxima of Little Egrets at Thorney Deeps, 1991 - 94.

Reports from other coastal areas have included, at Pagham Harbour, three on 22 August 1991, five on 12 June 1993, six on 26 September 1993 and 12 on 6 September 1994, and, in the lower Cuckmere Valley, three from 22 to 29 August 1992 and four on 13 September 1992 and 6 May 1994.

The cumulative monthly totals for 1962-88 and 1989-94 show that the pattern of occurrence has changed, with the largest numbers now recorded in August and September rather than in late spring when the species is now least frequent.

	Jan	Feb	Mar	Apr	May	Jun	Jul	Aug	Sep	Oct	Nov	Dec
1962-88	-	-	-	1	17	2	3	2	1	-	-	-
1989-94	53	56	53	53	30	22	61	208	201	148	141	129

Unusually, there were five well inland at Pulborough Brooks on 28 July 1993 and singles in both June and August 1994. Other inland records for 1989-94 were of singles at Weir Wood Reservoir on 14 August 1989, Kneppmill Pond on 26 October 1989 and at Bewl Water from 25 July to 4 September 1992 and on 27 April 1993. *Barry Collins*

Great White Egret *Egretta alba*

Status:- A very rare vagrant (two records).

First recorded in 1985, there are two records:

1985: A plumed adult on the eastern part of Thorney Great Deep on 15 June departed west into Hampshire.
1990: One in the middle of Pagham Harbour on 5 August.

The 1990 individual was seen on the Isle of Wight on 6 August and was presumably that recorded at Dungeness, Kent on 8 August (Rogers *et al* 1991).

There were over 60 records of this cosmopolitan heron in the British Isles during 1962-94. None of these were before 1974 and most have been since 1980. The nearest breeding population is in the Netherlands, which was colonised in the 1970s (Dymond *et al* 1989), and these birds winter in the north Mediterranean. *Richard Fairbank*

Grey Heron *Ardea cinerea*

Status:- A fairly common resident.

The Atlas map shows the tetrad distribution of the current 15 heronries in Sussex. The nests are all in trees of a variety of species, both coniferous and deciduous. The heronries are often occupied over very many years, and there are also reports of single nests which may be used for one or a few years. At some sites, nests of Rooks and Herons are interspersed or in adjacent parts of the same wood, without much interaction.

Historically heronries have been mentioned in estate records, so that we know of one at Iden in 1297 and one of 150 nests near Herstmonceux in around 1550. Walpole-Bond gives an account of all heronries known up to 1938. Cawkell (1935) gives more detail, published updates in 1937 and 1948 and has made his personal notes available.

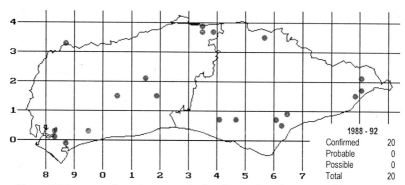

Since 1928 counts have been made for the national census of heronries, and we have reasonably complete annual counts for Sussex since 1950. The 1928 census of six Sussex heronries revealed 292-300 nests, a marked change from 1866 when one alone in Great Sowdens Wood near Brede contained about 400 nests. In 1938 twelve heronries and a solitary nest totalled 328. Counts were incomplete during and after the war but consecutive counts at Leasam showed a decrease from 70 in 1946 to 52 in 1947, following prolonged hard weather in the intervening winter. In 1950 there were 225 nests in Sussex, in 1960 145 and in 1962 127, but in 1963 after the very prolonged cold winter the total had dropped to 73. Fig. 6 shows a gradual recovery with 160 nests in 1969 and more than 193 in 1976. Since then the numbers have ranged between a low of 177 in 1986 and a high of 221 in 1982 but have been mostly just over the 200 level. The remarkable storm of October 1987 severely damaged the trees at some sites, and in the following spring some heronries had fewer nests but others more, so that there was no significant change in the county total.

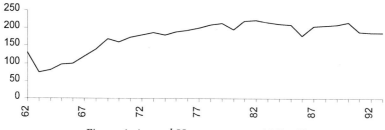

Figure 6. Annual Heronry counts, 1962 - 93.

The sites currently and recently occupied are discussed in order from west to east, grouped according to habitat where relevant:

Fishbourne and Sidlesham

The heronry at Old Park Wood, Fishbourne is on the edge of Chichester Channel. It was recorded, without a count, in 1872 and there is a record of a single nest in the area in 1878. It was then extinct for 52 years, during which time there was a heronry of up to 30 nests in Goodwood Park. Since a single nest in 1931 and four the following year, Old Park Wood has been occupied continuously, increasing slowly to 37 nests in 1962. After the following hard winter the number dropped to 21 and has ranged between 16 and 37 since then. Between 1946 and 1951 there was a satellite heronry 4 km distant on the opposite side of Chichester Channel at Itchenor with up to 18 nests. Since 1960 there has also been a heronry, usually of six to eight nests, at Sidlesham, immediately north of Pagham Harbour. This is 12 km from Old Park Wood, but clearly in the same habitat area.

Gillham's Moor

In the northwest of the county a heronry of four nests was found in 1992 in woodland at Gillham's Moor near Liphook, almost on the border with Surrey. It is thought that there may have been a heronry there for some years. Prior to this the only records from this area were of two nests at Rogate in 1963 and in 1964.

Flansham

In 1987 a tree near Yapton was noticed to contain one and possibly two nests. The tree was blown over in the October 1987 storm. In the following year herons attempted to nest in the fallen tree and adjacent low hedgerow, but then moved nearer to Flansham. In 1990 there were eight nests, in 1991 nine and in 1992 16. This new heronry is on the coastal plain, with its rifes and ditches, and near to the lower Arun Valley.

North Park Wood, Parham

A heronry established at Michelgrove in Angmering Park in about 1810, moved to Parham Park, some 8 km north, between 1826 and 1832, possibly due to tree felling at Michelgrove. Parham is on the east side of the Arun Valley and close to Amberley Wild Brooks and to Pulborough Brooks. There were 117 nests here in 1872 and 100 in 1876. About 30 nests were recorded in 1901 but in 1911 there were 60 to 80. The count in the 1928 census was 58 and in 1935 it was 45. In 1947 after a hard winter there were 29 nests but by 1950, 46 and the totals remained at about or a little over 40 nests for the next 15 years. In 1963 after an exceptionally hard winter there were only 11 nests and thereafter a gradual recovery to 41 in 1970. Totals remained at this level with minor fluctuations until the trees were badly damaged in the October 1987 storm, following which there were only 19 nests in 1988-90, 22 in 1991 and 17 in 1992-93.

Wyckham Wood near Henfield, and Knepp

In the Adur Valley a nest was recorded in Wyckham Wood in 1951 and in 1959 there were 13 nests. It is suspected that counts of nine or fewer nests between 1960 and 1977 were made from the nearby river bank and not from under the trees. An accurate count in 1978 found 15 nests and counts have ranged between 13 and 21 since, except for ten in 1989. Birds from this colony have been watched flying the 9 km down the Adur to Shoreham-by-Sea to feed, and returning with food for the young.

Several nests were noticed in 1975 at Knepp, some 8 km NNW of Wyckham Wood on the western arm of the upper Adur. There was a count of eight in the following year and the totals have been between nine and 16 since. The founding of this heronry does not correspond with any change in numbers at Wyckham Wood.

Firle, Glynde Place and Iford

On the edge of the Glynde Levels and near the Ouse valley, the heronry at Firle Park was established in 1917. It is on an island in the Decoy Lake and mainly in *Ilex* trees, but in some years there have been a few nests elsewhere in the park. At the 1928 census there were 20 nests, and between 24 and 34 in the late 1930s. Post-war counts were less than ten, during which period the main heronry was 4 km to the north at Glynde Place, and the low counts of five in 1963 and in 1964 do not necessarily reflect the effects of the preceding cold winters. In 1968 there were 34 nests and the counts have ranged between 30 and 44 since with a peak of 48 in 1990. In 1992 there was a drop to 15, probably due to estate work underneath the trees early in the breeding season.

Nesting at Glynde Place started in 1939, at about the time that numbers in Firle Park became low. In 1955 there were 31 nests here and only three reported at Firle. There was then a steady reduction to three nests in 1960 and 1961 and none in 1962, without a corresponding increase at Firle Park. Up to eight nests were counted each year between 1964 and 1970, but none since.

In the Ouse valley south of Lewes there have been two nests in a wood near Iford each year since 1990. This is near an earlier heronry of up to five nests immediately south of Lewes between 1936 and 1941.

Eridge Old Park

This heronry was founded between 1885 and 1890 and had eight nests in 1928. There are lakes in the park, and the site, south of Tunbridge Wells, is some 5 km from the upper reaches of the River Medway in Kent, but we have no positive information on the main foraging area of these birds. There were 15 nests in 1935 and 24 in the following year, but only eight reported in 1943 and in 1944. By 1948 there were 34. There were then between 29 and 38 in most years until 22 in 1962 and only 11 in 1963. The numbers have stayed low, with seven in 1969, 19 in 1985 and in 1989, and between nine and 18 in the intervening years. In 1992 and in 1993 the count has again been 11 nests.

Bewl Water

Six nests were built in woodland at the recently constructed Bewl Water reservoir in 1978 and four in 1979. The site was then disturbed by woodcutting and the herons deserted it.

Westdean and Charleston

In the lower Cuckmere valley there was a nest at Westdean in 1921 or 1922 and one in 1924. No more were reported until two nests in 1936 and then three or four annually until 1939. In 1946 there were three and in 1947 one, but none thereafter. Then in 1992, herons were seen carrying nesting material into a wood at Charleston and in 1993 eight nests were found there. Charleston and Westdean are only 1 km apart.

Glynleigh, Priesthawes, Wartling, Westham and Pevensey

The Herstmonceux and Wartling area, on the edge of Pevensey Levels, had a heronry of 150 nests in 1550. Originally in Heron Wood, Herstmonceux, by 1835 it was described as a small heronry at Windmill Hill Place. Fifty nests were noted in 1879, and between 25 and 35 from 1900 to 1907. In 1928 there were 46 or 48 nests. In the 1930s there were between 30 and 36 nests but tree felling caused a gradual transfer to Glynleigh, 7 km southwest, by 1948.

The Glynleigh heronry started in 1933 with "a few" nests and in 1937 there were ten. Counts then fluctuated between eight and 19, with a high count of 34 in 1955. In 1962 there were seven, in 1969 one, and none the following year. Meanwhile in 1962 three nests were found 1 km away at Priesthawes and numbers here built up to eight or ten nests between 1970 and 1975 as Glynleigh declined. From 1979 Priesthawes in turn declined to two or three nests in each year, the last being in 1989, but it was not until 1988 that it was noticed that there were six nests back at Glynleigh. In 1993 there were nine nests there.

The present Wartling heronries have developed from two nests near Boreham Street in 1959 and two near Wartling in 1963. Counts were less than ten until 1979, and 14 in 1981. Since then there have been two small heronries 0.5 km apart with a combined total of up to 18 nests.

There was a nest at Westham church in 1963, and one, two or three nests there in each subsequent year until 1991. Nearby at Pevensey there were up to three nests from 1979 to 1986.

Leasam, Winchelsea and Pett

The heronry in Leasam Wood, north of Rye, was founded with three nests in 1936, but is clearly related to earlier and larger heronries in the same area, overlooking the Brede and Tillingham river valleys and close to the Rother Levels and to Walland Marsh in Kent. There is an old record of a heronry at Iden prior to 1297. A heronry originally in Great Park Wood, Udimore, moved 1 km north to Great Sowdens Wood in 1840 and in about 1866 contained 400 nests. By 1886 there were 200 nests and in 1896 15 to 17. Meanwhile Aldershaw heronry, another 1 km north, was founded in 1892 and by 1928 contained about 106 nests. There were 121 nests in 1938 but then followed a rapid decline as birds moved to Leasam with one nest in 1944 and none thereafter. Leasam House had two or three nests in 1936 and 33 in 1942. In 1943, now in Leasam Wood, there were 50 nests and in 1946 70. Numbers declined to ten in 1962, before the hard winter, and to five in the following year, after which there was a very gradual recovery to the recent peak of 60 nests in 1984. In most years since the total has been between 45 and 50, but only 38 in 1993.

In the same part of Sussex there was a small heronry at Winchelsea from 1933 or 1934, usually of between two and five nests. In 1943 there were ten, but in the following year it was deserted. A single nest was again found here in 1990, and there were two nests in 1992 and in 1993.

In 1935 there was a single nest in an oak tree on the low cliff at the back of Pett Level, and from 1979 to 1986 there were up to four nests annually at what is clearly the same site.

Outside the breeding season Grey Herons are recorded in suitable habitat throughout Sussex and in all months. As well as along the edges of rivers and streams, ponds, lakes and reservoirs they feed on the shore at low tide and are common in the harbours and estuaries. They regularly visit ponds in suburban gardens. When feeding they are normally solitary or well spaced out, but there is a record of 15 feeding together at Hammer Trout Farm in April 1984. They are also frequently seen resting in daytime "roosts", there being counts of up to 46 together at Thorney Deeps in August, September and October and similar numbers in the same months at Weir Wood Reservoir. There are frequent counts of up to 35 birds at Rye Harbour from October to January and up to 20 birds have been reported at Pagham Harbour, Shoreham-by-Sea and Bewl Water.

Recorded movements are difficult to interpret. The county records contain no evidence of any change in population size in the winter, and the BTO Winter Atlas found no evidence of an increase in the south of Britain during the colder 1981/82 winter. The available ringing recoveries are all of birds ringed as nestlings, and show post-fledging dispersal rather than migration. Of 40 nestlings ringed at Aldershaw in April 1928, one was recovered in Ireland, two in Belgium and one in Spain. Nestlings ringed at Aldershaw in 1935 were recovered in Hampshire, Essex, Belgium and Holland and one ringed in 1939 was recovered near Reading. Nestlings ringed in 1967, 1970, 1971 and 1972 were recovered respectively in Belgium, Hampshire, Worcester and Berkshire. Seven birds ringed as nestlings elsewhere in Britain and found in Sussex were ringed in Essex, Suffolk and Norfolk. A nestling ringed in Denmark in May 1986 was found dead at Hammer in July 1987.

Single herons and small groups are frequently reported flying offshore, apparently departing, arriving and coasting east and west, in most months of the year and with no clear pattern. Fourteen flew south from Selsey Bill in

September 1981 and ten in October 1990. Thirty-eight flew west in formation over Beachy Head in October 1988. Some of these observations may be of relatively local movements, and the summer and autumn observations particularly could be of dispersing juvenile birds. Records of coastal movements during the breeding season may be of wandering immature birds.

Barrie Watson

Purple Heron   *Ardea purpurea*

Status:- A rare vagrant (44 records).

Eleven were recorded before 1962 (des Forges & Harber), although one record, for May, has not been traced. The earliest was found dead at Pett on 20 April 1940 and the latest flew east over the Rother Estuary, Rye Harbour on 2 November 1957 (*SxBR* 10: 5). Other dated records were in April, May (3), June, September and October and include individuals killed at Catsfield (October 1851) and Heathfield (16 May 1887) and obtained near Worthing (28 September 1848). The two remaining records were of birds killed at Abbott's Wood (autumn 1885) and Lewes (undated in 1822), the former being shot by a poacher who mistook it for a roosting Pheasant.

Thirty-three have been seen since the beginning of 1962, with a notable peak in the early 1980s (fig. 7). The subsequent reduction in records may reflect the species decline throughout much of Europe, the Dutch population, for example, fell by 60-70% between 1981 and 1991 (Tucker & Heath 1994).

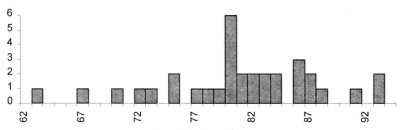

Figure 7. Annual totals of Purple Herons, 1962 - 94.

Most records were of single birds but three sub-adults were seen at Filsham Reedbed on 11 April 1980 and two flew north there on 26 June 1986. Most were recorded on one day only, the longest stay recorded being a juvenile at Chidmere Pond which was seen on 5 and 18 June 1983. A probable adult at the Severals, Church Norton on 4 April 1981 is the earliest to be recorded in the county to date, while a first-year with a broken wing at Sidlesham on 22 November 1963 is the latest. The latter was taken into care but later died. The cumulative monthly totals of all dated records are shown below.

Apr	May	Jun	Jul	Aug	Sep	Oct	Nov
8	14	7	2	3	2	4	2

Since the beginning of 1962 just over one third of all records have been at Filsham (12) with five at Pagham Harbour, four at Pett Level or Icklesham and three in the lower Cuckmere Valley. Less expected were individuals that flew west over Bognor promenade (30 August 1982), east past Brighton

Marina (7 May 1984), west over Lancing (28 May 1981) and east over Steyning (21 September 1980). The remaining individuals were recorded at Arundel (31 July 1982), Chidmere Pond (June 1983), near Ford Station (15 June 1967), Glynde Reach (28 May 1973) and Weir Wood Reservoir (8 July 1975).

There are between ten and 25 records of this normally retiring heron in Britain in most years (Evans 1995). It has a widespread breeding distribution throughout Europe, southern Asia and East Africa, but despite some extended stays in late spring, breeding has not been recorded in Britain. European birds winter in sub-Saharan Africa.   *Richard Fairbank*

Black Stork   *Ciconia nigra*

Status:- A very rare vagrant (five records).

Prior to 1962 there was only one record, at Icklesham on 9 August 1958, moving to Corkwood Farm, Iden where it remained for at least three weeks to 14 September (des Forges & Harber). It was moulting from first-winter into adult plumage and had earlier been seen at Stone Cliff, Kent on 7 August.

All four recent records have been seen since 1989:

1989:   One flying southeast over Wych Cross on 26 May.
1991:   One over Cissbury Ring on 26 August drifted slowly west.
1993:   One flying northeast over Sidlesham Ferry at 14:10 hrs, east over Shoreham-by-Sea at 15:05 hrs and over Icklesham during late afternoon on 16 September.
1994:   One arrived from the east at Littlehampton Marina on 17 September and drifted off west at 07:20 hrs. It was seen slowly circling west over Pagham Harbour between 09:30 and 10:00 hrs and was later seen over Hampshire and Dorset.

There were just over 90 records of this spectacular stork in the British Isles during 1962-94. A marked increase in records, evident during the 1980s, probably reflects increasing populations across Europe (Tucker & Heath 1994). It breeds in Iberia, from eastern Europe to central Asia and in southern Africa. Most European birds winter in sub-Saharan Africa.   *Richard Fairbank*

White Stork   *Ciconia ciconia*

Status:- A rare vagrant, mainly in spring (65 individuals recorded).

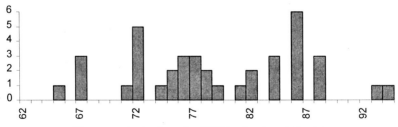

Figure 8. Annual totals of White Storks, 1962 - 94.

Until 1929 there were about 20 records involving about 27 birds (des Forges & Harber). The next was not until 1965 when there was one at Bodiam on 19 September. Subsequently, there have been records of White

Storks in 16 of the 29 years between 1966 and 1994 (fig. 8), covering all months except March. It is difficult to assess the numbers involved accurately, given that the majority of the records have been of birds seen in flight only and that some are known to have occurred at more than one locality, but a total of about 38 birds (excluding known escapes) during 1962-94 is reasonable.

With the exception of two over Etchingham on 6 June 1986 and a party of five over Polegate on 25 April 1972, all have been single birds. Most have occurred in the period late April to early June, with scattered records through to September. One overwintered at Adversane from September 1974 to 16 February 1975 but the only other winter record was of one over Goring on 31 December 1978. The earliest recorded in spring was one that flew north over Hastings on 6 April 1981. The cumulative monthly totals for the period 1962-94 are shown below.

Jan	Feb	Mar	Apr	May	Jun	Jul	Aug	Sep	Oct	Nov	Dec
1	1	-	12	9	9	3	2	4	1	1	2

White Storks have occurred widely in the county with the majority being seen either at sites on or near the coast, or in the river valleys. A few have been seen on inland fields, including one at Cottendean, Stonegate from 25 to 28 May 1986, which was observed feeding on earthworms in silage fields, and one on the Downs at Madehurst on 2-3 May 1993. An unusual record was that of a bird at Wartling from 9 to 11 May 1984 which was first seen in car headlights as it roosted in the heronry there.

The totals given above do not include known escapes from captivity. One such bird was that at Ashburnham from 30 September to at least 17 December 1978. It was found dead at South Heighton on 17 January 1979 and was traced through the ring it was carrying to Nieuwpoort Zoo in the Netherlands, from where it had escaped in the spring of 1978. Reports of two birds together at a number of localities in August 1990 and of a single bird in November-December 1990 were thought to relate to two free-flying birds that wandered to and from Whipsnade Zoo during the latter half of that year. They ranged widely and were seen in counties as far apart as Norfolk and Cornwall (*Birding World* 3: 260-261, 296, 331, 405).

British records of this species have shown a distinct bias to the south and east coasts. There were 322 White Storks recorded in Britain and Ireland in the period 1958-86 and about 70 prior to this (Dymond, Fraser & Gantlett 1989). Thus Sussex has contributed a significant proportion (approximately 16%) of these records, with only Kent recording a similar proportion, where at least 28 had occurred up until December 1976 (Taylor, Davenport & Flegg 1981).

There is an old ringing recovery of a bird ringed as a nestling in Denmark in July 1922 and shot from the roof of the workhouse at East Preston on 7 October of the same year.   *Michael Prince*

Glossy Ibis   *Plegadis falcinellus*

Status:- A rare vagrant (about 40 recorded but only five recently).

Prior to 1962 about 35 were recorded, the most recent being two at Fishbourne and two or three at Sidlesham in autumn 1909 (Walpole-Bond). Other old records were in May (2), August (1), September (21), October (4) and November (2). These include four at the River Rother near Beckley in September and October 1903, four at Fishbourne in late September 1906 and 12 there in early September 1908, four of which were shot. Of two at Piddinghoe in May 1850, one (an adult male) was shot and is in the Booth Museum (BoMNH 207875), as is an adult shot between Arundel and Ford on 20 August 1876 (BoMNH 207874).

Five individuals have been recorded since 1962:

1965:   One at Pagham Harbour on 22-23 April.
1986:   One flying east over Mill Hill, Shoreham-by-Sea on 18 September.
        One, presumably the same individual, flying northeast towards Castle Water, Rye Harbour on 19 September.
1987:   Two at Pett Level Pools from 25 to 27 April.
1988:   One on the banks of the River Ouse, near Hamsey Church, Lewes on 24 October departed north.
        One, presumably the same individual, at Cooden Beach on 27 October and at Hooe Level, Norman's Bay from 5 to 11 November.

Since 1962, records have been in April, September and October-November and, with the exception of the sighting near Lewes, they have been widely scattered along or near the coast.

There were nearly 60 records of this slim, silhouette-like species in the British Isles during 1962-94. It breeds from eastern Europe to southern Asia and Australia. Most European birds winter in sub-Saharan Africa. There are other populations in coastal southeast USA and the Caribbean and in southern Africa.   *Richard Fairbank*

Spoonbill   *Platalea leucorodia*

Status:- A very scarce visitor, most frequent in spring and autumn.

Until 1961 des Forges & Harber reported a total of over 120 including a maximum of seven in 1950. Between 1962 and 1994, a total of about 108 was recorded (fig. 9), suggesting little change in status. The average of about three per year in each of the last three decades is roughly the same as that for the period 1947-61 (43 birds in 15 years). Excluding a party of 20 that flew west offshore at Langney Point on 1 September 1964, most were recorded at Pagham Harbour/Sidlesham Ferry (35 birds), Rye Harbour (20) and Cuckmere Haven (13), although several were seen at more than one locality. One stayed at Amberley Wild Brooks from 31 December 1950 to 15 April 1951 while more recent inland records were of an adult that flew north there on 7 October 1977, a juvenile at Coldwaltham Brooks and Arundel WWT on 12 October 1986 and an adult at Weir Wood Reservoir on 26 August 1990.

The earliest recorded in spring was an adult at Thorney Island on 3-4 March 1989. An immature overwintered at Rye Harbour and Northpoint Gravel Pit from 5 October 1989 to 3 January 1990 but the only other recent record outside the period March to early November was of an immature over Newhaven Harbour on 28 December 1970.

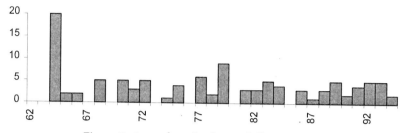

Figure 9. Annual totals of Spoonbills, 1962 - 94.

With the exception of the flock at Langney Point in 1964, the largest parties recorded were five that flew west at the same site in October 1947 and, more recently, five at Cuckmere Haven from 3 to 6 May 1979, four at Sidlesham Ferry on 12 April 1983 and four at Pagham Harbour on 25-26 September 1979. Although several birds were only seen in flight, many others remained for a day and 30% stayed for two days or more.

A few colour-ringed Spoonbills have been seen in Sussex. There are four recoveries, all of birds ringed as nestlings at various sites in the Netherlands. These include the individual that wintered at Rye Harbour in 1989/90 which had been ringed in June 1989. The others were all adults; one at Cuckmere Haven in May 1982 had been ringed in July 1978, a colour-ringed bird in the flock of five at the same site in May 1979 had been ringed in May 1974 and one at Rye Harbour on 17 August 1975 was ringed in July 1972.

The Spoonbill bred in Britain until the 17th century (Snow 1971). Now the nearest breeding colonies to this country are in the Netherlands, and as the recoveries of ringed birds demonstrate, this is probably the origin of most Spoonbills in Sussex, particularly as the Dutch population migrates along the Atlantic coast to winter in northwest Africa (BWP).

The cumulative monthly totals for the period 1962-94 are shown below.

Jan	Feb	Mar	Apr	May	Jun	Jul	Aug	Sep	Oct	Nov	Dec
1	-	5	15	18	16	4	6	32	14	5	2

A bird considered to be a hybrid Spoonbill x African Spoonbill *P. alba*, of captive origin, was seen at various localities including Chichester Gravel Pits and Pett Level in 1989 and 1990. Instead of the yellow-tipped black bill and black legs of an adult Spoonbill, it showed a grey bill and grey legs. The African Spoonbill has a bare red face and bright pink legs (BWP).

Michael Prince

Greater Flamingo   *Phoenicopterus ruber*

Status:- One old record of doubtful origin.

One shot one and a half miles west of Jury's Gap on 1 August 1916 was quite possibly a wild bird, while one seen several times at Norman's Bay in spring 1931 was believed to be an escape from captivity. Most recent records certainly refer to escapes (although the pink-kneed Chilean Flamingo *P. chilensis* is much more regularly at large).

Currently not on the British List due to the high likelihood of escape from captivity; the occurrence of wild individuals is well within the realms of possibility, although until one arrives wearing a continental ring the species status seems unlikely to change. *Richard Fairbank*

Mute Swan *Cygnus olor*

Status:- A fairly common resident.

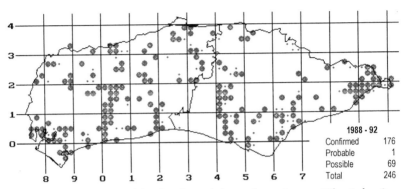

1988 - 92	
Confirmed	176
Probable	1
Possible	69
Total	246

The Mute Swan is widely distributed throughout Sussex. The Atlas Survey confirmed breeding during 1988-92 in all of the 10-km squares lying wholly within the county with the exception of TQ30, TQ31 and TQ52. In TQ01 (Arun Valley) there were records of confirmed breeding in 11 of the 25 tetrads and with sightings in another two, while, in the extreme east, in TQ91 (Camber) breeding was recorded in seven of the nine land-based tetrads.

The most recent census of Mute Swans in Sussex, in the spring of 1990, was carried out as part of a national survey of the species organised by the BTO, WWT and SOC. A total of 1111 birds was found, comprising 175 pairs which were known to have nested, an additional 52 territorial pairs, and 657 non-breeding birds (Hughes 1991b). Based on an estimated population of 890 birds in 1983 (Hughes & Watson 1984), these figures indicate an increase in the total population of approximately 20%. This increase was probably due in part to the ban in early 1987 on most sizes of lead weights for fishing, which was believed to have contributed, nationally, to a 49% increase in population between 1983 and 1990 (Delany 1990), and partially to a more thorough search of East Guldeford Level, east of Rye, which was not adequately covered in 1983.

The 1990 survey also looked at the habitats used by Mute Swans in the months of April and May. The results, shown in table 3, confirm that the major river valleys provide the most important habitat for territorial pairs and non-breeders alike. Ponds and lakes are also an important breeding habitat but they are of far less significance to non-breeders.

The Atlas map further confirms the importance of the levels as a habitat for this species although Hughes (1991b) drew attention to a decline in numbers of territorial pairs on Pevensey Levels (TQ60 and TQ61). A decrease from 26 pairs in 1976 to 24 in 1983, 23 in 1987 (Hitchings 1988) and 21 in 1990, would seem to indicate a gradual deterioration of the breeding habitat.

	% of nesting and territorial birds	% of non-breeding birds	% of total population
Levels and ditches	46.7	62.4	56.0
Ponds and lakes	30.8	10.2	18.6
Estuary and coast	4.0	12.0	8.7
Rivers (non-tidal)	3.5	0.8	1.9
Rivers (tidal)	6.6	5.2	5.8
Gravel pits	4.0	7.9	6.3
Reservoirs	1.3	1.4	1.4
Canals	3.1	0	1.3

Table 3. Mute Swan habitats in Sussex, April-May 1990.

In the winter months, sizeable herds may be found on the permanent grasslands of the levels and major river valleys, at suitable localities along the coast and on reservoirs. Winter counts at various localities are summarised in table 4.

	69-74	74-79	79-84	84-89	89-94	Peak counts
Chichester Harbour	58	62	86	103	91	138, Nov 1986
Chichester GP		33**	35*	41	64	118, Oct 1991
Arun Valley		124*	102	144	104	185, Nov 1988
Lewes Brooks				67**	78*	106, Nov 1992
Pevensey Levels		160**	32**		96	137, Dec 1991
Rye Harbour		24*	36	61	66	121, Sep 1993

Table 4. Five year means of maxima and peak counts of Mute Swans, 1969/70 - 93/94.

A herd of 200 on East Guldeford Level in November-December 1990 is the largest to be recorded in the county in recent years.

Of 652 Mute Swans ringed in Sussex and subsequently recovered, 260 had moved less than 10 km, 369 between 10 and 99 km and 23 further than this. These include seven recovered in France, three in the Netherlands, two in Denmark and singles in Germany and Sweden. The latter bird, caught at Eastbourne in February 1963, was controlled on Insto Island, Lycke, 1080 km northeast, in January 1966. A further 631 have been ringed outside Sussex and recovered within the county, of which ten had moved more than 100 km, from Hertfordshire (4), Dorset (3), Berkshire, Essex and the Netherlands (1 each). The latter, ringed at Veluwemeer, Oost Flevoland in May 1961 was caught in Pagham Harbour, 494 km WSW, in February 1963.   *Mike Mason*

Bewick's Swan   *Cygnus columbianus*

Status:- A scarce winter visitor and passage migrant.

Bewick's Swan overwinter annually at a few wet grassland sites in the interior of Sussex and they are now considered a regular feature of the winter months. Prior to 1940 the species had not been recorded inland and as recently as 1961 it was an irregular visitor with most birds still being seen at, or near, the coast (des Forges & Harber). Up to 1953 it was reported even more rarely than the Whooper Swan, although Nisbet (1959) considered that at that period Bewick's Swan was often mis-identified and reported as the latter.

In the 1960s first arrivals usually occurred during November, and October dates were exceptional. In the 1970s and 1980s the reverse was true with first birds usually arriving by the last week of October. The earliest dates for birds known to settle in Sussex were 15 October 1989 and 16 October 1990 (both in the Arun Valley) though parties likely to be overflying the county have been noted as early as 10 October in 1970. Hughes (1992), with a perspective of 30 years of records from 1961 to 1990, pointed out that first arrivals were twice as likely to be inland than at the coast. In years when the first reports were for the latter, there was a bias to sites in East Sussex, for example, the Midrips, Rye Harbour, Icklesham and Cuckmere Haven. Very few of these early birds have stayed at their site of arrival for more than one or two days, and that is equally true for both coastal and inland sites.

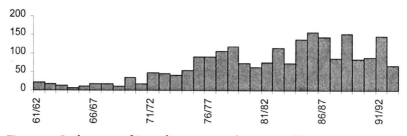

Figure 10. Peak counts of Bewick's Swans in the Arun valley, 1961/62 - 92/93.

The Arun Valley is the most regular, and numerically the most important, site for Bewick's Swans in Sussex (fig. 10). Here they graze various areas of agriculturally improved land, principally between Pulborough and North Stoke. These areas are sufficiently well spaced so that if disturbance occurs at one site, the birds have a selection of alternative sites from which to choose. A safe roost site is also a requirement and this changed from Kneppmill Pond during the mid-1960s and 1970s to the SWT reserve at Waltham Brooks which became the main roosting site until 1989/90. The WWT reserve at Arundel was also used as an alternative roost until March 1990, at least. Both sites have now largely been abandoned in favour of the recently created RSPB reserve at Pulborough Brooks, although birds do still roost from time to time at Arundel WWT.

In the Adur Valley, birds are usually found between Steyning and Henfield, especially in the vicinity of Stretham Manor and Wyckham Farm. In recent years they have been seen with increasing frequency to the north of Henfield near Bines Bridge, Ashurst. This is only 5 km from Kneppmill Pond and specific counts at the latter site, for example, 23 on 17 January 1988, have correlated well with the numbers using the Adur Valley, suggesting that this water may now be used as the safe haven/roost by birds from the Adur Valley. While Glynde Levels was for many years the favoured site in the Ouse Valley, this area has become drier since controlled flooding ceased in 1980, and the birds are now most likely to be found between Lewes and Southease.

In the far east of the county, the River Rother forms the boundary between Sussex and Kent for part of its course and it bisects both Wet Level and Wittersham Levels which provide ideal habitat. Birds in this area probably form but a small part of a population which wanders widely over the entire Rother Valley and Walland Marsh in Kent and are known to roost, in some years at least, on the ARC pit at Dungeness, Kent.

The increase in birds recorded in Sussex has been broadly in line with the national trend; the Winter Atlas reported that at the Ouse Washes in East Anglia, numbers grew steadily from a handful in the 1940s to top 1000 for the first time in 1971. The increase was maintained through the 1970s and 1980s. Shrubb noted that the average number seen per year in Sussex rose from just over one to 14 between 1952 and 1962, to 70 or more per year between 1963 and 1972, and to over 100 between 1973 and 1976. The trend continued subsequently and the sum of the peak counts at seven sites from 1975/76 to 1992/93 fell below 100 in only the winters of 1980/81 and 1983/84, while in seven winters it exceeded 150, peaking in excess of 270 in 1991/92. Hughes calculated that the mean January count for Sussex in the late 1980s amounted to 125, constituting approximately 1.5% of the numbers wintering in Britain. Table 5 summarises counts at the main localities. Sites which regularly hold 70 or more are considered to be of national importance for the species (Waters & Cranswick 1993).

	69-74	74-79	79-84	84-89	89-94	Peak counts
Arun Valley	37	92	80	136	81	158, Jan 1986
Adur Valley	4	6	13	15	22	84, Feb 1991
Ouse Valley	3	8	3	13	10	30, Jan 1985

Table 5. Five year means of maxima and peak counts of Bewick's Swans, 1969/70 - 93/94.

Return movements normally start during March; however the date varies considerably and is presumably attributable to prevailing weather conditions. Occasionally some linger into April as in 1972 when 30 were still present at

Amberley on 6th. The latest, however, were four at Henfield Brooks on 26 April 1991. Observation of the herd composition in the Arun Valley has shown that departure is staggered with parties leaving over a period of days, if not weeks. There is also evidence of early departures being replaced by new arrivals. Migrating birds follow both inland and coastal routes. Sightings in 1979, 1982 and 1986 of birds climbing northeast at dusk over West Chiltington and of 16 birds arriving from the southwest at Bewl Water on 6 March 1983 are evidence of an inland route being followed. Coastal records for March include 15 flying southeast over Ferring on 2 March 1980, 13 east at Jury's Gap on 8 March 1987 and 25 over Rye Harbour on 4 March 1992.

A bird colour-marked at Slimbridge, Gloucestershire in January 1982 was seen at Barcombe Reservoir on 18 February 1985. Another bird fitted with a neck collar at Khabuicka on the Russkii Zavorot Peninsula, USSR in August 1992 was recorded in the Arun Valley in the winter of 1992/93, on 20 October 1993 and 25 January 1995. It was also observed in Kreis Ludwigslust, Germany in March-April 1993 and March 1994 and at the site where it was first caught in May-June 1993 and July 1994.   *Mike Mason*

Whooper Swan   *Cygnus cygnus*
Status:- A very scarce winter visitor and passage migrant.

The Whooper Swan is recorded principally from December to March, in generally small numbers on the permanent grassland of the river valleys and levels and more occasionally on reservoirs and estuaries. It is now scarcer than Bewick's Swans in Sussex, as shown by the approximate total of 342 recorded in 21 of the 33 of the winters between 1961/62 and 1993/94 (fig. 11).

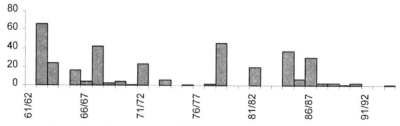

Figure 11. Winter totals of Whooper Swans, 1961/62 - 93/94.

Shrubb tabulated approximate monthly totals for the years 1947 to 1976 and showed only two records for October and November, these being one flying southwest over Pevensey on 16 October 1969 and two on the Adur Levels on 13 November 1971. The former is still the earliest county record. Since 1976 the pattern has changed and there were October records of ten birds in the period 1977-94 including four adults flying east at Beachy Head on 26 October 1985 and a second-winter bird at Bewl Water on 17 October 1993. Numbers in November similarly increased to 15 birds in the same period, including a herd of four which stayed briefly at West Chidham on 29 November 1978.

In the months December to February, records peak in the latter month. Severe weather will lead to influxes of birds; about 42 were recorded in

1946/47, 40-50 in early 1956, 66 in 1962/63, 46 in 1978/79 and 37 in early 1985, including 16 that flew west over Pagham Harbour on 16 January. This was the largest party to be recorded in the county since 1968, when 34 flew east over Pevensey Bay on 7 March 1968. A herd of 40 was recorded at Rye Harbour on 24 December 1938.

In the seventeen years from 1978 to 1994 inclusive there were only two records after the end of February. In 1978, two were seen on Glynde Levels on 5 March and on 4 March 1979 a party of six flew over Henfield Brooks. The latest recorded date is 2 May 1956, an immature at Rye Harbour that had been present since 3 March. The Winter Atlas stated that Whooper Swans are normally present in Britain until mid-April; the earlier departures from Sussex may support the suggestion that the birds visiting the south of England may be from the Continent rather than from the breeding stock in Iceland. Evidence to support this theory is provided by the recovery of a bird that had been ringed as a juvenile at Shoreham-by-Sea on 2 February 1963. It was found dead at Burgsvik, Sweden, 1392 km ENE, on 29 February 1964 and, at the time, it was the first recorded movement of this species between the British Isles and Scandinavia.

A probable escape associated with Mute Swans on Pevensey Levels and Lewes Brooks from 23 November 1985 to 24 January 1987.   *Mike Mason*

Bean Goose   *Anser fabalis*

Status:- A very scarce winter visitor and passage migrant.

This is the rarest of the grey geese to be recorded in Sussex as shown by the total of only five records comprising 27 birds during 1919-59 (des Forges & Harber). A total of approximately 321 Bean Geese was recorded in 19 of the 33 winters between 1961/62 and 1993/94 (fig. 12), although some single birds, particularly those associating with Canada Geese, were likely to have been of captive origin. As with Pink-footed Goose, the largest numbers occurred during severe weather in early 1963 and 1979. At least 45 were recorded in the 1963 influx including a flock of 17 at Greatham Bridge and in the Wiggonholt/Pulborough Brooks area from 1 February to 17 March. A minimum of 101 in early 1979 included 18 that flew northeast over Pevensey Levels on 24 February and 22 feeding there the following day. A flock of 26 near Climping on 2 February 1985 is the largest party ever recorded in Sussex.

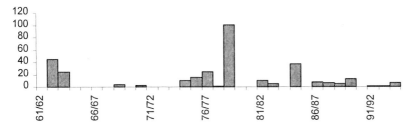

Figure 12. Winter totals of Bean Geese, 1961/62 - 93/94.

The approximate cumulative monthly totals of all records for the period 1962-94 are shown below.

Sep	Oct	Nov	Dec	Jan	Feb	Mar	Apr
1	11	1	52	60	206	36	12

Most records have been of small feeding flocks on the levels and coastal plain but ten at Litlington on 14 October 1974 and 11 which arrived from the direction of the sea at Birling Gap on 1 April 1990, were very likely to have been on migration. These are the earliest and latest birds to be recorded in the county, except for singles at Amberley Wild Brooks on 26 April 1978 and at Weir Wood Reservoir on 21 September 1993 which may well have been of captive origin.

Of forty which were racially assigned, 35 showed the characteristics of the tundra race *A.f. rossicus* and the remainder of the western race *A.f. fabalis*.

Paul James

Pink-footed Goose *Anser brachyrhynchus*

Status:- A scarce winter visitor and passage migrant.

Since 1961/62 there have been records of Pink-footed Geese of presumed wild origin in 22 winters, totalling approximately 663 birds (fig. 13). However, the severe winters of 1962/63 and 1978/79 were the only ones in which substantial numbers were recorded. The totals of 174 and *ca.* 200 respectively for these winters were the largest for the county, exceeding the total of 166 reported in 1955/56.

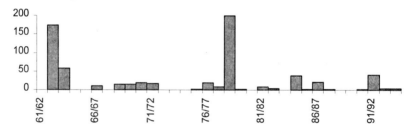

Figure 13. Winter totals of Pink-footed Geese, 1961/62 - 93/94.

The largest flocks recorded in the influxes that occurred in early 1963 and 1979 were 45 over West Wittering on 6 January 1963, 60 on Pevensey Levels on 27 January 1963, up to 100 with White-fronted Geese at North Bersted from 2-4 February 1979 and 72 on Pevensey Levels on 3 March 1979. Since 1979 all flocks have been of seven or less except for 32 over Brighton on 10 February 1985, 14 over Eastbourne on 11 January 1987, 15 over Hooe Level on 26 November 1988, 40 flying west over Rye Harbour on 17 November 1991 and 16 flying east at Glyne Gap on 4 February 1993.

In addition to wild birds, there have been a number of reports in recent years of likely escapes from captivity. These have been of single birds, often associating with flocks of Canada Geese, and usually on inland waters.

The cumulative monthly totals of all records (excluding those birds considered to originate from wildfowl collections) for 1962-94 are shown below:

Sep	Oct	Nov	Dec	Jan	Feb	Mar	Apr
12	2	93	37	286	217	112	13

The earliest recorded in autumn were five that flew south over Wartling on 1 September 1962 and seven (two of which were shot) at the Midrips on 5 September 1963. There are three records of flocks observed flying up-Channel in spring comprising 20 off Brighton on 4 April 1961 and seven and 12 off Beachy Head on 30 March 1971 and 7 April 1969 respectively. The latter are the latest to be recorded in the county except for one that flew west off Littlehampton on 25 April 1988 and an injured individual that remained at Piddinghoe until 13 May 1956.

Single birds ringed in Iceland in July 1953 and the Netherlands in December 1959 were shot in the county in February 1958 and January 1963 respectively, the latter at Bishopstone.   *Paul James*

White-fronted Goose   *Anser albifrons*

Status:- A scarce winter visitor and passage migrant.

Although recorded annually, there is no regular wintering population in Sussex, and birds rarely remain for more than a few days, except in severe weather. Most are seen in the period November to March but since 1982 there have been a number of October records. A few have been seen in April, May and June and single birds in July and September, although these are likely to have been injured or escapes from captivity.

In autumn and early winter, small skeins have been observed flying in a westerly direction, perhaps to the Avon Valley in Hampshire where a wintering flock was established in 1940 (Cohen 1963). During harsh weather, larger movements may take place and sizeable flocks may take up residence on the lowland pastures of the levels, coastal plain and river valleys. The numbers recorded each winter are very variable, ranging since 1947 from just three in 1960/61 to about 1670 in the severe winter of 1962/63, including a flock of *ca.* 400 in the Sidlesham area from 27 January to 6 March 1963. A considerable influx in the winter of 1978/79 was characterised by many feeding flocks in suitable localities throughout the county and also a confusing series of movements. It is impossible to give a precise total for this period although counts made on 24-25 February 1979, including totals of 858 on Pevensey Levels and 330 on Pett Level, suggest an absolute minimum of 1580 birds. From mid-February, flocks may sometimes be seen moving eastwards 'en route' to their Siberian breeding grounds, for example 300 over Hurst Green on 1 March 1986. Passage may continue into early spring, for birds were heard calling over both Findon and Lancing after dark on 9 April 1985.

All Sussex records are assumed to refer to the race *albifrons*, except for one showing the characteristics of the Greenland race *flavirostris* at Wiggonholt on 27 January 1956.

One ringed in Gloucestershire in March 1959 was shot at an unspecified locality in the county in January 1963.   *Paul James*

Greylag Goose   *Anser anser*

Status:- A fairly common introduced resident and winter visitor, scarce passage migrant.

Until the mid-1960s, the Greylag Goose only occurred as a rare winter visitor, particularly in severe winters. Shrubb noted that no more than about 25 birds were recorded in any year after 1947, except in 1953, when a party of 67 was seen. Subsequently, a feral population has become established and this expanded rapidly during the 1980s.

As a result of introductions by the Wildfowlers' Association of Great Britain and Ireland (WAGBI), successful breeding occurred in the Lake District in 1963 and, by 1971, more than 1000 geese had been released in Britain (Harrison 1973). Although WAGBI ceased introductions in the early 1970s, the introduced stock and other free-winged offspring from wildfowl collections formed local populations of feral geese, which by 1983 were estimated to total more than 3000 (Owen, Atkinson-Willes & Salmon 1986). There were, however, no major introductions into Sussex and Hughes (1987b) attributed the increasing number of records of feral birds in the county since the early 1970s to developments in neighbouring counties.

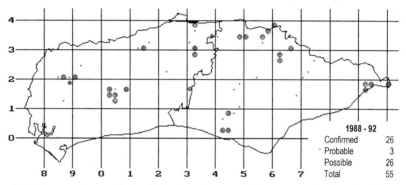

1988 - 92	
Confirmed	26
Probable	3
Possible	26
Total	55

The first undisputed feral birds to be seen in Sussex were four in the Rye Harbour area in April 1969. These were assumed to have dispersed from Dungeness, Kent where an introduction was made in 1968. A single bird was at Weir Wood Reservoir in February 1971 while throughout the early 1970s one or two Greylags were often reported associating with the Canada Geese at Petworth Park and in the Arun Valley. In spring 1974 two seen on Amberley Wild Brooks appeared paired but successful breeding was not proven until 1977 when a pair nested in Petworth Park. Although there is no proof, it seems likely that the Arun Valley and Petworth Park birds dispersed from Stratfield Saye, Hampshire, where a feral population became established following the introduction of a pair of pinioned birds in 1963 (Clark 1984). Although breeding did not occur in Petworth Park in 1978 or 1979, a pair again nested there in 1980. In 1981 birds bred for the first time in Parham Park and in 1982, a pair behaved territorially at Bewl Water. Breeding was successful at the gravel pits at Scotney Court in 1984 where at least eight young were reared. In 1985 five pairs bred successfully in the county and it is

140

possible that a similar number were unsuccessful. In addition there were approximately 20 non-breeders, indicating a total population of probably less than 50. At the time the geese were concentrated in three clusters, in the southeast, northeast and northwest of Sussex, and these small sub-populations were struggling to hold their own due to competition with the larger Canada Goose. A survey of introduced geese in the summer of 1991, organised by the WWT, found a total of 216 birds in Sussex, of which 107 were adult, 34 juveniles and 75 unaged (Rettke-Grover & Hughes 1993). It was apparent, therefore, that a considerable and quite rapid change had occurred since 1985. The Atlas map shows the three clusters previously identified, together with a new cluster centred on the Ouse Valley where the figures for TQ40, TQ41 and TQ43 comprised 40% of the total birds counted in Sussex in the WWT census. Birds were first recorded in TQ13 at Broadbridge Heath in 1985 and this flock had increased to 30 in 1988 and 60 in 1991. Elsewhere, population growth has been far less obvious though expansion is undoubtedly occurring given that 13 pairs were known to have bred successfully at nine sites in 1990. A more detailed account of feral Greylag Geese in Sussex, on which this summary is based, has been provided by Hughes (1987b).

In addition to feral geese at established localities, there have been a number of other records that do not fit the recent pattern of occurrence. Some have been in winter, such as a flock of 65 on Glynde Levels on 5 December 1982. These records could relate to cold weather movements of feral stock from the low countries, where widespread introductions have been made since 1955, but equally they could be unusual movements of feral birds from southern England, or even, perhaps, wild birds, as in 1953.

Regrettably, recent introductions have now made it impossible to identify true migrants which are 'en route' to their wintering grounds (e.g. eight flying west off Worthing on 28 September 1978) or have wintered elsewhere (e.g. three flying east off Langney Point with Brent Geese on 16 March 1991), particularly as birds that use the west European flyway between the Baltic and the Coto Donana, Spain, have now been infiltrated by feral stock from the low countries (Ellwood et al 1971). Similarly, the origin of flocks of 38, 34 and

17 that flew east over West Wittering, Lancing and Pagham Harbour respectively on 9 February 1985 must remain uncertain.

Since the mid-1980s, there has been a considerable increase in the number of birds wintering in the county (table 6). The largest concentrations have been at Scotney Court Gravel Pit, where 166 were recorded in late December 1991, and at Weir Wood Reservoir, where there were 206 on 26 January 1992. The latter total is the largest yet recorded in Sussex although as feral Greylags are now firmly established, it is likely that this will soon be exceeded.

	79	80	81	82	83	84	85	86	87	88	89	90	91	92	93
Arun Valley	12	32	19	24	20	36	21	31	37	43	34	75	59	40	100
Weir Wood Res.	17	15	9	15	23	30	16	2	11	99	22		206	150	76
Glynde Levels									14	29	56	5			
Bewl Water	2	3	5	2	2	11	7	1	1	2	1				
Rye Harbour	12	6	22	6	5	5	13	35	17	1					62
Scotney Court GP										137	166	63			53

Table 6. Maximum winter counts (November-February) of feral Greylag Geese, 1979/80 - 1993/94.

There have been four recoveries within the county of birds ringed at Sevenoaks, Kent while one ringed at the Zwin Reserve, Belgium in June 1966 was shot at East Grinstead on 20 January 1976. *Paul James*

Snow Goose *Anser caerulescens*

Status:- All records probably relate to escapes.

Perhaps the most likely candidates for being genuine vagrants were a flock of three white morph adults and four juveniles which flew north over Ferring on 2 March 1984. All other records, including 14 white morph adults seen in the Pagham/Bracklesham area (and in Hampshire) from 19 January to 12 March 1983 and five white morph adults at Bewl Water from 6 to 8 December 1988, almost certainly relate to escapes or birds from feral populations.

It is very likely that fewer than ten genuine vagrants are recorded in the British Isles in most years, mainly in the northwest (Evans 1993a). Juveniles are more likely to be wild, as are blue morph individuals, but there are growing feral populations in Britain. At least 160 were at large in summer 1991, including a flock of 12 (11 white morph adults and a juvenile) in Hampshire (Delaney 1993). Vagrancy in southeast England is unlikely to be proved other than by a ringing recovery, as was the case with a flock of 18 in the Netherlands in April 1980 which included one that had been ringed in Manitoba, Canada (*Brit. Birds* 75: 25).

Snow Geese breed across arctic North America and winter in southern USA and Mexico. *Richard Fairbank*

Canada Goose *Branta canadensis*

Status:- A fairly common introduced resident and partial migrant.

The Canada Goose was first introduced into England from North America in the second half of the 17th century. Further introductions followed in the 18th and 19th centuries, the birds being released on private waters, either for shooting purposes or as ornamental waterfowl. By the 1930s they were living in a semi-feral state in several parts of the country and the species was admitted to the British List. The first national Canada Goose census was organised by the BTO in July 1953 (Blurton Jones 1956) when there were about 2600-3600 in Britain, including about 350 pairs and about 750 goslings. Since then, the species has flourished, so much so that the peak numbers in Britain in October 1990 (38,000 birds) exceeded the equivalent figure for the previous season by almost 4000 birds (Kirby *et al* 1991). Canada Geese are now a considerable nuisance to farmers, and in urban areas they may damage lawns, foul footpaths and destroy lakeside vegetation.

Very little is known about the introduction of Canada Geese into Sussex although it is probable that the first introductions took place in the second half of the 19th century (Hughes 1973). Birds were present at Kneppmill Pond at the turn of the century and at Warnham Mill Pond during 1908-10. The exact date of introduction to Petworth Park is uncertain but it is known to have been between 1918 and 1930 and Petworth was almost certainly the origin of 11 geese which visited Lurgashall Mill Pond in April 1930. The BTO survey of 1953 found a total of 23-50 birds in Sussex and between 1947 and 1976 breeding was proved at a total of 22 sites. Further censuses in January 1967 and 1968, and July 1971 recorded totals of about 290 in 1967-68, and 326, including 98 young, in 1971.

A more recent review of the status of the Canada Goose in Sussex by Hughes & Watson (1986), based on data collected by a survey of inland waters (1983-85), gave a total for the county of *ca*. 239 pairs at 133 sites. They also found that the number of 10-km squares in which the species was present had increased from 27 in 1972 to 39 in 1983-85 and that there was a much greater density within the squares as indicated by the number of occupied tetrads (47 in 1972 and 171 in 1983-85).

As the Canada Goose population was still expanding rapidly and there was a need for reliable information on distribution and numbers, the WWT organised a survey of introduced geese in the summer of 1991. In Sussex, a total of 180 sites was visited, comprising about 80% of the potential habitat (Rettke-Grover & Hughes 1993). Birds were found at 80 sites and in a total of 33 10-km squares. By far the largest numbers were in TQ63 with 389 at Bewl Water. Other large concentrations included 237 at Weir Wood Reservoir, 260 at Arundel WWT, 116 in Petworth Park, 112 at Darwell Reservoir and 110 at Rye Harbour. The total for the whole county was 2578 (of which 660 were young) but as at least one potentially important site was not visited, a rounded up figure of 2700 was considered realistic. This estimate represented a 600% increase since 1976 and this compared with a 505% increase for the southeast region as a whole and a 218% increase nationally.

As the Atlas map shows, Canada Geese are now widespread in Sussex. Ponds and lakes are widely utilised for breeding and other favoured habitats include sand and gravel pits, reservoirs and wildfowl collections. Shrubb suggested that the failure of many pairs to attempt breeding was due to a dearth of suitable habitat in the county but this appears not to be the case, as birds have recently taken to nesting on many smaller waters and also along rivers and streams.

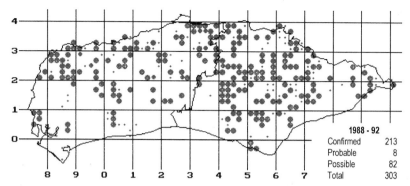

1988 - 92	
Confirmed	213
Probable	8
Possible	82
Total	303

After nesting, Canada Geese may assemble in large flocks to moult, when they are flightless and more easily caught for ringing. Of 1022 birds ringed in the county between 1974 and 1984, 728 were trapped at Petworth Park. That Petworth is a significant moulting ground is indicated by five birds first ringed at Chichester but controlled at least twice at Petworth, by five others relocated from north Hampshire to Chichester but subsequently found at Petworth and by 43 transported to Chichester from Petworth which subsequently returned (Hughes & Watson 1986). From about 1950, a moult migration evolved among the non-breeders of the central Yorkshire sub-population, of which an increasing number spent the moulting period on the Beauly Firth (Highland), 400-450 km north of their home range (Walker 1970). Ringing studies have shown that birds from Sussex may, too, moult at this site. Two geese ringed as juveniles at Chichester, one in 1976 and one in 1977, were controlled on the Beauly Firth in July 1978, and in June 1979 one of these was found in Petworth Park. Also in 1979, six other geese ringed on the Beauly Firth were controlled at Petworth in July.

Counts in recent years have shown that the largest numbers in Sussex are present in autumn, when the local population is augmented by birds from neighbouring counties. Confirmation of this was obtained in July 1979 when 14 ringed geese were controlled in Petworth Park. In addition to the seven ringed on the Beauly Firth (see above), three had been ringed in Hampshire but more surprisingly, one in Worcestershire. Table 7 which summarises the peak autumn counts at the main sites for Canada Geese in Sussex, shows the big increase that took place in the early 1980s. Since then, numbers have fallen, presumably due to the effectiveness of control measures now used at some sites.

	79-81	82-84	85-87	88-90	91-93
Chichester Gravel Pits	168	169	80	90	60
Arun Valley (Pulborough-Amberley)	200	1050	600	600	911
Ardingly/Weir Wood Reservoirs	98	208	278	505	110
Barcombe Reservoir	4	217	278	380	300
Arlington Reservoir	450	850	385	500	542
Bewl Water	1000	1158	1500	1100	1000
Darwell Reservoir	17	-	340	415	200
Rye Harbour/Scotney Court Gravel Pit	200	229	350	340	252

Table 7. Peak autumn counts of Canada Geese, 1979 - 93.

A flock of 1500 at Bewl Water in September 1986 is the largest yet recorded in the county.

The Canada Geese introduced into the west Palearctic are of the race *canadensis*. However, there have been occasional sightings of birds showing the characteristics of one of the smaller races that have occurred in an apparently wild state in Ireland and western Scotland (BWP). Those seen in Sussex are of captive origin and have included several records of singles at Bewl Water between 1978 and 1991, one of which was present between August 1984 and December 1985. Other singles were recorded at Battle and Northpoint Gravel Pit near Rye in early 1993 while two were seen at Plashett Park on 26 May 1991 and probably the same at Arlington Reservoir on 1 September 1991.

Paul James

Barnacle Goose   *Branta leucopsis*

Status:- A very scarce winter visitor, usually in severe weather, and an increasing feral resident.

The only influx of note prior to 1962 was that of about 55 birds in February 1956. Since then, there have been major influxes in each of the winters 1962/63, 1978/79, 1980/81, 1984/85 and 1993/94, presumably involving birds displaced westwards by freezing conditions in their usual Dutch wintering grounds.

With the exception of the influx in late 1993, all the others have been associated with severe weather in late winter. In 1963, a total of 39 was recorded, comprising 25 on Pett Level on 4 and 6 January, eight on Shoreham Airport on 13 February and six on Rottingdean Golf Course on 26 January. In 1979, about 96 were recorded between 4 February and 4 March with totals of 59 on Pevensey Levels, 31 at Pett Level and 6 in the lower Cuckmere Valley. The third influx in 1981 was remarkably similar with a total of 103 recorded in the period 19 to 27 February, comprising 68 on Pevensey Levels, 28 at Pett Level and seven in the Cuckmere Valley. In 1985, the influx spanned the period 20 January to 19 February with 91 birds recorded, comprising 56 at Camber, 26 in the Bosham/Thorney area and nine at Pagham Harbour. The last influx in 1993 differed from the others in that it occurred earlier in the winter before the onset of any severe winter weather. The total number of birds was unclear but the largest flocks recorded were 48 at Pevensey Levels on 28 November, 15 at Pulborough Brooks from 28 November into 1994, 21 at Thorney Island from 29 November to 11 December, 38 at Henfield Levels from 3 to 12 December and 34 in Pagham Harbour from 14 to 16 December.

Outside the major influxes, the largest flock of apparently wild birds was one of 28 at Pett Level on 4-5 December 1982 although flocks of five to 27 have been recorded on 16 occasions, mainly in the east of the county at Pett Level, Rye Harbour and more recently at Scotney Court Gravel Pit.

The true status of the species in Sussex is now clouded by the presence of feral birds in the county, following the establishment of a free-flying flock of 20 at Arundel WWT in 1980. A survey of introduced geese in summer 1991 found a total of 63 Barnacle Geese, of which 44 were at Arundel and 17 at

Plashett Park (Rettke-Grover & Hughes 1993). These totals included two young and one young respectively while in 1992, two pairs raised at least seven young at the latter site. Flocks of up to ten birds are now recorded regularly on inland waters, often in the company of Canada Geese. Occasional larger flocks, for example 24 at Weir Wood Reservoir in February 1992, 24 at Arlington Reservoir in December 1992 and January 1993, 22 at Barcombe Reservoir in February 1993 and 24 in the Cuckmere Valley in December 1993 are also likely to be of feral origin. *Tony J Wilson*

Brent Goose *Branta bernicla*

Status:- A very common winter visitor and passage migrant

Numbers of Dark-bellied Brent Geese *B.b. bernicla*, which winter only on the North Sea and English Channel coasts, have continued to rise in Sussex since the re-establishment of a regular wintering population in Chichester Harbour in 1952/53. This increase has also occurred nationally. Although the overall trend is upward, there are peaks and troughs (fig. 14), approximately on a 3-year cycle. This reflects the success or otherwise of the breeding season. Dark-bellied Brent Geese breed in western Siberia; the fluctuation in numbers has recently been linked to the abundance of lemmings, and the effects this has on prey selection by arctic foxes (Underhill *et al* 1993).

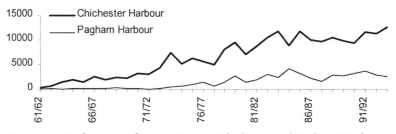

Figure 14. Peak counts of Brent Geese in Chichester and Pagham Harbours, 1961/62 - 93/94.

As numbers have increased, arrival dates have become earlier. Shrubb stated that birds "occasionally" arrive in September; by the mid-1980s arrivals in this month were more frequent, and they are now common, especially in poor breeding seasons.

Brent Geese traditionally fed intertidally. However, the trend towards feeding on grassland and winter cereals, which was first noted in Sussex in 1973/74 (Shrubb), has increased, a practice which has caused problems for coastal farmers. In years when high numbers occur, birds may venture some two miles inland to feed. Exceptionally, flocks may travel further, as in both 1991 and 1993, when 1800 and 1900 respectively were recorded on winter wheat at Barnham during December. Studies of the feeding distribution of Brent Geese in the Chichester area were carried out in 1979/80 (Round 1982) and in 1982/83 (Prater 1983a). The latter found that all the birds present on 16 October were feeding intertidally but on 13 November, 62% had moved to feeding on grass and 19% on winter cereals. By 11-12 December the proportion of birds feeding on grass had increased to 86% whereas the proportion feeding on winter cereals peaked at 23% on 19 March. Until 1991/92, flocks remained relatively faithful to their own area, but a season of high numbers and intensive scaring by farmers caused mixing in the Sidlesham/Bracklesham area, and into Hampshire.

The highest numbers occur in Chichester Harbour, with Pagham Harbour the other major site in Sussex (table 8). In the late 1970s and early 1980s a sizeable flock was also recorded at Bracklesham. Sites which regularly hold 2500 or more are considered to be of international importance for the species (Waters & Cranswick 1993).

	69-74	74-79	79-84	84-89	89-94	Peak counts
Chichester Harbour	4085	6206	9524	10163	10967	12647, Jan 1994
Pagham Harbour	191	1076	2327	3035	3042	4219, Jan 1985

Table 8. Five year means of maxima and peak counts of Brent Geese, 1969/70 - 93/94

These data show there has been a slightly slower increase recently; this is thought to be due to a combination of pressure from farmers and a shortage of refuge sites. In the 1970s Chichester Harbour was thought to be one of the few British sites able to accommodate increasing numbers (Prater 1975); maybe this is no longer the case.

Other sites at which Brent Geese have occurred in winter, all since 1980, include Climping, Cuckmere Haven, Newhaven, Pett Level, Pevensey Levels, and Rye Harbour. In very cold weather, birds may also visit additional sites such as Arlington Reservoir and the fields adjacent to Ferring Rife, where there were flocks of 93 and 101 respectively in January 1985, and Shoreham-by-Sea and Coldwaltham Brooks where flocks of 58 and 67 were recorded in January 1987.

Brent Geese migrate up-Channel in spring. Daily numbers vary; occasionally large totals are recorded, especially on days of southeasterly winds, such as 3961 off Glyne Gap, Bexhill on 9 March 1993, 3891 flying east at Splash Point, Seaford on 28 March 1993, 3785 off Brighton and 3218 off Worthing on 21 March 1985 and 3319 off Splash Point, Seaford and 2590 off Worthing on 29 March 1992. Passage continues into May.

As a result of licensed shooting by farmers for scaring purposes, some individuals inevitably are injured and are unable to migrate north to breed. Since 1983, numbers remaining through the summer have increased; the highest was 24 in Chichester Harbour in 1986.

Although a number of large down-Channel movements have occurred in autumn (e.g. 2986 off Worthing on 23-24 October 1982 and 2566 there on 2 November 1986), the totals recorded at this time of year are generally lower than those in spring, perhaps reflecting the comparative lack of sea-watching in autumn.

Brent Geese are also now reported passing over inland sites on both spring and autumn migration, especially around dusk. This has increased since the early 1980s. An exceptional inland passage occurred from 5 November 1982 for about ten days associated with strong southeasterly winds with heavy rain and cloud, for example 775 were recorded from Bewl Water on 6th, and 532 at

Weir Wood Reservoir on the same day.

A colour ringing scheme, organised in the Netherlands, has enabled some interesting observations to be made. Some birds survive over ten years, as shown by one ringed in 1974 and seen in Chichester Harbour in 1989/90. Most are faithful to a particular grazing site, sometimes being seen in 3-4 consecutive winters in the same field, and never elsewhere. Colour ringing has also revealed that some pairs stay together in their winter quarters. A bird marked with a metal ring at Taymyr, Russia on 31 August 1990 was found alive in a garden at Pevensey Bay, 5347 km WSW, on 7 April 1994.

Individuals of the Pale-bellied race *B.b. hrota* now occur annually. This race breeds in northeast Greenland, Spitsbergen and Franz Josef Land, and normally winters in Ireland, Denmark and northeast England (BWP). One or two usually winter in Chichester and Pagham Harbours; others have occurred at a variety of sites in the county, usually singly. Larger groups include 11 flying west at Selsey Bill on 20 April 1962 and 16 which flew west over Langney Point on 6 December 1962. An exceptional flock of 17 was at Pett Level from 10 to 31 January 1982 and there were six at Cuckmere Haven on 25 February 1986. During severe weather in January 1985 one was at Arlington Reservoir with a flock of Dark-bellied birds that peaked at 93. At Sidlesham Ferry one on 13 November 1983 was apparently paired with a Dark-bellied bird, together with a juvenile of intermediate colour.

A regular Black Brant *B.b. nigricans*, first seen at Marker Point, Thorney Island on 2 November 1986, returned to the same area every winter until 1993/94. Earlier in 1986, one at Pagham Harbour from 26 January to 8 March and at Bosham on 31 January was the first county record of this race. In 1987 one was again at Pagham Harbour on 11 January. In January 1989 a different individual appeared in the northern part of Thorney Island with six juveniles, thought to be the product of interbreeding with *bernicla*. This was the first British record of presumed hybrid young. What was believed to be the same bird reappeared from 12 January to 12 March 1990 and from 13 January to 10 February 1991, accompanied in the latter year by two hybrid young. The Marker Point individual was also seen with four young, all resembling *bernicla*, from 25 October 1991 to 15 February 1992. Black Brants breed in the Canadian Arctic, Alaska and northeast Siberia and usually winter on both sides of the north Pacific (BWP).   *Anne de Potier*

Red-breasted Goose   *Branta ruficollis*

Status:- A very rare vagrant (three winter records involving two individuals).

One was recorded before 1962, consorting with up to 117 White-fronted Geese in the Arun Valley at Amberley from 8 to 17 February 1958 (Mills & Watson 1958).

Since the beginning of 1962 there have been two further records of an adult associating with Brent Geese:

1986:   An adult at Pagham Harbour from 30 January to 3 March.
1987:   An adult, presumably the same, at Pagham Harbour from 23 to 27 January.

In addition to the above, an unringed adult was at Amberley Wild Brooks, with White-fronted Geese, on 18 December 1993 and at Pulborough Brooks, sometimes consorting with presumed wild Barnacle Geese, from 19 to 31 December 1993. It was probably an escape from captivity, also being reported from Arundel WWT, with free-flying Barnacle Geese, during this period.

There have been over 26 records of this elegant goose in the British Isles during 1962-94. It breeds in arctic Siberia and winters from southeast Europe (where it appears to be increasing) to the Caspian Sea.   *Richard Fairbank*

Egyptian Goose   *Alopochen aegyptiacus*

Status:- A rare visitor.

Although there is a long established feral population of Egyptian Geese in East Anglia, it is likely that Sussex records of this species refer to birds that have escaped from captivity. The first published record for the county was of one with Canada Geese at Sidlesham Ferry on 15 December 1978. Approximately 23 have been recorded since, most of which were single birds. There were, however, two in the west of the county between 1 January and 28 April 1980 which may have been those recorded at Rye Harbour in November of the same year. More recently, two were present at Weir Wood Reservoir between 19 September and 25 November 1985, at Waltham Brooks on 24 June 1988 and Icklesham on 2 June 1989, and singles at the latter site on 8 June 1993 and at Pulborough Brooks from 27 to 30 December 1994. Three were recorded at Pagham Harbour on 9 February 1984. It is likely that the above records involve some duplication, given that birds may remain in the county for lengthy periods, as shown by one in the Arun Valley from 1983 to 1987.   *Tony J Wilson*

Ruddy Shelduck   *Tadorna ferruginea*

Status:- A rare vagrant (20 old records, several recent escapes).

There are about 20 old records, three in April and the remainder between 25 August and late October (des Forges & Harber). These include three off

Beachy Head on 12 October 1892 and three shot at Selsey in late October 1892 which were part of a big influx into northwest Europe in which birds reached Iceland and Greenland (Madge & Burn 1988). The most recent record of presumed genuine wild birds was that of six shot at Rye Harbour during August and September 1940 (four being bagged on 7 September). One shot at Harting on 12 September 1890 is in the Booth Museum (BoMNH 204034).

There have been an unknown number of records since 1962, although 34 individuals were recorded during 1980-94 and the species has been seen in every month. These include three at Weir Wood Reservoir on 29 May 1988, three at Pagham Harbour from 19 to 24 August 1992 (reappearing at Littlehampton Golf Course on 26th) and three at Arlington Reservoir on 30 August 1994. All are considered to have been escapes from captivity although the origin of the three at Arlington and indeed one at Pagham Harbour North Wall from 13 November 1994 into 1995, may be more questionable as they may possibly have been part of an apparent national influx in autumn 1994.

All recent records of this colourful species in the British Isles are deemed to be escapes, the last wild birds occurring during the winter of 1945/46. Many recorded in Europe in autumn 1994 are thought to have possibly originated from southern Iraq where their marshland habitat is being drained. The *BOURC* is currently considering reinstating the species to Category A of the British List (i.e. recorded in an apparently wild state at least once since 1958) on the strength of these. Others, particularly family parties, are probably wanderers from continental feral populations although these may not, as yet, be sufficiently established to give the individuals any credibility here (Barthel 1991, Perkins 1992, Vinicombe, Marchant & Knox 1993). In the wild it breeds from southeast Europe across Asia wintering in Turkey and southern Asia, rarely erupting northwest. There are also resident populations in northwest Africa and Ethiopia.   *Richard Fairbank*

Shelduck   *Tadorna tadorna*

Status:- A fairly common breeder and common winter visitor.

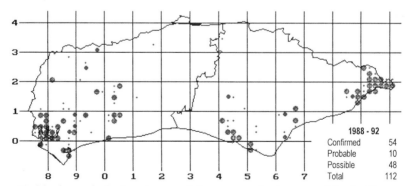

Shelduck regularly breed around the western harbours and in the Rye area; other coastal sites where successful breeding has occurred since 1976 include the lower Cuckmere Valley, Newhaven Tide Mills and Pett Level. Data on broods of downy young suggest that breeding is most successful at Pagham Harbour; however at Rye Harbour, where data have been collected on downy young and fledging success, it is clear that heavy mortality is common. Productivity is therefore lower than counts of downy young might suggest. This was confirmed during the 1992 national breeding survey, which was preceded, in Sussex, by pilot censuses at Chichester Harbour and Rye Harbour during the preceding two seasons (Yates & de Potier 1994). During the three years, productivity at these sites was 0.67-1.69 and 0.23-0.93 young per pair respectively. There are occasional very successful seasons, as in 1989 at Rye, when over 80 young were raised, compared with an average of just over 20 for this site. Around Chichester Harbour, numbers of downy young can vary by over 100% from year to year; there is also evidence that fewer young have been produced recently than in the 1970s. The total number of pairs breeding or holding territory in Sussex in 1992 was 215, an increase on Shrubb's 1979 estimate of 100-150.

The Atlas map shows that Shelduck also breed inland, particularly at various sites in the Arun Valley. The localities used for nesting and the success rate are, however, not consistent from year to year. Numbers are low compared with those at the main coastal sites, representing only some 6% of the total county population (Yates & de Potier 1994). Shrubb referred to regular breeding at Chichester Gravel Pits and up until 1987, pairs at this site, which is now no longer used, regularly produced an average of about ten downy young.

Every summer, pairs remain in Sussex which take up territory but either do not breed or fail to produce young. These may be in areas in which the physical conditions vary, making them suitable for nesting only in certain years. Counts at the main coastal sites in spring show that the number of non-breeders exceeds the number of territorial pairs, sometimes considerably. The 1992 survey showed that, in Sussex, there were 669 non-breeders, of which 482 were in Chichester Harbour and 125 at Pagham Harbour. These figures are within the range given by Shrubb. Pairs found inland are less likely to be intentional non-breeders.

	69-74	74-79	79-84	84-89	89-94	Peak counts
Chichester Harbour	3289	2181	2828	2884	2022	4552, Jan 1982
Pagham Harbour	732	710	653	666	452	1048, Jan 1987
Arundel WWT			35*	40	67	88, Mar 1994
Cuckmere Valley		15**	33	30	18	53, Mar 1987
Rye Harbour		50*	69	117	105	184, Jan 1991

Table 9. Five year means of winter maxima and peak counts of Shelducks, 1969/70 - 93/94.

Most adults depart in June and July for moulting grounds, thought to be at the Heligoland Bight in the German Waddensee (BWP). A few remain later into the summer to care for growing ducklings, which group themselves into 'crèches'. Shelduck return comparatively late from their moulting grounds, but linger correspondingly late in the spring. The wintering population builds up slowly from October onwards. The peak usually occurs in January or February, but is sometimes in December and occasionally as late as March (table 10), and its timing is usually linked with the weather. Cold conditions generally lead to an increase in numbers and the use of additional sites, sometimes only in transit. Table 9 summarises counts at the main localities. Sites which regularly hold 2500 or more birds are considered to be of international importance for the species (Waters & Cranswick 1993).

	Sep	Oct	Nov	Dec	Jan	Feb	Mar
Maximum	353	1010	1722	2880	5455	4397	3312
Mean	143	434	724	1961	2858	3125	2165
Minimum	41	136	252	1275	1562	1665	1133

Table 10. Monthly totals of Shelducks, 1974/75 - 93/94.

The largest totals so far recorded in the county are 5400+ in March 1968 and 5455 in January 1982. These peaks are reflected in data for individual sites, as in 1968 when there were 4900 in Chichester Harbour, the largest ever count for this locality. There are some exceptional cold weather records, such as 400 at Newhaven on 19 January 1985, a site at which over 20 is rarely recorded. When conditions are particularly hostile, birds leave Sussex, but this is unusual.

Movements of Shelduck may be observed at coastal sites, the scale of which is shown by the cumulative monthly totals recorded at Worthing in the period 1978-93:

	Jul	Aug	Sep	Oct	Nov	Dec	Jan	Feb	Mar	Apr	May	Jun
Flying west	1	46	62	349	679	1161	1253	174	222	581	590	9
Flying east	29	71	8	36	14	33	139	58	453	696	1275	72

Observations have revealed that these are predominantly up-Channel in spring and summer but down-Channel in autumn and winter. Many of the eastbound birds in spring are seen in the evenings during settled weather in May but the largest westward movements have been associated with cold weather, for example 518 off Worthing on 15 December 1981.

Seven Shelduck ringed abroad have been recovered in Sussex. Of these, five originated from western Germany and the others from northern France and Sweden. The latter, ringed at Degerhamn, Oland in May 1981, was found dead at Pagham Harbour, 1289 km WSW, in February 1987. Four birds have been ringed in Sussex and recovered outside the county, in western Germany (2), northern France and South Wales.   *Anne de Potier*

Mandarin   *Aix galericulata*

Status:- A scarce but increasing introduced resident.

The Mandarin was first imported into Britain from the Far East before 1745 but the naturalised population here is descended from escapes and deliberate releases from captivity since the early twentieth century (New Atlas). The species was admitted to category C of the British and Irish list in 1971.

In Sussex the earliest record of a Mandarin that could not be traced back to a known escapee was of a drake at Knepp Castle in January 1965. In April 1969 a pair was discovered, near ideal nesting habitat, on a small water in St Leonard's Forest and on the same day two drakes were found on the lakes at

Leonardslee. Neither of the waters were revisited in 1970 but in June 1971 breeding was proved for the first time, at the original water in St Leonard's Forest. In 1979, ten years after the first birds were seen, a complete search revealed a minimum of four pairs in St Leonard's Forest and two pairs at Leonardslee (Hughes & Codd 1980).

Elsewhere, birds of unknown origin occurred at both Dower House Farm, Blackboys and Heathfield Park prior to 1972. In that year and again in 1974 birds were introduced into Possingworth Park resulting in successful breeding in nest boxes in each of the years 1975-77. At other sites, breeding was suspected at Newick Place in 1976 and it was confirmed at Maresfield in 1975, Horam in 1978 and Vines Cross in 1979. By 1981 it was clear that this population in central East Sussex was much larger than previously imagined. Large post-breeding flocks began to appear at the wildfowl collection at Dower House Farm, where 45 were present at the end of 1980 and 60 in December 1981 (Hughes & Codd 1982). Given that Mandarins are often difficult to locate in the breeding season, these post-breeding flocks gave a good indication of the numbers breeding locally.

At about this time, further populations became established in the north of the county in the Copthorne/East Grinstead area, in the northwest in the Lurgashall/Shillinglee area and in the south at Swanbourne Lake, Arundel. Hughes & Codd estimated that in 1981 the county population was in the region of 150-175 birds, a rapid expansion from just one known pair in 1971.

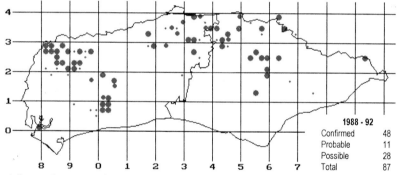

1988 - 92	
Confirmed	48
Probable	11
Possible	28
Total	87

The Atlas map shows that the species is now well established in Sussex with the main strongholds being in the areas already described, especially in the northwest. In 1990 a total of 25 pairs was reported from 23 sites in West Sussex and 12 pairs at 11 sites in East Sussex. A pair at Swanbourne Lake raised 11 young. This ability to raise large broods is clearly an advantage to the species as it colonises new areas.

The Mandarin differs from our native ducks by being more arboreal and this has allowed it to successfully exploit a vacant ecological niche in Britain for a hole-nesting duck. The species normally nests in tree cavities but it will also readily accept nesting boxes when they are provided. The preferred habitat is flowing or standing fresh waters with a dense growth of marginal trees and shrubs, especially where these overhang the water's edge, and where there is an abundance of emergent vegetation to provide shelter (New Atlas).

Oak, beech and sweet chestnut trees are required to provide acorns, beechmast and chestnuts which are the staple food in autumn and winter. The extent to which Mandarins in Sussex are reliant on the provision of food in winter, at the various wildfowl collections, is open to conjecture.

Post-breeding and winter flocks may be quite sizeable. These have included 43 at Lurgashall in September 1986, 50 at Arundel WWT in December 1986, 59 at Chithurst on 1 October 1990 and 84 at Shillinglee Mill Pond on 16 December 1987. It is believed that the latter birds had been displaced from Witley Park, Surrey by the great storm in October of that year.

Mandarins are mainly sedentary but very occasionally they are recorded at sea. In 1990, singles flew east past Worthing and Brighton Marina on 29 April and Seaford on 3 May and west past the latter locality on 30 April.

Martin Kalaher

Wigeon *Anas penelope*

Status:- A common winter visitor and passage migrant

Although a common winter visitor, Wigeon are usually confined to a few localities in the county. Since a large expanse of water on which to roost safely is required, it is not surprising that the species tends to congregate at a small number of favoured sites, of which Chichester and Pagham Harbours, the Arun and Cuckmere Valleys and Arlington Reservoir and Bewl Water are numerically the most important (table 11). Despite the large number of Wigeon that visit the county, Sussex has held only 1.4% of the British population and 0.5% of the northwest European population in recent winters.

	69-74	74-79	79-84	84-89	89-94	Peak counts
Chichester Harbour	716	580	985	1436	1196	2485, Jan 1987
Pagham Harbour	193	147	335	1939	989	4528, Jan 1987
Arun Valley	1334	488	435	701	1419	2535, Feb 1994
Glynde Levels	1166	1064	758	286*	50	2000, winter 1973/74
Cuckmere Valley	56	118	183	748	846	1192, Jan 1994
Arlington Reservoir	650**	1208	1088	885	110	3200, Jan 1985
Bewl Water		150**	199	670	452	1170 Jan 1987
Rye Harbour	140	82	68	600	119	2000, Jan 1985

Table 11. Five year means of winter maxima and peak counts of Wigeon, 1969/70 - 93/94.

	Sep	Oct	Nov	Dec	Jan	Feb	Mar
Maximum	695	2391	3481	5430	16314	6112	3825
Mean	179	832	1527	2754	4959	3220	1398
Minimum	24	21	212	929	1525	1409	578

Table 12. Monthly totals of Wigeon, 1974/75 - 93/94.

A few returning birds can usually be found in the second or third week of August, typically at coastal sites. Exceptionally, birds may appear in July, as in 1987, when there was a female at Bewl Water on 3rd, eight that flew in off the sea at Cuckmere Haven on 5th and a drake at Thorney Island on 19th. Numbers begin to build up in September and then increase rapidly in late autumn, reaching a peak in December or January (table 12). Some coastal passage may be observed in autumn although the numbers involved are small as shown by the cumulative monthly totals recorded at Worthing in the period 1978-93:

	Jul	Aug	Sep	Oct	Nov	Dec	Jan	Feb	Mar	Apr	May	Jun
Flying west	-	4	151	193	784	1080	4077	522	16	-	-	-
Flying east	-	-	19	68	65	116	244	107	374	16	4	-

The onset of severe weather may result in large influxes, such as in January 1985, when the total for the whole county reached 16,314 including 3447 in Pagham Harbour alone. This compares with a county total of just 1525 in January 1990. In such conditions, large numbers may be recorded along the coast, as at Worthing on 7 January 1985 when 735 flew west. The sea itself may be used as a roosting site and in early 1985 several flocks were reported between Climping and the Midrips including one of 1000+ off Newhaven on 19 January. January 1987 was another exceptionally cold month in which large numbers of Wigeon were recorded in the county, resulting in a peak count for the month of 11,919 and a record count for Bewl Water of 1170. Again there was a great deal of coastal movement including 1500 that flew south over Rye on 11 January and 1692 that flew west off Worthing on 16 January. The largest flocks recorded roosting on the sea during January 1987 were 4000 off Selsey Bill, 2500 in Rye Bay and 1000 off Climping. Wintering birds disperse from mid-February onwards and a small passage up-Channel may be observed in spring. Occasionally larger numbers are recorded, as on 31 March 1990, when totals of 819, 497 and 330 flew east at Seaford, Selsey Bill and Worthing respectively.

Oversummering birds are reported, almost annually, but the only record of successful breeding was in 1984 when a pair, probably of feral origin, raised two young at Swanbourne Lake.

Of the six Wigeon ringed abroad and recovered in Sussex, five had originated from the Netherlands. The other, ringed at Mikhaylovka in the former USSR in July 1949, was shot at Chichester, 5255 km west, in January 1954. Such a recovery supports national ringing data that indicates that most of the Wigeon wintering in southeast England originate from Finland, the Baltic States, the Ukraine and northwest Russia (Owen, Atkinson-Willes & Salmon 1986). Single birds trapped at Icklesham in October 1991 were shot on the Ribble Marshes, 394 km northwest, 20 days later, and at Pelves, France, 172 km ESE, in December 1992.   *Martin Kalaher*

American Wigeon
Anas americana

Status:- One record of doubtful origin.

A pair at Pett Level Pools on 1 June 1991 was, due to the unusual date, widely regarded as having escaped from captivity.

This duck is one of the most obvious gaps in the Sussex list with nearly 250 recorded in the British Isles during 1962-94, including six in Hampshire (Clark & Eyre 1993) and ten in Kent (J Cantello & T Hodge *in litt.*). It breeds in North America wintering south to Central America.   *Richard Fairbank*

Gadwall
Anas strepera

Status:- A very scarce breeder and fairly common winter visitor which has increased significantly in recent years; passage migrant.

The Gadwall population in Sussex has increased dramatically since the early 1960s (fig. 15), in line with the national trend. Prior to 1962, only about 145 had been recorded (des Forges & Harber) and no more than 17 in any one year. As recently as 31 December 1968, a flock of 26 at Chichester Gravel Pits was a county record whereas, nowadays, such numbers are commonplace. Gadwall are essentially vegetarian and show a strong preference for flooded meadows, gravel pits, lakes and reservoirs with plentiful submerged vegetation. There are now a large number of sites in the county that have held flocks of 20 or more and counts at those that have held 50 or more are summarised in table 13.

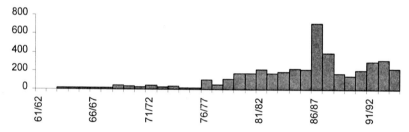

Figure 15. Peak winter totals of Gadwall, 1961/62 - 93/94.

Although there were four at Darwell Reservoir on 14 July 1968, at non-breeding localities the first returning birds do not normally appear until early to mid-August. Numbers in the county build up thereafter to reach a peak, usually in December or January (table 14).

	69-74	74-79	79-84	84-89	89-94	Peak counts
Chichester Harbour		4	37	9	12	61, Nov 1982
Chichester GP	19	32*	22*	28	37	69, Feb 1992
Swanbourne Lake		30*	76	84	32	149, Jan 1987
Arundel WWT			59	108	49	285, Jan 1988
Pulborough Brooks					40	57, Jan 1993
Bewl Water			20	116	57	230, Jan 1987
Pannel Valley					42*	63, Dec 1991
Rye Harbour		23*	1	17	37	81, Nov 1982

Table 13. Five year means of winter maxima and peak counts of Gadwall, 1969/70 - 93/94.

This peak varies considerably and is very dependent on the severity of the winter. A typical figure in recent years is 200-300, but in January 1987, following a cold spell, a record total of 714 was recorded. Dispersal usually occurs by mid-March and, by early April, only the summering population remains.

	Sep	Oct	Nov	Dec	Jan	Feb	Mar
Maximum	120	133	257	398	714	213	141
Mean	54	71	127	165	188	133	65
Minimum	2	1	2	12	34	50	0

Table 14. Monthly totals of Gadwall, 1976/77 - 93/94.

Sea-watching has shown that small numbers of Gadwall move up-Channel in spring. Most records are for the last week of March and the first two weeks of April; six off Seaford on 21 May 1989 were unusually late.

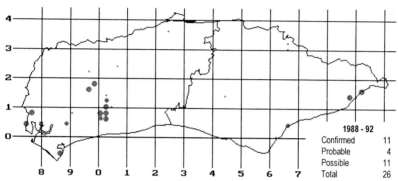

	1988 - 92
Confirmed	11
Probable	4
Possible	11
Total	26

Increasing numbers of Gadwall now summer in the county and in most years a few pairs breed. In 1976, three feral pairs at Arundel WWT produced 24 free-flying young which no doubt formed the nucleus for the breeding population in the Arun Valley, shown by the Atlas map. Occasional pairs may also breed at other sites in the county and these have included Aldsworth Pond, Burton Mill Pond, Chingford Pond, Pagham Harbour, Pett Level and Rye Harbour. It is unlikely, however, that the county population currently exceeds ten pairs.

One ringed at Icklesham in December 1991 was shot at Fowlmere, Norfolk, 172 km north, in November 1992, while singles ringed at Abberton Reservoir, Essex in September 1981 and August 1982 were shot at Lyminster, 145 km southwest, in November 1982 and Stopham, 135 km southwest, in December 1983. One ringed as a duckling in Schleswig-Holstein, Germany in June 1991 was controlled at Icklesham, 748 km WSW, in January 1993.

Martin Kalaher

Baikal Teal   *Anas formosa*

Status:- One old record recently regarded as unproven.

A male shot at Battle on 14 November 1927 was regarded as an escape by Walpole-Bond, commenting that "as an importation, this duck is often kept in this country more or less at liberty".

157

This striking east Asian duck has enjoyed an on-off relationship with the British List. The latest review has rejected all British records either due to the likelihood of escape or unproven identification (*BOURC* 1993b); the Battle individual fitting into the latter category. *Richard Fairbank*

Teal *Anas crecca*

Status:- A scarce resident and common winter visitor and passage migrant.

Shrubb reported a breeding population of about 50 to 60 pairs but considered that this was probably an underestimate. He thought it unlikely that there had been a marked change since 1938, when 75-150 pairs were thought to breed (Walpole-Bond). The favoured breeding sites were reported by Shrubb to be "lakes or ponds with good marginal vegetation" or "small, sometimes, quite insignificant, streams and marshes in the interior". Extensive grass marshes were rarely used for nesting.

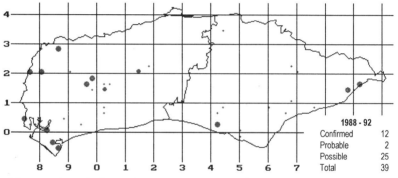

	1988 - 92
Confirmed	12
Probable	2
Possible	25
Total	39

The results of the Atlas Survey suggest that the number of pairs has declined significantly since the 1970s, given that breeding was confirmed or probable in only 14 tetrads and possible in a further 25. Furthermore, some of these may not be occupied in every year. However, at Pulborough Brooks RSPB reserve, where extensive habitat management has been carried out since the late 1980s, a remarkable 21 pairs raised at least 20 young in 1993. Allowing for perhaps 5-10 pairs elsewhere in the county indicates a minimum population of 25-30 pairs.

Flocks begin to build up from late July onwards at favoured sites such as Arundel WWT, Rye Harbour, Sidlesham Ferry and Thorney Deeps. Appreciable numbers do not usually arrive until September, after which they increase steadily, reaching a peak in mid-winter (table 16), the largest of which in recent years has been 5738 in December 1981. Counts at the main localities are summarised in table 15. Sites which regularly hold 1400 or more birds are considered to be of national importance (Waters & Cranswick 1993).

Shrubb referred to a decline in the winter population due to improved drainage of many extensive areas of wet grassland. Nowadays, it is unusual for the winter peak to exceed 4000 but in 1960 and 1962, the Amberley/ Pulborough marshes alone held up to 3000 birds. The creation of suitable habitat at Pulborough Brooks has restored numbers to much their former level, as shown by a count of 2697 at this locality in January 1993.

	69-74	74-79	79-84	84-89	89-94	Peak counts
Chichester Harbour	371	1220	2392	1838	1287	3253 Dec 1981
Pagham Harbour	166	352	726	425	1020	1636, Feb 1994
Arundel WWT		298**	161	172	197	357, Dec 1985
Arun Valley	750	588	699	542	2000	2697, Jan 1993
Glynde Levels	424	239	348	175*	128	800, winter 1973/74
Cuckmere Valley	105	104	136	97**		300, winter 1970/71
Bewl Water		98**	90	114	77	250, Jan 1985
Darwell Reservoir	69*	106**	107	213*	244*	509, Jan 1986
Powdermill Reservoir	40**	64*	17*	60	156	258, Jan 1993
Pannel Valley					233*	300, Dec 1990
Rye Harbour	105	70*	62	112	278	400, Dec 1991

Table 15. Five year means of winter maxima and peak counts of Teal, 1969/70 - 93/94.

	Sep	Oct	Nov	Dec	Jan	Feb	Mar
Maximum	1881	2457	5095	5738	5188	5231	1449
Mean	797	1234	2467	3344	3134	2400	949
Minimum	222	264	1002	2056	1473	1199	296

Table 16. Monthly totals of Teal, 1976/77 - 93/94.

Departure takes place in late February and March. Through passage is indicated by occasional small flocks moving up-Channel between March and mid-May and down-Channel in autumn, up to the end of November. The scale of these movements is shown by the cumulative monthly totals recorded at Worthing in the period 1978-93:

	Jul	Aug	Sep	Oct	Nov	Dec	Jan	Feb	Mar	Apr	May	Jun
Flying west	-	73	117	118	287	55	103	34	11	2	2	-
Flying east	-	9	1	13	38	8	40	41	748	13	28	-

The largest movement was on 31 March 1990 when 529 flew east at Worthing and 250 at Seaford.

There have been 14 recoveries of foreign-ringed Teal in the county. These originated from the Netherlands (9), Denmark (3) and France and Poland (1 each). The latter, ringed at Slonsk on 5 July 1981 was shot at Offham, 1068 km west, in mid-December of the same year. Of nine Teal ringed at Icklesham and recovered overseas, seven were in France. The remaining birds, ringed on 7 December 1988 and 22 October 1991, were shot at Zirni, Latvia, 1549 km ENE, on 26 August 1989 and near Kalajoki, Finland, 1994 km northeast, on 20 August 1993.

There have been five records of drakes of the Nearctic race *A.c. carolinensis*, the Green-winged Teal, as follows:

1961:   One at the Midrips on 19 and 22 March.
1975:   One in the Cuckmere Valley on 21-22 March.
1989:   One at Arundel WWT from 21 April to 2 May.
1990:   One at Arundel WWT from 10 to 24 March.
1991:   One at Arundel WWT from 26 January to 22 March.

The Arundel records are thought to refer to the same returning individual.

Martin Kalaher

Mallard

Anas platyrhynchos

Status:- A common resident and winter visitor.

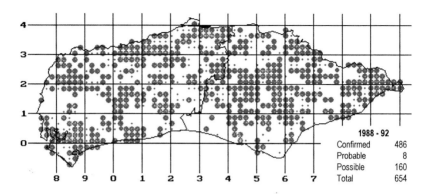

1988 - 92	
Confirmed	486
Probable	8
Possible	160
Total	654

The Atlas map shows the Mallard to be widely distributed in Sussex. The species is highly adaptable and is likely to be found on virtually any body of water in the county. It is only absent from the Downs, where there is a very little suitable habitat. A variety of nest-sites may be utilised, of which an old Magpie's nest, fully 15-20 feet above the ground, at Sidlesham in 1984 was one of the more unusual. The largest concentrations occur at wetland sites, as shown by surveys of Pevensey Levels in 1987 (Hitchings 1988) and the Arun Valley in 1991 that revealed totals of 47 pairs and over 200 pairs respectively. Recent records suggest populations of up to 80 pairs at Rye Harbour, 60 pairs at Bewl Water and 40 pairs at Icklesham, although there are probably other sites holding similar numbers for which no counts are available. Assuming a density of 5-10 pairs for each tetrad in which breeding was confirmed or probable indicates a county population of 2500-5000 pairs.

Mallard can breed in the winter as shown by the discovery at Arundel WWT of broods of seven on 24 February 1984 and ten on 13 December 1983. Winter broods are very unlikely to survive long, and the latter was decimated within three days. Information on breeding success is very scant. However, a count of 67 males, 20 females, nine broods and 42 young at Bewl Water in June 1991 suggests that it is low. There is, however, considerable variation and in some years it is very much better, as in 1992 when 64 pairs, 21 broods and 144 young were counted at the same site. Nesting ducks are generally very secretive and it may be that counts of post-breeding flocks in August provide better estimates of breeding success. At Bewl Water, for example, the breeding population in 1986 was an estimated 51 pairs whereas 775 were counted on 22 August. Another large post-breeding flock of 750 feeding on stubble at North Stoke on 20 August 1980 was evidence of the large numbers breeding in the Arun Valley, long before the 1991 survey took place.

After the breeding season, Mallard tend to congregate on undisturbed open stretches of water. As the winter progresses, numbers increase gradually to reach a peak of 3000-5000 in December or January before declining in February and March when birds return to their breeding sites. The counts at

160

the main localities are summarised in table 17 although it should be noted that other sites not listed are known to attract substantial numbers on occasions.

	69-74	74-79	79-84	84-89	89-94	Peak counts
Chichester Harbour	170	495	540	596	516	1075, Jan 1976
Pagham Harbour	202	228	337	407	376	486, Nov 1990
Chichester GP	355	211	258	159	153	487, Jan 1982
Petworth Park		147**	149	98	81*	205, Sep 1980
Swanbourne Lake		401*	270	157	142	441, Dec 1978
Arundel WWT		384**	655	708	792	1003, Dec 1981
Arun Valley	194	279	175	211	427	645, Jan 1993
Angmering Decoy			154**	193*	150	260, Sep 1984
Kneppmill Pond	180	166	226	200	114	390, Dec 1983
Ardingly Reservoir		136**	136	167	117	264, Nov 1986
Weir Wood Reservoir	271	198	133	118	118	500, winter 1969/70
Barcombe Reservoir	298	258	122	171	122*	700, winter 1970/71
Glynde Levels	217	155	175	150*	184	500, winter 1973/74
Arlington Reservoir		317*	576	543	291	1000, Jan 1985
Bewl Water		610**	681	625	446	1016, Sep 1983
Darwell Reservoir	125	310	429	291	294	711, Feb 1981
Alexandra Park, Hastings		178**	245	225	231*	332, Jan 1982
Rye Harbour	488	141	340	470	321	1000, winter 1969/70

Table 17. Five year means of maxima and peak counts of Mallards, 1969/70 - 93/94.

Small numbers of Mallard may be observed passing offshore as shown by the cumulative monthly totals recorded at Worthing in the period 1978-93:

	Jul	Aug	Sep	Oct	Nov	Dec	Jan	Feb	Mar	Apr	May	Jun
Flying west	-	10	26	47	132	44	120	6	13	12	8	1
Flying east	1	6	11	13	10	14	9	15	81	57	50	8

The largest movement was of 44 flying west off Worthing on 19 November 1985.

Of the 66 recoveries of Sussex-ringed Mallard, 53 were from within the county, nine from other parts of southern England and one from France. The latter bird, ringed at Icklesham on 7 September 1990, was shot at Ploermel, 399 km southwest, on 15 December 1991. *Martin Kalaher*

Pintail *Anas acuta*

Status:- A fairly common winter visitor and passage migrant which occasionally summers and has bred.

Pintail bred in Sussex in 1925 and 1936 and probably attempted to do so in 1970. In the Rye area, where pairs remained late in spring throughout the 1980s, a female was seen with three young in 1988. A feral pair hatched four young at Arundel WWT in 1985, none of which survived, a fate shared by four broods that hatched from feral pairs at the same site in 1986. In addition to these records of proved breeding, one was present at Thorney Island throughout June and July 1976 and a pair at Pulborough Brooks in June 1991. Prolonged stays such as these would appear to be unusual and, more commonly, birds are reported on one date only, as in 1990 when there were singles at Thorney Island on 20 June, Waltham Brooks on 22 June, and Pett Pools on 25 July. Whether these summering birds are genuinely attempting to breed, or simply sick or injured, is open to speculation.

Although up to eight were noted at Rye Harbour in July 1978, the first returning birds are not normally noted until August. Typically, these occur at coastal sites but occasionally there are inland sightings as in 1984, when one was recorded at Waltham Brooks on 11 August and three at Weir Wood Reservoir on 16 August. In 1992, there were three at Bewl Water on 31 August. Numbers build up slowly throughout the autumn to reach a peak, normally in December or January (table 19). A county total of 886 in January 1986 was thought to be the highest ever although this figure has since been exceeded by totals of 945 in November 1990 and 1064 in January 1994, indicating an increase in the winter population. Table 18 summarises counts at the main localities. Sites which regularly hold 280 or more birds are considered to be of national importance for the species (Waters & Cranswick 1993).

	69-74	74-79	79-84	84-89	89-94	Peak counts
Chichester Harbour	102	154	163	125	211	321, Jan 1992
Pagham Harbour	49	136	168	345	512	839, Nov 1990
Arun Valley	53	69	31	63	312	472, Jan 1993

Table 18. Five year means of winter maxima and peak counts of Pintail, 1969/70 - 93/94.

	Sep	Oct	Nov	Dec	Jan	Feb	Mar
Maximum	46	133	944	779	1070	873	470
Mean	11	52	274	353	440	338	144
Minimum	0	0	85	93	98	137	4

Table 19. Monthly totals of Pintail, 1976/77 - 93/94.

In the Arun Valley, numbers declined during the 1970s and 1980s due to a lack of regular winter flooding, resulting from raised river banks and improved drainage. More recently, the management of water levels at Pulborough Brooks RSPB Reserve has restored numbers to their previous levels, as shown by counts of 344 in January 1991 and 472 in January 1993. It is unusual to record more than 20 away from the western harbours and Arun Valley but exceptions have included up to 61 at Chichester Gravel Pits in the winter of 1975/76, 25 at Bewl Water on 6 November 1982 and 66 on the Adur Levels on 2 February 1988. Most have departed by late March and just the odd straggler remains into May.

Sea-watching has shown that small numbers of Pintail pass westward in autumn and winter and eastward between March and early May. Some indication of the scale of these movements is provided by the cumulative monthly totals for Worthing for the period 1978-93 shown below.

	Jul	Aug	Sep	Oct	Nov	Dec	Jan	Feb	Mar	Apr	May	Jun
Flying west	-	10	3	59	63	14	92	3	18	2	4	-
Flying east	-	-	4	16	1	4	13	18	478	37	11	-

Occasionally, larger movements are recorded, such as those of 279 off Worthing, 123 off Seaford and 61 off Beachy Head on 31 March 1990, 71 off Seaford on 4 March 1991 and 46 off Brighton Marina on 13 March 1993.

There have been four recoveries of foreign-ringed Pintail in Sussex. Single birds ringed in the Netherlands in February 1958 and September 1976 were shot at Beckley in January 1961 and in Chichester Harbour in October 1976. A female ringed at Nakskov, Denmark in November 1966 was shot at Bosham, 467 km WSW, in December 1969 and a male ringed at St Quentin-en-Tourmont, France in February 1975 was shot, also at Bosham, 183 km WNW, in January 1976. A number of Pintail have been ringed at Icklesham and, of these, three were recovered in France and one in Sweden. The latter bird, ringed in January 1992, was shot at Trolle Ljungby, Scania, 1086 km ENE, in September 1992. *Martin Kalaher*

Garganey *Anas querquedula*
Status:- A scarce passage migrant and rare summer visitor.

Until 1961 up to 12 pairs bred annually (des Forges & Harber). However, between 1962 and 1976 breeding was proved only five times, although other records for the breeding season suggested a population of up to seven pairs in some years (Shrubb). Since 1976 the number of pairs has varied between none (in five years) to ten in 1989, although the average is about two. An increase in the number of breeding records in the last five years may be attributed to improved habitat management of a number of wetland sites, especially Pett Level and Pulborough Brooks RSPB Reserve. The species is very secretive, remaining hidden in dense vegetation for much of the breeding season, thus making successful breeding difficult to prove. An analysis of the records of passage birds for the period 1962-93 suggests a decline during the late 1970s and early 1980s and shows that there has been a recent increase in the number of occurrences, perhaps reflecting the upturn in the breeding population in the late 1980s (fig. 16).

The Garganey is an early spring migrant. Since 1962, first arrival dates have been in February in five years, March in 25 years and early April in two, with the average for the 32 years being 13 March. Singles at Pulborough Brooks on 2 February 1993 and shot at Langney Point on 21 February are the earliest to be recorded in that month. Passage generally peaks between mid-March and mid-April although the total recorded each spring varies considerably. Shrubb refers to a maximum of 40 but, more recently, totals have varied between just four in 1985 and 38 in 1991. Singles or pairs are noted passing up-Channel in most springs, often with flocks of Common Scoters. In 1990 over 20 were recorded, including a party of 12 on 18 March that was seen from a number of sea-watching localities. Passage may continue into early June as shown by a record of three males at Pagham Harbour on 5 June 1983.

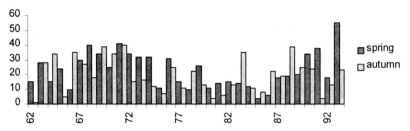

Figure 16. Spring and autumn totals of Garganeys, 1962 - 93.

Autumn passage invariably begins in early July and peaks between late July and late August. In years when breeding success is high, totals of up to 40 have occurred in any one autumn and as many as 23 have been noted together at Sidlesham Ferry on 12 August 1969 and at Icklesham on 5 August 1989. The peak counts are usually in the Pett Level/Rye Harbour area although pairs or singles may appear at other suitable localities. It is not unusual for the species to linger into October and since 1976 there have been four later records, of which singles at Rye Harbour on 15 November 1986 and at Bewl Water from 23 October to 13 December 1994 were the latest.

There are two winter records, a pair near Horsham on 19 January 1947 and one at Icklesham from 24 January to 24 April 1994.

Males ringed at Icklesham on 4 April 1992 and on 5 August 1993 were controlled at Abberton Reservoir, Essex, 102 km north, on 23 April 1992 and shot in Department Somme, France, 88 km southeast, on 2 September 1993.

Tony J Wilson

Blue-winged Teal   *Anas discors*

Status:- A very rare vagrant (two records).

One was recorded before 1962, being shot at Worth on 17 January 1922 (des Forges & Harber). It was probably the fifth British record but it was not included in the *Handbook of British Birds* (Witherby *et al* 1940).

A male at the Severals, Church Norton on 12 May 1970 and at Ivy Lake, Chichester on 13-14 May 1970 is the only comparatively recent record.

An eclipse male at Swanbourne Lake, Arundel from at least 2 to 27 November 1991 was considered to have escaped, probably from the adjacent Arundel WWT. It was full-winged but had slightly aberrant primaries on its right wing (white spots at the tips), a feature shown more obviously by a female in the WWT collection!

164

There have been over 170 records in the British Isles during 1962-94 but several records in southeast England have been tainted by the possibility of escape. It breeds in North America south of the Arctic circle wintering from southern USA south to Peru and northern Brazil.   *Richard Fairbank*

Shoveler   *Anas clypeata*

Status:- A very scarce resident and fairly common winter visitor and passage migrant.

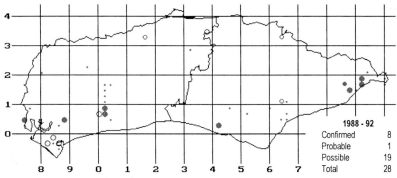

1988 - 92	
Confirmed	8
Probable	1
Possible	19
Total	28

Small numbers of Shoveler summer annually and in most years a handful of pairs are proved to breed. des Forges & Harber referred to nesting in a number of widely scattered localities, but only to the extent of a few pairs and irregularly. The species bred in 15 years between 1965 and 1987, involving 22 pairs, while during the Atlas Survey (1988-92), breeding was confirmed in eight tetrads. In 1993, eight pairs bred at Pulborough Brooks and possibly three pairs on Pevensey Levels. The distribution shown by the Atlas map, which also displays tetrads with additional breeding records during 1962-87 as open symbols, reflects the species' preference for marshland or rough pasture adjacent to shallow open water (New Atlas). Of those localities where breeding has been confirmed in recent years, the most regularly used have been Sidlesham Ferry, where pairs were proved to have bred in seven years between 1978 and 1993, and Rye Harbour, where pairs bred in 1983-84 and 1992. At Icklesham, where extensive habitat management has been carried out, there were five broods in 1989, while in 1990 11 pairs bred but most of the young were predated. Summer records of pairs and single birds, usually drakes, are reported annually from a number of other localities, some of which may be suitable for nesting. Small non-breeding flocks occur in some years, as in 1991 at Pulborough Brooks, when there were nine drakes and five ducks from April to late May.

Returning birds sometimes begin to congregate by mid-July, normally only at a few coastal sites such as Pagham Lagoon, where there were ten on 14 July 1989, Thorney Deeps, where 14 were recorded on 17 July 1990, and Rye Harbour. By contrast, few are reported inland before the end of August. However, there were 16 at Weir Wood Reservoir on 15 August 1981 and two at Darwell Reservoir on 27 August 1990.

Numbers build up slowly throughout September and October but more rapidly in November, reaching a peak in December or January. A gradual decrease follows in February and March (table 21). This pattern of occurrence is quite different to that for the country as a whole where the largest numbers are normally present in October. As the winter progresses, these birds move to France, the Iberian peninsula and Ireland, so reducing the wintering population to two-thirds of the peak figure. Occasionally, Sussex does follow the national pattern more closely, as in 1991 when the peak count of 290 occurred in September. Table 20 summarises counts at the main localities.

	69-74	74-79	79-84	84-89	89-94	Peak counts
Pagham Harbour	11	41	16	15	41	52, Nov 1991
Chichester Gravel Pits	110	186*	136*	31	39	261, Jan 1980
Arun Valley	75	168	41	81	149	300, Mar 1978
Arundel WWT			51	33	21	70, Jan 1981
Arlington Reservoir	28**	44	35	29	79	176, Dec 1992
Pannel Valley					55*	150, Sep 1991
Pett Level	50**	29*	19*	31*	27	66, Mar 1979
Rye Harbour	17	27*	36	45	81	110, Dec 1989

Table 20. Five year means of winter maxima and peak counts of Shoveler, 1969/70 - 93/94.

	Sep	Oct	Nov	Dec	Jan	Feb	Mar
Maximum	290	215	295	486	451	347	447
Mean	71	99	159	236	243	214	155
Minimum	10	26	56	52	85	52	65

Table 21. Monthly totals of Shoveler, 1976/77 - 93/94.

The high county totals for March in recent years suggest that there is a marked spring passage, probably involving birds that have wintered to the south and west. At Rye Harbour, for example, there were 220 on 7 March 1992, decreasing to 105 by 5 April, and 30 by 17 April.

Sea-watching has shown that there is a very light autumn passage at coastal sites, although at Selsey Bill a total of 77 flew west in November 1992, including 67 on 9th. The cumulative monthly totals recorded at Worthing during 1978-93, shown below, indicate that there is a more marked eastward passage in spring, typically between mid-March and late April. Earlier records include 84 off Seaford on 3 March 1991 while notably late were 37 off Goring on 10 May 1981, and a small party off Beachy Head on 20 May 1972. In some years very few are recorded but in others there may be exceptional numbers, as in 1990 when there were 819 off Seaford, 497 off Selsey Bill and 330 off Worthing on 31 March.

	Jul	Aug	Sep	Oct	Nov	Dec	Jan	Feb	Mar	Apr	May	Jun
Flying west	1	6	37	16	17	5	43	-	10	21	6	-
Flying east	-	-	1	4	3	-	10	10	466	317	25	-

The only recovery of a foreign-ringed Shoveler in Sussex was that of a female ringed at Haarsteg, the Netherlands on 8 March 1962 and shot at Knepp, 396 km WSW, on 12 September 1964. A male, ringed at Icklesham on 12 January 1990, was found dead at Kroshonzero, USSR, 2318 km ENE, on 4 May 1992.   *Martin Kalaher*

Red-crested Pochard   *Netta rufina*

Status:- Possibly a rare winter visitor and passage migrant, although many of the records probably relate to birds that have escaped from captivity or are of feral origin.

The first for the county was a female at Thorney Great Deep from 3 October to 16 December 1948. A further eight were recorded up to 1961 (des Forges & Harber), after which there were records in 23 years up to 1994 (fig. 17). It is not possible, however, to give an exact total for the period 1962-94 given that some birds apparently remained in the county for long periods, during which time they were recorded at a number of different localities.

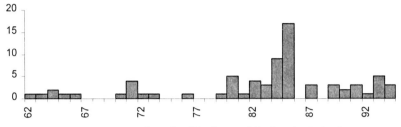

Figure 17. Annual totals of Red-crested Pochard, 1962 - 94

Most of those recorded were at Arlington Reservoir, Bewl Water, Chichester Gravel Pits, Darwell Reservoir and Rye Harbour although some duplication is likely. All records involved one or two apart from three at Arlington Reservoir on 30 May 1971, four there on 15 August 1985 and an exceptional 12 (five males and seven females) at Bewl Water on 30 December 1985. Genuinely wild birds, such as the two observed in a flock of Wigeon on the sea off Newhaven on 10 February 1991, will probably have come from Denmark, Holland or northern Germany where there are small breeding populations. However, one or two pairs have nested almost annually in Britain since 1968 (Baatsen 1990) and it is now thought that the feral population in this country exceeds the wild population in each of these countries combined (Harrop 1991). There are significant feral populations at Cotswold Water Park, Gloucestershire and St James' Park, London and these are likely to be the source of the 50-100 birds estimated to winter in Britain (Winter Atlas).   *Richard Kelly*

Pochard   *Aythya ferina*

Status:- A rare breeder and fairly common winter visitor and passage migrant.

des Forges & Harber referred to nine instances of proved breeding, the first near Three Bridges in 1876 and the most recent at Rye Harbour in 1960. A pair may have bred in 1973 while in 1977 two pairs were successful at Chichester Gravel Pits, raising 15 young. A pair bred at the same site the following year and again in 1982 and 1984. In the last 15 years, pairs have also bred successfully at Rye Harbour (1980-81), Forest Mere (1981), and Church Norton (1986-87), while at Bewl Water, a pair nested unsuccessfully in 1982-

167

84. At Arundel WWT, where a feral population has been established since the early 1980s, there were four broods totalling 27 young in 1985 but only 4-5 of these fledged. In addition to showing the 1988-92 distribution, the Atlas map displays, as open circles, tetrads with additional breeding records during 1962-87. Summering birds have also been recorded at a number of other sites in recent years and it is quite possible that some broods have been overlooked.

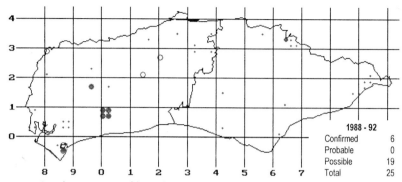

	1988 - 92	
Confirmed	6
Probable	0
Possible	19
Total	25

Despite the paucity of breeding pairs, quite sizeable flocks of Pochard may be recorded in late summer, especially at Chichester Gravel Pits, where there were 45 on 28 July 1984 and 60 by 18 August. Numbers build up gradually through September and October but it is not normally until November that a marked influx occurs (table 23). The county total may reach about a thousand in December or January but this figure is sometimes exceeded, particularly during cold weather when birds frequent unfrozen stretches of still water, or move to rivers or the sea. Table 22 summarises counts at the main localities.

	69-74	74-79	79-84	84-89	89-94	Peak counts
Chichester Gravel Pits	371	197*	245	213	163	465, winter 1971/72
Arundel WWT		208**	311	379	457	582, Feb 1991
Kneppmill Pond	171	14	22	37	27	410, winter 1972/73
Ardingly Reservoir		97**	22	18	17	118, Feb 1978
Weir Wood Reservoir	126	151	100	77	56	330, Dec 1977
Barcombe Reservoir	52	57	20	43	71	150, winter 1975/76
Arlington Reservoir	130**	61*	71	25	45	220, Dec 1981
Bewl Water		380**	138	135	77	380, Dec 1978
Darwell Reservoir	77	63	15	12*	46	140, winter 1972/73
Rye Harbour	395	211	171	199	217	500, winter 1969/70

Table 22. Five year means of winter maxima and peak counts of Pochard, 1969/70 - 93/94.

	Sep	Oct	Nov	Dec	Jan	Feb	Mar
Maximum	358	726	1091	1174	1221	1058	625
Mean	133	333	644	876	909	791	329
Minimum	23	47	228	398	604	252	22

Table 23. Monthly totals of Pochard, 1976/77 - 93/94.

Small numbers of Pochard may also be recorded at localities not listed in the table. In January 1984, when counts were made at an additional 146 sites, a total of 46 was found, of which 25 were at Forest Mere and the remaining 21 at eight small waters in the High Weald. On the coast, Widewater, Lancing and Brooklands, East Worthing are now regular sites for this attractive species, particularly during cold weather. In such conditions, small flocks may also appear at more unusual localities. Such was the case in January 1985, when ten were recorded in the lower Cuckmere Valley, and February 1991, when 34 were found on the Adur at Shoreham-by-Sea. Birds may also appear on deep flood water in the river valleys, for example in early 1990, when up to 112 were recorded at Pulborough Brooks.

There is very little passage observed at coastal sites, the extent of which is shown by the cumulative monthly totals recorded at Worthing in the period 1978-93:

	Jul	Aug	Sep	Oct	Nov	Dec	Jan	Feb	Mar	Apr	May	Jun
Flying west	-	3	-	32	42	1	149	21	-	7	-	1
Flying east	-	-	-	4	4	-	-	-	276	14	22	-

Very rarely, large movements are observed, the most notable of which was one of 236 flying east in small flocks off Worthing on 12 March 1984.

Of six foreign-ringed Pochard recovered in Sussex, four were from Latvia and two from the Netherlands. The birds of Latvian origin tie in well with national ringing data that indicate that most wintering Pochard in this country are from the Baltic countries and Russia (Owen, Attkinson-Willes & Salmon 1986). There have also been four recoveries within the county during the winter months of birds ringed at Abberton Reservoir, Essex, where there is a large post-breeding moult gathering. One ringed at Blunham, Bedfordshire in December 1980 was found dead at Worthing almost ten years later in June 1990.

Martin Kalaher

Ring-necked Duck   *Aythya collaris*

Status:- A very rare vagrant (one record).

A first-winter male at Portfield Gravel Pits, Chichester from 4 to 31 December 1982 is surprisingly the only county record. It spent long periods asleep which seems to be normal behaviour for this species when it is being observed!

With about 350 records in the British Isles during 1962-94, more might be expected to have appeared in Sussex. There have been annual sightings in Hampshire since 1985, although perhaps involving only four individuals (Clark & Eyre 1993), and also six in Kent (J Cantello & T Hodge *in litt.*). It breeds in North America and winters south to Central America.

Richard Fairbank

Ferruginous Duck   *Aythya nyroca*

Status:- A rare vagrant (21 to 23 individuals recorded in autumn and winter but many are probably escapes).

Prior to 1962 there were four records involving nine individuals (des Forges & Harber). Three were shot at Langney Point on 15 August 1903 (an unusual date) and Walpole-Bond gives a lengthy, but unconvincing, account of three together at Warnham Mill Pond on 20 March 1908 and also describes one seen briefly at Amberley on 24 March 1926 as being "not too friendly". Two present between Rye Harbour and the Midrips from 17 November 1946 to 22 February 1947, when one was shot (Cawkell 1947), would seem to have the best credentials for being wild birds of all those recorded in Sussex.

Twelve to 14 individuals have been recorded since the beginning of 1960:

1976: A male photographed at Chichester Gravel Pits in March (*Brit. Birds* 70: plate 29).
1977: A male at Weir Wood Reservoir from 6 February to 6 March and 29 October to 21 January 1978.
  A male between Rye and Winchelsea on 11 September was presumably that at Pett Pools on 12 December and Rye Harbour to the end of the year.
1978: A male, presumably the Rye individual, at Shorndene Reservoir, Hastings from 6 to 21 January, Castle Water, Rye Harbour on 12 February and at Pett Pools from 26 January to 22 February (*Brit. Birds* 71: plate 205).
  A male, presumably that at Weir Wood Reservoir to 21 January, at Ardingly Reservoir from 4 February to 10 March.
1979: A male at Arundel WWT from 14 January to 4 March and again from 15 September to mid February 1980.
  A female at the Crumbles Gravel Pits on 2 December and 6 January 1980.
1980: A female, presumably that at the Crumbles to 6 January, at Arlington Reservoir on 12-13 January.
  A female, possibly the same, at the Long Pit, Rye Harbour on 26 January.
  A female, possibly the same, at the Crumbles Gravel Pits on 12 October.
1981: An immature male at Scotney Court Gravel Pit between 6 March and 17 May, a rather late departure.
  A male at Weir Wood Reservoir on 9 November.
1985: A female at Weir Wood Reservoir from 3 to 13 February.
1987: A male at Ivy Lake, Chichester on 10 and 13 January.
  A male, probably in its first year, at the Crumbles Gravel Pits from 16 September to 3 October.
1991: A juvenile male at Weir Wood Reservoir on 2-3 December.
1993: A male at Camber Gravel Pits from 3 to 5 January.

Perhaps surprisingly, Weir Wood Reservoir has hosted most recent records (4), with three seen on the Crumbles Gravel Pits, two at Chichester Gravel Pits and Rye Harbour and singles at Ardingly Reservoir, Arlington Reservoir, Arundel WWT, Camber, Hastings, Pett Pools and Scotney Court Gravel Pit.

With the exception of the trio shot in August 1903 and the late staying Scotney Court Gravel Pit juvenile of 1981, all sightings have fallen between 11 September and 24 March. Even so, few of the above have a particularly distinguished pedigree. Not only do escapes have to be contended with but also the possible confusion with similar looking *Aythya* hybrids (Harris, Tucker & Vinicombe 1989). Any records on unusual dates, involving protracted stays or in unusual locations are best regarded as suspect and without being overly harsh the Sussex total could readily be halved.

The true status in Britain of this difficult species is hard to assess due to escaped individuals. Between eight and 13 were recorded annually during 1990-92 (Evans 1993a). It breeds discontinuously from Spain to western China and winters from North Africa and the Mediterranean to India. It has dramatically declined over much of its European range and is now regarded as globally threatened (Tucker & Heath 1994).   *Richard Fairbank*

Tufted Duck   *Aythya fuligula*

Status:- A fairly common breeding species and winter visitor.

As shown on the Atlas map, the Tufted Duck can be found throughout much of Sussex. As it is a diving duck, it requires deep water so the favoured habitats are lakes, reservoirs, flooded gravel pits and large ponds. The most important breeding sites numerically are Bewl Water and Rye Harbour in the east of the county and Chichester Gravel Pits in the west.

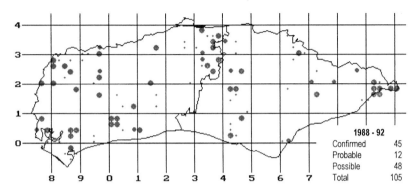

	1988 - 92	
	Confirmed	45
	Probable	12
	Possible	48
	Total	105

The Tufted Duck is generally under-recorded as a breeding species. However, in 1985 a search of inland waters revealed a total of 126 pairs at 41 sites and, of these, 33 pairs were known to have bred at 19 sites. In 1991, a comprehensive survey of breeding wildfowl and waders in the Arun Valley found 23 pairs, suggesting that the vast network of dykes in this area provides suitable habitat for breeding pairs.

Breeding success is very variable, as the following examples illustrate. At Chichester Gravel Pits in 1980, approximately 25 pairs produced 151 young but predation was very heavy with pike thought to be the likely culprit. In 1981, a total of 101 young from 19 broods was counted and in 1988, at the same locality, 22 pairs attempted breeding but only six broods totalling 20 young were seen. At Bewl Water in 1986, nine out of 13 pairs raised 54 young, but in the following year when 17 pairs were present, only two broods of five young each were seen. The birds at Rye Harbour are currently the most successful in the county although even here results can vary considerably. In 1992 there were 12 broods but in 1988 only two out of 13 pairs were successful, rearing eight and five young. A female at Arundel WWT in 1984 was accompanied by 21 ducklings but it is likely that these were the product of two birds laying in the same nest.

Moult gatherings may assemble after the breeding season and these are supplemented by the arrival of wintering birds from mid-October. Winter flocks usually build up to a peak in January or February (table 25) although at some localities more are recorded in November than December, indicating passage. The peak count for the winter has remained remarkably constant over the past 25 years and that of 1516 in January 1992 is the largest yet recorded. Table 24 summarises counts at the main localities.

	69-74	74-79	79-84	84-89	89-94	Peak counts
Chichester GP	309	193*	271*	319	248	400, winter 1972/73
Swanbourne Lake		59*	110	93	201	243, Dec 1993
Arundel WWT		203*	220	358	321	444, Jan 1987
Weir Wood Reservoir	140	134	90	63	38	290, winter 1974/75
Bewl Water		220*	153	188	163	288, Jan 1987
Darwell Reservoir	66	124	40	20*	32	188, winter 1974/75
Rye Harbour	98	135	133	127	147	234, Feb 1978

Table 24. Five year means of winter maxima and peak counts of Tufted Ducks, 1969/70 - 93/94.

	Sep	Oct	Nov	Dec	Jan	Feb	Mar
Maximum	667	748	1088	1216	1516	1237	1086
Mean	428	534	771	910	1059	972	768
Minimum	77	131	273	429	464	490	217

Table 25. Monthly totals of Tufted Ducks, 1976/77 - 93/94.

In severe weather birds may be forced to leave frozen lakes and gravel pits for the warmer coast. Flocks may then appear in less regular locations or in higher numbers than usual. In January 1985, for example, 103 flew west off Worthing on 7th and there were 20 on the sea at Jury's Gap, 20 in the lower Cuckmere Valley and 40 at Newhaven Tide Mills. In such conditions, tidal rivers normally remain ice-free and in early 1985, totals of 30 and 20 were recorded on the Arun and Adur respectively.

The departure of wintering birds is in March and early April. Spring passage is indicated by small movements up-Channel that have included, in 1990 at Splash Point, Seaford, 22 in 75 hours of sea-watching in March and a further 16 in 146 hours in April. The largest movement so far recorded was on 27 March 1968 when 47 flew east off Beachy Head.

A total of 16 Tufted Ducks have been ringed outside the county and recovered within Sussex. Of these, four had moved between 10 and 99 km and the remainder over 100 km. Single birds ringed at Lake Zhuvintas, Lithuania in August 1964 and at Suomenoja, Finland in July 1971 were shot at Rye Harbour in November 1964 and January 1973 respectively. The former had travelled 1589 km and the latter 1815 km.   *Martin Kalaher*

Scaup   *Aythya marila*

Status:- A scarce winter visitor and passage migrant; rare in summer.

Scaup are recorded primarily along the coast, especially during periods of hard weather, when large influxes may occur. In such conditions, small numbers may also appear on the larger inland waters. No recent change in status is apparent. In mild winters, county totals of between five and 30 are typical, but in hard winters, totals of 100 or more may be recorded.

Scaup are very rarely observed on autumn migration along the coast, but in 1971 a single bird flew west past Langney Point on the early date of 3 August. Wintering birds usually arrive from October onwards, but there have also been several records for August and September and, in 1987, one appeared at Rye Harbour on 4 July. This may have been a wandering summering bird, but its arrival with an influx of Pochard indicates that it could also have been a very early migrant.

Hard weather influxes usually occur in January or February and totals of 100 or more were recorded in ten of the winters between 1961/62 and 1992/93 (fig. 18). The largest influx was in February 1991 when 335 birds were recorded on 8th, including 230 at Scotney Court Gravel Pit alone. This flock subsequently increased to 280 by 10 March but it is likely that most (or all) of the additional birds may have been from elsewhere in the vicinity rather than additional arrivals from further afield. Even this number is eclipsed, however, by a flock estimated at 5000, which was present in Rye Bay in early 1947.

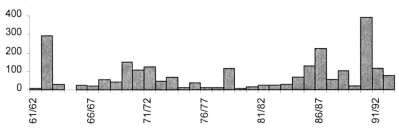

Figure 18. Winter totals of Scaup, 1961/62 - 92/93.

The Rye area frequently holds the largest numbers in the county, but Pagham and Chichester Harbours also hold small numbers virtually annually and the species also occurs, albeit less regularly, all along the coast, particularly in Seaford and Pevensey Bays and at the Crumbles. Inland, small numbers regularly occur at Arlington, Barcombe and Weir Wood Reservoirs, Bewl Water and Chichester Gravel Pits. A count of up to seven at Arlington Reservoir during November 1972 is the highest recorded for an inland locality in the county.

Hard weather movements are sometimes observed on the coast. For example, in January 1979, when there was another marked influx into the county, 19 flew west past Shoreham-by-Sea on 1st and nine west past Rye Harbour three days later. Numbers in this influx dropped markedly towards the end of the month, perhaps as birds moved further west, but there was evidence of a return passage in mid-February.

Wintering Scaup leave the county mainly during March. As with Goldeneye, coastal passage is more marked in spring than in autumn, with small numbers regularly recorded moving east between late March and early May. Most day totals are in single figures but higher numbers have been recorded as follows: 15 flying east past Selsey Bill on 5 April 1974, 12 flying east past Beachy Head on 8 April 1979, 15 flying east past Selsey Bill on 3 April 1985, and 11 flying east past Seaford on 26 March 1989:

Scaup are very scarce in Sussex between May and September, but they were records for this period in 23 of the 32 years between 1962 and 1993 (including coastal migrants in early May). The cumulative monthly totals are shown below.

May	Jun	Jul	Aug	Sep
32	8	14	5	19

National ringing data indicate that most Scaup wintering in Britain originate from Iceland but the large hard weather influxes probably involve continental birds. The single ringing recovery from Sussex involved a bird ringed at Lake Myvatn, Iceland on 7 July 1950 and recovered at Chichester on 6 February 1954.

Jon Curson

Eider   *Somateria mollissima*

Status:- A scarce winter visitor and passage migrant; non-breeding birds summer annually.

des Forges & Harber referred to an average of about 13 birds per year between 1946 and 1954. After 1954, the species became more common and in 1958 about 200 were recorded. Since then, the number reported each year has fluctuated widely, but it does appear that the increase first noted in the late 1950s has now halted.

Westward movements in autumn and early winter are occasionally observed, such as those of 54 off Langney Point on 23 October 1963, 121 off Selsey Bill and 63 off Worthing on 4 December 1982 and 77 at the latter site on 15 December 1988. There is a gradual build up throughout the autumn period until mid-winter when the largest numbers are normally present. Shrubb reported that the total numbers recorded wintering between 1960 and 1976 varied between 20 in the winter of 1960/61 and 250 in that of 1962/63. On average about 70-80 were usually present. That the wintering population continued to increase after 1976 is shown by a range for the period up to 1992 of 32-379 and a January average of 105. However, the numbers wintering can fluctuate very considerably as shown by totals of 379 in January 1989 but only four in January the following year. The high total in 1989 was due primarily to the presence of 220 in Pevensey Bay. This is the largest flock recorded in the county, yet previously no flock exceeding 98 had been found at this site. Other favoured localities are Chichester Harbour and the Pagham Harbour/Selsey Bill area, where flocks in excess of 100 have been recorded, and Rye Bay where the largest count was 72 in November 1971. A flock of 50 was noted off Lancing in December 1980.

Evidence of a marked return passage is provided by increases in wintering flocks in early spring and by coastal movements up-Channel. During the late 1970s and early 1980s, a flock of up to 200 regularly built up off Selsey Bill, the presence of which made passage at this site difficult to assess. In 1982, the totals recorded passing east off Worthing and Beachy Head were 372 and 202 respectively while in 1984 they were 410 and 172 . In both these years, there was a significant build up in the wintering flock off Selsey Bill in March. In 1983, when the flock at Selsey was smaller, totals of only 60 and 82 were noted at Worthing and Beachy Head. Passage is usually heaviest during the first three weeks of April, as shown by eastward movements of 184 off Worthing on 18 April 1982 and 159 off Seaford between 2 and 6 April 1991. Large numbers may also occur later in the spring, as in 1984, when 137 flew east off Goring on 31 May, a very late date for so large a number. The cumulative monthly totals recorded at Worthing in the period 1978-93 are shown below.

	Jul	Aug	Sep	Oct	Nov	Dec	Jan	Feb	Mar	Apr	May	Jun
Flying west	12	41	55	36	170	399	180	58	74	46	20	16
Flying east	-	1	28	86	117	65	137	88	389	1099	314	18

Shrubb referred to the occurrence of non-breeding Eider during the summer months in all but three years between 1960 and 1976. During this period, the largest flocks recorded were 27 off the Seven Sisters in 1962 and off Fairlight in 1976. Since then, between five and 110 have been recorded annually. Birds may occur anywhere along the coast although most records have been for the extreme west of the county. The largest total so far recorded of 110 in July 1989 comprised 70 in Chichester Harbour and 40 at Pagham Harbour.

The only inland records have been of a female at Arlington Reservoir on 3-4 December 1983, an immature male on the River Adur at South Stoke on 21 February 1987 and a male at Barcombe Reservoir on 25 October 1988.

Tony J Wilson

Long-tailed Duck   *Clangula hyemalis*

Status:- A scarce passage migrant and winter visitor.

Most Long-tailed Ducks in Sussex are recorded as singles or small groups during the winter months, or passing at sea in spring and autumn.

Shrubb noted an increase in the number of records between 1948 and 1963 but stated that this was partly due to an increase in observer activity. This trend has continued, as demonstrated in table 26, although some duplication in the monthly totals is likely due to the presence of overwintering birds.

	Total	Annual mean	Jul	Aug	Sep	Oct	Nov	Dec	Jan	Feb	Mar	Apr	May	Jun
1953-62	100	10	1	-	-	12	37	22	30	9	12	11	1	-
1963-72	223	22	-	-	-	22	73	64	51	39	48	29	4	-
1973-82	144	14	1	1	-	10	39	45	28	35	33	24	10	-
1983-92	287	29	1	2	1	6	64	68	83	102	100	85	31	1
Total	754		3	3	1	50	213	199	192	185	193	149	46	1

Table 26. 10-year totals of Long-tailed Ducks, 1953/62 - 1983/92.

The first usually arrive at the end of October or the beginning of November; earlier records include singles at the Crumbles on 23 August 1985 and at Bewl Water and Worthing on 4 October 1989.

A small passage down-Channel is noted in November, usually of single birds, although six flew west past Church Norton on 11 November 1988. Shrubb noted that a large proportion of birds were transient and that westerly passage continued until late January. Since 1976, most birds recorded from December onwards have been wintering. The most favoured localities are Rye Bay and in the western harbours, particularly Chichester Harbour, where ten were recorded together in December 1988 and 13 in December 1991. Numbers are usually stable in January but increase to reach a peak in February, as regular counts from Chichester Harbour demonstrate. For example, in 1989, 12 in January had increased to 20 in February falling to 12 on 7 March, ten on 25 March, nine on 8 April and one on 2 May. In 1992, 14 were at the same site on 7 January, increasing to 20 by 6 February and then decreasing to 14 by 24 February, 13 by 5 April and six on 19 April. Also in 1989, a similar situation occurred at Rye Harbour where a count of six on 18 January had increased to 13 by early February. The presence of wintering flocks of this size is a fairly new occurrence and prior to 1977 the largest gathering recorded was that of nine in Chichester Harbour on 26 January 1958. Away from the two main wintering sites it is rare to record more than two together and most records of threes are from inland sites (see below).

Spring passage is generally noted in April and May involving singles or pairs moving east offshore. Exceptionally, two flew east off Seaford on the early date 4 March 1980. The maximum number recorded in any one spring was 27 in 1989 coinciding with peak wintering numbers being recorded. Prior to 1977, the latest spring record was on 6 May although birds are now regularly recorded in May with the latest record being one east off Beachy Head on 22nd in 1988.

There are four summer records for the county totalling six birds, the most recent of which was a female that remained at Rye Harbour from 27 May to 16 August 1985. Three were recorded at this locality on 17 July 1960, a male at Chichester Gravel Pits on 10 July 1975 and one at the same site from 12 to 21 August 1976.

There were records of Long-tailed Ducks at inland localities in twenty of the winters between 1961/62 and 1993/94 totalling about 56 birds. These were at Chichester Gravel Pits (19), Barcombe Reservoir (8), Darwell Reservoir (7), Bewl Water (6), Arlington Reservoir, the Arun Valley and Weir Wood Reservoir (4 each) and Parham Pond and Kneppmill Pond (2 each). About one third of these were single birds but two were seen together nine times and three together at Bewl Water in late 1982 to 4 May 1983, at Chichester Gravel Pits from November 1982 to 17 April 1983 and from 12 December 1990 to February 1991 and at Darwell Reservoir on 13 November 1988 and from 12 February to 12 March 1989. There appears to have been a small increase in inland records in recent years given that 33 of the 56 recorded have been since the winter of 1976/77.   *Tony J Wilson*

Common Scoter
Melanitta nigra

Status:- A common spring passage migrant and fairly common winter visitor; scarcer in summer and autumn.

Common Scoters occur off the Sussex coast throughout the year but it is normally only during the winter months and in spring that substantial numbers are recorded. Shrubb noted a decrease, particularly during the winter, and this has continued to the present day.

Autumn passage is infrequently recorded and always on a small scale. At Selsey Bill, for example, totals of 12 flew east and 224 west in July-August 1981 and 279 east and 175 west during the autumn of 1982. A total of 250 flying west at Beachy Head on 15 September 1968 appears to be the largest movement recorded in the county in autumn.

The main wintering locality for this species in Sussex is Rye Bay. Since 1962, counts at this site, between October and December, have varied considerably from a low of just six in 1981 to a maximum of 1000 in December 1982. The largest numbers are usually present in January and February, averaging about 350, although between 1000 and 1100 have occurred on three occasions since 1964. This is a considerable reduction from the 1940s and 1950s when peak counts of 2000-5000 were noted regularly. Maxima at other sites in the east of the county have included 442 off Bexhill on 1 December 1991 and up to 250 offshore between Seaford and Cuckmere Haven. The species is much scarcer in winter off West Sussex and in many years there are no records other than occasional small flocks moving offshore. Recent exceptions have included a flock of up to 250 off Selsey Bill in 1981/82 and 350 off Shoreham-by-Sea on 5 December 1991.

There is a large spring passage up-Channel and the species is often the most numerous recorded on sea-watches at this time of the year. This is particularly so at Beachy Head and Splash Point, Seaford where considerably more are observed than at sea-watching sites further to the west, probably due to birds flying across the Channel in a northeasterly direction. At Selsey Bill, spring totals for the period 1979-92 ranged between 918 in 1985 and 7716 in 1992, with an average of 3095. At Beachy Head, where 22,102 were recorded in 1968, 20,184 in 1976 and 19,319 in 1979 but no more than 9000 since, the average spring total for the period 1968-91 was 8283, demonstrating the larger numbers recorded at sites further east. At Seaford, where a considerable number of hours have been spent sea-watching in recent years, the average spring total during 1988-93 was 11,121.

The largest movements are usually noted in the first three weeks of April. Thus, on 8 April 1979, during light southeasterly winds, 13,293 were counted flying east off Beachy Head. This movement was also observed elsewhere along the coastal with totals of 8106 recorded at Seaford Head, 4500 at Ferring but only 2063 at Selsey Bill. Other large movements at Beachy Head have included 7100 on 15 April 1968 and 12,200 on 7 April 1969. Passage often continues into June and even July; for example, at Selsey Bill a total of 640 flew east in June 1970 and in 1991, 635 flew east and 271 flew west during June and July. At Seaford, 574 flew east but only two west during the same period.

The number of birds summering in the county varies considerably. In Rye Bay, recent counts have fluctuated between none in a number of years and 550 in 1978, although up to 3000 were recorded there in 1956. Elsewhere, counts of between ten and 80 are regular, particularly at the other main wintering localities, although the species has been noted a number of times off the coast between Brighton and Rottingdean. A count of 350 off Langney Point on 9 August 1987 was exceptional.

Common Scoters have become more regular inland in recent years although this may merely reflect increased observer activity. des Forges & Harber gave about 14 inland records up to 1961 while more recently there have been 42 records comprising 135 birds. Of those recorded in the period 1962-93, most were at Weir Wood Reservoir (73), including flocks of 25 on 25 June 1972 and 11 on 24 August 1986, and Bewl Water (26). The cumulative monthly totals of all inland records during 1962-93 are shown below.

Jan	Feb	Mar	Apr	May	Jun	Jul	Aug	Sep	Oct	Nov	Dec
8	2	7	41	8	38	7	11	5	2	6	0

The totals show an expected peak in April, when coastal passage is heaviest, but also a surprising secondary peak in June, when the species is quite scarce in coastal waters. Regardless of the season, birds rarely remain for more than one day.   *Tony J Wilson*

Surf Scoter   *Melanitta perspicillata*

Status:- A very rare vagrant (three records).

First recorded in the county in 1966, there have been three records:

1966: A female on gravel pits at Rye Harbour on 3 December.
1977: A female or immature, sometimes with Common Scoter, off Pett Level from 23 November to 2 December.
1991: A male with Common Scoter off Splash Point, Seaford from 13 to 20 April.

More might be expected in flocks of Common Scoter passing east along the coast in spring, if only they were closer.

There were over 300 records of this large-billed duck in the British Isles during 1962-94. It breeds across northern North America wintering on the Atlantic and Pacific coasts south to northern Mexico.   *Richard Fairbank*

Velvet Scoter
Melanitta fusca

Status:- A scarce passage migrant and winter visitor along the coast; rare inland.

The status of the Velvet Scoter in Sussex has not changed in recent years. It is recorded in small numbers during the winter months but in appreciably larger numbers during the spring, as shown by the approximate cumulative monthly totals for 1962-76 and 1977-93 below.

	Jul	Aug	Sep	Oct	Nov	Dec	Jan	Feb	Mar	Apr	May
1962-76	1	1	13	48	104	132	56	207	52	349	453
1977-93	9	2	29	107	181	224	196	94	283	1336	453
Total	10	3	42	155	285	356	252	301	335	1685	906

Shrubb noted an arrival date as early as 10 July but since 1962 there have only been four sightings in this month, comprising singles at Brighton on 23 July 1976, off Church Norton on 12 July 1987 and 7 July 1991 and a flock of seven flying east off Rye Harbour on 12 July 1990. The only recent August records were one at Rye on 12-13 August 1972 and in 1984 when two flew west off Worthing on 2nd. In most years, the first birds are seen in October but numbers rarely reaching double figures during the month. In October 1991, however, a total of about 54 was recorded in the county.

Shrubb stated that in many winters fewer than 20 are seen. This trend has continued as shown by average totals for December and January for the period 1977-93 of 14 and 12 respectively. In some winters, larger totals may be recorded, for example 90 in 1958, 102 in early 1974 (including a flock of 100 in Rye Bay) and about 125 in 1991/92. Singles or small flocks are the norm and, since 1976, the only flocks of over 30 recorded in winter were 32 that flew east off Pett Level on 5 December 1982 and 33 off Bexhill on 1 December 1991. Most wintering birds are found in the east of the county, particularly in Rye Bay, although groups of 10-20 birds have been seen on a number of occasions on the sea between Worthing and Hove. Severe weather may result in a small influx; as in the cold spell in early 1987 when 42 were recorded, the highest January total since 1974.

Regular sea-watching in recent years has shown that this species is most numerous on spring passage, which has been noted in the period from 1 March to 30 May (1982, Rye Bay). The number recorded passing up-Channel each spring has varied considerably. Low numbers were recorded in the 1960s when fewer hours were spent sea-watching but even since regular observations started, totals as low as 12 in 1971 and 25 in 1977 have been reported. By contrast, spring totals of 289 and 313 were recorded in 1976 and 1984 respectively. The largest movements are associated with those of Common Scoters during periods of southeasterly winds. A flock of 300 was in Rye Bay on 8 May 1951 and, since 1975, day counts of 50 or more have been recorded on eight occasions, including 110 flying past Beachy Head on 2 May 1976, 76 also off Beachy Head on 7 May 1981, 66 at the same site on 10 April 1991 and 76 flying past Splash Point, Seaford on 21 April 1992. The sea-watching localities in the east of the county usually produce the largest numbers, as shown by average spring totals at Selsey Bill and Beachy Head for the period 1979-88 of 45 and 75 respectively.

There are only eight inland records of Velvet Scoters for the county, two of which are very old. More recently, singles were recorded at Weir Wood Reservoir on 1 February 1970 and from 20 to 22 November 1985, at Darwell Reservoir on 12 November 1972 and on the River Adur at Henfield from 28 to 31 December 1986 and two at Bewl Water on 18 November 1985. The most unusual inland record, however, was that of a party of 14 at Arlington Reservoir on 1 April 1991.

A female ringed at Siunaskari, Finland on 2 July 1961 was found dead at Pett Level, 1724 km southwest, on 3 March 1963.   *Tony J Wilson*

Barrow's Goldeneye   *Bucephala islandica*

Status:- One record of a presumed escape.

An adult male at Bewl Water from 7 January to late March 1979 (*Brit. Birds* 72: plate 151) and again between December 1979 and May 1980 was widely regarded as having escaped from captivity.

There is just one record of this species in Britain (Strathclyde in November-December 1979). It breeds from Iceland to northeastern Canada and from northwestern USA to southern Alaska. Icelandic birds are resident while those in North America winter mainly along northern coastal USA.

Richard Fairbank

Goldeneye   *Bucephala clangula*

Status:- A fairly common winter visitor; very rare in summer.

Goldeneye winter regularly at just five sites in Sussex. However, scattered individuals or small numbers occur more widely, especially during hard weather, and there have been records for all the large waters, the main rivers and for a number of coastal sites. No recent change in status is apparent; the higher numbers recorded since 1965 probably reflect increased observer coverage. There may, however, have been an increase in the percentage of adult males wintering in Chichester Harbour; prior to 1940 they were noted by Walpole-Bond as being extremely rare, but since the 1960s, adult males have accounted for 15-30% of the total numbers recorded there.

Goldeneye seem to be remarkably scarce on autumn migration, as shown by a few records in the period between 29 October and 14 December, mainly at Langney Point and Selsey Bill. Most counts have been in single figures but 27 flew west past Selsey Bill on 13 November 1983.

Wintering birds arrive from mid to late October and build up to reach a peak in January or February (table 28). They occur regularly at just three coastal sites (Chichester Harbour, Pagham Harbour and Rye Harbour) and at two inland waters (Bewl Water and Weir Wood Reservoir). Of these, Chichester Harbour is by far the most important site, with numbers there greater than at all the other sites added together (table 27). At Chichester Harbour, the largest concentrations so far recorded were of 225 on 16 January 1971 and 234 on 1 January 1974. However, both these counts, which were made from boats, are considerably higher than the maximum counts made from the shore, thus suggesting that counting from the shore may significantly underestimate numbers of the species. Neither count is included in the tables below.

	69-74	74-79	79-84	84-89	89-94	Peak counts
Chichester Harbour	66	79	64	86	73	139, Jan 1987
Pagham Harbour	3	5	3	14	11	31, Jan 1985
Weir Wood Reservoir		2*	4	8	5	11, Mar 1985
Bewl Water		17**	5	7	5	18, Feb 1987
Rye Harbour		6*	6	7	5	12, Feb 1987

Table 27. Five year means of winter maxima and peak counts of Goldeneye, 1969/70 - 93/94.

	Oct	Nov	Dec	Jan	Feb	Mar
Maximum	8	54	84	190	138	136
Mean	1	25	50	84	72	44
Minimum	0	4	22	41	32	5

Table 28. Monthly totals of Goldeneye, 1976/77 - 93/94.

Away from the main sites, small numbers occur, especially in periods of hard weather, on the other large bodies of water and on the lower reaches of the main rivers, as well as at scattered localities along the coast. Goldeneye were particularly widespread during hard weather in January 1985, January-February 1989 and February 1991. Cold weather movements may occur along the coast during such periods; for example, on 8 January 1985, 30 flew west at West Kingston and ten west at Selsey Bill.

Numbers begin to fall rapidly towards the end of March as birds leave for their breeding grounds in Scandinavia and western Russia. Spring passage along the coast is rather more evident than in autumn; small numbers are regularly recorded from mid-March to the end of April, with a small but distinct peak in late March. Most day totals have been in single figures but 16 flew east past Hastings on 19 March 1980. The latest spring migrants recorded were singles flying east off Selsey Bill on 10 May 1963, Beachy Head on 12 May 1977 and Hove on 23 May 1984.

Goldeneye are very rare in Sussex in summer, but have occurred in six of the 32 years since 1962 as follows:

1982: Singles at Rye Harbour on 16 July and Barcombe Reservoir on 11 August.
1985: One on Thorney Deeps from 9 June to 17 August had a slightly damaged wing.
1987: A female on Thorney Deeps on 19 July.
1988: A female at Chichester Gravel Pits from 29 May to at least 6 July.
1990: One at Fishbourne from 5 May to 6 July.
1992: One summered at Thorney Deeps.

Additionally, there was one at Rye Harbour on 31 July 1959 (des Forges & Harber). *Jon Curson*

Smew *Mergus albellus*

Status: A very scarce winter visitor except in severe weather when larger numbers may occur.

Smew are recorded annually in Sussex although numbers vary considerably from winter to winter (fig. 19). Gravel pits and reservoirs are the favoured localities although river systems are sometimes frequented when other waters are frozen. Birds are only rarely recorded on the open sea.

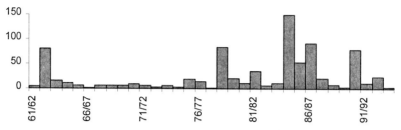

Figure 19. Winter totals of Smew, 1961/62 - 93/94.

In the period 1962-94 only 15 were recorded in November, of which one in the lower Cuckmere Valley on 3 November 1974 was the earliest. The number of birds recorded in December has been remarkably consistent, averaging three per year in the 20 years to 1976 and four per year in the 16 years after. The largest total for the month was just 14 during cold weather in 1981, 13 of which arrived on 19-20th.

The largest numbers occur during severe weather in January and February. Since 1947, there have been eight influxes involving 50 or more birds. Prior to 1962, these were in 1954 (*ca.* 50 birds) and 1956 (*ca.* 100) although the true numbers present were almost certainly greater as coverage was considerably less thorough than it is today. The totals recorded in the main influxes since 1962 are shown in table 29 below.

	1962/63	1978/79	1984/85	1985/86	1986/87	1990/91
Arlington Reservoir		7	1	-	-	-
Bewl Water		17	-	1	16	-
Crumbles GP		8	22	3	16	2
Cuckmere Valley	15	15	-	-	-	3
Northpoint GP		-	36	27	26	22
Pagham Harbour	14	5	5	1	6	2
Pett Level	1	10	2	-	6	1
River Adur	6	-	47	-	-	3
Rye Harbour		5	2	-	3	19
Thorney Island	-		1	1	9	-
Other sites	44	17	34	21	10	27
Total	80	84	150	54	92	79

Table 29. Minimum totals of Smew in five winters between 1962/63 and 1990/91.

The exact number present in each winter is often confused by the fact that groups may wander in search of ice free waters. Prior to 1977, the largest flock recorded was one of 22 at Manhood End in February 1956 but this has since been exceeded by an impressive gathering of 47 on an unfrozen stretch of the River Adur at Henfield on 20 January 1985, a somewhat unusual location for so large a number. There have been an additional 12 flocks of 15 or more birds, most in the east of the county. Four of these have been in the Northpoint Gravel Pit/Camber area and may represent displacement from Dungeness, Kent where the largest flock in the country is regularly recorded.

Even during severe weather it is very unusual to find Smew on the open sea and only then when most inland waters have frozen. This happened in January 1985 when a small number of birds were seen along the coast; one which stayed at Brighton Marina for five days was particularly noteworthy.

In milder winters, when considerably fewer Smew are noted, totals have varied between one in 1966/67 and 1977/78 and 35 in 1981/82 with an average of 12. Favoured localities are Pagham Harbour and Lagoon, Pett Level/Rye Harbour and the Crumbles. At Pagham between one and six have been seen in 14 of the 16 winters since 1976/77.

There is a rapid dispersal in March and it is rare for the total for the whole month to exceed six. An exception to this was in 1986 when 43 were reported during the month including 27 at Northpoint Gravel Pit. The latest spring record is of one that remained at Rye Harbour until 23 April 1977. This remains the only county record for the month.

The approximate cumulative monthly totals of all records during 1962-94 are shown below.

Nov	Dec	Jan	Feb	Mar	Apr
15	110	599	605	157	1

Tony J Wilson

Red-breasted Merganser   *Mergus serrator*

Status:- A fairly common winter visitor and passage migrant to the coast; a few summer annually.

Red-breasted Mergansers are most frequently recorded in winter, especially in Chichester Harbour and the Pagham/Selsey area, where numbers have increased in recent years (table 30), and also in spring passing up-Channel.

Although the main arrival normally starts in October, there has been an increasing tendency for the first returning birds to be recorded in September. Shrubb mentioned only four records for the month whereas birds are now frequently recorded before October, even allowing for the likelihood that some individuals may have summered in the county. A total of 35 in September 1980 was notable. Autumn movements do not usually occur on the same scale as in spring and counts of over 50 in a day are unusual. Some larger movements have, however, been observed including 200 that flew west at Selsey Bill on 19 November 1972 and 247 that did likewise on 9 November 1992. The wintering population is normally established by late November but westerly movements may continue into January and February in some years. Unlike the other species of sawbill, it appears that numbers are little affected by the onset of severe weather. Sites which regularly hold 100 or more birds are considered to be of national importance for the species (Waters & Cranswick 1993).

	69-74	74-79	79-84	84-89	89-94	Peak counts
Chichester Harbour	37	41	67	88	130	151, Dec 1990
Pagham Harbour	7	9	25	20	62	118, Mar 1993

Table 30. Five year means of winter maxima of Red-breasted Mergansers, 1969/70 - 93/94.

Away from Chichester and Pagham Harbours, the largest gatherings recorded have been off Atherington, where there were 87 on 23 November 1991, and offshore between Ferring and Shoreham-by-Sea, where the largest counts have been 78 on 26 February 1977, 80 on 28 December 1991 and 110 on 8 March 1992. As noted by Shrubb, the species is very scarce east of Brighton in winter and the only sizeable flocks recorded in East Sussex remain those of 45 in Seaford Bay on 25 February 1956 and 30 off Langney Point on 17 January 1965.

Spring passage up-Channel is recorded between early March and mid to late May but is heaviest in late March and the first three weeks of April. Counts of 50-100 in a day are annual while larger eastward movements have included 234 off Beachy Head on 15 April 1968, 199 at the same site on 8 April 1979 and 224 off Splash Point, Seaford on 29 March 1992.

A small number of birds have been recorded almost annually in summer since 1970, mainly in Chichester and Pagham Harbours. In most years, less than five have been noted but in 1980 and 1984 there were totals of 12 and 20 respectively. The latter figure included two flocks totalling 19 on 2 June which were likely to have been late migrants. The only other large counts were of ten in Chichester Harbour on 27 June 1980 and in Pagham Harbour on 3 August 1993.

Between 1962 and 1993 there were inland records in 19 years totalling about 105 birds. Most were at Bewl Water (33 birds), Weir Wood Reservoir (24), Southease (14), Darwell Reservoir (7) and Arlington Reservoir (6). Excluded from these totals are flocks of 60 that flew south over Bewl Water on 6 November 1982 (on which date there were also 13 on the reservoir) and 30 that flew southwest over nearby Hurst Green on 13 November 1983. Inland birds are normally recorded on single dates only, but there have been five stays of a week or more, including three at Bewl Water from 10 to 20 December 1978 and up to eight at Weir Wood Reservoir between 20 and 27 January 1987.

The cumulative monthly totals of all inland records in the period 1962-93 are shown below.

Oct	Nov	Dec	Jan	Feb	Mar	Apr	May
3	109	14	29	15	19	6	2

Tony J Wilson

Goosander   *Mergus merganser*

Status:- A scarce winter visitor and passage migrant

The number of Goosanders recorded in the county each winter varies considerably, with the largest numbers occurring during periods of severe weather. Shrubb did not note any change in status in the years up to 1976, although more recently a slight increase has been apparent, as shown in fig 20.

Goosanders are rarely recorded before mid-October and the average return date since 1976 has been 9 November. There have been occasional earlier records, including singles on the River Adur at Steyning on 16, 23 and 29 September 1992 and at Pagham Harbour on 1 October in the same year, and three at Church Norton on 2 October 1983.

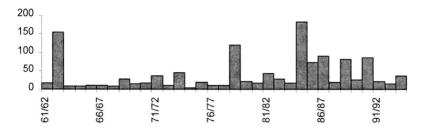

Figure 20. Winter totals of Goosanders, 1961/62 - 93/94.

Numbers are slow to build up during November and December. The average counts for these months since 1976 have been seven and ten respectively and no more than 30 have been recorded in either month in recent years. Evidence of overland passage at this time is provided by records of a single flying over the Downs at Lewes on 7 December 1980 and two over the Downs at Telscombe on 3 December 1989. The monthly average for January is 32 but far larger numbers may occur during periods of cold weather. Such influxes are usually associated with those of other species such as Smew and grey geese. Since 1962, there have been three influxes of over 100 although exact numbers are often very difficult to assess as birds frequently move between sites, particularly when inland waters become frozen. The first of these influxes was in 1962/63 when about 154 were recorded, the second in early 1979 when about 120 were seen and the largest in January 1985 when as many as 180 were recorded. During the 1985 influx, a flock of 55 was noted at Arlington Reservoir and one of 50 on the River Arun; these are the largest recorded in the county since a flock of 50 at Burpham on 30 January 1963.

Counts for winters when the weather is less severe have varied between five in 1974/75 and 90 in 1986/87. This is an increase since Shrubb, when the maximum influx noted during a normal winter was about 30. The most favoured sites are Arlington Reservoir, Bewl Water, Pagham Harbour and Weir Wood Reservoir although birds can be found on any inland water, even occasionally on comparatively small ponds. The species is also more likely to be found along the coast than its congener the Smew and there have been a number of sightings of birds passing at sea.

Birds generally leave fairly rapidly during March and most have gone by mid-month. Unusually, a pair was noted displaying at Bewl Water on 18 March 1984. There is a small spring passage up-Channel during late March and April and in the period 1962-94 there were five such records for May, totalling nine birds, the latest of which was a male that flew east past Hove on 15 May 1984. However, an earlier record of two males flying east at Selsey Bill on 20 May 1961 remains the latest date in the spring.

The species has only been recorded twice during the summer months; in 1972 an injured bird was seen at Lurgashall Mill Pond on 22 July and in 1987, a female spent much of the summer and early autumn at Bewl Water.

The approximate cumulative monthly totals for the periods 1962-76 and 1977-94 are shown overleaf.

	Sep	Oct	Nov	Dec	Jan	Feb	Mar	Apr	May
1962-76	0	9	50	124	210	160	80	17	5
1977-94	2	27	152	161	524	264	141	35	9
Total	2	36	202	285	734	424	221	52	14

The British breeding range of the Goosander has spread dramatically southward during the passed few decades (New Atlas) but it is likely that Goosanders seen in Sussex originate from the Baltic regions and Scandinavia (BWP).

Tony J Wilson

Ruddy Duck   *Oxyura jamaicensis*

Status:- A very scarce resident and scarce winter visitor.

The Ruddy Duck is a native of North America that has established a self-supporting population in this country. Three pairs were imported into Britain by the Wildfowl and Wetlands Trust in 1948, and they began breeding in the collection at Slimbridge, Gloucestershire the following year. Up to 20 young escaped in 1957 and it is thought that these birds were those that commenced breeding in Avon in 1960 and Staffordshire in 1961. Numbers gradually increased and by the winter of 1975/76, the British population was an estimated 375 birds (Vinicombe & Chandler 1982). The species was admitted to the British and Irish list in 1971.

The first records for Sussex were treated as escapes and it was not until 1978, when a total of nine was recorded, that occurrences were listed in the *Sussex Bird Report*. In 1979, a male and a female, possibly unpaired, remained at Chichester Gravel Pits throughout the year, and a pair raised three young at Pett Pools. This was the first breeding record for the county. Although a pair was seen displaying at Weir Wood Reservoir in 1980, the next record of confirmed breeding was not until 1982, when a pair was seen with three young at Chichester Gravel Pits. A pair was again successful at this site in 1983, while at Arundel WWT, three young were raised from a second brood.

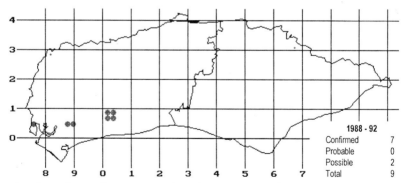

	1988 - 92
Confirmed	7
Probable	0
Possible	2
Total	9

During the Atlas Survey, breeding was confirmed at both Arundel WWT/Swanbourne Lake and Chichester Gravel Pits, and also at Thorney Island, where a pair bred for the first time in 1988. In 1993, two pairs each raised five young at Rye Harbour.

The species is more numerous in the winter, particularly in harsh weather, when birds may disperse from the main breeding areas in Avon and the West Midlands (Owen, Atkinson-Willes & Salmon 1986). This was especially apparent in early 1982 when over 50 were present in the county, including maximum counts of 16 at Chichester Gravel Pits on 17 January and 19 at the Crumbles on 19 January. There were also 4-5 at Rye Harbour on 23-24 January and smaller numbers at 11 other sites. Prior to this influx, the most recorded in any one winter was 12 in 1978/79. Counts at various localities indicate that the winter population has remained fairly constant in recent years at a level of about 20-30.

Concern has been expressed over the spread of Ruddy Ducks into Europe, where they now interbreed with White-headed Ducks, producing viable hybrids. It is thought that the less numerous and less vigorous White-headed Ducks could well be swamped by invading Ruddy Ducks, leading to local extinctions of the former (Everett & Prytherch 1993). At the International Ruddy Duck Workshop held at the Wildfowl and Wetlands Trust, Arundel in March 1993, it was recommended that action be taken to halt and reverse the range expansion of the Ruddy Duck. Research into suggested techniques such as arresting breeding (by coating the eggs with paraffin), shooting birds and also trapping and deporting them to North America is now taking place (Gantlett 1993). We wait, with interest, to see what effect, if any, these proposals have on the numbers recorded in Sussex.   *Richard Kelly*

Honey Buzzard   *Pernis apivorus*

Status:- A very scarce spring and autumn passage migrant; has bred.

For the period 1837 to 1961, des Forges & Harber gave about 60 records, all but three of which were prior to 1939. Of those in spring, one was in May but the rest in June, while those in autumn were between late August and early November with most in September and October. Shrubb described the Honey Buzzard as a rare passage migrant. He stated that although the number recorded in the county had greatly increased in recent years, no real change in status may have occurred and there was no evidence that the species had ever nested in Sussex.

Between 1962 and 1994 there were published records comprising about 80 birds. Most were from localities on or near the coast and 23 of those up until 1976 from the Beachy Head area. However, only ten were recorded there between 1977 and 1994.

Recently, some information not previously published for security reasons, has been released about inland sightings of Honey Buzzards. In consequence, it is now possible to mention that in 1971, a pair was seen in one locality, display was observed and breeding suspected. In 1972 and 1974, two birds thought to be paired were present but breeding was not confirmed. In 1975, a single bird was seen on two occasions and in 1976, two adults were seen. Finally, two juveniles were observed together on 26 August.

In another area, single birds were seen in the summer months, in every year from 1976 to 1982. Two different Honey Buzzards were observed there in 1980 and no less than three different birds were seen separately in 1982.

Single birds were recorded at other localities in the interior of the county in 1981, 1982, 1984 and 1994 while in 1990, a bird was seen in Ashdown Forest on 3 June. Fig. 21 shows all records of Honey Buzzards for the period 1962-94.

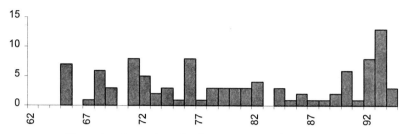

Figure 21. Annual totals of Honey Buzzards, 1962 - 94.

The cumulative monthly totals of all migrant Honey Buzzards recorded in the county during 1962-94 are shown below.

	May	Jun	Jul	Aug	Sep	Oct	Nov
1962-76	3	3	-	5	18	2	-
1977-94	11	7	2	5	19	2	1
Total	14	10	2	10	37	4	1

Most were single birds except for three together at Beachy Head on 12 September 1965 and two together at St Leonards on 25 May 1992, Beachy Head on 12 September 1993, East Wittering on 22 September 1993 and Lancing Clump on 24 September 1993. Two, possibly four birds, were recorded at Beachy Head on 16 September 1968. The extreme dates in this period were 9 May (1971, Beachy Head) and 1 November (1979, Maynards Green).

C M James

Black Kite
Milvus migrans

Status:- A rare, mainly spring, vagrant (15 records involving 13 individuals).

First recorded in the county in 1970, 13 individuals have been seen including ten during the 1980s:

1970: One at Birling Gap on 12 April arrived from the southeast and departed west along the cliffs (the tenth British record).
1976: One near Herstmonceux on 13 November.
1977: One north over Cissbury Ring on 5 May.
1980: One at Chanctonbury Hill on 12-13 July when it flew off west during the early morning.
One, presumably the same, west over Sidlesham Ferry at 11:10 GMT (and Emery Down, Hampshire at 16:50 GMT) on 13 July.
1983: One over Chapel Common on 2 May.
1984: One east over Cliff End, Pett on 30 April.
1986: One east over Pagham Harbour on 26 April.
One, probably the same individual, east along the coast at Covehurst, Fairlight on 26 April, being seen subsequently over Dungeness, Kent.
One over Whitbread Hollow, Beachy Head on 29 April.
1987: One drifted slowly west over Beachy Head and Birling Gap on 4 May.

188

1988: One north over Pevensey Bridge Level on 14 May.
1989: One over Beachy Head on 29 April.
       One east over Pilsey Island, Chichester Harbour on 6 May.
1990: One soaring over Icklesham, Pett Level and a nearby oak wood on 7 July.

Most have been fly-overs in spring with late April and early May the favoured time, eight individuals occurring in the period 26 April to 6 May. In total there are six records for April, five for May, three for July and a very isolated one for November (which is currently under review). Four have been recorded at Beachy Head, three at Fairlight or Pett, two at both Pagham Harbour and the Downs north of Worthing and singles at Chapel Common, Chichester Harbour, Herstmonceux and Pevensey.

One, of a pair, escaped from captivity at Pippingford Park on 12 March 1974. Its mate was then released and one or the other was seen at Edenbridge to at least 4 April.

There were nearly 220 records of this scavenging raptor in the British Isles during 1962-94, most of them since 1980. It breeds throughout Europe (excluding Scandinavia), Africa, Asia and Australia. The European population winters in sub-Saharan Africa.   *Richard Fairbank*

Red Kite   *Milvus milvus*

Status:- A rare visitor recorded in all months except July. Formerly bred.

The Red Kite ceased breeding in Sussex sometime before 1825 and it is now recorded mainly in winter and as a passage migrant in both spring and autumn. From about 1843 to 1937 a total of 18 was seen or shot but in the following 24 years to 1961, only three were recorded (des Forges & Harber). There were no records between 1962 and 1965 but between 1966 and 1994, about 64 were recorded (fig. 22).

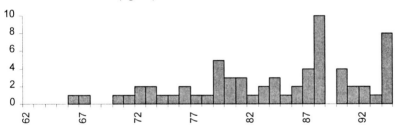

Figure 22. Annual totals of Red Kites, 1962 - 94.

The cumulative monthly totals for the period 1962-93 are shown below.

Jan	Feb	Mar	Apr	May	Jun	Jul	Aug	Sep	Oct	Nov	Dec
5	2	10	8	6	3	-	4	1	5	8	5

The peak in March and April coincides with the national trend and is usually associated with the displacement of continental migrants following periods of easterly winds. This was especially obvious in 1988 when four were recorded between 5 March and 5 April out of a total of nine for the year, the most this century. A similar pattern occurred in Hampshire where three out of the four recorded in 1988 were seen in March (Clark & Eyre 1993). There is no evidence to suggest that sightings in late spring are becoming more frequent but there are records up to 18 June (1984, Battle).

In autumn most have occurred between late October and mid-December with a peak in early November. The earliest were at Arlington Reservoir on 7 August 1994 and at Duncton on 11 August 1973; the former, a wing-tagged individual, remained in the Selmeston area until the year end.

Birds in winter are thought to largely originate from the Welsh breeding population, since there is a dispersal of juveniles from central Wales south and east into England (BWP). This has been verified by ringing recoveries.

Of those recorded from 1962 onwards, 16 were on the Downs between Chilgrove and Friston, 11 in the Beachy Head/lower Cuckmere Valley area, 11 in the Hastings/Pett area and five in the Pagham Harbour/Sidlesham area. Three were found dead due to poisoning, two in 1979 and one in 1980, all at inland sites well away from the more favoured areas listed above. This suggests that some birds may be overlooked in the interior of the county.

It has yet to be seen what effect the introduction of birds of Scandinavian and Spanish origin into England and Scotland may have in Sussex. These bred for the first time in England in 1992 (New Atlas). A wing-tagged individual, presumably from this reintroduction scheme, was seen in the Selmeston area between 7 August 1994 and the end of the year while in neighbouring Hampshire at least three wing-tagged birds have been seen since November 1991 (Clark & Eyre 1993). The record of persecution of birds of prey in the county has hardly been impressive so if this spectacular species is to make a comeback, it will be interesting to see if any change of attitude prevails.

Clive Hope

White-tailed Eagle   *Haliaeetus albicilla*

Status:- Formerly a rare vagrant (up to 50 old records) but only recorded once since 1929.

There are an indeterminate number of very old records, possibly as many as 50 (des Forges & Harber). These include one shot at Camber in the early spring of 1837 which recovered and was kept in captivity for many years (Walpole-Bond), one shot while feeding on a dead 'turtle' at Birling Gap in December 1859 (Arnold 1936) and a juvenile female shot near Lancing on 19 November 1863 which is in the Booth Museum (BoMNH 207172). There are only four records, involving six individuals, since the turn of the century when an adult was seen at Beachy Head (Walpole-Bond). Three frequented St Leonards Forest in the winter of 1902/03, with others seen there on 7 March 1908 and at Firle Beacon on 20 March 1929 and off Selsey Bill on 30 July 1961. The last, and most recent record, was an adult observed fishing for ten minutes and seen to take a fish 400 yards offshore although it was possibly of captive origin due to the very unusual date.

Most might be expected in the winter, along the coast or in open country, with the records for St Leonards Forest and that for July being particularly unusual.

There were 22 records of this huge raptor in the British Isles during 1962-94. Most have been seen since 1980 and include two in Kent (winter 1988/89 and October 1990). It is mainly resident, breeding from Greenland, Iceland and Scandinavia to northeast Asia, and is being reintroduced into western Scotland where seven young were fledged in 1992 (Ogilvie *et al* 1995). Some Scandinavian and east European birds winter south and west to northern France (Dymond, Fraser & Gantlett 1989) and it is from these that any future records might be expected.   *Richard Fairbank*

Marsh Harrier   *Circus aeruginosus*

Status:- A scarce spring and autumn passage migrant and rare winter visitor.

The status of the Marsh Harrier in Sussex reflects the increase that has occurred in the breeding population in Britain from just one pair in 1971 to 83 breeding males and 91 females in 1991 (Ogilvie *et al* 1994). This has resulted in an increase in the number of sightings in the county with approximately 470 birds recorded in the period 1962-94 (fig. 23).

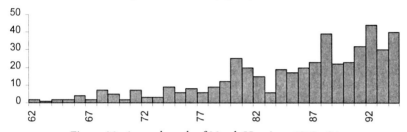

Figure 23. Annual totals of Marsh Harriers, 1962 - 94.

Analysis of the records confirms this steady increase, as shown by the average number recorded annually in each 5-year period since 1962:

1962-66	1967-71	1972-76	1977-81	1982-86	1987-91
2.6	4.8	5.6	14.8	15.6	28.0

In 1992, the best year so far, probably 44 different individuals were seen in the county.

Most of the Marsh Harriers that nest in Britain are found in the east between Kent and the Humber (New Atlas). There are no breeding records for Sussex but, as the Kent population is currently increasing, it is conceivable that nesting may one day occur. Suitable habitat in the county is, however, limited since the species requires undisturbed reedbeds or cereal fields with sympathetic land ownership. An adult male summered near Selsey from 21 June to late August 1981.

The cumulative monthly totals for the period 1962-94 shown below confirm that most birds have been recorded in May followed by September and August. This pattern has been consistent throughout the period under review, even in past years when records were considerably fewer.

Jan	Feb	Mar	Apr	May	Jun	Jul	Aug	Sep	Oct	Nov	Dec
2	1	8	46	145	18	6	99	135	30	6	6

In most springs, birds are seen to arrive from over the sea, as on 5 May 1984 when five apparently different individuals arrived.

Most sightings are of single birds although two together have occurred on a number of occasions, almost always in autumn. Three were seen together at Cissbury on 4 September 1981 and four together at Beachy Head on 24 September 1989, on which date possibly six different birds were present in the area (T J Wilson *pers. comm.*).

Over 90% of the records have come from the Rye area and Beachy Head in the east of the county and the Selsey peninsula and Chichester Harbour in the west. Most of the remainder have been on the Downs, especially in the Cissbury/Chanctonbury area where, during the 1980s, there were reports from farm workers of birds appearing after the autumn harvest. There is no recent information to indicate whether this is still the case although changes in agricultural practices may have caused a reduction in records from this area.

Clive Hope

Hen Harrier *Circus cyaneus*

Status:- A scarce, but regular, winter visitor and passage migrant.

In Sussex, most Hen Harriers occur on coastal farmland and marshes, in the river valleys and on the Downs. A few birds are also found on the heaths and commons in the northwest of the county and in Ashdown Forest.

Between 1947 and 1961 des Forges & Harber recorded an average of about ten per year, but noted that some decline was evident towards the end of the period. However, between 1966 and 1976 the average doubled to about 20 per year (Shrubb) while between 1977 and 1992 it more than doubled again to 48 per year. Prior to 1976, the most noted in any one year was 25 in 1967 whereas in 1979, at least 72 were recorded. Of these, most were seen in the early part of the year when the county experienced sub-zero temperatures and heavy snowfalls. Reports from the 66 localities where birds were observed suggested that a minimum of 16 adult or sub-adult males and 41-43 ringtails was seen up to the end of April, although the true total may have been double the estimate. Exceptional numbers were also recorded in 1991 and 1992 when the approximate annual totals were 72 and 76 respectively (fig. 24).

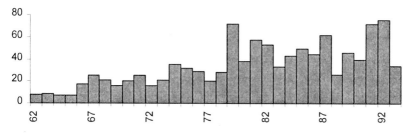

Figure 24. Annual totals of Hen Harriers, 1962 - 93.

The Hen Harrier is well known for roosting communally. Although such behaviour was first noted on the south coast in Kent in 1953 (Walker 1953), it was not recorded in Sussex until 1977, but from then up to 1982, seven definite roost sites were located. On the Selsey peninsula, where communal roosting was first observed during the winter of 1978/79, three different roost sites were used during the period 1978-83, one two years in succession. The largest numbers were recorded in early 1979 when between three and ten ringtails and an adult male roosted in a reedbed at Sidlesham. A second roost held at least seven different individuals (but no more than six at any one time) in the winter of 1981/82. Analysis of pellets from the latter roost showed that small birds made up almost 85% of the total prey items (Lord & Janman 1984).

Until the mid-1970s, it was very unusual to record Hen Harriers before October. However, in the period 1976-93, there were nine records for August and 26 for September, of which one at No Man's Land on 4 August 1976 was the earliest. Numbers increase significantly in October, probably as a result of passage through or into the county. Since 1962, five have been recorded arriving over the sea in autumn between 14 September and 31 December. Singles flew out to sea at Littlehampton on 13 January 1985 and at Beachy Head on 27 January 1974. Prior to 1968, there were no published records later than April. However, in the period up to 1993, there were 29 records for May and two for June, of which a ringtail at Beachy Head from 25 May to 3 June 1991 and a male at Duddleswell, Ashdown Forest on 19 June 1989 were the latest. Of six migrants recorded in spring, all flew north in from the sea during the period 13 March-22 May.

The cumulative monthly totals of all records for the periods 1962-76 and 1977-93 are shown below:

	Aug	Sep	Oct	Nov	Dec	Jan	Feb	Mar	Apr	May	June
1962-76	1	3	50	82	79	76	52	68	39	5	-
1977-93	8	27	89	148	172	276	219	154	93	24	2
Total	9	30	139	230	251	352	271	222	132	29	2

The origin of our wintering population is suggested by the recovery in Sussex of two birds that were ringed outside the county. The first, a female ringed in Oost-Vlanderen, Belgium in November 1984, was regrettably killed at Amberley, 312 km west, a year later while the second, a male ringed as a nestling in the Highland Region in July 1992, was found dead at West Firle, 839 km SSE, the following November. Two birds carrying wing-tags at Rye

193

Harbour in the latter part of 1991 had been marked as nestlings earlier that year in Scotland.   *Martin Kalaher*

Montagu's Harrier   *Circus pygargus*

Status:- A very scarce spring and autumn visitor; formerly bred in small numbers.

This, the rarest of the harriers recorded in Sussex, has always been a scarce species. Walpole-Bond recorded that it bred regularly, although not annually, and suggested that between five and, at the very most, ten pairs were involved. Sadly there has been a marked decline in the fortunes of this species in the county as only one pair has bred successfully since 1938. On 18 May 1962 a pair was first seen at Lullington Heath, the first of four eggs was laid on 9 June and the young fledged on four different dates between 10 and 19 August. All were then seen hunting together in late August.

More recently, birds have summered and breeding may have been attempted on downland between Worthing and Steyning. In May and June 1969 a male and female were recorded in the same valley, although not together, while in May and June 1973 there were many more sightings of both sexes in the same area. The number of birds involved in 1973 was unclear but in 1974 at least three, a melanistic male and two females, were recorded including a pair that held territory throughout June and July. Three were seen together on 18 August 1974, one remained until 12 September, but neither nesting activity nor young birds were observed. In 1975 there were unsubstantiated reports of a male seen by a local gamekeeper while in 1976 there was a female in June and two immatures from 8 to 24 August. In 1977 the only record was of a male on 18 June and although birds were recorded regularly in this area in 1980 and 1981, the dates suggest that they were autumn passage migrants.

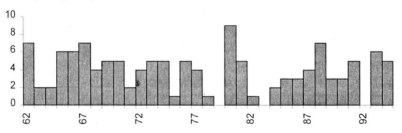

Figure 25. Annual totals of Montagu's Harriers, 1962 - 94.

As a passage migrant the species has also been in decline although not as obviously as a breeding species. Presumably this reflects the decrease recorded in the northwest European population since the 1950s (BWP) and particularly the reduction in the British breeding population over the same period (New Atlas). Between 1947 and 1961, a period when the species was reasonably successful with up to 30 pairs breeding in Britain (New Atlas), des Forges & Harber recorded an average of about five per year. In the following 15 years, during which time the British breeding population crashed, Shrubb reported a total of 55, an average of less than four per year. Between 1977 and 1994, a period in which up to 15 pairs bred annually in Britain (Ogilvie *et al* 1995), a total of 61 was recorded so maintaining an average of between three and four birds per year. The number of birds recorded annually in the period 1962-94 is shown in fig. 25.

Unlike the other harriers, this species has never been recorded in winter. Shrubb reports an early date of 17 April but the earliest recorded in the period 1962-94 was at Stoughton Down on 21 April 1985 and the latest were at Beachy Head on 18 October 1973 and on the Downs near Steyning on 21-22 October 1972. The cumulative monthly totals shown below, which exclude birds known to have summered, reveal clear peaks in May and August and also indicate that in the most recent years more have been seen in autumn than in spring. An unusual autumn influx, coincident with an arrival of Marsh Harriers, occurred in 1980, the best year for this species in recent times.

	Apr	May	Jun	Jul	Aug	Sep	Oct
1962-76	1	25	7	4	13	7	3
1977-94	3	15	7	4	19	14	1
Total	4	40	14	8	32	21	4

Most records have been of a single birds and, apart from the groups previously mentioned, the only other record of three birds was on 3 September 1980 when a male and two ringtails were watched soaring over the downs north of Worthing in the company of three Marsh Harriers and two Buzzards.

This species prefers open country and it is not surprising, therefore, that most of the records since 1962 have been for the open downland east of the Arun Valley through to Beachy Head. Only two records, however, have come from downland west of the Arun Valley. Most of the remaining records were for the coastal plain or river valleys; the most favoured sites being the Selsey peninsula (20), between Rye and the Midrips (12) and Pevensey Levels (6). Few records exist for areas far north of the Downs with only two records from Ashdown Forest on 18 May 1971 and 1 May 1974, one at East Grinstead on 16 May 1988 and most remarkably, a male which flew into a window at West Hoathly on 28 May 1991 and survived to fly away.

Melanistic forms occur rarely (BWP) but three have been seen in the county: at Sidlesham on 22 August 1962, summering on the Downs in 1974 and at Camber on 3 June 1985.   *John Newnham*

Goshawk   *Accipiter gentilis*

Status:- A very scarce visitor, mainly in winter; has bred and now appears to be resident in the county.

Goshawks bred in one area of the county from 1938 (possibly from 1926 or even earlier) to 1951, when a pair raised young from a nest at Cocking near Midhurst. Hosking (1970) published some information about this happening and disclosed that one of the adults carried jesses. No evidence has come to light of subsequent breeding at this site.

Between 1948 and 1961 the only published records were of singles at Sidlesham on 20 May 1961 and Beachy Head on 9 September 1961. In the following 31 years to 1992 about 34 were recorded (fig. 26). These included a pair at a downland locality in 1976 that may have bred, given that the male was observed displaying and carrying food, and pairs observed in suitable breeding habitat in October 1989 and March 1990.

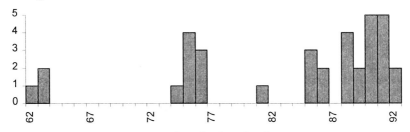

Figure 26. Annual totals of Goshawks, 1962 - 92.

When all the records for 1962-92 were listed, it was evident that over half of the birds were on or within two miles of the coast, with six at Beachy Head alone. A male, first seen at Church Norton on 16 April 1990, was again present at this locality from 6 November 1990 to 7 May 1991, 28 November 1991 to 31 May 1992, 7 February to 13 April 1993 and from 22 September to 31 October 1993. The large number of occurrences in coastal areas perhaps reflects the distribution of observers rather than a preference by Goshawks in Sussex for more open country.

The cumulative monthly totals for the period 1962-92 are shown below.

Jan	Feb	Mar	Apr	May	Jun	Jul	Aug	Sep	Oct	Nov	Dec
4	5	4	6	2	1	1	2	8	8	7	1

The number of Goshawks nationally was estimated at 200 pairs in 1988 (New Atlas) and the population is thought to be currently expanding, despite persecution. There is much suitable nesting habitat for the species in Sussex and reports from a number of different areas since 1990 (not all fully documented) suggest that there are now several pairs resident in the county.

C M James

Sparrowhawk   *Accipiter nisus*

Status:- A fairly common resident; passage migrant.

The Sparrowhawk declined markedly in the late 1950s following the introduction of organochlorine pesticides in agriculture but, happily, the species has now made a remarkable recovery from the impact of these chemicals. It is the second commonest raptor in Sussex, after the Kestrel. However, personal observations suggest it is almost certainly more numerous than the latter species in well-wooded areas, as in TQ01 which probably holds 25-30 breeding pairs.

Large tracts of coniferous woodland are favoured for nesting, but broad-leaved woodland and tall scrub are also commonly used. Where such habitat is lacking, Sparrowhawks will nest in riparian trees and even thick overgrown hedgerows (New Atlas). As Sussex has so much suitable woodland and small birds in abundance, it is not surprising that the Atlas map shows the species to be widespread and only absent from a few areas, such as Pevensey Levels, where there is a lack of suitable habitat for nesting. Although normally associated with rural areas, it is clear that in recent years the Sparrowhawk has colonised many towns, being recorded in seven such sites in 1970-74 and 19 in 1980-83 (Shrubb 1984). Worthing now holds 5-6 pairs.

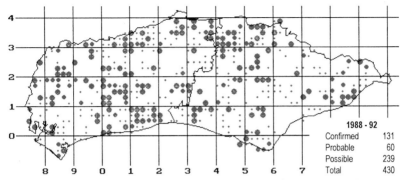

1988 - 92	
Confirmed	131
Probable	60
Possible	239
Total	430

The Sparrowhawk has never been the subject of a SOS breeding survey but by taking known breeding densities for well-watched areas, it is possible to calculate, reasonably accurately, the likely number of pairs in the county. Shrubb suggested a county population of not more than 300 pairs in the late 1970s but in 1980, breeding records indicated a minimum density of one pair per 600-700 ha and a total of over 600 pairs in the county (*SxBR* 33: 19-20). An arbitrary figure of two pairs per occupied tetrad where breeding was confirmed or probable would suggest a current population of about 380 pairs, although the presence of birds in a further 227 tetrads indicates possibly as many as 800 pairs, a far cry from the early 1960s, when just 38 breeding season sites were reported for 1960-64 and none in 1961!

The breeding success of Sparrowhawks in Sussex would appear to be low but the information available is fairly limited. A figure of 2-3 young per pair seems to be the average. There is also evidence to suggest that the recovery of the species has been accompanied by an increase in percentage of successful pairs and in the number of broods with three or more young (Shrubb 1984).

Presumed passage migrants are recorded at coastal sites almost annually. The extreme dates since 1965 are 23 February and 6 May in spring and 9 August and 17 December in autumn, with marked peaks in April and September. Most records have been of single birds and both emigration and immigration have occurred at each season.

Winter sightings are common. Shrubb (1984) analysed 531 records of birds seen outside the breeding season, for which the sex of the bird was known, and found that 61% were females and 39% males. This apparent preponderance of females can be attributed to a number of factors. They tend to hunt in more open habitats, they range more widely in their hunting, and in late winter, those still unattached will be actively seeking a mate.

Ringing recoveries suggest that Sussex birds do not roam far. The furthest venturer was a female, ringed as a nestling at Bosham in June 1988, and found dead at Swindon, Wiltshire in April 1989. An adult male ringed at Sandwich

Bay, Kent in April 1982 was seen at Faygate in February 1984 but found dead one month later at Ifield.

Two foreign-ringed birds have been recovered in Sussex. A female ringed in Gelderland, Netherlands in August 1976 was killed at Horsham a year later. Another female ringed in Halland, Sweden in April 1983 was found dead at Birdham, 1099 km away, in February 1984, having possibly overwintered.

Martin Kalaher

Buzzard   *Buteo buteo*

Status:- A rare resident, scarce passage migrant and possible winter visitor.

Although, historically, Buzzards must have been common in the county, relentless persecution in the 19th century by gamekeepers extirpated the Sussex population by the 1880s, breeding being last recorded in 1882 in Ashdown Forest. Reduced gamekeeper pressure in the 1914-18 war may have allowed the species to regain a toehold in the county, but it was not apparently until the 1950s that a small population permanently re-established itself in central West Sussex.

Although breeding has occurred regularly in this area, and sporadically in other parts of the county, there has been little sign of any increase in numbers. Shrubb referred to the presence of up to four pairs in the county between 1950 and 1956 and to between one and seven pairs between 1965 and 1976. During the Atlas Survey, breeding was confirmed in two tetrads and probable in eight, thus suggesting a county population of up to ten pairs. The Atlas map also shows the tetrads (as open circles) where Buzzards were recorded in the period 1976-87 but not in 1988-92.

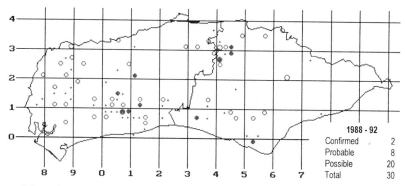

1988 - 92	
Confirmed	2
Probable	8
Possible	20
Total	30

Although nesting Buzzards are usually quite obvious, very few broods have been reported in the county in the past 30 years. Shrubb, for example, referred to only six in the period 1964-70. One reason for this is probably the difficulty of locating nesting territories due to the sparseness of the population and the very large amount of suitable habitat available. It may also be that Buzzards display less in areas where they nest at very low densities, due to a lack of intra-specific competition for territorial space, and are consequently less obvious during the breeding season.

In the 1970s, a reintroduction programme was started in Ashdown Forest which involved birds being released over a number of years, including four in 1982. These reintroduced birds bred for the first time in 1985 and it is quite possible that records of Buzzards in other areas of Sussex in the past 15-20 years have related to wandering birds from this programme as well as genuine migrants.

Probably the main reason for the Buzzard's continued rarity as a breeding species in Sussex is the well-publicised use of organochlorine pesticides until a few years ago, although deliberate persecution still appears to be a local problem; a number of birds killed in recent years included two found on gamekeepers' gibbets in 1971. However, there is no doubt that most gamekeepers are more tolerant these days and that the use of pesticides has declined dramatically in the last few years. The presence of large areas of suitable habitat in Sussex and the fact that neighbouring Hampshire holds 100-130 pairs (Clark & Eyre 1993) lends hope that the species may finally re-establish itself in the county on a firmer footing.

It is thought that most of the Buzzards that breed in Sussex are largely resident although there may be some dispersal of juveniles in winter. Passage is indicated by the appearance of birds mainly at the coast, but also at inland sites where breeding does not occur. Most spring records have fallen in the period mid-April to mid-May, although March records are not uncommon. Presumed migrants have also been reported in February and June. Autumn passage, which has been recorded between mid-July and late November, is typically more pronounced than that in spring. At Beachy Head, where between 1965 and 1976 a total of about 70 Buzzards was recorded between early August and late October, there was a pronounced peak in the third week of September. This total includes 12 in 1976 alone, including four on

4 October. Autumn migrants at Beachy Head have been fewer in recent years with about 36 recorded in the 17 years between 1977 and 1993; 23 of these were in September.

Records outside the main migration periods are perhaps more likely to refer to wandering resident or introduced birds, though it is noteworthy that one at Ferring on 20 December 1971 flew in off the sea.

One ringed as a nestling in Hampshire in June 1957 was found dead near Bosham the following April, 43 km distant.   *Martin Kalaher & Jon Curson*

Rough-legged Buzzard   *Buteo lagopus*
Status:- A rare winter visitor and passage migrant.

As there were just two records between 1938 and 1961 (in November 1956 and November 1957) and less than ten between 1977 and 1994, the Rough-legged Buzzard ranks as one of our scarcest birds of prey. There were, however, exceptional influxes into Britain in the autumn and winter periods of 1966/67, 1973/74 and 1974/75, all of which resulted in birds reaching Sussex. Such influxes are closely linked with the population dynamics of voles and lemmings within the breeding range of the species in northern Scandinavia and the Arctic (Brown 1976). The arrival of birds in Britain either follows a crash in rodent numbers due to their poor breeding success or a surplus of birds after a good breeding season whereby the available food supply is inadequate to sustain them. The influx in 1966/67 was the largest for 50 years and at least 57 birds were present, mainly in southeast England (Scott 1968). A minimum of six stayed to winter in the county through to March. A similar total wintered in 1973/74 but this was eclipsed by the 45-50 recorded in the autumn of 1974 including 15 or more that arrived from the sea at Beachy Head on 22 October. At least 20 stayed to winter, the majority favouring open areas of downland with small woods for roosting (Shrubb). The influx of 1974/75 was the largest ever recorded in Britain, with about 100 wintering (Scott 1978). A further influx occurred in autumn 1975 with four present in October increasing to 8-9 by January 1976. However, since the beginning of 1977 only 9-10 have been recorded as follows:

1977:   One flying east over Pound Hill on 1 February.
        One in the Cissbury/Chanctonbury area on 19 November.
1979:   One at Rye Harbour on 6-7 January.
        One at Lullington Heath on 5 February.
1982:   One in the Arun valley on 14 February.
1985:   One at Birling Gap on 19 October.
        One, possibly the same, at Balsdean on 26 October.
        Singles at South Heighton and South Stoke on 14 December.
1987:   One over Horsham on 28 November.

Given that there was an influx of over 100 Rough-legged Buzzards into Britain in October 1994 (Nightingale & Allsopp 1995), it seems very surprising that none were recorded in Sussex.

The cumulative monthly totals for the period 1962-94 are shown below.

Sep	Oct	Nov	Dec	Jan	Feb	Mar	Apr
1	46	23	39	35	39	30	6

The extreme dates were 11 September (1970, Udimore) and 26 April (1975, Alfriston).

Most birds have been seen on the Downs, particularly between Beachy Head and the Cuckmere Valley and in the Cissbury/Chanctonbury area, but other favoured localities have included Glynde Levels and the coast between Rye and the Midrips.   *Clive Hope*

Osprey   *Pandion haliaetus*

Status:- A scarce passage migrant.

Ospreys were once considered very rare birds in Sussex (Shrubb) but since 1949 they have been recorded annually. Between 1962 and 1989 there was a gradual increase in the annual totals, followed by a sharper rise from 1990 onwards (fig. 27).

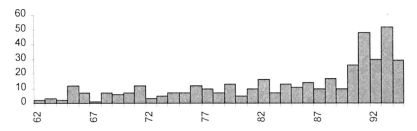

Figure 27. Annual totals of Ospreys, 1962 - 94.

Although Ospreys first returned to nest successfully in Scotland in 1954, the number of breeding pairs only started to increase rapidly in the 1980s (New Atlas). By 1992 there were 76 pairs (Ogilvie *et al* 1995) and, although there is no definite evidence, it would seem safe to assume that the increase in records in Sussex is associated with the growth of the Scottish population and not simply the greater number of observers active in the county.

Ospreys have been recorded in every month of the year except January and February. The earliest ever was one at Bewl Water on 24 March 1993 while the latest was at Arlington Reservoir on 9 December 1994. The cumulative monthly totals shown below reveal that in spring most are recorded in May while in autumn the main passage is in September. The totals also show that there has been a tendency for spring migrants to arrive earlier in recent years and that the proportion of spring records in each period has increased successively from 16% in 1947-61 to 34% in 1962-76 and 45% in 1977-94. Furthermore, the totals demonstrate an increase in summer and early autumn records yet virtually no change in the number of late autumn occurrences.

	Mar	Apr	May	Jun	Jul	Aug	Sep	Oct	Nov	Dec
1947-61	-	-	8	-	3	8	17	13	1	-
1962-76	-	8	21	4	1	16	47	1	-	-
1977-94	3	51	83	18	16	65	87	19	5	1
Total	3	59	112	22	20	89	151	33	6	1

In addition to those recorded on passage, there have been a number of recent sightings of non-breeding birds during the summer months, mainly at Weir Wood Reservoir and Bewl Water.

Although most sightings are of single birds, two have been seen together on a number of occasions. More unusual were three together at Weir Wood Reservoir on 30 August 1976 and up to four in Chichester Harbour almost daily from 11 to 27 September 1991.

Most of the Ospreys recorded in Sussex have been in Chichester and Pagham Harbours (18%) and at inland waters (43%), especially Weir Wood Reservoir and Bewl Water. In spring, it is unusual for birds to linger more than a few days but in autumn, birds may remain for several weeks at a time. Stays from late August to early October have been recorded at both Chichester Harbour and Weir Wood Reservoir while exceptionally, in 1994, individuals remained in Chichester Harbour from early September until mid-November and at Arlington Reservoir until 9 December.

Roger Jackson & John Newnham

Lesser Kestrel   *Falco naumanni*

Status:- One record, no longer considered to be acceptable.

A record of a male seen in flight and perched on a post on the Downs at No Man's Land, north of Cissbury Ring on 4 November 1973 has recently been reviewed and is considered to be inadequately documented (Rogers *et al* 1995).

There are now only six surviving records of this species in the British Isles for the period 1962-94, half having been deleted following a national review. It breeds from Iberia to China wintering mainly in sub-Saharan Africa.

Richard Fairbank

Kestrel   *Falco tinnunculus*

Status:- A fairly common resident and passage migrant.

The population of this familiar and charismatic species in Sussex has grown steadily over the last 20 to 30 years. This reflects its tolerance and adaptability to the wide range of habitats with which the county is endowed. These include urban areas, farmland with copses, heathland, chalk downland, coastal cliffs and the grass verges of highways. Nest sites are often in holes in trees and cliffs although buildings may also be used. These have included blocks of flats, a brewery, churches, a hospital, power stations, racecourse stands and railway stations. Prey items frequently include small birds as well as the more usual rodents. The chicks of Little Terns and Ringed Plover have been taken at Rye Harbour in most years while at Sidlesham, House Sparrows and Starlings are among the prey caught.

A survey of the breeding population in the period 1964-67 found the species to be generally distributed and reasonably numerous, with a total of 238 occupied territories in just over half the county and birds present in a further 71 localities. Breeding densities in ten areas ranged between 0.11 and 0.39 pairs per km² and a total of 600 pairs was estimated for the whole county

(Shrubb 1969). The survey also revealed a decline along the chalk cliffs, where only ten pairs were found, a figure markedly lower than that given by Walpole-Bond who recorded 30-60 pairs annually and nearly 100 pairs in 1919.

A further survey in 1978, restricted to the Weald in the vicinity of Horsham and Crawley, found 65 pairs at a density of 0.16 pairs per km² (Hughes & Dougharty 1979). This represented an increase in the study area of 45% since 1967. Records submitted for 1979 indicated similar increases on the coastal plain at Sidlesham, on the Downs north of Worthing and in the Horsham area, where densities had increased by 40%, 44% and 32% respectively, compared with 1964-67. All breeding season records for 1980 were plotted on maps, from which it was possible to estimate spacing between occupied territories which averaged 2.1 km apart. Extrapolated for the whole county, this figure gave an average density of 0.28 pairs per km² or a county population of about 1150 pairs. Even allowing for a more realistic estimate of 800 pairs, it was clear that a substantial increase of not less than 33% had occurred since 1967.

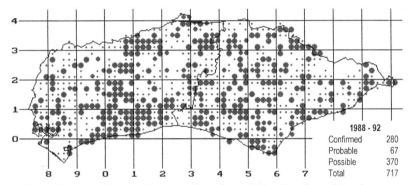

1988 - 92	
Confirmed	280
Probable	67
Possible	370
Total	717

The Atlas map shows the Kestrel to be widely distributed in the county. Applying a density of 0.28 pairs per km² to the 717 tetrads in which Kestrels were recorded during the Atlas Survey, indicates a county population of about 800 pairs, suggesting little change in status in the last decade. This estimate equates to an average density of 21 pairs per 10-km square, a figure that compares well with the national average of 20 pairs per 10-km square (New Atlas).

In autumn, large concentrations are sometimes reported. These have included 18 at Long Furlong on 14 September 1978 and at Chanctonbury on 15 September 1984, 15 between Amberley and Burpham on 5 November 1976 and 22 October 1977 and in the Cissbury area on 13 November 1976 and 19 October 1977. A total of 23 was recorded on Pevensey Levels on 13 December 1992.

Although some adults remain in their breeding territories throughout the winter, there have been a number of sightings at coastal sites in both spring and autumn suggesting passage. Both immigration and emigration have been observed and also coasting movements, but the exact scale of the latter is difficult to determine due to the presence of resident pairs at coastal sites. The number of birds recorded is generally small and less than ten per year is the norm. In 1969, a total of 13 was recorded at Selsey in the spring while in 1970, the best year, 12 were reported at the coast in spring and 17 in autumn, including a total of six, all flying west, at Langney Point between 30 September and 2 October.

Ringing data has shown that Kestrels from Sussex can venture some distance from their capture site. Of 52 recoveries of Sussex-ringed birds, many of which had been ringed as nestlings, 48 were within southern England, one in Wales, one in Scotland and two in Belgium. Similarly, of 45 birds, mostly nestlings, ringed elsewhere in Britain and subsequently found in Sussex, 29 had come from southern counties, 12 from northern England and four from Scotland.

There have also been three incidences of foreign-ringed birds recovered in Sussex. All had been ringed as nestlings in the Netherlands in 1980s and were found here in their first year.   *Clive Hope*

Red-footed Falcon   *Falco vespertinus*

Status:- A rare vagrant (22 records involving 26 individuals).

Prior to 1962 there were ten records of eleven individuals. Five occurred in May and singles were obtained near Arundel on 4 July 1894 and at Fairlight on 11 October 1884. The remaining four, including a pair shot at Brighton in 1855, were undated. Those in May included an adult male shot and wounded on the airfield at Thorney Island on 31 May 1956 which was taken into care, but subsequently died, and an adult male obtained near Brighton Racecourse on 20 May 1873 (BoMNH 207240).

Fifteen individuals have been accepted since the beginning of 1962:

1968:   A juvenile at Sidlesham during the evening of 8 September.
1973:   A second-summer male flying east over Whitbread Hollow, Beachy Head on 10 May.
        A male flying west over Belle Tout, Beachy Head on 1 June.
        A female at Lock Farm, Iden on 13 June.
1979:   An immature female at Cissbury Ring from 25 May to 1 June.
1987:   A female at Bullock Hill, Woodingdean on 3 July.
1989:   A female at Newmarket Hill, Woodingdean from 29 May to 3 June and a first summer male there from 30 May to 1 June. Despite the period of overlap they were rarely seen together.
        A first-summer female at Hooe Level, Norman's Bay on 1 June.
1990:   A female at Balsdean on 20 May.
1992:   A female at Pett Level on 5 June arrived from the west and alighted on a post for a few minutes before departing east.
        Two first-summer males and a female at Powdermill Reservoir on 9 June, one first-summer male remaining to 14 June.
1994:   A female at Icklesham from 30 May to 12 June.

Records in 1973 and 1992 were part of large national influxes (see below). Even ignoring these occurrences, there appears to have been a slight recent increase in sightings (fig. 28), possibly due to better observer coverage away from the coast.

Most individuals since 1962 have arrived in May (6) and June (7) with one in early July and one in September. Four have been seen on the Downs immediately to the east of Brighton, three (together) at Powdermill Reservoir, two at both Beachy Head and Icklesham/Pett and singles at Cissbury, Pevensey, Rye Harbour and Sidlesham.

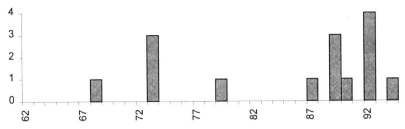

Figure 28. Annual totals of Red-footed Falcons, 1962 - 94.

There were over 500 records of this elegant falcon in the British Isles during 1962-94 including 42 in spring 1973 (Dymond *et al* 1989) and nearly 120 during May-June 1992 (Nightingale & Allsopp 1994). It breeds from eastern Europe to Mongolia and winters in southern Africa.

Richard Fairbank

Merlin *Falco columbarius*

Status:- A scarce but regular winter visitor and passage migrant.

Although Shrubb recorded little change in status for this mobile and easily missed falcon between 1961 and 1976, the approximate cumulative monthly totals for the periods 1962-76 and 1977-93 shown below, indicate that there has been an increase in the number of Merlins recorded in the county. Whether this is a genuine increase or merely the result of greater observer activity is not clear.

	Jul	Aug	Sep	Oct	Nov	Dec	Jan	Feb	Mar	Apr	May
1962-76	-	2	22	68	38	32	37	18	15	9	1
1977-93	3	17	108	214	153	117	111	84	73	58	5
Total	3	19	130	282	191	149	148	102	88	67	6

Merlins are found mainly on coastal farmland and marshes and a high proportion of recent records have been for Chichester and Pagham Harbours, the Beachy Head area, Pevensey Levels and from Pett to the Midrips. Other favoured areas include the river valleys of the Arun, Adur, Ouse and Cuckmere and the coastal plain between Bognor and Littlehampton. Most records are of single birds or two together, but there were three at Thorney Island on 13 October 1989 and at Rye Harbour on 4 December 1990.

The cumulative monthly totals indicate that autumn passage migrants contribute significantly to the total number of sightings. Since 1962, there have been 11 autumn records of birds apparently on migration, of which seven flew out to sea and four arrived over the sea. The earliest ever recorded in autumn were singles at Roedean, Brighton on 3 July 1993 and at Balsdean on 17 July 1978 while other first dates for returning birds between 1962 and 1993 covered the period 7 August to 9 October with the average (including the July birds) 5 September.

Wintering Merlins leave from February onwards, and between 1967 and 1993 the last dates fell between 14 February and 11 May, with an average departure date of 12 April. Of the six recorded in May, all were at coastal sites including singles that flew north off the sea at Selsey Bill on 7 May 1981 and at Brighton Marina on 11 May 1993. The latter was the latest county record.

There have been three ringing recoveries which give some clues to the origin of the Merlins that winter in Sussex. Females found dead at Brighton in November 1986 and at Selsey in September 1989 had been ringed as nestlings during the previous breeding seasons in Gwynedd and West Yorkshire respectively. One fledged from an Icelandic nest in July 1990 was seen at Beachy Head, 1847 km SSE, in October of that year and allowed observers to approach close enough to read the ring number in the field.   *Clive Hope*

Hobby   *Falco subbuteo*

Status:- A scarce breeding summer visitor and regular passage migrant.

Hobbies have long been associated with the heathlands of Sussex where they can be seen hawking for insects, particularly on warm summer evenings. In recent years, however, following a marked increase in the number of pairs breeding in Britain, they have also frequented farmland with pine clumps. In the 1950s, when the British population was put at 60-90 pairs (New Atlas), the available records suggested a maximum population of only about 12 pairs in the county. Between 1962 and 1976 there was an increase to between 20 and 25 pairs while a further increase is indicated by the results of the Atlas Survey in which Hobbies were recorded in 118 tetrads. Although breeding was confirmed in only 15 tetrads and probable in 21, the species is often unobtrusive except in courtship or with young (New Atlas), so it is quite likely that many of the birds in the 'seen' category relate to those which are breeding in the immediate vicinity. The current population may be 50 pairs or more, based on the assumption that pairs are present in tetrads where only possible breeding was recorded. The Atlas map which also shows, as open circles, additional breeding records from 1976-87 demonstrates how widespread the species may be.

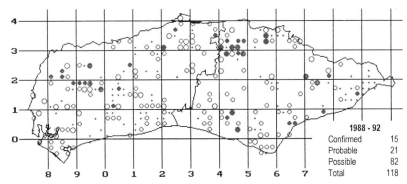

1988 - 92	
Confirmed	15
Probable	21
Possible	82
Total	118

Hobbies are one of the later summer visitors to arrive. Between 1970 and 1993 first dates were in the period 12 April to 2 May with an average arrival date of 23 April. Singles at the Midrips on 12 April 1971 and at Littlehampton on 13 April 1987 are the earliest for the county. There are annual records of birds seen arriving off the sea during sea-watches. In most springs fewer than 30 migrants are reported so totals of 45 in 1992 and 1993 were noteworthy, perhaps reflecting the species' recent increase as a breeding bird in Britain.

Larger numbers are recorded in autumn, often involving what are probably family parties; for example, seven seen hawking dragonflies at Pulborough Brooks on 15 September 1991 and a party of three at Burton Mill Pond on 21 October of the same year. Coastal localities with fresh water are especially favoured, but Hobbies may be recorded at other coastal sites and at many inland localities. The recent increase in the species in Britain is reflected in the number of migrants recorded passing through the county in autumn. In the 1960s autumn totals in single figures were the norm, and in the 1970s the totals ranged from three to 23. Numbers increased steadily throughout the 1980s, with totals averaging 22 in the first half of the decade and 37 in the second. In the 1990s, numbers increased more dramatically with 52 recorded in autumn 1990, 77 in 1991, 90 in 1992 and an astonishing 212 in 1993. Even allowing for duplicity of records in 1993, this last figure is a significant increase compared with the previous autumn's total and a huge increase compared with the number of autumn migrants just five years previously.

Most Hobbies depart the county in late September and early October, with relatively few lingering into late October. One at Selsey Bill on 31 October 1965 is the latest record for the county.

There are only two ringing recoveries for Sussex; one found dead at Sompting in September 1982 had been ringed as a nestling near Guildford, Surrey the previous July and a nestling ringed in the Netherlands in July 1991 was found dead in Brighton in May 1993.   *Mike Scott-Ham*

Gyr Falcon   *Falco rusticolis*

Status:- A very rare vagrant (three records).

Two were recorded before 1962 (des Forges & Harber). A grey morph adult shot while devouring a pigeon on a wheat stack at Mayfield in January

207

1845 is illustrated in Borrer (1891) while a white morph adult female shot at Bullock Hill, Woodingdean on 26 September 1882 was reported to have been present for a day or two and was likened to "a newspaper blown along by the wind". Both are in the Booth Museum (BoMNH 207231 and 207235 respectively).

A white morph individual present on the Downs between Cissbury and Chanctonbury Rings from 11 to 24 March 1972 is the only comparatively recent record.

There were over 100 records in the British Isles during 1962-94, with a record seven in 'early spring' 1972 which included one in Surrey in mid-March. It has a circumpolar distribution north of 60°N but is declining in the south of its range due to persecution and climatic change. The predominantly white 'high arctic' populations are the more migratory, most British birds being from Greenland (BWP). *Richard Fairbank*

Peregrine *Falco peregrinus*

Status:- A scarce breeding resident, passage migrant and winter visitor.

In his *A History of Sussex Birds*, Walpole-Bond wrote that in 1904, when he first started searching Sussex systematically, "seven pairs of breeding falcons held sway on our sea-bastions". In subsequent years there were frequently "eight or nine eyries to a year, on several occasions ten, and sometimes actually 12". He continued that "the cliff-frontage affected by the birds reaches in all little more than 16 miles" and that "at least two steep, lofty unworked chalk pits well inland, now and again, marshal each its pair of breeding Peregrines".

Walpole-Bond added that the breeding pairs were "resident, each couple confining itself the calender through to its ancestral cliff together with the country behind and adjoining", including downland and levels. Birds of the year, on the other hand, "when capable of fending for themselves in late summer or early autumn" were "driven from the home-domains by their

208

remorseless parents and forced to seek pastures new". For about the next six months, they could be met with "almost anywhere in the county, provided the country be more or less open". Unoccupied cliffs, barren downland, vicinities of ponds, heaths and marshes suited the birds. In wooded areas, it was "nothing phenomenal to see a Peregrine perched in one of them" while in towns, the spire of a church or cathedral provided "a suitable stance".

In 1940, the Air Ministry organised the destruction of Peregrines, in various parts of Britain, in an attempt to safeguard carrier-pigeons but it is not known for certain how long this continued in Sussex and how many birds were shot. The records indicate, however, that six territories were occupied in 1941, seven in 1943 and eight in 1945. Subsequently four pairs bred in 1946, five pairs were reported from the cliffs in 1947 and six pairs attempted to breed in 1948. Probably only four pairs did so in 1949. In 1951, six pairs were seen on the coast in the breeding season and some of these raised young. In 1952, young were raised at three sites and in the following year four pairs were reported from the chalk cliffs. Five or six pairs were recorded in 1954, Peregrines were present on some sea-cliffs in 1955 and breeding was confirmed on 20 May 1956 when an adult together with a juvenile was seen near Seaford Head. This was the last record of breeding by Peregrines in the county until 1990, when a single pair bred successfully at Beachy Head.

In Sussex, as elsewhere in Britain, the decline in the number of Peregrines was attributed to the organochlorine pesticides accumulated from their prey. In 1961, the Government Advisory Committee on Pesticides and other Toxic Chemicals recommended that a voluntary ban be placed on the use of aldrin, dieldrin and heptachlor to dress spring sown cereals. The ban was effective from the spring of 1962 and in 1964 and 1969, further restrictions were recommended. In 1967, the Peregrine population in Britain, began to show the upward trend, which is probably still continuing. There was little evidence, however, of more than a modest recovery in Sussex until 1985 when the number of records showed a marked increase. Some of these were, of course, duplications when an individual bird was reported by more than one observer. By 1989, the position had improved still further for 26 birds were recorded on various dates. Once again, there were duplications in these figures. In 1990, no less than 106 reports were received, mainly from localities on or near the coast and in 1991 and 1992 there were nearly 200 sightings. By 1994 the resident population of this magnificent bird, in Sussex, had increased to at least three pairs.

The marked increase that has occurred in the number of Peregrines recorded in Sussex has been accompanied by a return to roosting on tall buildings, as was noted in Walpole-Bond's day. In late 1992, single birds were observed on the spire of Chichester Cathedral and on the chimney stack of the old Southwick Power Station, while in early 1994 a bird that hunted Starlings going to roost on the West Pier at Brighton was believed to roost on the roof of the nearby Bedford Hotel. It was also seen perched on the facade of the Metropole Hotel and was still present in the area in December of that year.

A first-winter male Peregrine, ringed as a nestling in Nordland, Norway, was found dead in a bramble bush at Stone Hall, Haywards Heath, 1957 km southwest, on 5 January 1983. Peregrines that breed in temperate and subarctic Europe are basically non-migratory but many individuals (especially juveniles) wander extensively in autumn and winter (BWP).   *C M James*

Black Grouse   *Tetrao tetrix*

Status:- Formerly resident; the native stock apparently became extinct by about the mid-19th century. Introductions survived until the 1930s.

Although Walpole-Bond gave the impression that this once quite numerous species was still indigenous to the county until at least 1880, it is more widely accepted that the native stock survived until around the mid-19th century.

Walpole-Bond stated that in Sussex the Black Grouse chiefly occurred on "thinly treed, healthy bracken-grown parts of forest-land, as well as on our larger commons and, possibly, certain wooded stretches of the Downs". Both Ashdown and St Leonard's Forests appear to have supported most birds while smaller numbers occurred at a number of other sites, for example, Harting, Lewes and Lower Beeding.

As early as 1840, a number of birds were introduced to Hollycombe and Black Down. Subsequent releases to these areas followed and the descendants of these birds survived into the 1930s. A greyhen flushed in Ashdown Forest in 1937 was the last county record.   *Tony Cook*

Red-legged Partridge   *Alectoris rufa*

Status:- A common, introduced resident.

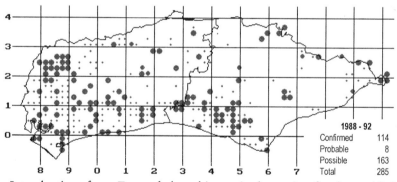

	1988 - 92
Confirmed	114
Probable	8
Possible	163
Total	285

Introductions from France led to this species becoming firmly established in the county about 1841. Walpole-Bond described the Red-legged Partridge as "quite common" but it is likely that a marked decline occurred thereafter (Shrubb) until, perhaps, the early 1960s when populations were supplemented with the release of captive-reared birds (New Atlas), a practice that continued until the early 1980s.

Its choice of habitat is similar to that of the Grey Partridge, occurring mainly on farmland, although it is much more tolerant of wooded landscapes. In the more open parts of the South Downs it is now almost absent (New

Atlas). The current status of the species in Sussex is confused by the existence of released captive-bred Chukars *A. chukar* and *A. rufa* x *A. chukar* hybrids, known as "ogridges". In September 1970, more than 2000 Chukars and "ogridges" were released from North Farm, Washington on to the South Downs. Some birds seen at the time were reported as Rock Partridges (*SxBR* 24: 21) but this species is thought never to have been released in Britain. Introductions continued on a regular basis until 1980s, involving on average 2700 birds per year. These introduced birds are difficult to tell apart from pure Red-legs and no attempt has been made to distinguish between them on the Atlas map above. The preponderance of Atlas records in West Sussex, particularly in the extreme northwest of the county, may reflect where most captive-rearing and releasing has occurred.

Recent estimates have suggested that stocks of Red-legged Partridges now rarely exceed densities of more than five pairs per km² (Marchant *et al* 1990). Applying a lower density of three to four pairs per km² to the occupied tetrads indicates a county population of 3200-4400 pairs but one that is likely to be distorted by the effect of artificial stocking.

Research by the Game Conservancy has shown that the introduction of captive bred Chukar hybrids increasingly dilutes the stock of pure Red-legs and also reduces breeding success. These factors, together with the shooting of these mixed populations of *Alectoris* partridges, can locally drive wild Red-legs to extinction. However, this problem should now diminish, as the licence under which hybrid releases were allowed ceased in December 1992.

Few have been recorded away from breeding areas although one crossing the A259 at the King Alfred, Hove on 9 May 1991 was unusual.   *Tony Cook*

Grey Partridge   *Perdix perdix*
Status:- A fairly common but decreasing resident.

This highly sedentary species is found mainly on arable farmland, especially where flanked with taller and denser cover such as hedgerows and rank herbage. The Atlas map shows a widespread but patchy distribution, with the main concentrations along the Downs (particularly the more open downland to the east of the River Arun), adjacent to Chichester and Pagham Harbours, and in the Rye area. It is, however, absent from large areas of the county, especially in the Weald. The distribution is broadly similar to that of the Red-legged Partridge although it appears to be more restricted to the Downs and coastal plain. This may be due, in part, to *Alectoris* partridges being released more extensively into the Weald, especially in West Sussex.

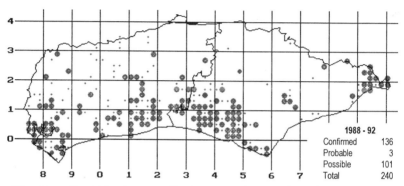

1988 - 92	
Confirmed	136
Probable	3
Possible	101
Total	240

The Grey Partridge is generally less conspicuous than the Red-leg as it is more crepuscular and less vocal. There is a monogamous pair bond and for 7-8 months of the year, flocks are established which consist of family groups. Five to 15 birds commonly make up such coveys, but larger flocks may sometimes be seen, for example, 34 at Stanmer in November 1984 and 40 at Rye Harbour in December 1986.

Studies have shown that the Grey Partridge has suffered a long term national decline. This has been especially marked since 1950 and is thought to be due to post-war changes in agricultural practice. These have included the removal of field boundary habitat, which has led to increased nest predation where pairs have been unable to space themselves adequately (Marchant *et al* 1990), and the increased use of herbicides in cereals, so reducing the amount of insect food available for chicks (Potts 1986). Shrubb considered climatic factors to be another cause of the decline, at least at a local level, referring to "a series of cold damp summers, particularly in the 1950s, that contributed to high chick mortality on the coastal plain".

During the Atlas Survey, there were records in 240 tetrads, with breeding confirmed in 136, probable in three and possible in 101. However, given the sedentary nature of the species, each record is likely to refer to breeding birds. Assuming a density of up to five pairs per occupied tetrad indicates a county population of up to 1200 pairs.   *Tony Cook*

Quail   *Coturnix coturnix*

Status:- A scarce summer visitor, recorded in variable numbers from year to year. Formerly occasional in winter.

The Quail, Europe's only migratory gamebird, is recorded annually in Sussex. It is thought that it breeds in the county in most years but this is difficult to prove. Most records refer to males calling at dusk or dawn, but this is by no means an indication of breeding as they call regularly when they first arrive but much less frequently when they have acquired a mate, unless there are other males holding territory nearby (Moreau 1951). Proof of breeding is dependent on sightings of broods or nests, usually during harvesting activities.

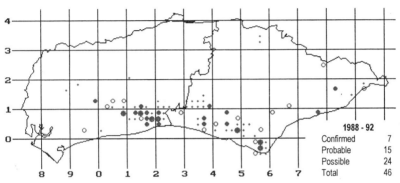

1988 - 92	
Confirmed	7
Probable	15
Possible	24
Total	46

The Atlas map shows the tetrads in which Quails were recorded in the period 1988-92 and also those (as open circles) where birds were recorded in 1976-87 but not 1988-92. Most were found within 10 km of the coast between the River Arun and Beachy Head, a distribution that reflects the species preference for rolling chalk downland with cereal crops such as barley and winter wheat. Other suitable breeding habitats include fields of clover, legumes, oilseed rape and unmown grass and rank set-aside. Walpole-Bond stated that birds in autumn and winter favoured "stubbles, levels, fields of roots, rape and even cabbage patches".

There are considerable annual fluctuations in Quail numbers, the largest numbers being associated with warm dry springs and south-easterly winds (68-72 BTO Atlas), conditions in which migrants may overshoot. Since 1960, the largest influxes have been in 1964 (20 recorded), 1970 (38), 1987 (32) and 1989 (46 calling males at 31 localities and three singles in autumn). The latest 'Quail year' proved to be an exceptional one, with an estimated 2600 calling males in Britain (New Atlas).

Although Quails have been recorded as early as 21 March (1921, St Leonards and 1973, Lancing), the first males are not usually heard calling before mid-May. In some years, arrivals may occur well into June or even July. It is believed that these summer movements are of birds shifting their breeding grounds from areas where conditions have deteriorated (Moreau 1951).

Autumn migrants have been noted between early August and early October. des Forges & Harber referred to about ten records for December, two or three for January and one for February, all but four of which were prior to 1900. A further five have been recorded since 1960: at Winchelsea on 13 January 1966, Sidlesham on 6-7 February 1966, Shoreham-by-Sea on 8 March 1967, Earnley on 31 January 1968, and Southease on 8 February 1976.

Tony Cook

Pheasant   *Phasianus colchicus*

Status:- A very common resident.

The Pheasant was introduced to Britain probably by the Normans in the late 11th century and, according to Walpole-Bond, was known in Sussex by about 1245. From the 18th century other races, especially *P.c. torquatus*, were added to the initial introductions of chiefly *P.c. colchicus*, and these birds, together with resultant crosses, have long constituted the Pheasant population in Britain.

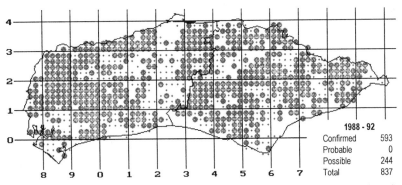

1988 - 92	
Confirmed	593
Probable	0
Possible	244
Total	837

Pheasants are found in a wide range of habitats but especially on farmland with woodland edges. The Atlas map above reflects this preference with birds only absent from the more urbanised areas of the county between Littlehampton and Brighton and around Crawley, Eastbourne, Bexhill and Hastings. The absence of the species from Pevensey Levels and from the levels between Rye and the Kent border is perhaps due to a lack of adequate cover for nesting in these areas.

In autumn, large numbers of hand-reared birds are released on many of the sporting estates in the county. Most, however, are shot and do not survive to the following breeding season. Very little information has been published about the Pheasant in Sussex so estimating the size of breeding population is difficult. The New Atlas gives an average breeding density in Britain of 3.9 territorial males and 7.3 females per km^2 and, if these figures are applied to the 593 tetrads in the county in which breeding was confirmed, a county population in excess of 9000 males and 17000 females is indicated. This figure may be on the low side given that the Hampshire population has been estimated at 21,000 territorial males, 17,000 non-territorial males and 40,000 hens (Robertson, Tapper & Stoate 1989).

Tony Cook

Golden Pheasant — *Chrysolophus pictus*

Status:- A scarce introduced resident.

The Golden Pheasant, a native of the uplands of central China, became established in Britain after a series of introductions made during the 19th and 20th centuries. It was not admitted to category C of the British List until 1971.

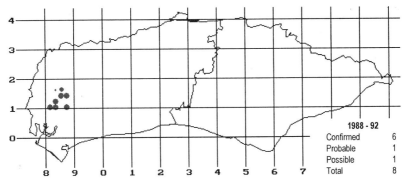

	1988 - 92	
	Confirmed	6
	Probable	1
	Possible	1
	Total	8

Two colonies exist to the north of Chichester which may have become established as far back as the late 1960s, given that those present at Queen Elizabeth Country Park, Hampshire since the early 1970s are thought to have spread from West Sussex (Clark & Eyre 1993). One colony is in 117 ha of dense yew forest and bordering habitats at Kingley Vale NNR where birds have been present since 1968 (Williamson & Williamson 1973). Published territory counts from here have ranged from 11 in 1983 to a peak of 22 in 1987, dropping back to 13 by 1990. A flavistic male first recorded at this site in December 1990 points to a weakened gene pool through inbreeding. The other colony is in 12 ha of mainly conifer plantation at West Dean Woods where there have been up to four territories annually since at least 1983. Single birds may occasionally be reported from other sites including Rewell Wood in March 1971, Singletonhill Plantation in March 1987 and May 1990 and Ebernoe Common in January 1992.

The county population appears stable but is unlikely to grow due to the species' sedentary nature and preference for dense dark woodland with a relatively bare floor.   *Tony Cook*

Lady Amherst's Pheasant — *Chrysolophus amherstiae*

Status:- A rare introduced, but not established, resident or escape from captivity.

This native of southwest China and adjacent parts of Tibet and upper Burma was brought into Britain in the early 19th century and introduced for ornamental reasons (New Atlas). Its stronghold in this country is centred around Bedfordshire, Buckinghamshire and Hertfordshire and as with the previous species, it was admitted to category C of the British List in 1971.

When properly established, it favours relatively young, dense conifer plantations with little floor cover. However, records from elsewhere, including those in Sussex, show that single birds may occur in a variety of woodland habitats, sometimes with dense undergrowth. In recent years, males have been recorded at Herstmonceux Castle in July 1982, Wiggonholt Common in December 1988, Sailor's Copse, Poling from October 1990 to April 1991, Shopham Bridge in April 1993, Sutton in August 1993 and Burton Mill Pond in November 1993 but all probably relate to escapes or deliberate releases rather than birds from established feral populations. Such individuals can hardly represent a viable population and so this sedentary species has not been admitted to the county list.   *Tony Cook*

Water Rail   *Rallus aquaticus*

Status:- A scarce resident, winter visitor and passage migrant.

Prior to 1962, the only estimate of the size of the breeding population was that given by Walpole-Bond who considered that about 50 pairs nested annually. More recently, an incomplete census between 1962 and 1966, that revealed only about 15 pairs (*SxBR* 19: 53-4), was thought to have under-estimated the population, as between 1962 and 1976 there were records from 35 sites, involving a possible 38 pairs (Shrubb). During the Atlas Survey, breeding was confirmed or probable in 14 tetrads, and possible in a further 14. It is likely, however, that some pairs were overlooked, due to the species' preference for dense aquatic vegetation, and because it is largely silent by day during the breeding season.

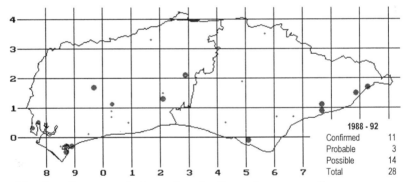

Non-breeding records show that the first migrants usually start to appear in late August but that the majority of wintering birds arrive between late September and mid-November. Although Water Rails typically occur in wetland habitats such as overgrown streams and ditches and reedbeds, passage birds are sometimes noted in drier areas, especially at Beachy Head, where they have occasionally been trapped.

The wintering population reaches a peak between late November and February (table 31) and then gradually decreases during March and early April, when birds return to their breeding grounds. Water Rails may be widely distributed during the winter months, especially in severe weather when they become more conspicuous as they are forced into the open to seek out ice-free areas in which to feed. At most sites fewer than five are recorded, but Arundel WWT has regularly held 10-20 birds in winter since the early 1970s and Icklesham up to 40 since the late 1980s.

		Sep	Oct	Nov	Dec	Jan	Feb	Mar	Apr
Number of birds	Maximum	27	60	83	71	74	65	40	13
	Average	9	25	35	44	38	35	20	15
	Minimum	3	6	13	17	13	2	3	2
Number of sites	Maximum	9	9	13	17	23	23	12	8
	Average	4	7	9	11	12	11	7	5
	Minimum	2	3	6	6	8	2	3	2

Table 31. Winter totals of Water Rails, 1982 - 93.

The largest number of birds recorded in any month in the period 1982-93 was 83 in November 1987. 1987 also produced the highest totals for September, October and December whereas those for January and February were recorded in 1985. The minimum totals shown in the table may merely reflect under-recording or may be due to an absence of harsh weather in that particular winter.

Few Water Rails are trapped for ringing but, even so, there are two recoveries that may indicate the origins of the birds that winter in the county. One ringed near Sidlesham in September 1966 was found dead in Utrecht, the Netherlands, 424 km ENE, in March 1974, while one ringed in Braunschweig, Germany, in August 1975 was found dead at Brede, 687 km west, in April 1977.

Richard Kelly

Spotted Crake   *Porzana porzana*

Status:- A very scarce spring and autumn passage migrant and rare winter visitor.

The Spotted Crake is of less than annual occurrence in Sussex, having been recorded in 23 of the 33 years since 1962 (fig. 29). It is, however, a very skulking species, seen mainly at dawn and dusk, so it is likely that many birds are missed.

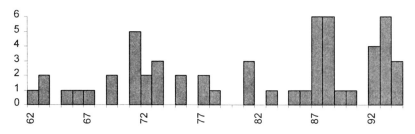

Figure 29. Annual totals of Spotted Crakes, 1962 - 94.

Between 1962 and 1994, about 65 were recorded. Of these, 40 were in autumn and, although there have been records as early as 1 August (1893, Polegate and 1914, Pett), most were in the period mid-August and mid-October. des Forges & Harber referred to eight records for December-February; more recently there have been five comprising singles at Charleston Reedbed on 4 December 1971 and 16 December 1977, the Crumbles on 2 January 1965, Hampden Park, Eastbourne on 3 January 1971 and at Amberley Wild Brooks on 16 February 1975, the latter found freshly dead. One at Combe Haven on 11 March 1986 may well have been a wintering bird but one at Icklesham on 26-27 March 1989 seems more likely to have been an early spring migrant, the majority of which have occurred in April. There is no evidence that the species has ever nested in the county although, at Combe Haven, two males were recorded from 26 May 1981. Both were still present in June and one remained until 5 August. More recently, up to three males have been heard giving their distinctive "whiplash" call at this site in spring.

Of those recorded since the beginning of 1962, 15 were at Combe Haven and 13 at Icklesham, including four different birds trapped between 16 August and 1 October 1992. Other favoured localities have been the lower Cuckmere Valley (8), Pagham Harbour (6) and Arundel WWT (5). Stays of one or two days are typical but, at Arundel, there was one from 26 August to 29 September 1987, with three there on 28-29 August and two on 30th. One remained at Pagham Harbour from 30 August to 11 September 1988.

The general pattern of occurrence is shown by the cumulative monthly totals for the period 1962-94.

Aug	Sep	Oct	Nov	Dec	Jan	Feb	Mar	Apr	May	Jun	Jul
12	14	11	5	2	2	1	2	8	8	5	2

The Spotted Crake breeds mainly in eastern central Europe, but also in France, Spain and a few other western European countries. It winters in the Mediterranean, North Africa, East Africa and the Middle East. Annual numbers recorded in Britain are in the order of 30-100 birds.   *Richard Kelly*

Sora Rail   *Porzana carolina*

Status:- A very rare vagrant (one record).

An adult present at the eastern end of Pagham Lagoon from at least 26 October to 24 December 1985 often gave exceptional views (*Brit. Birds* 79:

plates 30, 31 and 278). It was the 11th to be recorded in Britain and the first in southeast England.

There were just seven records of this species, a close relative of the Spotted Crake, in the British Isles during 1962-94. It breeds across North America and winters south to northern Peru. *Richard Fairbank*

Little Crake *Porzana parva*

Status:- A rare vagrant (13, mostly old, records).

Eleven were recorded prior to 1962: the first British record at Catsfield near Battle on 29 March 1791, nine during the 1800s and a female at Eastbourne on 3 March 1913. The latter, the earliest dated arrival, entered the Fisherman's Institute on Eastbourne sea front where it was mistaken for a mouse and hit by a thrown boot (Arnold 1936). One at Worthing on 22 October 1894 is the only autumn record, although three are undated, the remainder being in March (4) and April (3). A female at Pevensey on 14 April 1869 hunted out of reeds in a brick pit by a dog and caught alive in a hastily hurled hat is in the Booth Museum (BoMNH 204905). One included erroneously by des Forges & Harber from Pevensey on 1 June 1931 was in 1921 (Walpole-Bond) but in any event should be discounted as it was one of the Hastings Rarities (Nicholson & Ferguson-Lees 1962).

Two have been recorded since the beginning of 1962:

1968: An adult female first seen on the lawn at Hodcombe, Beachy Head on 15 April was trapped. It walked off into a nearby cornfield when released, never to be seen again.

1985: An extremely confiding female present in a ditch in the lower Cuckmere Valley, just south of Exceat, from at least 6 to 16 March (*Brit. Birds* 78: plates 99-101).

The two recent records continue the pattern of most occurrences being in March or April.

There were nearly 30 records of this long-winged crake in the British Isles during 1962-94. It breeds discontinuously from Spain to Kazakhstan wintering mainly in East Africa. *Richard Fairbank*

Baillon's Crake *Porzana pusilla*

Status:- A very rare vagrant (six records).

Five were recorded prior to 1962 (des Forges & Harber). A very exhausted individual was caught at Eastbourne on 6 August 1874 and a female was caught in a bird-catcher's net near Ditchling Road, Brighton on 2 September 1894, the latter being in the Booth Museum (BoMNH 207826). One was shot near Lancing on 13 November 1900, one was killed at Pevensey on 16 May 1939 and one was seen at Sedlescombe on 27 December 1941 and 5 and 9 January 1942 (Moore 1942).

An adult female trapped at Icklesham on 11 August 1992 is the only recent record. It had been attracted by taped vocalisations.

No clear pattern emerges with one record in each of May, September, November and December and two in August.

There were only ten records of this diminutive crake in the British Isles during 1962-94. It breeds from Iberia east to Japan and south to Australia and southern Africa. European populations migrate to sub-Saharan Africa.

Richard Fairbank

Corncrake   *Crex crex*

Status:- A rare passage migrant that formerly bred.

As a breeding bird, the Corncrake was mainly found in the western half of the county within 12 miles of the coast (des Forges & Harber) and, although there were still 25 pairs in 1938, breeding ceased about 1945. None have bred since but single birds were heard calling on the edge of Chailey Common on 7 June 1955 and at Woodman's Green, Linchmere for about a week up to 17 June 1969. There was also one near Harting from 12 to 15 May 1969.

The Corncrake is now an increasingly rare migrant in Sussex as shown by annual totals for the period 1962-94 (fig. 30). The number of records has halved in successive 10-year periods since 1962, with 39 during 1962-71, 19 during 1972-81 and nine during 1982-91. 1967 was the first year without a single record. This reduction in the number of records reflects the recent decrease that has occurred in the breeding population in Britain. The species is now absent from Wales and rare in England, the Isle of Man and Scotland, where the Inner and Outer Hebrides support 90% of the British population (Hudson, Stowe & Aspinall 1990).

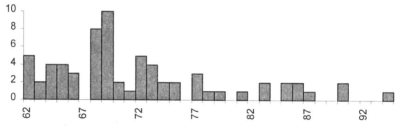

Figure 30. Annual totals of Corncrakes, 1962 - 94.

The earliest spring record is for 9 April 1961, when one was heard calling at Selsey Bill. Subsequent spring migrants have occurred between 19 April and 26 May, while those in autumn have been between 1 July and 27 October. Birds are almost always recorded on one day only, although one at Combe Haven on 1 October 1987 was seen again the following day. Of the 69 recorded in the period 1962-94, 22 were at Beachy Head and 14 on the Selsey peninsula, reflecting the species' preference for arable fields and rough grassland and the density of birdwatchers in these areas.

The cumulative monthly totals for the period 1962-94 are shown below:

Apr	May	Jun	Jul	Aug	Sep	Oct	Nov	Dec
5	6	1	4	3	29	20	-	1

There are old records for November and December, including one caught by a dog at Hardham on 28 December 1908 (Walpole-Bond) but the only recent record for these months was of one at Cissbury on 9 December 1973.

Of those recorded in recent years, one of the most unusual was a bird that was observed being carried by a fox at Littlehampton West Beach on 22 September 1990.   *Richard Kelly*

Moorhen   *Gallinula chloropus*

Status:- A very common resident and winter visitor.

The Moorhen is the commonest riparian species in lowland Britain and can be found in virtually all fresh water habitats, provided suitable emergent vegetation and bankside growth is available for nest building and feeding. Such habitats can range from large lakes to tiny farmyard ponds, large rivers to muddy ditches and extensive reedbeds to damp areas in grassy fields. In Sussex, the largest concentrations occur in the river valleys, on lakes and ponds and at coastal marshes, while smaller numbers breed on isolated village, farm and garden ponds. Few systematic counts of breeding pairs have been made and few breeding records are submitted, reflecting the ubiquitous nature of the species. Twenty-three pairs were recorded along 4 km of Chichester Canal in 1969 and 25 territories were located along 4 km of Aldingbourne Rife in 1988. Thorney Deeps held 24 pairs in 1988 and 1989, while there were 30 pairs at Rye Harbour in 1990 and up to ten pairs at Pulborough Brooks in 1991 and 1992.

The Sussex population is mostly sedentary. Recoveries of birds ringed in the county indicate movements over very small distances with eight recovered within 10 km of their ringing site and five just over 10 km. Indeed, it is unusual for resident birds to move more than 20 km (BWP). Although the population is probably stable overall, breeding habitat may be lost through improved drainage and the infilling of ponds on farmland and also through vegetation clearance of dykes, streams and waterways. The species is subject to temporary declines following severe winter weather, particularly prolonged frozen conditions. The CBC indices show that the population was greatly reduced after the severe winter of 1962/63 but made a rapid recovery and suffered only minor setbacks in the cold winters of 1978/79 and 1981/82. They also suffer from heavy nest predation, mainly caused by crows, mink and stoats (New Atlas). In 1979, 66 pairs were found on 935 ha of the Brede Valley. This population declined to only 15 pairs in 1981. Lower water levels and the presence of mink were the suspected cause. Further, in 1981, at Higham, seven pairs laid over 80 eggs but heavy predation by corvids left only 30 surviving young. However, owing to the pertinacious breeding potential of the species with second broods being common and third and fourth broods, although rare, a possibility, numbers usually make a rapid recovery from any set back.

The number of Moorhens that may breed in any particular tetrad will vary considerably. In some, there will be just one or two isolated pairs, while others will hold considerably more. Thus, in the absence of any census data, an assessment of the size of the county population is largely a matter of guesswork. Clark & Eyre (1993), suggested a range of 8-12 territories per occupied tetrad in Hampshire. Using this as a basis, it would indicate a Sussex population in the region of 4500-7000 pairs. This compares with the 1988/91 estimate of 240,000 territories in Britain (New Atlas).

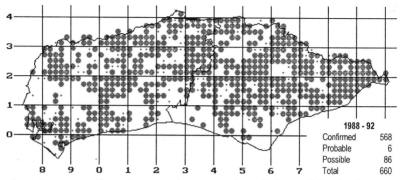

1988 - 92	
Confirmed	568
Probable	6
Possible	86
Total	660

In winter, numbers increase because of an influx of birds from areas unsuitable for overwintering. These visitors form small feeding flocks together with young birds without a territory. Residents stay in their territories defending a small part as a feeding area. Should this freeze, they will then join flocks on neutral ground until conditions improve (Winter Atlas). Groups of 50-100 are widespread, with concentrations of 100-200 being possible.

Sites with the higher wintering numbers include Chichester Harbour (197, February 1982), Chichester Gravel Pits (135, January 1984), Arundel WWT (154, early 1985) and Pagham Harbour (154, January 1982). Counts at Rye Harbour since 1983 have varied between 60-100, with 40 seen roosting in the tops of elders at Pett Pools on 31 December 1992. Sites that have yielded lower numbers have included Bewl Water (95, September 1993), Ifield Mill Pond (73, January 1992), Pevensey Levels (81, December 1992), Weir Wood Reservoir (64, December 1986) and Westhampnett Gravel Pit (50, January 1989). In earlier years, flocks of 105 at Manhood End, 80 at Harting Pond, 70 at Swanbourne Lake and 105 in the Arun Valley were noted (Shrubb).

Ringing data confirms that some of our winter population is of continental origin. Since 1962 there have been seven recoveries of foreign ringed birds. Six of these were ringed in the Netherlands and one in Belgium. The longest movement involved a bird ringed at Friesland, Netherlands on 25 August 1988 and shot at Pagham, 543 km WSW on December 1988. *Joe Nobbs*

Coot   *Fulica atra*

Status:- A common resident with numbers much increased by visitors outside the breeding season.

The Coot is a familiar Sussex bird. It breeds in any freshwater habitat that provides sufficient space and emergent vegetation for nest building. Coots may be found on lakes, larger ponds, reservoirs, flooded gravel pits, canals and slow-running rivers where they show a preference for fairly shallow water with room to dive to a muddy bottom. The main concentrations in Sussex during the breeding season are at Bewl Water (max. 46 pairs in 1980), Weir Wood Reservoir (max. 28 pairs in 1981), Thorney Deeps (24 pairs in 1988 and

1989) and Icklesham (25 pairs in 1990). Other sites holding 10-20 pairs include Aldingbourne Rife, Darwell Reservoir, Pannel Sewer, Pulborough Brooks and Rye Harbour. The species has never been the subject of a county survey, so estimating the total population is difficult because of the wide variation in density between tetrads. Assuming a density of two to five territories per occupied tetrad suggests a population in the range of 400-1000 pairs. In 1988-91, the British population was estimated at 46,000 individuals (New Atlas).

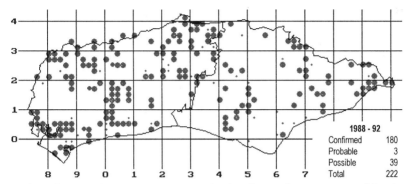

After the breeding season is over, the local population is joined by birds arriving to overwinter. This arrival commences in August and September with ringing evidence suggesting that some visitors may originate from as far away as Russia. They form into larger flocks with overall county numbers usually peaking in December or January and then declining in March and April as birds return to their breeding grounds. Numbers, however, are very variable, both from year to year and within each wintering period, depending on the severity of the weather and the availability of food sources. Maximum counts at individual sites (table 32) may occur in any of the winter months, thereby suggesting considerable local movement between sites. Little is known about such movements, although one pilot study found that some colour-marked individuals wandered over several counties during the course of a winter (Winter Atlas).

	69-74	74-79	79-84	84-89	89-94	Peak counts
Chichester Harbour	1037	782	408	308	145	2000, Feb 1974
Pagham Harbour		116**	160	110	71	281, Jan 1982
Chichester Gravel Pits			1013**	1184	1108	1584, Dec 1992
Arundel WWT		227*	169	89		294, Jan 1982
Ardingly Reservoir			98**	190	72	417, Jan 1987
Weir Wood Reservoir		255**	135*	55	17	280, Oct 1983
Arlington Reservoir			152*	73	17	280, Oct 1983
Bewl Water		414**	1398*	1118	302	2013, Jan 1987
Darwell Reservoir		123*	52	44	44	150, Jan 1977
Rye Harbour		417*	899	763	446	1057, Jan 1987

Table 32. Five year means of maxima and peak counts of Coot, 1969/70 - 93/94.

Significant concentrations recorded at localities not listed in the table include 350 at the Crumbles in January and December 1984, 350 on Pevensey Levels in December 1985 and 355 at Scotney Court Gravel Pit in early 1982.

Both the counts in table 30, and the maxima quoted by Shrubb for the period 1966-76 of 2335 in Chichester Harbour, 360 at Pagham Lagoon, 410 at Darwell Reservoir and 1900 at Rye Harbour, suggest that there has been a significant decline in the wintering population of this species at several sites. This may either be a result of loss of suitable feeding habitat or of milder winters. At Bewl Water, for example, where there was a record count of 2013 in January 1987, numbers have since declined probably as the result of the loss of canadian pondweed following the rapid lowering of water levels necessary to repair hurricane damage. The only site at present that regularly holds wintering numbers comparable to the peak count given in table 30 is Chichester Gravel Pits, a site of national importance (Waters & Cranswick 1993), holding around 1% of the national wintering population.

There have been two recoveries of foreign-ringed Coots in Sussex. One, ringed in the Netherlands in March 1958, was found at Rye Harbour in February 1963 and another, ringed as a chick in Latvia in June 1962, was found dead at Pulborough, 1689 km WSW in January 1963. Of those birds ringed in Sussex, two have been recovered abroad. Singles trapped at Icklesham on 18 July 1989 and 27 November 1990 were found dead in France, the first in the Pas-de-Calais region on 16 February 1991 and the second in Gironde, 632 km south, on 11 December 1990. Of seven birds ringed elsewhere in Britain and controlled/recovered in Sussex, four were from Abberton Reservoir, Essex, two from Dorset and one from St James's Park, London. The longest elapsed period between ringing and recovery was that of a bird ringed at Abbotsbury, Dorset on 23 December 1982 and recovered at Arundel on 12 May 1988.   *Joe Nobbs*

Crane   *Grus grus*

Status:- A rare visitor.

Until 1963 there were only two records for Sussex, one shot on Pevensey Levels in May 1849, which is in the Booth Museum (BoMNH 208191), and another shot at Pagham on 18 October 1854 (des Forges & Harber). An influx into southern England in late October and early November 1963 was, therefore, quite remarkable. The highest numbers were recorded in Sussex, where about 300 but possibly as many as 450 were seen, far exceeding the 50 or more that occurred in Hampshire (Clark & Eyre 1993). The total numbers involved were very difficult to judge as flocks covered large areas during their stay, sometimes appearing twice at the same locality within an hour. It was suspected, for example, that all or most of the birds recorded in the Sidlesham/Selsey area were part of a flock of about 100 that had previously been seen flying north over Stedham on 30 October. The main areas in which the birds were seen were Eastbourne to Lewes, the Adur and Arun Valleys, round Midhurst and East Harting and on the Selsey peninsula.

Additional to those in 1963 referred to above, a total of at least 27 was recorded in the period 1962-94 as follows:

1976: One near Crowborough on 16 April.
1978: One seen in the Ouse Valley near Lewes on 9 April and over Newhaven on 14 and 24 April.

1979:   Two adults at Selmeston on 14 April.
        An immature in the Brede valley from 24 December to at least 10 April 1980.
1982:   A first-winter on Pevensey Levels on 11 January.
        A first-winter on Lewes Brooks from 11 to 20 April.
1984:   Five flying west over Beachy Head on 5 April.
        Two over Combe Haven on 10 April.
        An immature on the Adur Levels at Small Dole from 29 April to 9 May was probably that seen at Herstmonceux on 9 May and at Combe Haven from 15 to 24 May.
1987:   An adult at Thorney Island on 27-28 September.
1989:   An adult flying northwest over Chailey Common on 19 September.
        An adult flying southeast past Selsey Bill on 29 October.
        Three adults at Icklesham on 16 November.
1991:   Two adults on Pevensey Bridge Level on 17-18 April were seen later on 18th at Minsmere, Suffolk.
1993:   Two flying east over Pagham Harbour, Patching and Newhaven on 24 October.
        One over Thorney Island on 11 December roosted overnight at Pulborough Brooks, leaving the next morning. What may have been the same bird was seen at West Wittering on 17 December.
1994:   An adult on the Adur Levels near Steyning from 6 to 10 November when it flew off south.

Although there were invasions of Cranes into Kent in the autumns of 1982 and 1985, none occurred in Sussex, despite most birds being recorded just over the county boundary in the Dungeness area.   *Richard Kelly*

Little Bustard   *Tetrax tetrax*

Status:- Formerly a rare vagrant (12 records but none since 1914).

There are 12 records of single individuals, all from well before 1962. Three occurrences are undated with one in April and two in each of October, November, December and January (des Forges & Harber).

There was an apparent influx in late autumn 1901 with singles shot at Pagham on 28 November, Eastergate on 30 November and Burpham on 16 December. The first, an adult female shot in a turnip field, is in the Booth Museum, as is the last, an adult shot at Wepham Farm (BoMNH 204032 and 204031 respectively). The most recent records were of birds obtained between Willingdon and Polegate on 9 April 1904 and at Goring on 12 January 1914.

There were only 12 records of this species in the British Isles during 1962-94. It has declined dramatically in Europe from early 1950s although populations are showing signs of recovery in some areas (Tucker & Heath 1994). It breeds discontinuously from Iberia and northwest Africa to Central Asia. The closest breeding population, in France, probably winters in Iberia (Dymond, Fraser & Gantlett 1989).   *Richard Fairbank*

Great Bustard   *Otis tarda*

Status:- Resident until about 1825. Otherwise two records but none since 1891.

There is ample evidence that the Great Bustard was once found on the Downs in Sussex although it is not entirely certain when the indigenous stock became extinct in the county. Some authors have suggested that it was as early as 1770 but Walpole-Bond was of the opinion that extinction occurred in the 1820s, a view supported by the presence of nine together in a turnip field above Patcham in 1810.

The only subsequent records have been of singles shot at Ripe on 12 January 1876 and at Pett on 6 January 1891 (des Forges & Harber). *Paul James*

Oystercatcher   *Haematopus ostralegus*

Status:- A scarce breeder, fairly common passage migrant and winter visitor.

The Oystercatcher became extinct as a breeding bird in Sussex about 1890, but re-established itself in the west of the county by about 1905. By 1945, there were two centres of population at opposite ends of the county, and as the Atlas map shows, this remains the situation today, with almost all the tetrads in which breeding was confirmed or probable in the vicinity of Chichester and Pagham Harbours and Rye Harbour. This distribution reflects the availability of suitable habitat that includes sand and shingle beaches, pasture and arable fields.

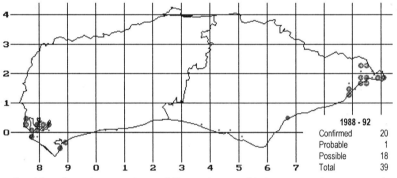

1988 - 92	
Confirmed	20
Probable	1
Possible	18
Total	39

Shrubb referred to maxima of five pairs at Chichester Harbour, 12 pairs at Pagham Harbour, ten pairs at Rye Harbour and two pairs at the Midrips and a total county population of not more than 20-25 pairs. There has since been an increase as shown by totals for the period 1984-92 of 17-27 pairs at Rye Harbour, 7-17 pairs at Pagham Harbour, 8-12 pairs at Chichester Harbour and about ten at other sites, giving a maximum estimate for the county of 66 pairs. This total is not significant when compared to an estimated British population of 33,000-43,000 pairs in the mid-1980s (Piersma 1986), but it is an important part of the sparse and restricted population of southern Britain. Although there has been a great increase in inland breeding in northern Britain, only a few birds nest more than 5 km from the shore in Sussex, these being on the levels of the eastern Rother.

Flocks of non-breeding birds also occur during the summer, with up to 400 recorded in Chichester Harbour, 250 at Rye Harbour and 80 in Pagham Harbour.

In winter, the Oystercatcher is gregarious, occurring mainly on sandy substrates where there are good numbers of marine worms or molluscs.

Flocks build up from July onwards, as birds from northwest Europe arrive to supplement the resident population, but the maximum numbers may occur in any month from September to February (table 34). The estuary counts (table 33) show a population that increased significantly between the early 1970s and early 1980s but has since declined.

	69-74	74-79	79-84	84-89	89-94	Peak counts
Chichester Harbour	868	1298	1626	1308	1253	2002, Sep 1980
Pagham Harbour	262	242	304	374	414	763, Sep 1993
Atherington / Climping	112*	186	285	224*	175	505, Jan 1983
Goring Gap			13*	19**	28*	33, Feb 1993
Adur Estuary					28	86, Feb 1993
Pevensey Bay			21	16*		31, Jan 1987
Glyne Gap				13		25, Jan 1987
Pett Level		108**	88*	72	51	166, Sep 1986
Rye Harbour	333*	415*	561	457	443	699, Jan 1984

Table 33. High tide roost counts of Oystercatchers: five year means of maxima and peak counts, 1969/70 - 93/94.

	Sep	Oct	Nov	Dec	Jan	Feb	Mar
Maximum	2531	2290	2790	2515	2627	2183	1788
Mean	1462	1702	1684	1639	1801	1647	1140
Minimum	97	623	892	916	810	712	413

Table 34. Monthly totals of Oystercatchers, 1974/75 - 93/94.

In spring, there is an eastward passage at coastal sites, the extent of which is masked by birds moving locally. Although totals of 738 flew east and 110 west at Brighton Marina in spring 1984, observations at Worthing suggest that some birds move eastward in the morning and return westward in the evening.

Oystercatchers were recorded inland in seven of the 13 years between 1962 and 1974 and annually thereafter. Apart from a flock of 39 that flew southwest over Ashcombe Bottom during cold weather on 7 January 1982, most have been recorded at Bewl Water (43), Weir Wood Reservoir (41, including 12 on 18 July 1965 and ten on 2 August 1984), Arlington Reservoir

(7) and Darwell Reservoir (6). The cumulative monthly totals of all published inland records for 1962-93 are shown below.

Jan	Feb	Mar	Apr	May	Jun	Jul	Aug	Sep	Oct	Nov	Dec
51	6	11	7	10	1	21	35	6	1	3	2

Sussex-ringed Oystercatchers do not seem to venture far, but a few ringed elsewhere have been recovered in the county. One found dead at Camber in September 1980 had been trapped as an adult in Lincolnshire in August 1975, and another recovered at Bracklesham Bay in December 1980 had been ringed in Cornwall in August 1979. A bird with an orange rump at Selsey Bill on 26 October 1980 had been colour-marked by the Wash Wader Study Group earlier that autumn. A chick ringed in Friesland, Netherlands in June 1961 and found dead at Selsey Bill, 524 km WSW, the following January is the only foreign-ringed Oystercatcher to be recovered in Sussex.

Site fidelity is shown by a leucistic individual first noted at Pilsey Island on January 1989. It returned by 30 July of that year and was also seen in July and December 1990 and January, October and November 1991.   *Dr B J Yates*

Black-winged Stilt   *Himantopus himantopus*

Status:- A rare, mainly spring vagrant.

There were 11 records of 14 individuals prior to 1962 (des Forges & Harber), although three have not been traced. Of these, one was undated, seven were in May, three in September and singles in June, August and December. Three were seen at Rye Harbour on 9 May 1949 and singles at two sites in the Rye area between 20 September and 5 October 1958 were seen together twice.

Since the beginning of 1962 there have been nine records involving at least seven (and possibly 11) individuals:

1978: One at Portfield and Westhampnett Gravel Pits, Chichester on 8 June.
       One, probably the same, at Ternery Pool, Rye Harbour on 11-12 June.
       One, probably the same, at Sidlesham Ferry from 19 to 23 June and from 11 to 18 July.
1984: Two near Boreham Street between 12 and 18 May.
       Two, probably the same, north over Combe Haven on 13 May.
1986: An adult east past Birling Gap on 2 May.
1987: One at Pagham Harbour on 19 May.
       One north over South Malling, near Lewes on 25 May.
1992: One at Bewl Water on 19 May.

Since 1962 all records have been in spring, with six individuals having arrived in May and one in early June. This contrasts with records before 1962 which were more evenly distributed between spring and autumn. Two have been recorded at Pagham Harbour with the other recent occurrences widely scattered. Six have been seen in the Rye area, but only one since 1962.

All three records in 1978 were assumed to relate to the same highly mobile individual which was also seen at Dungeness, Kent on 10, 16-17 and 24 June and 6 July (Rogers *et al* 1979).

There were over 180 records of this striking wader in the British Isles during 1962-94, including a pair which raised two young in Norfolk in 1987.

228

This cosmopolitan species has distinctive races on each continent. Most of the European population winters in sub-Saharan Africa.   *Richard Fairbank*

Avocet   *Recurvirostra avosetta*

Status:- A scarce winter visitor and passage migrant. Has bred.

From 1979 to 1984 up to two pairs of Avocets nested successfully at a site in Chichester Harbour. Two pairs were again present in 1985, but no young hatched, while in 1986 a pair was recorded on 15 March only. In 1987 a pair built a nest but this was destroyed. There have been no subsequent breeding attempts at this site though in 1994 a pair bred at Rye Harbour, but failed due to predation by foxes.

The number of Avocets recorded each year varies considerably. Shrubb documented an increase in spring numbers; this appears to have been maintained as shown by the cumulative monthly totals for the periods 1947-61, 1962-76, 1977-85 and 1986-94:

	Jul	Aug	Sep	Oct	Nov	Dec	Jan	Feb	Mar	Apr	May	Jun
1947-61	2	7	16	2	1	5	-	2	34	16	22	21
1962-76	8	4	1	22	5	39	44	42	65	128	143	49
1977-85	40	48	55	5	22	143	27	27	64	98	148	88
1986-94	48	29	39	25	82	56	32	33	109	264	224	84
Total	98	88	111	54	110	243	103	104	272	506	537	242

From the table it can be seen that numbers at other times of the year have also increased, probably reflecting both improved coverage and the growth of the breeding populations in some northwest European countries (BWP).

In spring, flocks of Avocets are regularly seen passing up-Channel. These are believed to be birds that have wintered in Iberia and tropical West Africa, though very early individuals could be from the population that winters in Devon. Double-figure flocks are not unusual, the largest of which were about 25 off Hove on 16 March 1954, 23 east past Beachy Head on both 13 and 14 April 1971 and 22 off Selsey Bill on 16 April 1989.

Avocets are less frequently recorded in autumn, though some sizeable flocks have occurred at this time of the year, including 21 at Camber on 8 October 1966, 24 at Pagham Harbour on 21 September 1982 and 18 that flew west at Rye Harbour on 26 August 1989. In some years, large flocks have also been seen in November-December, of which 54 flying west off Selsey Bill on 2 December 1982 and about 40 off Newhaven the same day were the largest.

A few Avocets winter in Sussex, mainly in Pagham Harbour, but also in Chichester Harbour. At the former site, where birds have been recorded every winter since 1967/68, counts of up to four are typical, though 12 wintered in 1969/70, up to seven in 1982/83 and six in 1978/79. In Chichester Harbour, where 1-3 were noted in the winters between 1965/66 and 1968/69 and two in February 1977, 1-2 have wintered annually since 1984/85. Few are recorded away from the western harbours in December-February, though singles occasionally occur at coastal sites such as Newhaven Tide Mills, Pett Level and Rye Harbour. One may have wintered in the Camber area in 1984/85.

Between 1962 and 1994, there were inland records totalling 45 birds, at Weir Wood Reservoir (11), Waltham Brooks (7), Chichester Gravel Pits,

Lewes, Stedham (5 each), Arlington Reservoir (4), Arundel WWT, Pulborough Brooks and Bewl Water (2 each), and Amberley, Barcombe Reservoir, and Horse Eye Level (1 each). The most unusual records were those of six that flew south at Waltham Brooks on 11 December 1986 and five seen, by the light of street lamps, over Lewes on the night of 16 September 1974. The cumulative monthly totals of inland records during 1962-94 are shown below.

Jul	Aug	Sep	Oct	Nov	Dec	Jan	Feb	Mar	Apr	May	Jun
1	2	6	-	3	7	-	1	-	4	16	5

Anne de Potier

Stone Curlew   *Burhinus oedicnemus*

Status:- Now a rare passage migrant but formerly a scarce breeding summer visitor and rare winter visitor.

Stone Curlews are one of Britain's rarest and most threatened breeding birds and have been declining since the middle of the last century. This decline has affected Sussex along with the rest of the country but, whereas in the last ten years the population in the two principal areas (Breckland and Wessex) has stabilised, in Sussex the species became extinct in the late 1980s. It was probably still fairly common as a breeding bird in the county at the turn of the century when 12 pairs were nesting at the Midrips alone (Walpole-Bond). Walpole-Bond estimated the population at 60 pairs in 1938, but the species was possibly already in decline by this time. By 1964 the population had fallen to 22-28 pairs; the following year there were 11-13 pairs, and by 1970 there were just eight or nine pairs (Prater 1986a). The decline continued through the 1970s; by 1980 the population was down to two pairs and only a single pair bred in 1981.

Prater (1986a) assumed the species to be extinct in the county as no breeding had been proved since 1981. However, in the late 1980s, a pair with a single chick was seen on the Downs and, as a result, the RSPB organised a thorough survey in 1991. Potentially suitable breeding sites were visited three times (once in the last week of March and then twice in April) during which tape recordings of calling Stone Curlews were played to initiate a response from any birds present. As a result of this survey, one bird was definitely located and another was suspected to be present. The first bird responded positively to tape on the Downs near Shoreham on 26 March, while a brief response was given by a second bird on the Downs near Chichester on 29 March. Further surveys of these areas in 1992 and 1993 failed to elicit any response to tape and the species was once again pronounced extinct in the county (Sinton 1994).

The long-term decline that has occurred in the Stone Curlew population is most likely due to changes in agricultural practices, in particular the large-scale conversion to arable land of the rolling central area of the Downs, which provided the most favoured nesting habitat for the species. The decrease in the intensity of grazing on the remaining downland, due to changes in animal husbandry and the effect of myxomatosis on the rabbit population, and the recent switch from spring sown crops to winter sown cereals both aggravated the decline in the latter years. In fact the absence of sheep and rabbits may be doubly significant as, in addition to keeping the turf short and suitable for nesting birds, their droppings encourage beetles and other invertebrates which may form an important part of the Stone Curlew's diet.

Stone Curlews have very specific habitat requirements in the form of open ground with sparse or short vegetation for feeding and patches of longer (but not too dense) vegetation in which the young can hide after they fledge. They are principally crepuscular and nocturnal feeders and locate their prey by sight; therefore they are unable to feed in areas where the vegetation is more than a few centimetres high. Following the large-scale conversion of the Downs to arable land, many Stone Curlews switched to nesting in fields of spring sown field crops such as beet, kale and maize which have a more open structure than other crops and thus provide better feeding areas for the birds (Sinton 1994). By contrast, winter sown cereals are too tall and dense by mid-March to provide suitable habitat for Stone Curlews and they will not attempt to nest in such areas. It was this switch to winter sown cereals on the Downs that was probably the final cause of the species' extinction in the county (Prater 1986a).

However, it may be that with sympathetic management, Stone Curlews can be encouraged to return to breed in Sussex. The key requirements identified by Sinton (1994) are that the areas of land on the Downs must be closely grazed or remain sparsely vegetated until at least mid-June and that these areas must be close (within 1 km) to good feeding habitat such as closely grazed pasture, rabbit warrens, manured spring sown arable land or pig fields. She also suggests a number of land management initiatives to enable these habitat requirements to be achieved on the Downs. These include promoting higher grazing intensities on chalk grassland areas, encouraging the growing of spring sown field crops rather than winter cereals in arable areas (and the use of farmyard manure on such areas), and promoting the establishment of fallow plots, spring sown game cover plots and grass margins along arable fields.

Stone Curlews formerly arrived in Sussex from mid-March and most breeding birds had arrived by mid-April, although migrants were recorded until late May. The earliest arrival date in the period 1962-94 was 8 March 1969 at West Chiltington. Very few spring migrants were recorded in the 1960s and 1970s, although an exceptional flock of 12 flew over Mile Oak on 27 April 1973.

Prior to 1947, autumn migration was quite pronounced in Sussex, with influxes occurring at any time between late August and November, following which birds often lingered for some time. Walpole-Bond indicated that flocks of 100 or more were not exceptional. However, since 1947 there have only been two such records. A flock of about 50 behind Worthing on 27 September 1955 had built up to 125 by 1 November, after which they departed. Although not of the same magnitude, there was a flock of 27 in the same area on 27 September 1959.

There is no recent indication of wintering, but this has been recorded on a number of occasions in the past, the most seen together being three (des Forges & Harber). A party of 12 seen near Burpham on 1 December 1958 may have comprised overwintering birds but they could also have been very late autumn migrants; this is the most recent county record for December-February.

Since 1981, when regular breeding ceased in Sussex, Stone Curlews have become rare spring and autumn migrants. There has also been a scattering of summer records but none of these have been in suitable breeding habitat. There were only three records in the period 1982-85. With the exception of the breeding pair in the late 1980s, and the bird heard responding to tape near Shoreham in 1991, the following are the only records for the period 1986-94:

1986:   One at Langney Point on 11 September.
1987:   One at Beachy Head on 8 August.
1988:   One at Glyne Gap on 2 October.
1990:   Singles at Beachy Head on 28 May and at Rye Harbour on 3 November.
1991:   One at Rye Harbour on 20 June, one at Pett Level on 29 June and two there on 3 July.
1992:   One at Selsey West Fields on 9 October.
1993:   One at Pett Level on 16 July.
1994:   One at Pagham Harbour on 2 May.

Jon Curson

Collared Pratincole   *Glareola pratincola*

Status:- A very rare vagrant (three records).

One was recorded prior to 1962, being shot at Kingston, near Lewes, on 31 August 1840 (des Forges & Harber). It is in the Booth Museum (BoMNH 204064).

There have been two records since the beginning of 1962:

1978:   One at Ternery Pool, Rye Harbour on 8-9 June.
1987:   One at Pagham Harbour on 4 July.

The former hawked insects over Ternery Pool from dawn to dusk while the latter was seen on the ground and feeding in flight between Sidlesham Ferry and Church Norton for much of the day.

There were nearly 50 records of this tern-like wader in the British Isles during 1962-94. It breeds from Spain to central Asia and in Africa and winters in sub-Saharan Africa, but mainly north of the Equator (Hayman, Marchant & Prater 1986).   *Richard Fairbank*

Oriental Pratincole   *Glareola maldivarum*

Status:- A very rare vagrant (one record).

One at Middle Bridge, Pevensey Levels on 29-30 August 1993 spent most of its time sitting motionless by a small muddy pool just north of the A259. It was possibly the individual that had been present in Norfolk between 14 May and 17 August (Gantlett & Millington 1993, *Brit. Birds* 87: plates 129 and 130). Assuming it to be different, it was the fourth British record of this eastern and southern Asian species. It winters as far south as Australia.   *Richard Fairbank*

Black-winged Pratincole   *Glareola nordmanni*

Status:- A very rare vagrant (one record).

One at Sidlesham Ferry on 14 October 1981 was seen on the ground and in flight for about an hour before departing east.

Single pratincoles seen at the Midrips on 21 August 1955 (Donovan 1958), Selsey Bill on 3 September 1975 and Church Norton on 7 October 1981 and 21 September 1993 were not specifically identified although all were thought most likely to have been Black-winged. It is probable that the individual at Church Norton in 1981 was the Black-winged that was subsequently seen at nearby Sidlesham Ferry a week later.

In the past all the above three species of pratincole have been considered conspecific, hence the 1955 individual was recorded by des Forges & Harber as *G. pratincola.*

During 1962-94 this central Asian species, which migrates to southern and western Africa, was specifically identified in Britain on 22 occasions. It has a generally more northerly breeding distribution than that of Collared Pratincole (Flint, Boehme & Kostin 1984) and it migrates further south.

Richard Fairbank

Little Ringed Plover   *Charadrius dubius*

Status:- A rare breeding summer visitor and scarce passage migrant.

Little Ringed Plovers have colonised Britain since 1938, when a pair bred in Hertfordshire (68-72 BTO Atlas). The first nesting activity in Sussex occurred in 1948, prior to which there were only four county records. In May of that year a pair made a scrape at Chichester Gravel Pits but apparently did not lay eggs. One bird was observed displaying on 13 June but none were seen after 20 June (Parrinder 1949, C M James *in litt.*). The following year two pairs bred at this locality, and from two and six pairs did so annually up to 1955. Between 1950 and 1953 from one to three pairs nested beside Chichester Harbour while in 1956 a pair bred at a new locality in the same general area (des Forges & Harber). Up to five pairs were present annually in the county until 1960 (Shrubb), single pairs bred in 1965 and 1970, the latter unsuccessfully, while another pair possibly did so in 1969.

Since 1970, Little Ringed Plovers have nested in the county regularly, although not every year. The number of pairs recorded in any one year has usually been in single figures, although 11 were present in 1988 and 13 in 1993. The Atlas map not only shows the distribution of breeding records during the Atlas Survey but also, as open circles, additional tetrads where Little Ringed Plovers bred in the period 1976-87. Breeding success is not usually very high and there have only been three years in which the number of young fledged is known to have reached double figures. Of six pairs that bred in 1984, four were successful, raising a total of ten young, while in 1986 five pairs raised 11 young. In 1988, 11 pairs attempted to breed and of these, six raised at least 12 young between them. It should be noted, however, that most breeding sites are private gravel pits and sand pits and that the effort put into confirming breeding has varied widely from year to year. Of nests that

233

have been monitored, reasons for failure have included predation by foxes and drowning of chicks during a heavy rainstorm.

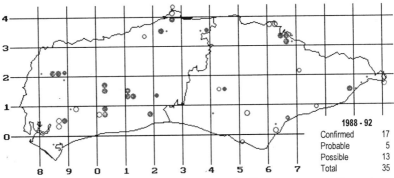

Little Ringed Plovers are early migrants, the first ones generally arriving in early to mid-March. The earliest ever was one at Fishbourne on 6 March 1990 while in other years during 1970-93 first arrivals were recorded up to 26 April, with the average 29 March. Passage in spring is heaviest in April (table 35) though, in some years, migrants have been recorded as late as the first week of June. In the period 1983-93, the average number of spring migrants per year was 22, with a low of 13 in 1988 and a high of 40 in 1990.

	1983	1984	1985	1986	1987	1988	1989	1990	1991	1992	1993	Total
March	2	-	1	-	1	4	6	10	3	2	4	33
April	7	19	11	14	5	10	4	18	8	1	11	108
May	4	18	15	8	10	8	12	12	6	4	8	105
Total	13	37	27	22	16	22	22	40	17	7	23	

	1983	1984	1985	1986	1987	1988	1989	1990	1991	1992	1993	Total
July	12	32	10	38	19	37	40	21	10	17	40	276
August	14	29	28	40	20	31	43	15	15	17	30	282
September	8	5	2	5	5	7	8	5	15	2	10	72
October	5	-	-	-	-	-	-	-	-	-	-	5
Total	39	66	40	83	44	75	91	41	40	36	80	

Table 35. Monthly totals of migrant Little Ringed Plovers, 1983 - 93.

Return passage, which is heavier than that in spring, begins in early July. As the table shows, there is a clear peak in July and August with numbers dropping off rapidly in September. In the period 1983-93, the average number of autumn migrants per year was 58, with a low of 36 in 1992 and a high of 91 in 1989. Interestingly, nearly half of those reported in 1989 were at Icklesham, whereas in other years the number of birds recorded at this site has been significantly lower when compared with the autumn total for the whole county. Flocks reaching double figures are rare but have included 11 at Sidlesham Ferry on 29 July 1989 and 18 at Middle Bridge, Pevensey Levels on 22 July 1993. The latest ever were two at Chichester Gravel Pits on 8 October 1983 compared with an average last date for the period 1970-93 of 21 September.

The only ringing recovery relates to a bird ringed as a chick at Thelford Gravel Pit, Warwickshire in June 1989 and controlled six weeks later at

Icklesham, 214 km southeast. The origin of a colour ringed juvenile seen at Pevensey Levels in mid-August 1988 (among a group of five birds) has not been traced.   *Jon Curson*

Ringed Plover   *Charadrius hiaticula*
Status:- A fairly common breeder, passage migrant and winter visitor.

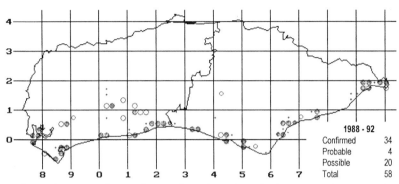

	1988 - 92
Confirmed	34
Probable	4
Possible	20
Total	58

The Atlas map above shows that the Ringed Plover continues to breed along the coast of Sussex, despite increased human disturbance and development on the shingle beaches where it nests. The map also shows that it occurs more widely than other shingle nesting species, such as the Oystercatcher and Little Tern, which are very restricted in their distribution. Of the 38 tetrads where breeding was confirmed or probable, all but three were coastal. The others were at Chichester Gravel Pits and on downland above Findon and Rackham, both habitats that were used more often in the past. This too is demonstrated on the map by open circles representing tetrads where Ringed Plovers were recorded breeding in the years 1976-87 but not during the period 1988-92.

East Sussex	1973	1984	West Sussex	1973	1984
Midrips	1	3	Shoreham Beach	-	9
Northpoint GP area	4	6	Widewater	-	4
Rye Harbour	16	46	Pagham Harbour	16	22
Crumbles	nc	3	Bracklesham Bay	nc	4
Newhaven Tide Mills	2	3	Chichester Harbour	13	23
Brighton Marina	-	3	Chichester GP	10	-
Portslade/Southwick Beach	5	-	Downs	1	-
Downs	1				
Total	29+	64	Total	40+	62

Table 36. Territorial pairs of Ringed Plovers, 1973 and 1984.

The last national survey of Ringed Plovers took place in 1984 and, in Sussex, a total of 128 territorial pairs was located (Prater 1985). The results of this census (table 36) indicated a 76% increase since the previous survey in 1973 (Prater 1976), but most of this increase was accounted for by the growth in the population at Rye Harbour where the use of electric fences (primarily to protect Little Terns) has increased breeding success. The survey also found

235

three pairs holding territory on arable downland, but they did not stay to nest. Most sites where Ringed Plovers nest suffer from disturbance, so it is not surprising that 69% of the pairs located in the 1984 survey were at protected sites. Of the habitats chosen, 83% were on shingle, 12% on sand/shingle, 3% on saltmarsh and 2% on man-made areas.

Prater (1989) estimated that in 1984 some 8480 pairs bred in Britain so the Sussex total at the time represented just 1.5% of the national population.

Outside the breeding season, most Ringed Plovers are found in Chichester and Pagham Harbours, although in winter small numbers are recorded along the whole coast. Counts have shown that numbers build up from late July onwards, reaching a peak between late August and mid-September. A secondary peak is sometimes apparent in November, after which numbers decline through until March when wintering birds probably depart. The estuary counts further show that there has been a steady and dramatic increase in wintering numbers since 1975. Shrubb stated that "it seems unlikely that the county's total wintering population often exceeds some 500 birds" whereas monthly counts (November-January) for the period 1984-92 were rarely below 500 and generally between 800 and 1000. Severe weather may reduce numbers dramatically as in January 1987 when the county total was just 179 (table 38), compared with 951 the previous month and 613 the following month, with the return of less harsh weather. Similarly, very cold weather in early 1985 reduced numbers from 1273 in December 1984 to 517 in January and 502 in February of that year. High tide roost counts at various localities are summarised in table 37.

	69-74	74-79	79-84	84-89	89-94	Peak counts
Chichester Harbour	330	468	488	628	1246	2083, Jan 1990
Pagham Harbour	214	203	256	264	315	477, Sep 1993
Atherington / Climping		24	71	41*	62	114, Dec 1993
Goring Gap		153*	138	255**	148*	328, Dec 1984
Adur Estuary		118*	158	150	280	446, Sep 1992
Newhaven		11*	32	38	27	52, Dec 1985
Cuckmere		23*	39	36	37	70, Dec 1982
Rye Harbour	41*	78*	59	171	79	501, Oct 1984

Table 37. High tide roost counts of Ringed Plovers:
five year means of maxima and peak counts, 1969/70 - 93/94.

	Sep	Oct	Nov	Dec	Jan	Feb	Mar
Maximum	2338	1540	1017	1295	2449	1089	407
Mean	900	763	608	649	760	548	215
Minimum	326	217	119	272	179	120	54

Table 38. Monthly totals of Ringed Plovers, 1974/75 - 93/94.

The British wintering population of Ringed Plover is localised and is internationally important; about 23,000 are present in winter, representing 64% of the European population (Prater in Batten et al 1990). Therefore, the increasing Sussex total is significant, representing 8% of the British wintering population. The localised major concentration in Chichester Harbour is of international importance being, after the Thames, the second most important site in Britain (Waters & Cranswick 1993).

Sea-watching has shown that small numbers of Ringed Plovers pass up-Channel in spring, usually in association with other waders, especially Sanderling. The largest numbers are recorded during May in settled weather, with winds from the east or northeast. At Worthing, totals of 80 were recorded in 1984, 64 in 1986 and 91 in 1988. This passage is also evident in Chichester Harbour where numbers increase from a low in March or April to reach a peak in mid-May. This is demonstrated by counts in 1993 of 174 on 6 March, 59 on 4 April and 562 on 12 May, the latter the highest May total for this site. This spring peak occurs when all local birds have started their breeding season and some may already have young.

Two foreign-ringed birds have been recovered in the county. One ringed at Revtangen, Norway in August 1961 was found dead in Chichester Harbour, 971 km SSW, in September 1962 and another ringed near Copenhagen, Denmark in July 1957 was found dead at Shoreham-by-Sea, 1005 km WSW, in January 1963.

It is likely that some of the birds that pass through Sussex are of the northern race *C.h. tundrae*. There are no recent published records of this race for the county although des Forges & Harber list six, all prior to 1938.

Dr B J Yates

Killdeer   *Charadrius vociferus*

Status:- A very rare vagrant (one record).

A very vocal individual was in fields near Sidlesham Sewage Farm during the late afternoon of 30 March 1974.

There were nearly 40 records of this noisy plover in the British Isles during 1962-94, most in late autumn, winter and early spring. It breeds across North America and the Caribbean and winters south to Peru where there is an isolated breeding population.   *Richard Fairbank*

Kentish Plover   *Charadrius alexandrinus*

Status:- A very scarce spring and autumn passage migrant. Formerly bred.

The Kentish Plover bred regularly in East Sussex until about 1920 and again between 1949 and 1956. It has not bred since, although a party of five, including three fledged juveniles, was seen at Pilsey Island on 17 September 1974, where an adult female had been present on 14 August. The breeding population was always small, and from 1949 onward it consisted of only one or two pairs (des Forges & Harber).

Between 1962 and 1994, a total of about 90 was recorded, with sightings in all but five years (fig. 31).

The earliest in spring was at Newhaven Tide Mills on 17 March 1969 and the latest at Langney Point on 1 June 1991 and at Pilsey Island on 13 June 1990. Singles at Shoreham-by-Sea on 26 June 1989 and Pilsey Island on 26-27 June 1981 were the earliest autumn records while those at Shoreham on 16 October 1991 and 8 November 1982 were the latest. One, first recorded at Worthing on 24 October 1981, remained to overwinter, being seen thereafter at either Goring or Shoreham until 15 March 1982. One at West Wittering on

13 February 1982 was considered to have been a different bird. The only other winter record for the period 1962-94 was of one in Chichester Harbour on 1 and 14 December 1963 although there is an old record for January 1894.

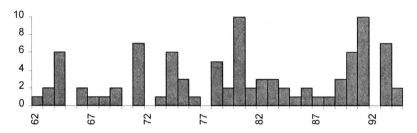

Figure 31. Annual totals of Kentish Plovers, 1962 - 94.

Most records have been of single birds. The largest flocks in recent years, apart from the five in September 1974, were four males at the Midrips on 5 April 1964 and threes at Sidlesham Ferry on 1 May 1980, Shoreham on 21 September 1980 (one remaining until 24th) and at Pilsey Island on 16 September 1993 (two remaining until 17th and one until 19th).

The most favoured localities in the period 1962-94 were Pilsey Island (*ca.* 32 birds), Rye Harbour (13), Shoreham (9), Pagham Harbour/Sidlesham Ferry (9), the Midrips (9) and Cuckmere Haven (7). One flying east past Brighton Marina on 11 May 1980 was unusual and the only inland record was of one at Chichester Gravel Pits on 4 August 1976.

The cumulative monthly totals during 1962-94 are given below.

Jan	Feb	Mar	Apr	May	Jun	Jul	Aug	Sep	Oct	Nov	Dec
1	2	6	24	23	4	5	6	16	6	2	2

In the period 1962-94, an average of 2-3 birds was recorded per year. This is a similar figure to that of 1-3 birds (away from breeding areas) given by des Forges & Harber for the period 1945-61. However, with increased observer activity and improved identification skills, it is likely that there has been a reduction in the number of Kentish Plovers occurring in Sussex. This would accord with the decline in its nearest breeding population on the north-west European coast (BWP).   *Richard Kelly*

Greater Sand Plover   *Charadrius leschenaultii*

Status:- A very rare vagrant (one record).

One present in Pagham Harbour from 9 December 1978 to 1 January 1979 was the first record of this species in Britain (Kitson, Marr & Porter 1980). It was most readily seen on a rising tide in the creek to the east of the Information Centre at Sidlesham Ferry. Sadly, it appeared moribund on the last date and it is likely that it perished in freezing weather.

There were ten records of this large-billed central Asian plover in the British Isles up to the end of 1994. It breeds from Turkey to central China and winters in coastal areas from southern Africa to Australia.   *Richard Fairbank*

Dotterel

Eudromias morinellus

Status:- A very scarce spring and autumn passage migrant; one winter record.

Although Dotterel were more frequent in the 19th century when parties of 20 or more were seen (Shrubb), a total of about 202 was recorded in Sussex in the period 1962-94 (fig. 32). Birds were noted in 26 years, of which 1985, 1986 and 1992 were the best this century.

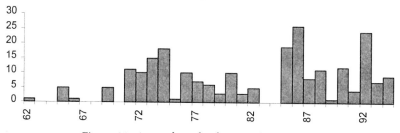

Figure 32. Annual totals of Dotterel, 1962 - 94.

Between 1962 and 1994, all those recorded in spring were either in April or May and, apart from one at Balsdean on 10 October 1981 and four over Beachy Head on 10 October 1993, all those in autumn were in August or September. There have been earlier spring records and the earliest ever relates to several 'secured' at East Blatchington, near Seaford on 22 March 1853. The latest spring record was of one at Newmarket Hill from 26 to 29 May 1991 although one at Pilsey Island on 28 April 1991 also remained until 29 May. The earliest recorded in autumn was at Rye Harbour on 10 August 1978 whereas the latest were one shot at Sidlesham on 10 November 1875 and another, also shot, a few days later in the same year at Earnley. One on fields near Ternery Pool at Rye Harbour from 27 January to 2 February 1992 and again on 22 February is the sole winter record for the county (*Brit. Birds* 85: plate 200).

The most regular site for Dotterel in recent years has been on the Downs between Woodingdean and Rodmell, in the vicinity of Balsdean, where at least 91 birds have been recorded since 1973 (table 39).

Year	Period(s) in which birds seen	Total number of birds
1974	10 September	3
1977	30 August	2
1981	10 October	1
1982	9-10 September	4
1985	28 August-26 September	11
1986	13 August-1 September	11
1987	19 April	3
	29 August-7 September	4
1988	15 April	6
	22-27 August	5
1989	23-29 August	1
1990	30 April	3
	23 August-17 September	4
1991	26-29 May	1
	24 August	1
1992	11 April-6 May	15
	15 August-22 September	8
1993	29 April	1
	10 May	1
1994	10-11 April	1
	23 August	1
	30 August-10 September	4

Table 39. Annual totals of Dotterel in the Balsdean area, 1974 - 94.

The Beachy Head area is another favoured locality. Between 1973 and 1985, there were records in six autumns totalling 25 birds. There were, however, none between 1986 and 1992 but in 1993, there were five.

The largest 'trips' recorded in recent springs were 14 near Balsdean on 29 April 1992 and 11 on Itford Hill from 19 to 22 May 1971. In autumn, there were 12 in a coastal field at Jury's Gap from 23 to 25 August 1986, 11 at Balsdean on 30-31 August 1986 and ten there on 1 September 1985.

The cumulative monthly totals for the period 1962-94 are shown below.

Jan	Feb	Mar	Apr	May	Jun	Jul	Aug	Sep	Oct	Nov	Dec
1	1	-	52	33	-	-	76	60	5	-	-

The breeding population in Scotland may now exceed 800 pairs (Spencer *et al* 1993), a far cry from the 100 pairs estimated at the time of the 68-72 BTO Atlas. As the Dotterel that pass through southern England are thought to belong to either the British or Scandinavian breeding populations (BWP), it may be that the recent increase in the number of birds recorded in Sussex may be linked to the growth of the Scottish population.   *Richard Kelly*

American Golden Plover   *Pluvialis dominica*
Status:- A very rare vagrant (one record).
One was present in stubble fields between Sidlesham Ferry and Church Norton from 14 to 17 September 1988 (Edwards 1989). It usually consorted with *ca.* 100 Golden Plover, flying to roost with them in Pagham Harbour.

There were just over 180 records of this species in the British Isles during 1962-94, so more might have been expected in the county. It breeds on the arctic tundra of North America and winters in central South America. The very closely related Pacific Golden Plover *P. fulva*, which has occurred in Britain 30 times up to the end of 1994 (Rogers *et al* 1995), is a likely candidate to be recorded in the county at some future date.   *Richard Fairbank*

Golden Plover   *Pluvialis apricaria*

Status:- A common winter visitor and passage migrant, rare in summer.

Golden Plovers are well known for their use of traditional wintering grounds, often using the same fields year after year. Grassland is the favoured feeding habitat, which is often shared with flocks of Lapwing and Black-headed Gulls. Permanent pastures are preferred to both leys and arable land, probably because of the higher densities of soil invertebrates on which they feed. However, fields of winter sown cereals and recently ploughed land may also be utilised, as may intertidal areas, especially in harsh weather. In the severest conditions, birds may leave the county completely, though they quickly return when the weather becomes milder. Such was the case in early 1987 when the species was virtually absent from Sussex between 11 January and 1 February. Prior to this, there was a large cold weather movement on 10 January, when 1200 flew north at Scotney Court Gravel Pit, 830 south at Upper Beeding in 2½ hours and 212 southwest at Worthing. A similar movement occurred during cold weather at the beginning of 1985.

Small numbers of birds usually begin to arrive in Sussex from late July onwards. However, the earliest recorded arrival was one at Thorney Deeps on 9 July 1989. Numbers tend to remain low until mid-September and sizeable flocks are present only from mid-October onwards. The largest numbers usually occur from December to February (table 42). There is a decline in March as birds return to their breeding grounds. There may, however, be an influx of migrants in late March and early April, as shown by counts of 361 at Thorney Deeps on 5 April 1989 and 221 at Pagham on 5 April 1988. These birds, which have presumably wintered further south, tend to be of the northern form which breeds predominantly in Iceland, northern Scandinavia and Russia (Hayman, Marchant & Prater 1986). Most have left by mid-April and few are seen between late May and mid-July. Shrubb referred to records of three at the Midrips on 21 June 1937 and singles at Hamsey from 16-30 June 1954, at Pagham on 9 June 1968 and Sidlesham Ferry on 13 and 21 June 1975. More recently, up to three were recorded in the Sidlesham Ferry area between 2 May and 31 July 1977 while in 1978, up to six summered in the Pagham Harbour area.

In winter the largest numbers are to be found on the Selsey peninsula, Pevensey Levels and in the Rye area. Counts at these sites sometimes exceed 2000 but totals of 500-1500 are more common. A maximum of 5300 was recorded at Pevensey Levels in February 1977 but this was exceptional as no other total of this magnitude has been recorded at this or any other site in the county. Co-ordinated counts were made in the winters of 1976/77 and 1977/78, as part of the BTO Wintering Golden Plover Survey, the results of which are summarised in table 40. These can be compared with the BoEE counts summarised in table 41.

	8-9 January 1977	27 November 1977	1 January 1978	5 February 1978
Selsey peninsula	1860	539	2124	1353
Ford Airport	nc	182	33	0
Adur Levels	11	1	0	0
Glynde/Ringmer	nc	nc	320	350
Pevensey Levels	2800	1100	850	1300
Pett Level, Winchelsea & Rye Harbour	490	293	437	500
Camber	405	383	2213	737
Total	5566	2498	5977	4240

Table 40. Co-ordinated counts of Golden Plovers, winters 1976/77 and 1977/78.

	69-74	74-79	79-84	84-89	89-94	Peak counts
Chichester Harbour	643	871	1087	1830	1657	2441, Jan 1986
Pagham Harbour	132	270	532	497	657	1077, Feb 1992
Pevensey Level	800**	2483*	1306	913*	190**	5300, Feb 1977
Pett Level		420	575	81	44	1000, Dec 1978
Rye Harbour		459*	441	510	526	1200, Feb 1988

Table 41. Five year means of winter maxima and peak counts of Golden Plovers, 1969/70 - 93/94.

	Sep	Oct	Nov	Dec	Jan	Feb	Mar
Maximum	766	1449	3781	4133	3651	5823	2701
Mean	202	409	1163	1587	1757	1507	710
Minimum	1	1	37	188	5	26	0

Table 42. Monthly totals of Golden Plovers, 1974/75 - 93/94

Although coverage has been variable, the records suggest a total wintering population for the county of 4000-7000 birds, with no evidence of any long term change. This compares with a British wintering population of 200,000-300,000 (Winter Atlas).

Ringing data suggests that birds wintering in southern England are largely of Scandinavian and Russian origin. British breeding birds tend to move to lowland habitat adjacent to their breeding areas (BWP). A bird shot at Pevensey Levels on 18 January 1986 had been ringed at Slijoe, West Vlaanderen, Belgium on 3 November 1985.   *Joe Nobbs*

Grey Plover   *Pluvialis squatarola*

Status:- A common winter visitor and passage migrant.

The British wintering population of Grey Plover originates from breeding areas on lowland tundra between the White Sea and the Taimyr Peninsula in western Siberia. However, birds from this area have an extremely wide wintering range which extends as far south as tropical West Africa (Branson & Minton 1976).

In non-breeding habitat, Grey Plovers feed in the intertidal zone, utilising areas of mud flats, saltings, islets and sandy beaches, where their diet consists of a variety of marine invertebrates. Because they are visual feeders, they need to forage on undisturbed areas in order to be successful. They tend, therefore, to be solitary in habit and are only seen in flocks at roosting sites, in the company of other waders, at high water (Winter Atlas).

The annual migration pattern is complex. Mostly immature non-breeding birds begin to arrive during the last half of July. These are followed by adults in full summer plumage in August. Numbers continue to increase with the arrival of juveniles from late August through to October. In November, after moulting, some adults and juveniles continue their migration to southwest Europe and West Africa, while others stay for the winter. At this time, additional birds also arrive from mainland Europe (Winter Atlas). This continual movement, which results in considerable fluctuations in monthly totals, makes assessing the size of the wintering population difficult. In most years, the largest numbers are recorded in September-October but the peak count may also occur in mid-winter or in March (table 44). In harsh weather, birds may be displaced from their normal feeding areas. Such was the case in January 1987 when a total of 111 flew west at Worthing including 63 on 11th.

The largest numbers occur in Chichester Harbour, which is a site of international importance for this species (Waters & Cranswick 1993), currently holding approximately 5% of the British wintering population, and in Pagham Harbour (table 43). The increase in numbers that has occurred at these sites reflects the increase in the northwest European wintering population (Smit & Piersma 1989). Reasons advanced for this growth include a succession of mild winters that have allowed birds to survive at the northern limit of their wintering range, successful breeding seasons and the imposing of various hunting bans over the last two or three decades (Rehfisch & Waters 1995).

	69-74	74-79	79-84	84-89	89-94	Peak counts
Chichester Harbour	1311	1530	1604	2352	2215	3901, Mar 1992
Pagham Harbour	199	295	552	979	815	1266, Dec 1982
Atherington / Climping		61	77	66	75	151, Dec 1993
Goring		79*	116	175**	142*	230, Feb 1984
Pett Level		40*	75*	65	55	135, Jan 1993
Rye Harbour	25*	39*	6*	39	16	70, Mar 1985

Table 43. High tide roost counts of Grey Plovers: five year means of maxima and peak counts, 1969/70 - 93/94.

	Sep	Oct	Nov	Dec	Jan	Feb	Mar
Maximum	3438	4180	3888	3747	2533	3509	4319
Mean	1935	1914	1969	1834	1771	1853	1947
Minimum	920	1034	822	784	714	901	1052

Table 44. Monthly totals of Grey Plovers, 1974/75 - 93/94.

Moderate numbers pass up-Channel in spring, as shown by the monthly totals recorded at Worthing in the period 1978-93:

	Jul	Aug	Sep	Oct	Nov	Dec	Jan	Feb	Mar	Apr	May	Jun
Flying west	-	157	111	151	124	126	148	35	47	36	83	12
Flying east	-	2	25	41	56	12	33	35	172	583	3075	4

The largest spring total for the county was that of 744 recorded at Worthing in 1993 while the largest movement in a single day was of 398, also at Worthing, on 7 May 1981. As the bulk of the local wintering population has dispersed by May, it is likely that those recorded in late spring have wintered further south in Africa. Grey Plovers tend to migrate in settled weather with winds from the southeast, usually in small flocks averaging five or in flocks of other wader species (Newnham 1985). Occasionally larger flocks are recorded such as those of 70 at Beachy Head on 3 May 1977 and 80 that passed both Worthing and Brighton on 11 May 1982.

A few birds summer regularly in Chichester and Pagham Harbours. These are mostly in winter plumage and presumably are immature non-breeders. Numbers vary from year to year but as many as 250 were recorded in Chichester Harbour on 20 June 1986.

Inland records are comparatively rare but have become more frequent since the 1970s, probably due to the increase in the northwest European wintering population. Between 1962 and 1993, a total of about 74 was recorded, at Arlington Reservoir (25), Bewl Water (14), West Chiltington (8), Weir Wood Reservoir (6), Lewes Brooks (5), Waltham Brooks (4), Crawley and Pulborough Brooks (3 each), Amberley Wild Brooks and Chichester Gravel Pits (2 each), and Ardingly and Barcombe Reservoirs (1 each). The cumulative monthly totals are shown below.

Jul	Aug	Sep	Oct	Nov	Dec	Jan	Feb	Mar	Apr	May	Jun
-	5	17	16	3	11	7	-	3	4	8	-

Joe Nobbs

Sociable Plover *Chettusia gregaria*

Status:- A very rare vagrant (two records).

First recorded in 1978, two individuals have been seen:

1978: One, probably an adult, opposite Chilver Bridge Farm, Arlington on 9-10 October.

1985: A juvenile moulting into first-winter plumage on the Downs near Steyning from 31 October moved onto the lower Adur Levels and Shoreham Airport from 9 November to 3 January 1986 (Newnham 1986a).

Both, as with most seen in Britain, consorted with Lapwing.

There were just over 30 records of this splendid central Asian plover in the British Isles during 1962-94. It winters from Sudan to Pakistan.

Richard Fairbank

Lapwing *Vanellus vanellus*

Status:- A fairly common but decreasing breeder and very common winter visitor.

In recent years there has been a fall in the number of Lapwings breeding nationally, with the most marked decline in southeast England (Shrubb & Lack 1991). Walpole-Bond recorded a steady decrease in the county from about 1885 to 1937, which des Forges & Harber noted as continuing. Shrubb reported that the severe winter of 1962/63 seriously depleted the breeding stock and that a further very sharp decline occurred after 1968. The Atlas map, which shows the breeding distribution in the period 1988-92, and also those tetrads where breeding was recorded between 1976 and 1987 but not

244

subsequently, confirms that there has been a 22% reduction in the number of tetrads holding breeding birds compared to 1976-87.

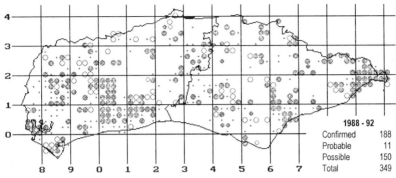

It is not possible to make an estimate of the size of the present breeding population from available records but the wetlands in the county were surveyed in 1982 as part of the Wet Meadows Wader Survey. Altogether 399 pairs were counted on 4992 ha of marsh, a figure that suggests a county population of considerably less than 1000 pairs. This total would be subject to considerable fluctuation from year to year if the changing fortunes of Lapwings at Rye Harbour (fig. 33) are representative of the county as whole. Even more unpredictable is breeding success. In a wet spring few chicks survive. For example, in both 1986 and 1987, 22 pairs nested at Rye Harbour but none were successful in rearing young.

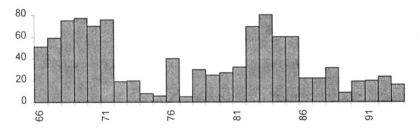

Figure 33. Annual totals of breeding pairs of Lapwings at Rye Harbour, 1966 - 93.

The favoured breeding habitat is mixed farmland where Lapwings show a preference for nesting in spring sown cereal crops with adjacent grass fields for feeding (Shrubb & Lack 1991). This habitat is in increasingly short supply in the county and most pairs are forced to seek alternatives (Shrubb 1985). The most important breeding areas are around Chichester and Pagham Harbours, the Arun Valley, especially Amberley Wild Brooks and Pulborough Brooks, Pevensey Levels, Pett Level and Rye Harbour. Lapwings also nest on downland, with the main concentration to the north of Worthing in the Cissbury/Chanctonbury area. The species' ability to adapt is illustrated by a report in 1969 of 14 pairs nesting in 1.2 ha of kale at Burpham.

Post-breeding flocks of 100-200 begin to gather in June or more occasionally in late May. Outside the breeding season, Lapwings show a preference for wet areas but they may also feed in autumn sown cereal crops. Particularly favoured as winter roosts and feeding areas are the coastal plain and lower river valleys where flocks of several thousand are commonplace. When Glynde Levels was allowed to flood during the winter months, large flocks gathered there, with 10,000-20,000 reported on several occasions in the 1960s and 1970s. More recently, water levels at this site have been subject to stricter control, and consequently only small flocks are now recorded. A count of 700 in February 1982 was the largest in recent years.

Wintering flocks increase in size from October to December as local birds are joined by continental immigrants. In most years, the largest numbers are present in December and January but drop rapidly from mid-February onwards. In January-February 1977, it was estimated that there was a minimum of 59,900 in the county made up of 24,402 recorded in the coastline wader count on 22 January and at least a further 35,500 elsewhere during that general period. This total appears to have been exceptional, given that in a typical winter half this number are present. Counts at the main localities are summarised in table 45.

	69-74	74-79	79-84	84-89	89-94	Peak counts
Chichester Harbour	1146	2359	2692	2749	3048	4071, Feb 1994
Pagham Harbour	282	899	1831	1407	1800	3250, Jan 1990
Atherington / Climping		88*	974	1109*		2300, Nov 1984
Adur Estuary		413*	1230	2949	1286	9000, Dec 1984
Newhaven		412*	1150	1150	1222	3000, Jan 1983
Cuckmere Valley		1025*	1156	1070	650	2600, Nov 1984
Pevensey Bay		11750**	7900	11000**		26000, Jan 1979
Pett Level		3625*	1602*	1235	1397	10000, Dec 1978
Rye Harbour	470*	2800*	1877	1797	2649	4000, Jan 1990

Table 45. Five year means of maxima and peak counts of Lapwings, 1969/70 - 93/94.

Numbers decrease rapidly with the onset of harsh weather, sometimes to such an extent that very few remain in the county. This is because Lapwings are unable to feed when the ground is frozen or snow covered. Under these conditions, spectacular cold weather movements may be observed, as on 31 December 1978, when 40,000 were estimated to have flown out to sea and a further 5000 flew in off the sea in the Shoreham area (Welfare 1979).

Return movements are sometimes noted in February or March but these are never on the same scale as autumn and cold weather movements.

Only a few Lapwings are ringed in Sussex, mainly as chicks. Of 21 recoveries, ten were in southern England, six in France, three in Spain and singles in Portugal and Morocco. All were in the winter months except the Moroccan bird which was recovered in August, so confirming that some Sussex-bred birds winter in France and Iberia. The origins of Lapwings wintering in Sussex are shown by the recovery of eight foreign-ringed birds, from Belgium (2), Germany (2) and France, the Netherlands, Sweden and the USSR (1 each). The latter, ringed as a chick at Kaliningrad in 1913 in the pioneer days of organised ringing schemes, was killed near Chichester, 1499 km away, in 1916. The Dutch ringed bird was 12 years old when found dead at Pulborough in January 1985.   *Robin T Pepper*

Knot   *Calidris canutus*

Status:- A common winter visitor and fairly common passage migrant.

The first Knot arrive in Sussex from early July onwards. Numbers then build up gradually, reaching an autumn peak in September, when birds from north-central Siberia pass through the county 'en route' to their wintering grounds in West Africa (BWP). The numbers involved are typically small as shown by maxima in recent years of 95 in Chichester Harbour in September 1993, 87 in Pagham Harbour on 27 September 1992, 53 at Rye Harbour on 1 September 1988 and 29 at Pett Level Pools on 10 September 1984. Visible movements in autumn are infrequently recorded; exceptions have included 250 at Rye Harbour on 19 August 1970, 500 at Pett on 15 August 1982, 120 at Climping on 12 August 1985 and 200 at Worthing the following day, all flying west or southwest.

In winter, the Knot is the most restricted of the commoner waders and only in Chichester and Pagham Harbours is it recorded regularly (table 46).

	69-74	74-79	79-84	84-89	89-94	Peak counts
Chichester Harbour	887	921	991	734	1911	3000, Jan 1993
Pagham Harbour	9	9	4	66	59	161, Jan 1985

Table 46. Five year means of maxima and peak counts of Knot, 1969/70 - 93/94.

	Sep	Oct	Nov	Dec	Jan	Feb	Mar
Maximum	139	310	1350	2556	3001	1620	650
Mean	25	232	383	633	744	556	196
Minimum	2	0	5	1	25	40	1

Table 47. Monthly totals of Knot, 1969/70 - 93/94.

The highest numbers are present from November to February (table 47) followed by a marked decrease in March as birds depart for their breeding grounds in northeast Canada and Greenland. Although the number of Knot wintering in Europe since the late 1960s has declined by *ca*. 50% (BWP), it appears that there has been a genuine increase in the number visiting Sussex. Although the peak count in each winter period has fluctuated widely, the total of 3000 in Chichester Harbour in January 1993 is the largest recorded at this locality, so far. The significance of this wintering population is, however, limited when compared to the 430,000 estimated to winter in Atlantic Europe in a normal year (BWP). Away from the Chichester and Pagham Harbours, the species is scarce in winter, but small numbers may occur along the coast, particularly during harsh weather. In January 1987, for example, there were up to nine at Langney Point, two at Rye Harbour and singles at Littlehampton, Newhaven Tide Mills and Shoreham.

Regular sea-watching has revealed that some Knot pass up-Channel each spring. These are believed to be birds returning to their breeding grounds in Siberia from West Africa. The number recorded each year is very variable but it is clear that most are seen during periods of east or northeast winds. Very large numbers occurred in 1990, when 2207 passed Splash Point, Seaford, 2170 between the 2 and 5 May including 1173 on 4th. By contrast, 1991 was a very poor year with just 94 recorded at Seaford, of which only 36 were in May. A few birds summer most years, mainly in the western harbours and at Rye Harbour.

Knot are almost exclusively found on or near the coast. The only inland record prior to 1962 was of one killed at Slinfold on 30 January 1907. Between 1962 and 1993, about 33 were recorded. These were at Bewl Water and Weir Wood Reservoir (10 each), Arlington Reservoir and Glynde (4 each), Barcombe Reservoir and Chichester Gravel Pits (2 each) and Pulborough Brooks (1). Most were recorded on one day only though a single bird remained at Weir Wood Reservoir from 22 September to 2 October 1983. The cumulative monthly totals were as follows:

Jul	Aug	Sep	Oct	Nov	Dec	Jan	Feb	Mar	Apr	May	Jun
-	1	14	3	1	2	4	-	4	4	1	-

Paul James

Sanderling   *Calidris alba*

Status:- A fairly common winter visitor and passage migrant.

Sanderling breed mainly well within the Arctic Circle in the extreme north of Alaska, Canada, Greenland, Svalbaard and Siberia. Due to the high latitude, their breeding season is necessarily very short with around eight weeks between peak arrivals and departures (Prater 1981). Adults leave the breeding grounds between mid-July and mid-August, while juveniles follow in late August and early September. Birds from northeast Canada, Greenland and Siberia pass through Britain on migration. Some of these stay to winter while others continue as far as South Africa (Hayman, Marchant & Prater 1986).

The main wintering site for Sanderling in Sussex is Chichester Harbour, where sufficient numbers occur for it to qualify as a site of national importance for the species (see below). The normal high tide roosting area is on Pilsey Island though in recent years a large proportion of the flock has occasionally roosted at Black Point, Hampshire. Birds disperse from the roosts to various feeding areas, eastward along the Sussex coast, across Spithead to Ryde Sands on the Isle of Wight and westward into Hampshire (Clark & Eyre 1993). Other favoured areas are the sandy shores between Middleton and Worthing and between Pett and Camber. The Sanderling is probably the most confusing species of wader in Sussex, in that its numbers vary wildly between sites and months. This reflects its high degree of mobility. Totals in some months even suggest that the main flock has not been counted (Prater 1981), as shown by counts for Chichester Harbour of just three in January 1985, one in February 1986 and four in January 1991.

Autumn migrants begin to appear in small numbers from about the second week of July, building up rapidly during the following weeks, to reach an autumn peak usually in September but occasionally in October. However, large counts recorded from Chichester Harbour of 559 in November 1981 and 601 in November 1987 suggest that passage may continue into November. In most years however, the largest numbers occur later in the winter (table 49). Nationally, in 1992, the January index for Sanderling rose for the fourth successive year to reach its highest recorded level (Cranswick, Kirby & Waters 1992). Unfortunately, this was not reflected in Sussex where recent counts in

248

winter at the main localities indicate that a marked decline has taken place (table 48). Increased recreational disturbance of these areas may be to blame. Sites which regularly hold 230 or more Sanderling in winter are considered to be of national importance for the species (Waters & Cranswick 1993).

	69-74	74-79	79-84	84-89	89-94	Peak counts
Chichester Harbour	325	317	410	401	279	600, Mar 1985
Pagham Harbour	64	30	11	26	13	132, Mar 1978
Atherington / Climping	355*	216	236	150*	75*	408, Jan 1972
Goring Gap	114*	186*	80	145**	109*	300, Jan 1973
Rye Harbour	46*	126	134	140	99	290, Jan 1985

Table 48. Five year means of maxima and peak counts of Sanderling, 1969/70 - 93/94.

	Sep	Oct	Nov	Dec	Jan	Feb	Mar
Maximum	502	452	820	673	752	788	722
Mean	218	180	283	209	375	311	364
Minimum	1	0	0	37	132	52	19

Table 49. Monthly totals of Sanderling, 1974/75 - 93/94.

Sanderling are regularly recorded passing up-Channel in spring, as shown by the monthly totals recorded at Worthing in the period 1978-93:

	Jul	Aug	Sep	Oct	Nov	Dec	Jan	Feb	Mar	Apr	May	Jun
Flying west	5	99	38	74	11	19	21	3	80	127	606	10
Flying east	2	-	4	23	-	3	-	-	261	1122	5634	71

Passage gradually increases throughout April and is heaviest in the first half of May although migration is still evident in early June (Newnham 1985). The most recorded in any one spring was 1101 at Worthing in 1993, while the most seen in one day was 277, also at Worthing, on 10 May 1993. Interestingly, a detailed study of the spring migration of Sanderling through Britain in 1979 (Ferns 1980) suggested that passage through east and southeast England was at a maximum in April rather than May, a finding supported by the largest spring count recorded at Pilsey Island of 700 on 19 April 1988.

A few non-breeders remain throughout the summer.

Inland, Sanderling are rare. Between 1962 and 1993, about 36 were recorded. These were at Arlington Reservoir (20, including 8 on 2 September 1976), Chichester Gravel Pits (9, including 5 on 22 May 1976), Weir Wood Reservoir (2), and Amberley Wild Brooks, Bewl Water, Lewes Brooks, Stedham and Waltham Brooks (1 each). The cumulative monthly totals were as follows:

Jul	Aug	Sep	Oct	Nov	Dec	Jan	Feb	Mar	Apr	May	Jun
-	4	14	-	1	-	-	1	-	2	13	1

Some evidence of the movements of Sanderling has been provided by sightings of marked birds. In spring 1985, the Merseyside Ringing Group took part in an international project to study the spring passage of waders, by colour-marking Sanderling on the Alt and Ribble estuaries. One of these birds was seen in Chichester Harbour on 21 July 1985 and up to three at Rye Harbour between 27 July and 12 August 1988. Another bird, colour-ringed in

Iceland in late May 1989, was seen roosting at Pilsey on 26 July and 1 August 1989 and from 3 to 29 September 1990. These birds almost certainly originate from the breeding population in northeast Greenland. The sighting of a colour-dyed bird in Ghana indicates that some or all of this population winter in tropical West Africa. National ringing data suggests that those wintering in Sussex may be of Siberian origin (BWP). *Joe Nobbs*

Semipalmated Sandpiper *Calidris pusilla*

Status:- A very rare vagrant (one record).

One was present at Rye Harbour from 2 to 4 August 1986. It could have been more obliging in its behaviour in that it usually gave only distant views, spending most of its time at the back of Ternery Pool.

There were just over 70 records of this stout-billed stint in the British Isles during 1962-94, most since 1980. It breeds on the arctic tundra of North America and winters on the coasts from central America south to Peru and Brazil. *Richard Fairbank*

Little Stint *Calidris minuta*

Status:- A passage migrant, scarce in autumn and very scarce in spring; a few winter in most years.

Little Stints are most regularly recorded at localities on or near the coast including Chichester and Pagham Harbours, Sidlesham Ferry, the River Adur at Shoreham-by-Sea, Newhaven Tide Mills, Cuckmere Haven, Pett Level Pools and Rye Harbour. Although they most often frequent the muddy margins of freshwater or brackish pools, they can also be found on estuarine mudflats. They are most numerous in autumn as the following table of cumulative monthly totals for the periods 1962-76 and 1977-93 shows.

	Jan	Feb	Mar	Apr	May	Jun	Jul	Aug	Sep	Oct	Nov	Dec
1962-76	10	7	13	6	36	6	34	162	307	100	13	13
1977-93	14	9	18	18	68	32	80	279	813	352	31	22
Total	24	16	31	24	104	38	114	441	1120	452	44	35

Returning adults arrive from late June onwards but numbers begin to increase from late August when the main passage, consisting of mostly juveniles, commences. The peak counts occur in September with numbers decreasing in October and a few lingering into November. Most are seen in ones and twos but parties of up to six are not uncommon and groups of seven to 13 are occasionally noted. Exceptional counts in autumn have included 26 at Pilsey Island on 9 September 1988, 34 there on 19 September 1990 and 46 on 17 September 1993, 31 at Sidlesham Ferry on 8 September 1993, 26 there 11 September 1978 and 31 at Pett Level the following day. In 1960, when an exceptional influx of 200-300 occurred, there were 31 at Sidlesham Ferry on 25 September and a maximum of 70 at the Midrips from 29 September to 1 October. The only autumn comparable to this in the period 1962-93 was 1993 when 215 were recorded. Although numbers appear to be increasing slowly (fig. 34), they are very variable and may reflect the incidence of easterly winds in which birds drift westwards from their normal migration routes from Scandinavia and Siberia, where they breed, to sub-Saharan Africa.

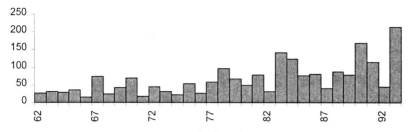

Figure 34. Autumn totals of Little Stints, 1962 - 93.

Small numbers of Little Stints, usually between one and three, winter in most years but they may easily be overlooked in the large flocks of Dunlin with which they may associate. The most favoured locality is Chichester Harbour where maxima have included 11 at Thorney Island on 27 December 1960 and five at the same locality on 5 December 1973. Other wintering individuals have occurred at Shoreham-by-Sea, Pett Level and Rye Harbour.

Only a few Little Stints, up to a dozen annually, are seen on spring passage. Most records for April probably relate to wintering individuals as the main movement occurs from early to mid-May and sometimes into June. The highest count was of four at Sidlesham Ferry on 22 May 1984, but single birds are much more usual. A party of five at Pett Level Pools on 17 June 1992 may have been late spring migrants or early autumn arrivals.

Inland records have come from Arlington, Darwell and Weir Wood Reservoirs, Arundel WWT, Chichester Gravel Pits, Gatwick and Waltham Brooks.

One bird ringed at the Midrips in September 1960 was found dead exactly one month later in Charente-Maritime, France, 592 km SSW.   *Chris Janman*

Temminck's Stint   *Calidris temminckii*

Status:- A very scarce spring and autumn passage migrant.

About eight were recorded between 1880 and 1946 and a further 19 between 1947 to 1961 (des Forges & Harber). Since then, there have been records in 28 years up to 1994, totalling 95 individuals (fig. 35). It is likely that increased observer activity and improving identification skills are responsible, at least in part, for this increase which has been reflected in Britain as a whole. Favoured localities in the period 1962-94 included Sidlesham Ferry (28 birds), Rye Harbour (14), Pett Level (12) and the lower Cuckmere Valley (12), reflecting the species preference for smaller muddy pools and puddles, rather than large open areas of mud. Inland records for the same period were at Arlington Reservoir (3), Weir Wood Reservoir (2), Waltham Brooks (2) and Arundel WWT, Chichester Gravel Pits and Darwell Reservoir (1 each).

Most are seen singly but occasionally two or three have occurred together. Exceptional parties of seven were recorded at Sidlesham Ferry on 7 May 1981 and in the lower Cuckmere Valley near Exceat Bridge on 8 May 1993.

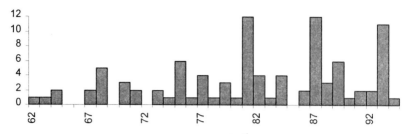

Figure 35. Annual totals of Temminck's Stints, 1962 - 94.

Apart from one at Thorney Island from 19 March to 9 April 1975, all spring records were in the period 1 May (1954, Rye Harbour) to 7 June (shot near Worthing, 1852), with most in mid to late May. Autumn records covered the period 5 July (1952, Rye Harbour) to 21 October (1975, Sidlesham Ferry), the latter having been present since 23 September.

One which overwintered at Thorney Island from 20 December 1975 to 15 February 1976 was possibly that recorded at the same site in March-April 1975, in which case it may have been there undetected since late 1974. There have been no other instances of overwintering in Sussex, although one is said to have been shot near Chichester about 20 December 1876.

The cumulative monthly totals for the period 1962-94 are shown below.

May	Jun	Jul	Aug	Sep	Oct	Nov	Dec	Jan	Feb	Mar	Apr
58	1	3	22	13	1	-	1	1	1	1	1

The Temminck's Stint breeds across northern Europe into Russia and winters in tropical Africa, extending just south of the Equator.   *Richard Kelly*

Least Sandpiper   *Calidris minutilla*
Status:- A very rare vagrant (two records).
First recorded in 1984, there have been two records:

1984:   An adult at Pett Level Pools on 28 July was present until dusk but had gone the following day (*Brit. Birds 77*: plate 240).
1995:   An adult at Sidlesham Ferry from 19 to 25 July (*Birding World* 8: plate 245).

There were nearly 30 records of this tiny yellow-legged stint in the British Isles during 1962-94. It breeds across North America and winters from southern USA to central South America.   *Richard Fairbank*

White-rumped Sandpiper   *Calidris fuscicollis*
Status:- A very rare autumn vagrant (ten records).
Four were recorded prior to 1962: one shot in company with a Red-necked Phalarope in a flooded meadow at Bexhill on 8 October 1857, one shot at Eastbourne on 12 November 1870, an adult at the Midrips from 30 August to 19 September 1948 (Blake, Blake & Cawkell 1949) and one at the western end of Thorney Great and Little Deeps and in Emsworth Channel from 9 to 28 November 1959 (des Forges & Harber).

Since the beginning of 1962 there have been six records:

1974: An adult at Sidlesham Ferry from 24 to 28 August.
1979: A juvenile at Pett Level Pools from 28 September to 3 October.
1981: An adult at Sidlesham Ferry from 1 to 15 August moved into Pagham Harbour at low tide.
1987: A juvenile at Sidlesham Ferry from 25 to 28 October.
1990: An adult at Sidlesham Ferry from 20 to 26 August (*Brit. Birds* 84: plate 72).
1993: One at Pett Level Pools on 19 September was only seen briefly on the ground and was consequently not aged.

All have been in autumn, with four arriving in August and two in each of September, October and November. All but one of those that were allowed to, stayed for at least four days. Sidlesham Ferry is the most favoured locality having hosted four of the last six records. The others were at Pett Level Pools.

There were over 325 records of this species in the British Isles during 1962-94. It breeds on the arctic tundra of North America and winters in coastal southern South America.   *Richard Fairbank*

Baird's Sandpiper   *Calidris bairdii*

Status:- A very rare autumn vagrant (six records).

One was recorded prior to 1962, on the Kent/Sussex border at the Wicks from 19 to 27 September 1952 (Fluke 1953, *Brit. Birds* 46: plates 44-46). It was the fourth British record.

Since the beginning of 1962 there have been five records:

1968: One at Northpoint Beach, Rye on 8 and 10 September.
1973: One at Arlington Reservoir from 11 to 18 September.
1978: An adult at the Long Pit, Rye Harbour on 23 July.
1981: An adult at Widewater, Lancing Beach on 18-19 August.
1989: A juvenile at Pett Level Pools on 17 September.

All have been in autumn, with one each in July and August and four in September. Rye Harbour has produced two records but, perhaps rather surprisingly, only one has been recorded in West Sussex. None have been seen at Sidlesham Ferry, perhaps reflecting the species' preference for drier habitats. The July record is one of the earliest to be reported in Britain in autumn.

There were nearly 170 records of this scaly wader in the British Isles during 1962-94. It breeds on the high arctic tundra of North America and winters inland in southern South America, often beside Andean lakes.

                    Richard Fairbank

Pectoral Sandpiper   *Calidris melanotos*

Status:- A rare vagrant, mainly in autumn (46 records).

Eleven were recorded prior to 1962: two arriving in August, five in September and four in October. The earliest were two at the Cuckmere Haven oxbows from 29 August to 1 September 1948 and the latest one at Sidlesham Ferry from 6 to 20 October 1957. Other records include two together at Thorney Island on 12 October 1947 (Ferguson-Lees 1948b) and singles there from 26 September to 3 October 1948 and on 2 October 1949.

Since the beginning of 1962 there have been a further 35 records and the species has been recorded in 17 of the last 21 years (fig. 36).

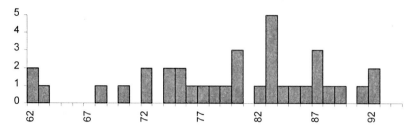

Figure 36. Annual totals of Pectoral Sandpipers, 1962 - 94.

Three have been recorded in spring, singles at Cuckmere Haven on 14 May 1977 and 18 May 1980 and at Pevensey Bridge Level from 11 to 14 May 1987. The earliest in autumn were in 1987, at Arundel WWT on 18 July and at Pett Level Pools from 24 July to 4 August while the latest were at Horse Eye Level on 16 October 1992 and one trapped at Selsey Sewage Farm on 2-3 November 1963. Most, however, were found in September (fig. 37).

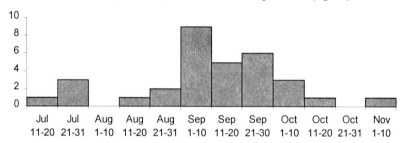

Figure 37. Cumulative 'autumn' arrival dates of Pectoral Sandpipers, 1962 - 94.

Records since 1962 have been widely scattered, although most were at recognised wader haunts. Pett Level Pools has held eight, including three together from 9 to 14 September 1983 and three have been found at both Rye Harbour and Selsey (including one on a small pool behind fishermen's huts on 14 September 1972). Arlington Reservoir, Chichester Gravel Pits, the lower Cuckmere Valley, Pevensey Levels, Waltham Brooks and Weir Wood Reservoir have all hosted two records as has Pagham Harbour (where perhaps more might be expected). Of those at Pagham Harbour, one was at Church Norton and the other at Sidlesham Ferry. A most unlikely venue was a small muddy pool at the edge of a pig field at Littlehampton West Beach which one frequented from 13 to 15 September 1980. Other records have been for Arundel WWT, Chichester Yacht Basin (21 to 27 September 1991), Icklesham (a male trapped on 13 August 1989), Newhaven Tide Mills (29-30 September 1962), Shoreham-by-Sea (on the River Adur opposite the airport on 26 September 1970) and Thorney Little Deep (31 August 1974). That only one should be recorded at Thorney in recent times is surprising considering the four seen there during 1947-49.

There have been between 40 and 80 records of this yellow-legged wader in the British Isles in most recent years (Fraser & Ryan 1992) and it is the commonest American wader to be recorded this side of the Atlantic. It breeds on the arctic tundra of North America and northern Siberia and it winters in southern South America and in small numbers in Australia. Most migrate to South America by way of a Great Circle route over the western Atlantic (Hayman, Marchant & Prater 1986).   *Richard Fairbank*

Curlew Sandpiper   *Calidris ferruginea*

Status:- A passage migrant, scarce in autumn and very scarce in spring; very rare in winter.

Curlew Sandpipers are most regularly recorded at the same localities previously outlined for Little Stint. They, too, are most numerous in autumn as the following table of cumulative monthly totals for the periods 1962-76 and 1977-93 shows.

	Jan	Feb	Mar	Apr	May	Jun	Jul	Aug	Sep	Oct	Nov	Dec
1962-76	0	0	1	1	18	1	34	429	460	59	13	0
1977-93	1	0	1	15	45	20	92	499	643	86	0	2
Total	1	0	2	16	63	21	126	928	1103	145	13	2

The breeding grounds of the species are on the Siberian tundra where, apparently, only the females incubate. Some males may leave as early as late June which may account for the small number of birds recorded in Sussex at this time. The autumn passage of adults reaches a peak in early August but the largest numbers occur from late August into September as the passage of juveniles reaches a peak. Numbers decrease rapidly in late September, some lingering into October, but few are seen after mid-month. Exceptional counts in autumn have included the following:

Locality	Count	Date
Pilsey Island	19	22 September 1985
Sidlesham Ferry	180	1 September 1969
	32	9 September 1978
	32	27 September 1987
	35	28 August 1981
Pett Level Pools	40	7 September 1975
	37	9 September 1978
	40	26 August 1981
Rye Harbour	56	14 August 1985

The Rye birds were all adults, roosting during a heavy rainstorm.

By far the largest numbers recorded in autumn were in 1969 when an exceptional influx of *ca.* 260 occurred, including a flock at Sidlesham Ferry that reached a maximum of 180 on 1 September (Shrubb). As with Little Stint, the numbers recorded each year vary considerably (fig. 38), depending on the success of the previous breeding season and the incidence of easterly winds to drift birds westwards from their usual migration route from Siberia to West Africa.

Instances of Curlew Sandpipers wintering in the county are extremely unusual, and all records have come from the Chichester Harbour area, in

1950, 1954, 1955, 1964 and 1987/88 (2). Very few are seen on spring passage which extends from mid-April to late May. The extreme dates are 3 April and 16 June and the maximum recorded in any one spring since 1977 was nine in 1992.

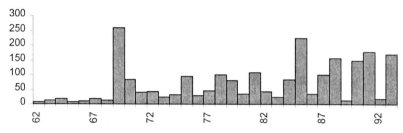

Figure 38. Autumn totals of Curlew Sandpipers, 1962 - 93.

There have been inland records for Arlington and Weir Wood Reservoirs, Bewl Water, Chichester Gravel Pits and Waltham Brooks.   Chris Janman

Purple Sandpiper   Calidris maritima

Status:- A scarce winter visitor and passage migrant; very rare in summer.

Purple Sandpipers winter regularly at several sites in Sussex although, of these, only one (Newhaven Harbour) has consistently held a wintering flock throughout the period 1962-93. Birds may also be found on seaweed covered rocks between Littlehampton and Goring-by-Sea and Eastbourne and Pett Level but no one site along these stretches of coast holds a wintering flock as regularly as Newhaven. Furthermore, it appears that birds move between sites as shown by the presence of a regular roost at Glyne Gap, between Bexhill and St Leonards, from 1966 to 1972, which was then abandoned in favour of a roost at Langney Point. This remained the main roost until 1982, after which the birds moved back to Glyne Gap. In the Littlehampton area, the largest and most regular roost is on the west pier at the mouth of the River Arun, but smaller numbers may also roost at Ferring and Goring; these smaller roosts sometimes, but not always, hold birds from Littlehampton. Since 1982 a few birds have roosted regularly at Brighton Marina. Other sites where small numbers have occurred in winter with some regularity include Selsey Bill, Pagham Harbour, Shoreham Harbour and Fairlight.

Traditionally, Newhaven has always held the largest wintering flock in Sussex. Since the early 1980s, however, the roost at Glyne Gap has consistently held higher numbers (table 50). Over the same period, the roost at Newhaven has become less regular on the east pier (the traditional roosting site) and the birds now spend more time on the western breakwater and, at low tide, along the undercliff between Newhaven and Peacehaven. It is also possible that a few of the Newhaven birds have moved to Brighton Marina in recent years.

	82/83	83/84	84/85	85/86	86/87	87/88	88/89	89/90	90/91	91/92	92/93
Littlehampton	11	9	16	7	5	4	3	2	3	2	1
Brighton Marina	2	4	2	3	6	9	0	9	2	2	0
Newhaven	33	30	25	28	30	25	30	20	10	10	11
Glyne Gap	11	35	44	43	44	38	11	26	30	17	20

Table 50. Peak counts of Purple Sandpipers, 1982/83 - 92/93.

County totals of wintering birds in the period 1962/63-92/93 varied from a low of 11 in 1964/65 to 90 in 1970/71 and 1971/72 (fig. 39). The highest count at any one site in the county was that of 51 at Glyne Gap on 12 December 1993.

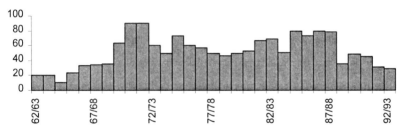

Figure 39. Peak county totals of Purple Sandpipers, 1962/63 - 92/93.

Purple Sandpipers are late in returning to their winter roost sites in Sussex. Although migrants are occasionally seen in August and September, wintering birds generally return during the latter half of October and November. They do not arrive 'en masse' but rather in small groups through the late autumn and early winter, with peak numbers generally not occurring until the New Year. The earliest date for an autumn migrant in the county is probably 5 August 1973, when one flew east past Selsey Bill, although a bird seen at Brighton Marina on 30 July 1981 may have been a very early migrant rather than a summering individual. In the period 1962-93, the earliest date that wintering birds returned to Newhaven was 16 October 1976; the two birds seen there on 26 August 1988 did not linger and were presumably on migration.

The spring departure of Purple Sandpipers follows the same pattern as their arrival, with birds leaving the roost sites in small groups from about mid-March. Most probably move eastwards along the coast; this would explain the high numbers often reported at Fairlight from mid-March to mid-May. Although there has been a paucity of records at this site since 1980, from 1967 to 1979 flocks of Purple Sandpipers were seen regularly there, sometimes during the winter but most often during the spring. Purple Sandpipers are also occasionally seen during spring sea-watches, most often from Selsey Bill in May, suggesting that small numbers of birds that have wintered outside the county pass along the Sussex coast. Some wintering birds linger at the main roost sites until mid-May, the latest date being 24 May when four birds were at Newhaven in 1974 and two were there in 1981. The latest ever spring migrant was one at Cuckmere Haven on 26 May 1978.

Purple Sandpipers are very rare in Sussex in summer; there have been just four records, perhaps relating to three birds, in June and July. One was at Black Rock, Brighton, on 4 June 1978 and either this individual or a second summering bird was at Selsey Bill on 3 July of the same year. One at Brighton Marina on 30 July 1981 was possibly a very early returning migrant rather than a summering bird (see above). Finally, one was at Newhaven on 15 July 1992.

Jon Curson

Dunlin   *Calidris alpina*

Status:- An abundant winter visitor and common passage migrant. Scarce in summer.

Dunlin are the most abundant of the estuarine waders in winter, occurring anywhere on the coast where mud is present. They generally feed in flocks, on wet mud, where their invertebrate prey tends to be nearer to the surface. At high tide, large roosting flocks are formed which may utilise salt marshes or shingle beaches. However, when these are covered by water, nearby areas of pasture and ploughed fields are used on which feeding may continue, particularly in mid-winter (Winter Atlas).

The main site for Dunlin in Sussex is Chichester Harbour, which is important both as a migratory staging post and for its wintering population. About 80% of the Dunlin that winter in the county are found there. It is also a site of international importance for the species (Waters & Cranswick 1993), holding about 6% of the British wintering population and just under 2% of the European population. High tide roost counts at this site and the other main localities in the county are summarised in table 51.

	69-74	74-79	79-84	84-89	89-94	Peak counts
Chichester Harbour	20667	25414	25554	22025	21447	32520, Oct 1985
Pagham Harbour	3436	4540	3460	3853	2715	6950, Dec 1976
Goring		672*	344	435**	396*	1040, Feb 1978
Adur Estuary		880	1154	1095	1252	1570, Jan 1982
Pett Level		91*	335*	151	239	840, Feb 1981
Rye Harbour		574*	431	640	164	1500, Jan 1985

Table 51. High tide roost counts of Dunlin: five year means of winter maxima and peak counts, 1969/70 - 93/94.

258

The population in Sussex reached over 30,000 in all but one of the winters between 1972/73 and 1977/78, in each of those between 1982/83 and 1985/86, and again in 1989/90. More recently, however, numbers have fallen, reflecting the national trend. Reasons advanced for this decline include poor breeding seasons and also habitat changes that have limited the availability of food resources, so resulting in a lower winter survival rate (Goss-Custard & Moser 1988).

Returning adults arrive from late June onwards followed by juveniles in August-September. Some birds then leave for their winter quarters and, such is the complexity of the autumn migration pattern, that numbers obtained from counts in October have fluctuated enormously. For example, in October 1985, a total of 33,618 was recorded compared with just 93 in October 1979. Clearly much depends on whether the presence of large numbers of migrants coincides with the date of the count! Numbers increase further in November (table 52) and remain at a high level throughout the winter except in hard weather when a partial exodus may occur. Such was the case in January 1987 when only 13,797 were counted compared with 24,151 the previous month.

	Sep	Oct	Nov	Dec	Jan	Feb	Mar
Maximum	7600	33618	33093	32345	33741	33348	14863
Mean	1840	11525	18448	22906	22174	19386	8024
Minimum	372	1396	11265	14580	4903	12521	1535

Table 52. Monthly totals of Dunlin, 1974/75 - 93/94.

Most depart for their breeding grounds in March or early April but numbers may increase again as migrants that have wintered in Africa pass through. For example, 2000 were recorded at Pilsey Sand on 10 May 1990, 2682 on 4 May 1991 and 3500 on 17 May 1991. Such counts have coincided with the timing of the peak movements up-Channel, the scale of which is shown by the cumulative monthly totals recorded at Worthing in the period 1978-93:

	Jul	Aug	Sep	Oct	Nov	Dec	Jan	Feb	Mar	Apr	May	Jun
Flying west	32	395	362	1345	871	97	19	-	245	261	563	4
Flying east	-	27	77	342	175	1	22	88	981	1442	2795	8

In some years large numbers are recorded, as in 1993, when there were 103 in April and 709 in May at Worthing and 1124 in May at Selsey Bill. The largest movement in one day was of 156 at Worthing on 2 May 1986. Autumn coastal passage begins in July but it is not until late October or early November that any significant movements are seen. These often occur after strong northerly winds and frequently are coincident with days of heavy Brent Goose passage. The largest movement was of 459 flying west at Worthing on 26 October 1980.

Small numbers of non-breeders summer in some years, mainly in Chichester and Pagham Harbours. At least 20 were recorded at the former site in 1988 and 26 at the latter in 1985 although in other years there has been none. At Rye Harbour, 5-7 may have summered in 1989 and two definitely did so in 1984 and 1985.

Inland records are fairly frequent but they involve relatively small numbers and sometimes only single birds. These usually occur during the main passage periods in spring and autumn. Regular sites include Arlington Reservoir, Bewl Water, Darwell Reservoir and Weir Wood Reservoir. However, larger flocks have been noted on floods in the river valleys, especially in hard weather, at sites such as the Adur Levels (max. 55 in early 1985), Amberley Wild Brooks (max. 100 on 26 March 1975), Glynde Levels (max. 125 on 24 February 1974) and Lewes Brooks (max. 200 in early 1977 and early 1988).

Three races of Dunlin are thought to occur in Sussex although they can only be separated, with great difficulty, in summer plumage. The birds that winter locally are of the nominate race *C.a. alpina*, which breeds in northern Fenno-Scandinavia and arctic Russia and moults on the southern coast of the North Sea. Those present in autumn and spring are thought to be of the race *C.a. schinzii*, which breeds in southeast Greenland, Iceland, Britain and southern Scandinavia, though it is likely that some birds of the race *C.a. arctica*, which breeds in northeast Greenland, also occur. Most *schinzii* moult and winter in northwest Africa though some may complete their autumn moult in southern England before moving to their winter quarters.

There have been 16 recoveries of foreign-ringed birds in Sussex. Of these, six were ringed in Sweden, four in Poland, two in Denmark and one each in Finland, Norway, Germany and the Netherlands, all in the period July to September. Recoveries were in January (6), March (5), February (2) and November, December and April (1 each). The timing of the recoveries would indicate that these birds are of the race *alpina* ringed either on their breeding grounds or while on migration. The longest movement involved a bird ringed in Norway on 27 August 1974 and controlled at Shoreham-by-Sea on 17 February 1976, 2674 km southwest, while the longest time lapse between ringing and recovery involved a bird ringed in Sweden on 19 July 1953 and found dead at Church Norton, almost ten years later, on 31 January 1963. Of 13 recoveries of birds ringed in Sussex, three were local, three elsewhere in England, six in France and one in Germany.   *Joe Nobbs*

Broad-billed Sandpiper   *Limicola falcinellus*

Status:- A very rare vagrant (seven, mostly old, records).

Five were recorded prior to 1962. Three were shot, at Shoreham Beach in late October 1845 and at Rye Harbour on 13 August 1887 and 12 October 1895, and two were seen, at the Midrips on 13 September 1934 (Ticehurst 1934) and Hove Lagoon on 6 March 1948. That from 1845 is in the Booth Museum (BoMNH 204250). The 1948 individual was an exceptionally early occurrence and the brief published account (*SxBR* 1: 23) lends it little support.

They have been only two records since the beginning of 1962:

1988:   An adult in summer plumage at Pevensey Bridge Level on 8 May.
1993:   An adult in summer plumage at Sidlesham Ferry on 1-2 May moved into
        Pagham Harbour at low tide.

No clear pattern emerges with one record in March and others in May (2), August (1), September (1) and October (2). The two most recent records, in early May, would seem to be the most typical.

There were just over 150 records of this species in the British Isles during 1962-94. It breeds in northern Scandinavia and central and eastern Siberia and it migrates to East Africa, southern Asia and Australia.   *Richard Fairbank*

Stilt Sandpiper   *Micropalama himantopus*

Status:- A very rare vagrant (three records).

First recorded in 1962, there have been three records, the most recent as long ago as 1972:

1962:   A non-breeding adult at Chichester Gravel Pits from 1 to 7 September was the second British record (Carter, Mead & Sheldon 1963).
1963:   A non-breeding adult at Manhood End, Chichester Harbour from 7 to 13 August was the fourth British record (Shrubb 1964).
1972:   An adult in summer plumage at Sidlesham Ferry on 14 July was the tenth British record.

Another would seem long overdue as there were three in Kent during 1985-90 (Evans 1994).

There were 25 records of this long-legged wader in the British Isles during 1962-94. It breeds on the arctic tundra of North America and winters in central South America.   *Richard Fairbank*

Buff-breasted Sandpiper   *Tryngites subruficollis*

Status:- A very rare autumn vagrant (eight records).

Three were recorded before 1962: one shot on the Sussex coast prior to autumn 1843, a male shot at Rye Harbour on 21 August 1934 (Harrison 1934) and one seen at the Midrips from 17 September to 2 October 1955 (des Forges & Harber).

Five have been recorded since the beginning of 1962:

1970:   One at Sidlesham Ferry on 5 September.
1973:   One at Camber on 6 September.
1974:   One at Sidlesham Ferry on 9-10 September.
1989:   One at Ternery Pool, Rye Harbour on 14 October.
1993:   One at Littleham Farm, Sidlesham from 18 to 23 September.

All records were in the autumn with one undated, one in August, five in September and one in October. Rye Harbour and Sidlesham Ferry have both held two with the remaining records, so far as is known, being either in the extreme east or west of the county. The 1993 individual consorted with a small party of Ruff in a large ploughed field. The short grass of airfields and golf courses are often favoured localities elsewhere in Britain.

There were about 500 records of this confiding wader in the British Isles during 1962-94. It breeds on the arctic tundra of North America and migrates to northern Argentina and adjacent grasslands.   *Richard Fairbank*

Ruff

Philomachus pugnax

Status:- A scarce winter visitor and passage migrant.

Ruff are probably best known to most Sussex birdwatchers as passage migrants rather than winter visitors. Winter flocks are often elusive because of their habit of feeding on flooded fields, and they are usually only obvious when they congregate at dusk at their few roost sites. Although des Forges & Harber considered that Ruff were primarily autumn passage migrants, they have wintered regularly in Sussex for many years and, from the early 1960s until the mid-1980s, wintering birds outnumbered those recorded on passage, sometimes dramatically so. Since the mid-1980s, the wintering population has declined and numbers of wintering and passage birds have been more equal.

Ruff winter regularly at only a handful of sites in the county. Most are recorded on the Selsey peninsula, especially at Sidlesham Ferry and Bracklesham, though smaller numbers also occur in Chichester Harbour and the Arun Valley and more occasionally at other sites such as Pevensey Levels and Rye Harbour. In the hard weather of early 1985 they were much more widespread with birds occurring on the upper Adur Levels and Lewes Brooks, as well as in a number of gardens in the county. There was even a report of one waiting on the roof of a house in Goring for food to be put out!

Numbers on the Selsey peninsula started to build up in the late 1960s and a flock of 120 at Bracklesham from 18 February to 17 March 1968 was the largest ever recorded in the county at that time. Over the next seven winters there were regularly flocks of 50-100 at Sidlesham Ferry, Bracklesham and Chidham, with a maximum count of 116 at the latter site on 19 December 1973. In the following winter a marked increase occurred as shown by the presence of 320 at Sidlesham Ferry from 14 to 25 February 1976. This flock subsequently broke up but then reformed in March and by 20 March there were 290 at Chichester Gravel Pits and an estimated 370 on the Selsey peninsula and surrounding area as a whole. There was a lull the following winter, with no more than 100 birds in the area, but in 1977/78 a single flock of 500 was recorded at Sidlesham Ferry while in 1978/79 numbers increased still further. The flock at Sidlesham totalled 540 on 29 December 1978 but there were an additional 500 birds elsewhere on the Selsey peninsula on this date, giving a minimum estimate of 1000 birds in the area. Nothing on this scale had been seen in Sussex previously and it appears that these numbers are unprecedented in western Europe in winter.

Hard weather in early 1979 resulted in the departure of most of this flock and by 29 January only 150 remained. Subsequently, numbers wintering on the Selsey peninsula have steadily declined. There were 300 or more in the area in each of the following four winters but in 1983/84 and 1984/85 the maximum counts recorded were 203 and 159 respectively. Why the numbers of Ruff wintering in Sussex should have shown such a pronounced peak between 1975/76 and 1982/83 is not clear, but this trend was also evident elsewhere in Britain, particularly in Hampshire, though on a smaller scale.

Elsewhere in Sussex, wintering flocks have been much more modest. At Amberley Wild Brooks, where 12 were noted in December 1972, the first sizeable flock to be recorded was in early 1974 when there 40 on 28 February, declining to 22 by 2 March. A flock of up to 50 wintered regularly at this locality until at least 1989/90, though they were often apparently absent for large parts of the winter. It was suggested that this flock may have flown to join the Sidlesham roost at night after feeding in the Arun Valley during the day, but this was never proved conclusively. More recently, numbers wintering at Amberley have declined slightly and a new winter flock has formed at Pulborough Brooks, following the establishment of the RSPB reserve there. In the latter part of 1993 the flock at Amberley totalled 15 while that at Pulborough totalled 50.

Despite the erratic nature of wintering flocks, it would appear that they start to build up from late October or early November, reaching a peak early in the New Year and then departing quite abruptly during March (or sometimes earlier if there is a sudden cold spell). This pattern was also mirrored in neighbouring Hampshire in the 1970s but since then, Ruff have become less regular there in winter than in Sussex.

Ruff are early spring migrants and flocks in March probably comprise passage as well as wintering birds. By late March migration is at a peak, though birds continue to be recorded throughout April and into May. Peak counts in spring have included 42 on Wet Level on 24 March 1967 and 30 at Amberley Wild Brooks on 5 April of the same year. The following table, covering the period 1962-93, shows that the numbers recorded in spring fluctuate widely.

	Jan	Feb	Mar	Apr	May	Jun	Jul	Aug	Sep	Oct	Nov	Dec
Maximum	502	487	407	72	66	21	75	165	126	122	403	1017
Mean	93	106	93	22	10	3	16	37	47	41	61	111
Minimum	7	0	1	0	0	0	1	8	8	0	0	2
Total	2983	3383	2962	689	334	108	501	1178	1491	1309	1958	3559

Ruff are generally scarce in mid-summer with far fewer records in June than in any other month. Even so, there were only six years in the period 1962-93 in which no Ruff were recorded in June while, in 1989 the surprisingly high total of 21 was recorded.

Autumn migration generally begins in July but occasionally in late June (as probably happened in 1989). Passage usually peaks in late August-early September and continues into October when numbers are augmented by the returning winter population. Numbers are usually fairly small but higher counts have included ca. 40 at Sidlesham Ferry on 3 September 1965, 75 at Chidham on 25 August 1968 and up to 80 at Sidlesham Ferry in September-October 1980.   *Jon Curson*

Jack Snipe   *Lymnocryptes minimus*

Status:- A scarce winter visitor and passage migrant.

The Jack Snipe is a regular winter visitor to the county but it has never been common. It is usually found in damp and boggy habitats, at both coastal and inland localities, including areas of shingle and heathland. Most are located when flushed at very close range and few are seen in the open, when the characteristic 'bobbing' action may be observed. Due to their habit of remaining hidden until almost trodden on, most birds are clearly overlooked.

Shrubb referred to annual totals of fewer than 30, except in occasional years, when over 50 were recorded. The table below, covering the period 1970/71-92/93, suggests little change in status in recent years, although the number recorded each winter depends, to some extent, on the discovery of concentrations of birds at favoured sites. In the 1970s, these included Glynde Levels, Newhaven Tide Mills and Thorney Deeps and, while the latter has continued to produce high counts, most are now recorded at Icklesham where there were 30 in October 1989 and again in October 1990. Other favoured sites in recent years have included Chichester Gravel Pits, Combe Haven, Glyne Gap, The Pells (Lewes), Pevensey Levels and Rye Harbour.

	Sep	Oct	Nov	Dec	Jan	Feb	Mar	Apr	May
Maximum	2	45	22	37	35	29	20	10	2
Mean	0	9	9	10	13	12	9	4	0
Minimum	0	0	1	1	1	1	0	0	0
Total	11	201	216	213	283	273	207	83	4

The table shows most have departed by April and very few linger into May; the latest spring record being at the Crumbles on 12 May 1951. Arrival of birds into Sussex usually commences in early to mid-October although occasionally there are earlier records, such as that of two at Icklesham on 1 September 1989. The earliest was one at Pagham on 29 August 1959.

Jack Snipe breed in northern Europe and winter from western and southern Europe to tropical Africa, India and southeast Asia. It has been estimated that the wintering population in Britain may possibly be as high as 100,000 (Winter Atlas).

One ringed at Icklesham on 1 November 1993 was shot at St-Font, Haute Loire, France, 706 km SSE, five days later.   *Richard Kelly*

Snipe   *Gallinago gallinago*

Status:- A fairly common breeder and common winter visitor.

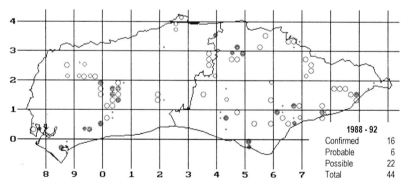

1988 - 92	
Confirmed	16
Probable	6
Possible	22
Total	44

Snipe are unobtrusive birds that are mainly crepuscular feeders. They are notoriously difficult to survey (Green 1985) and estimates of their numbers should be treated with caution. The loss of large areas of suitable breeding habitat due to changes in agricultural practice and river management is, however, indisputable. Breeding Snipe favour poorly drained pastures that are subject to winter flooding to provide then with an abundant supply of earthworms and insects. Modern pasture management reduces the quality of the habitat for Snipe by lowering the water table. This allows earlier and more intensive grazing by livestock, which further reduces the survival chances of the young due to an increased risk of trampling.

Population changes may be more obvious from changes in distribution than from counts made at the main breeding sites (Bibby, Burgess & Hill 1992). Evidence of a dramatic contraction of range in the county is provided by the Atlas map which shows the tetrads in which Snipe were recorded during 1988-92 and also those in which birds were found during 1976-87 but not during the Atlas Survey.

From data in Walpole-Bond, Shrubb calculated that the Snipe population in 1938 was a minimum of 500 pairs, but a survey carried out between 1965 and 1967 suggested that the population was then under 100 pairs (Shrubb 1968). A repeat survey of the same areas in 1980 and 1981 (Mitchell 1982) found an estimated 86 pairs. In a review of the ornithological status of Pevensey Levels, Hitchings (1988) stated that there may have been 100 pairs breeding in 1938 but that by 1965 there were only 25 pairs. In 1976 there were 17 pairs but by 1980 the population had declined still further to just three pairs; a survey in 1987 gave the same result. By contrast, in the Arun Valley, which is now the main breeding stronghold for this species in Sussex, numbers increased from eight pairs in 1982 to 84 pairs in 1991 (Corrigan 1993). Although the RSPB has been actively managing a large site in this area since 1989, the author concluded that the apparent increase was almost certainly due to the different methodologies used in the two surveys. From the information available, it is impossible to give more than a tentative estimate of the size of the current breeding population in the county but it is likely to be in the region of 130 to 250 pairs, assuming that some of the previous surveys may have underestimated breeding numbers.

	69-74	74-79	79-84	84-89	89-94	Peak counts
Chichester Harbour	145	261	259	144	127	541, Dec 1980
Pagham Harbour	9	55	199	52	30	546, Dec 1983
Newhaven		44*	28	73*	34*	200, Jan 1981
Cuckmere Valley		121*	138	44	13*	300, Dec 1981
Pevensey Levels		2150**	758	461	91**	2300, Feb1978
Pett Level		200*	253*	66	18	350, Mar 1982
Rye Harbour		120	49	154	37	265, Jan 1977

Table 53. Five year means of maxima and peak counts of Snipe, 1969/70 - 93/94.

	Sep	Oct	Nov	Dec	Jan	Feb	Mar
Maximum	173	525	1533	2891	2718	2824	2172
Mean	68	210	490	739	708	601	442
Minimum	5	26	64	57	15	10	19

Table 54. Monthly totals of Snipe, 1974/75 - 93/94.

After the breeding season, numbers are augmented by migrants from more northern parts of Britain and from around the Baltic. Arrivals start in late July and build up during the winter months. The distribution varies from that in the summer as more use is made of coastal sites such as Thorney Island.

Flocks or 'wisps' of Snipe are not so close knit as other waders, making counting more difficult, but there is no doubt that wintering numbers have declined. Counts of 1000 or more were made, mostly on Pevensey Levels, in seven of the years between 1966 and 1985. Since then the largest counts have been 900 in November 1991 and 500 in 1990, both at Pulborough Brooks. Numbers increase during cold weather until the ground becomes frozen, when birds seek more hospitable feeding grounds. During January and February 1979 such a spell almost emptied the county of this species when the coastline wader counts produced totals of only 218 and 281 respectively, compared to 2681 the previous January. Winter counts at the main localities are summarised in tables 53 and 54.

Although Snipe numbers show marked monthly and yearly variations, the 3-year moving average of the peak count in each of the winters between 1976/77 and 1993/94 (fig. 40) provide further evidence of a significant decline in the wintering population. The graph shows a six-fold decrease between 1976/77 and 1988/89 although it appears that, more recently, numbers have stabilised, albeit at a lower level. When interpreting the graph, it should be born in mind that the counts are made on a fixed day each month and that they may not represent the peak numbers recorded in that month. In some years not every site was counted but it is known that the records for the past four winters (1990/91-93/94) are complete.

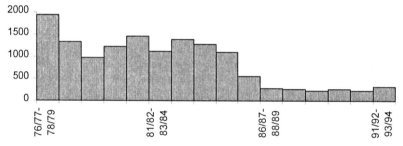

Figure 40. Moving averages of peak counts of Snipe, 1976/77 - 93/94.

Of the 17 Snipe ringed in Sussex and subsequently recovered, six were in the county or elsewhere in southern England, five in France, two in Spain and one in each of Germany, Ireland, the Netherlands and the former USSR, the latter ringed at Icklesham in August 1987 and found dead in the Borsky Region, 2920 km ENE, in August 1990. One of those recovered in Spain had been ringed as a chick at Brede in 1935. Foreign-ringed birds recovered in Sussex have largely originated from the countries bordering the Baltic. Of 12 birds in total, three each were from Denmark and Germany, two from Poland, and one each from Sweden and Finland. The other two birds, ringed in the Netherlands, may have been on autumn passage at the time of capture.

Robin T Pepper

Great Snipe
Gallinago media

Status:- A very rare autumn vagrant (20 records, but only two during the last 30 years).

Eighteen were recorded prior to 1962 of which five were undated, six in September, five in October and two in November (des Forges & Harber), although one record, for November, has not been traced. The earliest, a female shot near Patcham windmill on 18 September 1909, is in the Booth Museum (BoMNH 204065) while the latest was killed at Hellingly on 11 November 1893. Most were recorded before 1900, with subsequent records (all in September) at Arundel (obtained in 1906), Patcham, Roedean and the Midrips. The individual seen at the Roedean was flushed several times from a stubble field on 26 September 1920 (Walpole-Bond) while that at the Midrips was flushed on 30 September 1950, although the brief published notes are not particularly convincing (*SxBR* 3: 19).

Since the beginning of 1962 there have been only two records:

1964:   One at the edge of a small pool at the northeast side of Pagham Lagoon on 10 November was seen on the ground and in flight.
1975:   A female shot at Bodiam on about 27 September.

These records conform to the pattern of earlier (dated) occurrences between mid-September and mid-November.

There were just over 70 records of this species in the British Isles during 1962-94 compared with nearly 200 prior to 1962 reflecting its (continuing) decline in central in central and eastern Europe (Tucker & Heath 1994). It also breeds in Scandinavia and west Siberia and it winters in sub-Saharan Africa.

Richard Fairbank

Long-billed Dowitcher
Limnodromus scolopaceus

Status:- A very rare vagrant (four records).

Two were recorded before 1962 (des Forges & Harber). Both were at Thorney Island, one on a small marshy pool by the sea wall from 15 to 22 October 1950 (Douglas 1951) and the other at the western end of the Great and Little Deeps from 2 to 11 November 1959 (*SxBR* 12: 9, *Brit. Birds* 54: plate 56b). The latter was sometimes seen with the White-rumped Sandpiper present at the time.

Since the beginning of 1962 there have been two records:

1965:   One at Sidlesham Ferry Rubbish Dump from 14 February to 15 March.
1992:   An adult in summer plumage at Sidlesham Ferry from 21 to 23 May (*Birding World* 5: 168, *Brit. Birds* 86: plate 165).

The 1965 individual was originally identified as a Short-billed Dowitcher *L. griseus* but following a review, based on better understood identification criteria, it has been correctly assigned to Long-billed (Rogers *et al* 1981).

Two unidentified dowitchers have been recorded in the county, at Chidham on 4 April 1965 and at Willingdon Level, Eastbourne on 28 December 1985, although it is very likely both were Long-billed.

There were just over 170 records of this taxing wader in the British Isles during 1962-94, a further 100 records of indeterminate dowitchers, but only one acceptable record of a Short-billed Dowitcher (in southern Ireland). It breeds in northeast Siberia and in Alaska and winters in southern USA and Central America. Short-billed Dowitchers breed as close as Newfoundland and winter from southern USA to coastal Brazil. *Richard Fairbank*

Woodcock   *Scolopax rusticola*

Status:- A fairly common resident and winter visitor.

The Atlas map shows that Woodcock are largely confined to three distinct areas of Sussex. The first comprises the woodlands of the northwest of the county, stretching from the Hampshire and Surrey borders south to the western River Rother and east to the River Arun. Also included in this block are the forests of the Downs and the commons in West Sussex. The second block consists of the forest ridges of East Sussex, which project into West Sussex, while the third comprises a large area of the central Weald to the northwest of Bexhill and Hastings. The absence of Woodcock from the clay soils of the lowland Weald and coastal plain is probably related to the feeding requirements of the breeding females which need a ready supply of worms during daylight hours, within the safety of woods and cover.

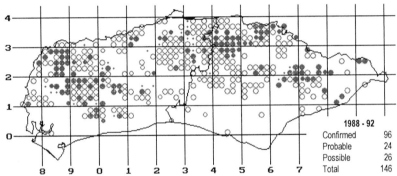

	1988 - 92	
	Confirmed	96
	Probable	24
	Possible	26
	Total	146

The distribution and status of the species in Sussex was reviewed by Hughes (1976) who reported that, in the period 1966 to 1975, Woodcock were found in a total of 310 tetrads involving 37 of the 56 10-km squares in the county. The distribution map he plotted identified two main areas of distribution, the first in the northwest of the county, as described above, and the second encompassing both the forest ridges and the central Weald of East Sussex, suggesting that some occupied tetrads may have been missed in the latter area during the Atlas Survey. Twenty-one new tetrads were added up to 1981 (des Forges 1982) and 24 by the Atlas Survey. The tetrads in which Woodcock were recorded between 1965 and 1987, but not between 1988 and 1992 are also shown on the map as open symbols. In both sets of data the large symbol, portraying confirmed breeding, mainly represents roding males.

Any meaningful estimate of the density of nests in favoured areas and much less an overall figure for the total county population is impossible from the available data, especially as there is no close correlation between the number of breeding females and the number of contacts an observer makes with roding males (Hirons 1981). Furthermore, birds may be seen flying from woodland to feed in early spring and be wrongly assumed to be roding. The 68-72 BTO Atlas did, however, suggest that there might be 10-25 pairs per 10-km square in which breeding was probable or confirmed, indicating a possible figure for Sussex of 380-950 pairs. More recent studies clearly point to a reduction in the British breeding population (Hoodless 1995) so the lower end of this range may be more appropriate.

Roding, by the males only, may start as early as mid-February and laying at the beginning of March. An average date for first clutches is mid-March. Repeat layings undoubtedly occur. Evidence of second broods is lacking but some late records, for example a clutch hatching near West Dean in West Sussex on 19 July, are indicative.

During winter, birds are more widely spread. They feed between dusk and dawn on worm-rich pasture and in large woods and lie up during the day in small patches of woodland and scrub. Where Woodcock do not nest, as on the Downs at Ashcombe Bottom, Castle Hill, Newmarket Hill and the Plumpton escarpment, birds may be seen in winter (Leverton 1994). Over a period of 15 years they have arrived at the very end of October or in the first two or three days of November and are to be found mostly in dense downland scrub by day, flying out to feed on open grassland at night. Numbers are low (exceptionally in one period of three hours seven were found) and the birds always solitary.

In hard weather, when food becomes difficult to find, birds may be displaced from their usual feeding areas and they may turn up in wholly uncharacteristic places such as town gardens and parks and on the seashore. In 1991, for example, only three were reported for January but the total for February, when there was a cold snap, was 133, including up to 11 at Selsey Bill and seven on Littlehampton Golf Course.

A partial albino Woodcock was shot near Bolney in October 1974.

Ringing recoveries suggest that Sussex birds are largely resident and are joined in winter by birds from the continent. Of seven ringed in Sussex, five were recovered within the county while the other two, ringed at Bexhill in 1964 and at Beachy Head on 9 November 1991, were recovered in northern France and Sweden respectively. The latter was a road casualty found 1221 km NNE in the Kalmar District on 5 April 1993. Of seven ringed overseas and recovered in Sussex, three had originated from the Netherlands and two each from France and Sweden.

Paul James

Black-tailed Godwit Limosa limosa

Status:- A common winter visitor and passage migrant; small numbers summer.

In winter, Black-tailed Godwits are almost entirely restricted to Chichester and Pagham Harbours (table 55). The first birds return from their breeding grounds in late June or early July, as shown by an increase at the latter site from 37 on 29 June 1993 to 99 on 7 July. Numbers build up rapidly thereafter to reach an autumn peak, often in September-October, though there has been a recent tendency for the largest numbers to be recorded earlier in the autumn, in July-August. Numbers then drop, sometimes considerably, as some birds move on to winter elsewhere on completion of their moult.

	69-74	74-79	79-84	84-89	89-94	Peak counts
Chichester Harbour	800	908	897	750	555	1400, Jan 1973
Pagham Harbour	217	338	370	249	146	716, Mar 1988

Table 55. High tide roost counts of Black-tailed Godwits: five year means of maxima and peak counts, 1969/70 - 93/94.

The monthly totals (table 56) fluctuate very markedly, partly due to an exodus in very cold weather, as in February 1979 and January 1987, and also because wintering birds are believed to move about the whole of the estuarine complex from Pagham Harbour to Portsmouth Harbour in Hampshire (Shrubb). An increase in numbers at Titchfield Haven, Hampshire has been linked with corresponding reductions in Chichester and Langstone Harbours (Clark & Eyre 1993). Although the peak count at Pagham Harbour was in March 1988 the numbers in both Chichester and Pagham Harbour have been relatively low since 1983/84 although these are slowly recovering.

	Sep	Oct	Nov	Dec	Jan	Feb	Mar
Maximum	1512	1430	1392	1400	1404	968	910
Mean	513	602	499	437	553	391	428
Minimum	5	99	26	0	0	30	1

Table 56. Monthly totals of Black-tailed Godwits, 1969/70 - 93/94.

Black-tailed Godwits are very mobile. At low tide, they are usually found feeding on estuaries where they show a preference for areas of finer sediments, unlike Bar-tailed Godwits which prefer sandier substrates. At high tide, they are liable to congregate on damp pastures, sometimes some distance from the intertidal feeding zone. In November 1982, 440 were regularly seen in a ploughed field at South Mundham, while on 5 March 1983, a flock of 800 was recorded on fields west of Selsey. Fields closer to the harbours can also attract high numbers, such as the 600 that used a pasture adjacent to the sea-wall at Nutbourne in November 1992.

Few are normally recorded away from Chichester and Pagham Harbours during the winter, though notable exceptions have included 25 at Amberley Wild Brooks on 16 and 24 December 1977 and 140 at Chichester Gravel Pits on 9 December 1990.

Black-tailed Godwits are essentially overland and nocturnal migrants so few are seen on spring sea-watches. Although there were still 700 in Chichester and Pagham Harbours on 18 April 1977, all had left by 7 May. On calm, clear evenings in late April, large numbers have been observed leaving Langstone Harbour, Hampshire in a northwest to north direction (Clark & Eyre 1993) and there is no reason to suppose that Sussex birds do not do likewise. Of those recorded passing up-Channel in spring, the largest flocks were of 40 at Brighton Marina on 16 March 1991 and 23 at Splash Point, Seaford on 4 May 1989. A flock of 35-40 flew east over Chichester Gravel Pits on 3 May 1988 and one of 17 flew north inland up the Cuckmere Valley on 25 May 1991. In most years, there are records of small numbers of birds pausing to feed at both coastal and inland sites in spring. An estimated 50 were present with Bar-tailed Godwits in the lower Cuckmere Valley on 4 May 1990 while other counts have included up to 22 on Pevensey Bridge Level in May 1988, 18 at Rye Harbour on 16 May 1982 and at Waltham Brooks on 6 May 1984, 15 at Icklesham on 14 May 1989 and up to 14 at Pulborough Brooks from 15 to 21 May 1992. A few pausing migrants may also be recorded in autumn, especially at Rye Harbour, where there were up to 16 in August 1978, and at Chichester Gravel Pits, where a number of flocks have included up to 31 from 8 to 19 September 1982, up to 27 from 16 July to 19 October 1983, 15-21 between 13 and 15 September 1981 and 15 on 15 October 1988.

Significant numbers remain through the summer at Pagham Harbour, where counts have suggested a slight increase in recent years. The summering flock at this site peaked at 130 in 1988, but the average since 1982 has been about 60. Recent counts in Chichester Harbour indicate an average of about 30 birds in June, but not necessarily all summering. Three were recorded in suitable breeding habitat at East Guldeford Level on 15 June 1980 as was a single bird at Horse Eye Level on 12 June 1982 but there is no evidence that they were territorial.

It is likely that two races of the Black-tailed Godwit occur in Sussex. Those which winter in Britain and Ireland are of the Icelandic breeding race *L.l. islandica* (Winter Atlas) whereas those recorded on passage in spring and autumn are most likely of the nominate race *L.l. limosa*. Birds of the latter race winter mainly in Africa north of the Equator and breed from western Europe into Asia. The only ringing recoveries involved one ringed in Charente-Maritime, France in October 1973 and killed at Pagham Harbour, 500 km north, the following September and a colour-ringed bird in Fishbourne Channel on 1 December 1995 that had been marked at Farlington Marshes, Hampshire on 18 September 1993.   *Anne de Potier*

Bar-tailed Godwit *Limosa lapponica*

Status:- A common winter visitor and passage migrant; a few summer.

In winter, Bar-tailed Godwits are almost entirely restricted to Chichester Harbour where they show a preference for areas of sandy substrates. The peak at this site, which usually occurs between December and February, has fluctuated around the 1000 mark since counts started in 1964. Sites which regularly hold 1000 or more birds are considered to be of international importance for the species (Waters & Cranswick 1993). Elsewhere only at Pagham Harbour are more than a few found; here there has been a tendency for larger numbers to be noted since 1980 (table 57). A few may also occur on the beaches between Atherington and Worthing and at Rye Harbour, especially in cold weather. For example, in January 1979 up to 59 were recorded at the latter site while in January 1987, there were up to 48 at Littlehampton West Beach, 40 at Rye Harbour and eight at Worthing. Severe weather can also lead to lower numbers, as in January 1986, when ten flew west past Selsey Bill on 10th and the county total was only 232 compared with 995 the previous month. Occasionally, individuals in summer plumage are noted during the winter, the most being four at Pilsey Island in December 1986.

	69-74	74-79	79-84	84-89	89-94	Peak counts
Chichester Harbour	1374	1004	987	1164	1295	2400, Dec 1988
Pagham Harbour	15	25	91	38	51	318, Oct 1980

Table 57. High tide roost counts of Bar-tailed Godwits:
five year means of maxima and peak counts, 1969/70 - 93/94.

Autumn passage starts in July, and in 1982 there were already 437 in Chichester Harbour by the 24th of that month. Numbers at this site, which have slowly recovered from a low in 1983, increase to reach a peak in September-October (table 58), prior to the main arrival of the wintering population. Away from Chichester and Pagham Harbours, only very small numbers are normally recorded, the main exceptions being 200 at Rye Harbour on 14 September 1968 and 57 at Goring in October 1991.

	Sep	Oct	Nov	Dec	Jan	Feb	Mar
Maximum	1611	1317	1075	2400	1416	1227	1171
Mean	572	618	662	908	704	687	264
Minimum	32	17	30	332	35	69	35

Table 58. Monthly totals of Bar-tailed Godwits, 1969/70 - 93/94.

Movements in autumn are much less frequently recorded and on a smaller scale than those in spring. The most exceptional record was that of 352 flying west at Pett Level on 15 August 1982. At Langney Point, a flock of 150 flew southwest on 14 September 1970, as did flocks of 100 and 160 at Worthing on 9 and 13 August 1985 respectively. Inland, 28 flew south over Slinfold on 30 July 1978 and 55 southwest over Chichester Gravel Pits on 15 August 1982.

The wintering population departs in March and this is followed by a marked spring passage up-Channel of birds returning from their wintering quarters in Mauritania and Morocco to the breeding grounds in northern

Scandinavia and Siberia (Prater 1981). The cumulative monthly totals recorded at Worthing in the period 1978-93 are shown below:

	Jul	Aug	Sep	Oct	Nov	Dec	Jan	Feb	Mar	Apr	May	Jun
Flying west	17	330	164	15	5	1	38	15	9	181	210	1
Flying east	-	11	10	10	3	5	72	54	53	31,266	18,517	36

Passage is heaviest in the last week of April and first week of May, especially in settled weather with winds from the east to northeast. Such conditions prevailed in 1984 when at least 9707 were noted passing the Sussex coast including 2019 at Brighton on 27 April and 3029 at Worthing and 2793 at Beachy Head on 29 April (Newnham 1985). Other large movements have included 6000 at Selsey Bill on 27-28 April 1963, 4009 at Worthing on 24 April 1984 and at Beachy Head, 3420 on 26 April 1973 and 3350 on 25-26 April 1971. In years when the overall numbers are low, the peak tends to occur in May rather than April. 1980 was an unusual year in that northerly winds resulted in some birds flying inland. At Rye Harbour, a total of 269 flew northeast on 25 April while inland, there were 14 northeast over Bewl Water on 3 May, 50 northeast over Weir Wood Reservoir on 4 May and 25 north over Lewes on 12 May. Other inland movements have included 200 north over Arlington Reservoir on 3 May 1971, 200 east over Ashdown Forest on 27 April 1984 (the date of peak passage past Worthing that year), 100 east over Chichester Gravel Pits on 3 May 1974 and 15 northeast over Herstmonceux on 3 May 1976.

Bar-tailed Godwits may pause briefly on their spring migration, though in general this has a sense of urgency and they do not linger. The largest numbers are recorded at Rye Harbour, where there were 500 on 1 May 1984 and 230 on 27 April 1975, and in Pagham Harbour where there were 400 on 27 April 1974. In Chichester Harbour, numbers in spring have increased considerably, particularly in recent years. In the 1960s it was unusual to record more than 50 whereas more recent counts have included 296 on 19 April 1992 and 253 on 1 May 1991.

Summering birds may be recorded in both Chichester and Pagham Harbours and at Rye Harbour. Counts for the former site, where summering is almost annual, have ranged between five and 160, with an average of about 65. At Pagham Harbour, where 20 summered in 1966 and five in 1985, none have done so since although 40 were recorded there on 15 June 1991 and 12 on 20 June 1993. At Rye Harbour, one summered in 1965 and 1-2 almost annually between 1979 and 1984.

Although migrating flocks of Bar-tailed Godwits have been recorded inland on a number of occasions, it is very unusual for birds to pause to feed away from the coast. Just 16 have been noted since 1971 at Arlington Reservoir (5), Waltham Brooks and Weir Wood Reservoir (4 each), Bewl Water (2) and Chichester Gravel Pits (1). The cumulative monthly totals are shown below.

Sep	Oct	Nov	Dec	Jan	Feb	Mar	Apr	May
2	1	1	-	-	-	-	9	3

One ringed in Rogaland, Norway in September 1939 was later found near Chichester, 967 km SSW, in November of that year and another ringed in

Texel, the Netherlands in December 1983 was found dead at West Wittering, 465 km WSW, in March 1985.   *Anne de Potier*

Whimbrel   *Numenius phaeopus*

Status:- A common passage migrant; a very scarce summering and wintering species.

Although Whimbrel have been recorded in every month of the year in Sussex, they are most frequently encountered in spring. Shrubb stated that the earliest record for spring arrival was of one at Chidham on 23 March 1971 and that passage always started in the first ten days of April. Indeed, prior to 1977, there were only two county records for March and the mean arrival date was 5 April. Since 1976, however, arrival has become earlier, so much so that in the period 1976-93 there were only seven springs in which the first birds were recorded in April. The mean arrival date for the county is now 27 March and, as the following table shows, of 59 birds recorded in March, 49 were in the period 1986-93 (including 42 in 1990-93).

1962-69	1970-77	1978-85	1986-93
-	2	8	49

The earlier start to spring passage has coincided with an increasing tendency for Whimbrel to occur in the county in winter. It is possible, therefore, that some March birds, such as those at Cuckmere Haven on 2 March 1991 and at Selsey Bill on 8 March 1987, may have wintered locally.

Up-Channel movements of Whimbrel are regularly recorded in spring, usually in the company of other waders, such as Bar-tailed Godwits, and also terns. This passage has been described by Cooper (1976a) and Newnham (1985) who both showed that the peak occurs in late April and early May and that there is considerable variation between years and sites. The total recorded each spring depends on the incidence of easterly winds during the peak passage period; in these conditions more are seen. Good years included 1976, when a total of 960 passed Beachy Head; 1984 when the total for the whole county exceeded 2121 (including 1231 at Brighton Marina); 1989 when the county total was at least 1156; and 1993 when the totals of 1407 and 1269 recorded at

Seaford and Worthing respectively were the highest ever for these sites. Totals such as these contrast with those for other years, for example 1986, when just 367 were recorded at all the regularly watched sites.

Between 1990 and 1993, the totals recorded annually at Selsey Bill, Worthing and Seaford averaged 308, 406 and 671 respectively, figures that compare favourably with an average of approximately 300 birds per spring at Beachy Head in the period 1968-75 (Cooper 1976a). Although the data for 1990-93 suggest that Whimbrel, like many other species observed passing up-Channel in spring, are seen in greater numbers at sites further east, the true picture is far less clear. Newnham (1985) showed that the number of Whimbrel recorded on the same date at different coastal sites may vary considerably. This feature is demonstrated in the following table which shows the dates on which more than 300 birds have been recorded at a single site in the county, together with the totals recorded at other sites on the same day, where known.

Date	Selsey Bill	Worthing	Brighton	Seaford	Beachy Head
19 Apr 1969	119*				330
19 Apr 1976					488
7 May 1987	1	205	457		
8 May 1987	7	141	391		
8 May 1989	38	336		53	44
6 May 1993	45	309		170	
7 May 1993	60	288		323	

* total for whole spring

Note:- Coverage invariably different at each site.

Analysis of data collected at Worthing in the period 1978-84 has shown that Whimbrel most often occur in small parties averaging three to five birds. Flocks of 30 to 50 are, however, regularly recorded while occasional larger parties have included those of 110 off Roedean on 1 May 1986 and 95 off Beachy Head on 9 May 1978.

Although large numbers of Whimbrel pass through the Solent in spring (Clark & Eyre 1993), the totals recorded at Selsey Bill are consistently lower than those for other sites in the county. This is most likely due to some birds turning northward before reaching Selsey and migrating overland. Parties of Whimbrel are regularly seen moving north or northeast during the spring, both at coastal and inland sites, and this would help to explain the widely differing totals recorded at sea-watching sites on the same day. Some of the largest flocks recorded have included 50 flying north over Seaford on 12 May 1965, 89 flying north over the Cuckmere Valley on 7 May 1987 and 46 flying northeast high over Pilsey Island on 8 May 1988. Whimbrel have also been observed leaving Chichester Harbour in an inland direction. A total of 79 departed northeast at East Chidham on 9 May 1978 and 107 did likewise during 11 to 13 May 1979.

In addition to these visible movements, flocks of Whimbrel are regularly recorded in both Chichester and Pagham Harbours. In most springs the peak counts at these sites fall between 40 and 80 birds though counts of 100 or more have been recorded on four occasions, including 120 in Pagham Harbour on 21 April 1983 and 117 at Chidham on 4 May 1985. Notably fewer stop over at other estuarine sites although, exceptionally, 70 were recorded at Cuckmere Haven on 5 May 1984.

In recent years there has been an increase in the number of Whimbrel feeding on pasture at both coastal and inland sites. This habit was first noted in 1968 when 36 were recorded at Bury on 12 May although, with the exception of 150 at the Midrips on 5 May 1970, only small numbers were noted in the 1970s. In the early 1980s, 36 were recorded near Arundel on 24 April 1982 and 30-35 at Amberley Wild Brooks between 25 April and 11 May 1984. Over 50 were recorded in the Arun Valley every spring between 1988 and 1993, including a peak count on 2 May 1992 when 200 were at South Stoke and 105 at Pulborough Brooks. Observations from the latter site suggest that Whimbrel, unlike other waders, choose the drier pastures on which to feed. At Pevensey Levels, where feeding on pasture was annual in the period 1987-93, the largest single gathering so far recorded was of 112 on Pevensey Bridge Level on 25 April 1993. Flocks have also been noted on Down, Horse Eye and Manxey Levels while noteworthy counts at other sites have included 98 at Pett Level on 5 May 1987, 55 at Icklesham on 19 April 1989, 47 at Combe Haven on 22 April 1993 and 40 at East Guldeford Level on 5 May 1990. Counts of birds feeding on pasture are summarised in table 59.

	76	77	78	79	80	81	82	83	84	85	86	87	88	89	90	91	92	93
Arun Valley	15	16	7	10	4	2	36	3	35	18	18	50	74	75	50	130	305	78
Pevensey Levels	-	-	4	1	7	1	-	-	-	10	-	25	40	28	60	103	120	112
Other sites	6	11	15	2	3	2	4	6	4	13	5	98	17	55	40	4	13	47

Table 59. Counts of Whimbrel feeding on pasture, 1976 - 93.

The increase that has occurred in the number of Whimbrel feeding on pasture has been accompanied by a dramatic increase in the number of birds roosting at Rye Harbour (fig. 41). Although the peak counts always occur in late April and early May, they do not coincide with the largest coastal movements of the spring. A similar, but larger, spring roost occurs at Steart Island, Somerset where 1500-2000 have been regularly recorded (Prater 1981). Birds that use this roost probably feed in the Severn estuary and on the Somerset and Gwent Levels while the birds that gather at Rye Harbour have presumably spent the day feeding on local pastures.

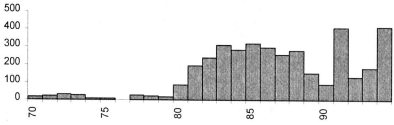

Figure 41. Peak counts of Whimbrel roosting at Rye Harbour, 1970 - 94.

Spring passage extends into June, and in most years small numbers are recorded in the first few days of the month. Notable were 15 that flew east over Bewl Water on 7 June 1987 and one that arrived from the south at Selsey

Bill on 14 June 1970. A few Whimbrel remain during the summer, mainly in Chichester and Pagham Harbours and at Rye Harbour. Typically one or two birds are involved but ten summered in Chichester Harbour in 1978 and seven at Rye Harbour in 1968.

Autumn passage commences in the second half of June as shown by records of one flying south over Upper Beeding on 19 June 1983, three flying west over Bewl Water on 20 June 1992 and two flying southwest there on 22 June 1981. Gatherings of 35 at Rye Harbour on 28 June 1972 and of up to 11 at Pilsey Island during the second half of month also indicate early return passage. In contrast to the spring, little visible migration is noted as shown by the cumulative monthly totals recorded at Worthing in the period 1978-93:

	Jul	Aug	Sep	Oct	Nov	Dec	Jan	Feb	Mar	Apr	May	Jun
Flying west	45	86	13	1	-	-	-	-	-	520	248	2
Flying east	3	13	-	-	-	-	-	-	32	4060	4633	-

Most records are of small parties moving in directions between south and west. Occasional larger groups have included 23 flying southwest at Selsey Bill on 6 August 1965, 40 over Rye Harbour on 19 August 1970, 30 off Langney Point on 30 July 1978 and 36 off Pett on 5 August 1986. Large flocks of between 100-1000 have been recorded flying high over the Netherlands during the autumn (BWP) and one can only speculate about an interesting record of 18 Whimbrel which alighted at Weir Wood Reservoir on 15 August 1982 after separating from a flock of 350-400 unidentified waders that continued flying high to the southwest.

During the autumn most Whimbrel are recorded in Chichester and Pagham Harbours, sites at which it was previously not unusual for the autumn peak to exceed 100 birds. Indeed three-figure counts were recorded in 14 of the 21 autumns in the period 1962-82, including a combined total for both sites of 295 on 28 August 1967. However, since 1982 the highest counts recorded have been just 64 at Chidham on 25 July 1987 and 70 in Pagham Harbour on 25 August 1991. This decline may be due, in part, to a lack of co-ordinated estuary counts in late July and August when Whimbrel numbers are at their highest, but it is interesting to note that autumn counts in Langstone Harbour, Hampshire have similarly declined (Clark & Eyre 1993). Counts at other sites in autumn are much lower than those in Chichester and Pagham Harbours and, even at Rye Harbour, where large numbers gather in the spring, the highest total has been only 50+ in August 1989. Only time will tell whether an exceptional record of 200 at Pulborough Brooks RSPB reserve on 10 August 1993 will be repeated in subsequent autumns.

The highest numbers in autumn are present between mid-July and mid-August and it would appear that by September most Whimbrel have left the county, as shown by the estuary counts for this month (table 60).

	69-74	74-79	79-84	84-89	89-94	Peak counts
Chichester Harbour	16*	11	13	16	6	35, Sep 1984
Pagham Harbour	5*	5*	2*	3	1	10, Sep 1970, 1977 & 1987

Table 60. September counts of Whimbrel in Chichester and Pagham Harbours: five year means of maxima and peak counts.

In 1979 a record of four at Parham Park on 17 September was the last for the year but in all other years a few have lingered into October. Shrubb noted seven November records between 1947 and 1976, including the latest on 25 November 1953 at Thorney Deeps. Between 1977 and 1993 there were November records in a further 11 years involving 16 birds, the latest of which was at East Head on 30 November 1978. The increase in November records is probably related to an increasing tendency for a few Whimbrel to winter in the county.

The first winter record for the county was of one in Pagham Harbour on 24 January 1965. None were then reported until early 1973 when one remained at this site from 2 January to 24 April. Further singles were recorded in Pagham Harbour from 19 January to 31 March 1975 and on 21 February 1981 and two in the lower Cuckmere Valley on 23 February 1981. Whimbrel were then reported in each of the winters between 1983/84 and 1993/94. Prior to 1986/87, all records were for January or February but since December 1986 there have been annual records in that month, totalling 15 birds and including four at Apuldram Manor Farm on 22 December 1992. Most of the 42 Whimbrel recorded between December and February have been seen in Chichester and Pagham Harbours but it is not known whether the same individuals return each year. Exceptions to those recorded in the western harbours were the two in the Cuckmere Valley referred to above, one on the River Adur near Lancing College on 20 February 1984 and a remarkable record of seven flying southwest over Weir Wood Reservoir on 1 January 1992. An increase in the number of Whimbrel wintering in southwest Ireland since the 1960s has been attributed to increased observer interest in wintering waders (Winter Atlas). However, most Sussex records are from localities which have been regularly watched for many years. The following table, which shows the number of winter (December-February) records in 8-year periods between 1962 and 1993, suggests that a real increase has occurred in Sussex.

1962-69	1970-77	1978-85	1986-93
1	2	5	34

Only one Whimbrel has been ringed in Sussex in recent years and, with no recoveries, ringing has added nothing to our knowledge of this species in the county. National ringing data and BWP suggest that some Whimbrel breeding in Iceland, the Faeroes, Fenno-Scandinavia and northwest Russia pass through Britain to and from their wintering quarters in tropical West Africa.

John Newnham

Curlew *Numenius arquata*

Status:- Formerly a very scarce breeder; common passage migrant and winter visitor.

des Forges & Harber reported that one to three pairs of Curlew nested annually in the county after 1932 and that breeding was largely confined to Ashdown Forest, though at least one other locality had been used in the past. Shrubb, however, referred to a maximum of six pairs in Ashdown Forest (in 1968) and one or two pairs in one area of the northwest of the county. Sadly it appears that the Curlew is now extinct as a breeding bird in Sussex as, although 1-2 pairs were recorded in Ashdown Forest throughout the 1980s, none have been seen there since May 1991. A pair was reported at Chapel Common, near Liphook in 1980, 1981 and 1983 while pairs noted at Waltham Brooks on 10 May 1980 and Horse Eye Level on 30 May 1985 may well have been on passage.

Curlew are one of the best known of our wintering waders, their melancholic cries echoing across the marshes. The preferred non-breeding habitat is inter-tidal mudflats, where they feed on worms, crabs and molluscs (Winter Atlas). However, during the winter months they may also utilise ploughed fields or pasture close to the shore. Saltmarsh is also used extensively. Individuals have been shown to specialise in their choice of winter habitat. This is possibly as a result of the individual Curlew's bill morphology. Birds with relatively short, thick, straighter bills tend to specialise in field habitats, while those with relatively long, slim, decurved bills tend to specialise in the inter-tidal zone (Evans 1988).

The main wintering areas in Sussex are in Chichester and Pagham Harbours and at Pett Level but elsewhere in the county few Curlew are seen. At Rye Harbour, birds form a nocturnal roost and although some of these undoubtedly fly in from the Romney/Walland Marsh area which extends into Kent, most arrive to roost from Pett Level.

Adults begin to return from their continental breeding grounds in mid-June, with numbers quickly increasing during July. The highest counts typically occur in September-October (table 62) coinciding with the arrival of large numbers of juveniles (Prater 1981). Numbers tend to decline thereafter, though occasional peaks are recorded in mid-winter. There are marked fluctuations in the monthly totals for any one winter, which may be due to birds moving away from the estuaries to feed during the day, resulting in under-counting (Shrubb). The gradual silting of the harbours may also have led to flocks roosting away from the main sites, so that they too remain uncounted. High tide roost counts at the main localities are summarised in table 61. Sites that regularly hold 1200 or more birds are considered to be of national importance for the species (Waters & Cranswick 1993).

	69-74	74-79	79-84	84-89	89-94	Peak counts
Chichester Harbour	1194	1685	1837	1780	1732	2652, Sep 1982
Pagham Harbour	258	394	375	458	542	909, Sep 1993
Pett Level		550*	525*	573	454	1800, Jan 1987
Rye Harbour	226*	196*	43	87	141	550, Oct 1974

*Table 61. High tide roost counts of Curlew:
five year means of maxima and peak counts, 1969/70 - 93/94.*

	Sep	Oct	Nov	Dec	Jan	Feb	Mar
Maximum	3446	2474	2383	2696	3343	2514	1972
Mean	2039	1720	1393	1470	1550	1608	1149
Minimum	918	995	602	434	770	712	573

Table 62. Monthly totals of Curlew, 1974/75 - 93/94.

Counts of 2321 at Chichester Harbour in December 1985 and 1814 at Pett Level and Rye Harbour in January 1988 were exceptional not only in their size but in that they far exceeded the counts at these localities in the previous month. Curlew tend to be faithful to their winter sites, with most birds staying in one area from the start of the autumn moult through to the commencement of spring migration (Winter Atlas). It may be that since the previous count there had been an influx of birds displaced from other areas by severe weather conditions. Certainly, very hard weather in the county can lead to a reduction in the numbers present. In January 1987 only 500 birds were present in Chichester Harbour compared with 980 in January 1986 and 975 in January 1988. The onset of severe conditions may also result in cold weather movements, as in early 1987, when a total of 59 birds flew northwest at Bewl Water during 12 to 14 January and 22 flew west at Worthing on 14 January.

Although numbers wintering in Pagham Harbour appear to have increased, there is some evidence of a decline in Chichester Harbour. There has been a similar decline in adjacent Langstone Harbour, where numbers have decreased from a mean of 1045 in the period 1975-80 to 769 in 1985-90 (Clark & Eyre 1993). This may be due to poor breeding seasons although, as the National Index for the species has not shown a decrease, it may be that local factors are affecting the suitability of these sites.

As well as feeding in fields close to the harbours, small groups of Curlew can also be found further inland. A number of autumn records have included 18 at Amberley Wild Brooks on 15 September 1990 and several reports of flocks feeding on chalk downland, for example, ten at Bignor Hill on 13 October 1979, 14 at Cissbury Ring from 17 to 27 October 1980 and eight there on 24 October 1989. The largest numbers in winter have been at North Stoke, where there were 90 in January 1985 and 1986, while other notable gatherings have included 61 at Combe Haven and 60 on Lewes Brooks, also in January 1985. A number of spring records, relating to migrants, include 32 at Nyewood on 4 May 1990, 25 at Waltham Brooks on 25 April 1988 and 20 at Harting Down on 1 April 1991. Summer records, such as those of ten at Weir Wood Reservoir on 25 June 1990 and 26 at Bewl Water on 28 June 1990, presumably relate to flocks of returning adults.

Spring passage commences in February as shown by a build up in numbers at the main sites as birds gather to return to their breeding grounds. Sea-watching at Worthing has revealed that the small movement up-Channel is mainly in March and April as is evident from the monthly totals recorded at this site in the period 1978-93:

	Jul	Aug	Sep	Oct	Nov	Dec	Jan	Feb	Mar	Apr	May	Jun
Flying west	196	68	116	45	72	42	139	60	20	121	37	342
Flying east	3	1	3	5	11	-	3	23	235	351	150	8

Small numbers of non-breeding birds, thought to be first-year individuals (Evans 1988), remain throughout the summer in Chichester and Pagham Harbours.

Observations at the main sea-watching localities have also shown that there is a marked westerly movement in June, probably of adult birds (BWP). This passage continues throughout the month and into July and August, with juveniles arriving later in the autumn.

There have been only ten recoveries of foreign-ringed Curlew in Sussex since 1959. Of these, five were ringed as chicks in Finland (3) and Belgium and the Netherlands (1 each). The remaining recoveries relate to birds ringed as fully grown individuals in the Netherlands (3) and Belgium and West Germany (1 each). A similar pattern of recoveries in Hampshire (Clark & Eyre 1993) points to these countries being the origin of our passage and wintering population. The life span of the birds ringed as chicks was fairly short; three were recovered shot within their first year, while one survived for three years and one for six years before being shot at Dell Quay. A fully grown individual ringed on 23 October 1957 in the Netherlands lived for nearly 19 years until it was found shot at Worthing on 14 February 1976.

Joe Nobbs

Upland Sandpiper   *Bartramia longicauda*

Status:- A very rare vagrant (one record).

A first-winter was at Bracklesham from 21 to 25 December 1979 (Porter 1981).

There were nearly 30 records of this species in the British Isles during 1962-94. It breeds on the North American grasslands and migrates to the central South American pampas.   *Richard Fairbank*

Spotted Redshank   *Tringa erythropus*

Status:- A scarce passage migrant and winter visitor.

des Forges & Harber noted that Spotted Redshanks had been recorded annually in winter, except in 1948 and 1951-52. Winter numbers in that period were typically three per annum but a remarkable concentration of 24 was reported in the lower Rother Valley on 13 January 1946. Since the early 1960s the species has been found to winter almost exclusively in Chichester Harbour (especially at Thorney Island) with occasional sightings at nearby Pagham Harbour and coastal sites in the east of the county. Exceptionally, there was one well inland at Weir Wood Reservoir on 20 January 1985. Up to three wintered annually in the county during the 1960s, increasing in the period 1969/70-78/79 to between three and 18, and in most winters approaching the latter figure. More recently, however, a decrease has occurred with no more than seven recorded in any winter in the period 1979/80-92/93, except for 12 in January 1980 and 14 in January 1987.

The presence of wintering birds obscures the arrival of spring migrants but passage probably commences in mid to late March and continues throughout April, with a peak late in that month, before finishing in mid-May. Occasional stragglers occur into early June. Most records are of ones and twos but eight were recorded at Horse Eye Level on 30 April 1975 and four at Rye Harbour on 25 April 1985. An unprecedented passage occurred in early May 1990, when 45 were recorded, including ten at Thorney Island on 2nd and 14 at Sidlesham Ferry on 3rd. The average total for April and May combined for the years 1965 to 1993 is 12. In some years, however, spring passage is very light or almost non-existent, as shown by totals of just five in April-May 1977 and four in April 1986, with none in May of that year.

Return passage commences with the arrival of normally single birds in mid, or more usually late June, although five were recorded at Thorney Island on 30 June 1963. These early individuals may well be failed breeders or females that have already left the males on their breeding grounds (BWP). Peak counts may occur at any time between mid-August, when males and juveniles start to arrive, and late September, although there is considerable variation from year to year. There has, however, been a significant decrease in autumn numbers from the high totals of the 1960s and 1970s (fig. 42). To illustrate this, a total of 135 was recorded in July to September 1967 compared with just 20 in the same period in 1992. Passage continues on a smaller scale throughout October to about mid-November though the numbers recorded in these months have also decreased since the 1970s. There were still ten in Chichester Harbour in November 1981 but only four in the whole county the following month.

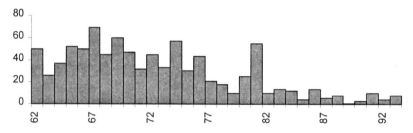

Figure 42. Peak autumn counts of Spotted Redshanks in Chichester Harbour, 1962 - 93.

As with wintering birds, the largest concentrations are recorded in Chichester Harbour where Shrubb referred to annual flocks of between 30 and 60 in the period 1965-76, and a peak count of 69 on 8 August 1967. Numbers have subsequently decreased at this site, in line with the trend for the whole county, as shown by maxima for the periods 1977-81 and 1982-93 of only 55 (in September 1981) and 14 respectively. Birds may also be recorded at other coastal sites in autumn, including Sidlesham Ferry, Pevensey Levels, Pett Level Pools and Rye Harbour. Numbers are typically small although 14 were recorded at the latter site on 19 August 1986.

Birds on migration are sometimes found at inland sites, including reservoirs (especially Bewl Water and Weir Wood Reservoir), gravel pits and in the river valleys. Typically singles are recorded but there were four on the Adur Levels near Steyning in October 1976, five at Weir Wood Reservoir on 2 September 1980 and three at Bewl Water on 3 September 1982.

With the growth in sea-watching since the early 1960s, small parties have occasionally been observed passing offshore in both spring and autumn, sometimes in the company of other waders such as Greenshank. Records have included six flying west at Selsey Bill on 23 August 1980 and three flying west at Worthing on 22 April 1986. *Dave Smith*

Redshank   *Tringa totanus*

Status:- A fairly common resident, passage migrant and winter visitor.

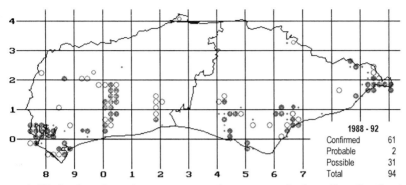

1988 - 92	
Confirmed	61
Probable	2
Possible	31
Total	94

It is likely that the Atlas map accurately portrays the breeding distribution of the Redshank in Sussex, given that the adults are very obvious when displaying and when caring for their young. Display by the males is noted from early March, but the first chicks do not appear until at least the second week of May. The main habitats occupied by breeding Redshank in Sussex are coastal marshes and the permanent grasslands of the river valleys and levels. The major concentrations are round Chichester and Pagham Harbours, at Rye Harbour, on Pevensey and Pett Levels and adjacent to the Arun, Ouse and eastern Rother. Breeding numbers are difficult to assess where the species is common, but a county survey in 1980-81 found a total of 212 pairs (Mitchell 1982). This figure represented a marked decline compared with 1965-67, when a survey found about 250 pairs (Shrubb 1968), and with 1938, when Walpole-Bond's account indicated a population of well over 300 pairs. The decrease in the number of pairs has been accompanied by a contraction of the breeding distribution. This is illustrated by the Atlas map which also shows, as open symbols, tetrads in which Redshank were recorded in the period 1976-87 but not during the Atlas Survey. The decline in both breeding numbers and distribution is considered to be a result of the loss of wet grasslands due to drainage and agricultural intensification. This reduction in habitat has also affected other species with similar requirements, for example, Yellow Wagtail and Snipe. At some sites, however, the reversal of previous drainage has quickly restored a good breeding population, most notably at Pulborough Brooks RSPB Reserve where there was an increase from ten pairs in 1990 to 38 pairs in 1992.

Following the end of the breeding season in June, there is a rapid build up at coastal sites of flocks of moulting and juvenile birds, as shown by counts at Thorney Deeps in 1990 of 474 on 27 June and 1381 on 25 July. Although Shrubb referred to autumn totals of 3000 or more for the western harbours and a peak count of 4200 on 5 September 1971, the numbers recorded in recent years have been lower, not exceeding 2500. A few migrants may occur at inland sites at this time, most notably a flock of 22 at Bewl Water on 30 August 1992. Winter numbers are usually highest in November (table 64), the county totals for this month in each of the five winters from 1989/90-1993/94 indicating that over 1.5% of the British wintering population of 75,000 occurs in Sussex.

	69-74	74-79	79-84	84-89	89-94	Peak counts
Chichester Harbour	2911	2387	2604	1844	1338	4110, Sep 1971
Pagham Harbour	387	392	521	395	389	616, Dec 1981
Adur Estuary		146	171	139	153	300, Feb 1983
Rye Harbour	50*	171*	146	194	128	304, Jan 1985

Table 63. High tide counts of Redshank:
five year means of maxima and peak counts for 1969/70 - 93/94.

	Sep	Oct	Nov	Dec	Jan	Feb	Mar
Maximum	3906	2706	3066	2560	3497	2743	2187
Mean	2035	1758	1934	1783	1695	1664	1300
Minimum	664	847	1169	1027	987	922	450

Table 64. Monthly totals of Redshank, 1974/75 - 93/94.

In addition to those localities listed in table 63, small flocks winter regularly on the shore between Ferring and Lancing and at Newhaven Tide Mills, Cuckmere Haven and Pett Level. Few, however, are recorded inland during the winter months except at Lewes Brooks where counts have included 61 in December 1982, 60 in early 1988 and 50 in January 1985. The onset of severe conditions may result in cold weather movements and high mortality, as in early 1985 when a total of 42 flew west at Worthing on 7-8 January and 70 were found dead at Pagham Harbour.

A very small spring passage is apparent at coastal sites, as shown by the cumulative monthly totals at Worthing for the period 1978-93 in the table below. The largest, and most unusual movement recorded at this locality was a total of 42 flying west in two flocks on 6 May 1986.

	Jul	Aug	Sep	Oct	Nov	Dec	Jan	Feb	Mar	Apr	May	Jun
Flying west	17	45	35	104	53	33	60	1	11	8	58	8
Flying east	1	10	23	54	33	4	20	28	77	33	112	-

Of thirteen recoveries of Sussex-ringed birds, only two, both ringed as chicks, were from outside southern England. The furthest, ringed at Selsey in July 1962, was found dead at Sarthe, France, 278 km SSE, in January 1963 while the other was shot at Baie de Somme, France in July 1988, having been ringed at Icklesham the previous May. There is only one record of a foreign-ringed bird found in Sussex, relating to an individual ringed in Latvia in May 1965 and shot in November 1966 in Pagham Harbour, 1714 km WSW. These recoveries suggest that at least some of the Redshank that breed in Sussex winter locally and that these are joined by birds from further afield.

Individuals can be very faithful to their wintering site, as illustrated by a leucistic bird that has returned to the River Adur at Shoreham-by-Sea every winter since 1985/86 and again present in 1995/96. *Dr B J Yates*

Marsh Sandpiper

Tringa stagnatilis

Status:- A very rare vagrant (seven records involving eight individuals).

Four were seen prior to 1962 (des Forges & Harber): two at the Wicks on 26 September 1937 (Ticehurst & Morley 1937) and singles at the eastern end of Thorney Great Deep on 22 April 1951 (des Forges & Paulson 1952) and in the lower Cuckmere Valley on 29 April 1951 (Alder & James 1952). Those at the Wicks were the second and third to be seen in Britain.

Four have been recorded since the beginning of 1962, including three during 1989-92:

1984: A summer plumaged adult at Waltham Brooks from 8 to 11 July.
1989: A first-summer at Icklesham on 23 May.
1990: An adult at Sidlesham Ferry from 30 June to 9 July.
1992: An adult at Icklesham around midday and at Ternery Pool, Rye Harbour during the evening of 4 July.

With the exception of the two in September 1937, all records have fallen between 22 April and 11 July. Two have been seen at Icklesham, two together at the Wicks and singles at the Cuckmere, Sidlesham Ferry, Thorney and Waltham Brooks.

There were over 70 records of this delicate fine-billed wader in the British Isles during 1962-94. It breeds from eastern Europe across Asia and winters in Africa, southern Asia and Australia. *Richard Fairbank*

Greenshank

Tringa nebularia

Status:- A fairly common passage migrant and scarce winter visitor.

Shrubb noted that parties of up to seven had been recorded in winter, but that the species did not winter every year. Wintering has, however, occurred annually from at least 1966 involving typically fewer than eight individuals although there were ten in February 1991 and 12 in December 1992. The vast majority of winter records have been for Chichester Harbour (especially

Thorney Island), followed by Pagham Harbour, with occasional singles at other sites including the lower Cuckmere Valley, Pett Level and Rye Harbour. Unusually, there was one inland at Arlington Reservoir on 21 January 1982.

Spring passage normally commences in mid-April though occasional birds noted in late March and the first two weeks of April may possibly be wintering birds on the move. Migration continues through May, with the odd straggler recorded in early June. The peak is usually in the last few days of April and the first ten days of May; notable concentrations at this time have included 11 that arrived from the south at Beachy Head on 13 May 1971; 15 well inland at Bewl Water on 7 May 1976; 24 that flew east at Rye Harbour on 8 May 1989; a remarkable total of 32, including a flock of 25, that flew east past Birling Gap on 2 May 1990; 25 that flew east at Worthing on 5 May 1993; and 11 at Waltham Brooks on 8 May 1993. Counts in Chichester Harbour have included 30 on 3 May 1988, 26 on 29 April 1991 and 28 on 10 May 1993. Sea-watching has shown that singles, small parties and occasional larger parties, such as those listed above, pass up-Channel in spring, sometimes in the company of other waders. A total of 34 was recorded at both Worthing and Seaford in 1991 and 65 at the former site between 28 April and 11 May 1993. However, in years when favourable east to southeast winds are absent, very few are noted.

By far the largest numbers occur on autumn passage, which begins in mid to late June and continues into November. Numbers build up rapidly in July and in some years there is evidence of two peaks, one between mid-July and mid-August and another between late August and mid-September. Ringing of Greenshank at Farlington Marshes, Hampshire indicates that these two peaks correspond to the main passage periods for adults and juveniles respectively (Clark & Eyre 1993). Numbers decrease slowly through October though there were still 115 at Thorney Island on 5 October 1991 and 99 there on 16 October 1990. In some years only a handful remain in November, as in 1972 when just five were recorded, but in other years much larger numbers occur, as in 1971 when there were 68.

The majority of autumn birds are recorded in Chichester Harbour. des Forges & Harber stated that 30 to 50 were regular there and that up to 70 had been counted together, while Shrubb referred to regular flocks of 50 to 100 and maxima of 135 on 5 September 1971 and 130 on 15 September 1974. More recently, numbers appear to have increased slightly as shown by regular counts of 100 or more and maxima of 143 on 15 August 1981, 137 on 28 August 1983 and 146 on 26 September 1991. Significant numbers may also be recorded in autumn in the east of the county, particularly at Rye Harbour, where there were 52 on 9 August 1975 and 50 in July 1985. Other counts in this area have included 48 at Camber on 2 August 1984 and 70 at Pett on 30 August 1985. Some visible movements are noted in autumn, for example, 31 that flew southwest over Sidlesham Ferry on 20 August 1992.

Greenshank are regularly recorded in small numbers at inland sites, especially in the autumn, while counts in double figures have included 13 at Darwell Reservoir on 22 August 1987, 11 at Weir Wood Reservoir on 19 August 1987 and ten there on 20 August 1989.

One ringed at Glynde Reach in August 1983 was found in Segou, Mali, 4265 km south, in February 1985 while one ringed at Icklesham on 28 August 1991 was shot in France at Rejet de Beaulieu, Nord on 1 August 1993.

Dave Smith

Lesser Yellowlegs *Tringa flavipes*

Status:- A very rare vagrant (eight records).

Two were seen prior to 1962 (des Forges & Harber): at Chichester Gravel Pits on 15 August 1947 (Ferguson-Lees & Smith 1948) and at Sidlesham Ferry on 13 September 1954.

Since the beginning of 1962 there have been six records:

1969:   One at Chichester Gravel Pits from 16 October to 3 November.
1970:   One at the Cuckmere Haven oxbows on 3-4 August.
1971:   One at Weir Wood Reservoir on 11-12 August.
1983:   A first-winter at Willingdon Level, Eastbourne from 3 February to 9 April.
1985:   One at Sidlesham Ferry on 27 April.
1988:   An adult on the beach opposite Pett Level Pools on 14 August was flushed by a dog and departed east.

It is likely that the individual seen in 1983 had arrived in Britain the previous autumn. Of the other records, one was in spring and six in autumn (from August to November). Two have been recorded at both Chichester Gravel Pits and Sidlesham Ferry with singles at Cuckmere Haven, Pett Level Pools, Weir Wood Reservoir and Willingdon Level.

There were almost 190 records of this slim wader in the British Isles during 1962-94. It breeds in Alaska and Canada and winters in the southern USA and throughout Central and South America.

Richard Fairbank

Green Sandpiper *Tringa ochropus*

Status:- A scarce spring and fairly common autumn passage migrant. Very scarce in winter.

des Forges & Harber reported that the number of wintering birds recorded annually in the period 1947-60 varied from two to 12, with an average of about six, while Shrubb referred to a wintering population of "usually five to ten birds annually". In the period 1977-93, the number of birds recorded in December varied from six to 23 annually (average 12) while totals for January varied from six to 21 (average 12). The most reported in any one winter were 42 in 1984/85 and 49 in 1988/89. Wintering birds are typically found in ones and twos on the margins of streams, ditches, farm ponds, gravel pits and sewage farms away from the coast. Up to six have been noted at Barnhorn Level, Chingford Pond, Darwell Reservoir and Pett Level in recent winters but the largest concentration recorded in the county was that of eight at Amberley on 12 February 1989.

Spring passage occurs from mid-March, as indicated by the appearance of birds at sites where they have not wintered. Passage is heaviest in April though the number recorded annually varies considerably. The largest party recorded at this time was eight at the Midrips on 13 April 1971. Passage may continue into mid-May, as shown by the arrival of singles from the south at Beachy Head on 11 May 1969 and at Selsey Bill on 17 May 1964, but in most years few are seen after the first week of that month.

Green Sandpipers are one the first waders to return from their breeding grounds and autumn passage may commence as early as the second week of June, after which there is a scattering of individuals through to the end of the month. Singles recorded at Runcton on 4 June 1964 and Bewl Water on 7 June 1992 could refer to either late spring or early autumn migrants. Numbers may reach a peak at any time between late July and late August but most frequently during the first week of August. Passage continues until the end of October. Until recently, the largest concentrations recorded in autumn were at Chichester Gravel Pits, where there were 21 on 19 August 1972 and 20 on 23 July 1983. Similar numbers have also been noted at Rye Harbour (max. 19 on 18 August 1990), Thorney Island (max. 20 on 25 August 1963) and Waltham Brooks (max. 17 on 10 July 1983 and 28 July 1990). Counts of eight or more have also been made at Bewl Water, Chingford Pond, Darwell Reservoir, Pevensey Levels and Pett Level and in the Adur, lower Cuckmere and Ouse Valleys.

The cumulative monthly totals, monthly maxima, minima and means for the period 1962-93 are shown below.

	Jan	Feb	Mar	Apr	May	Jun	Jul	Aug	Sep	Oct	Nov	Dec
Maximum	21	23	14	22	8	24	89	110	52	34	21	23
Mean	9	8	7	10	2	9	37	59	28	13	10	8
Minimum	0	0	0	0	0	1	8	14	11	4	1	0
Total	287	261	216	308	73	282	1187	1892	881	417	328	251

One ringed at Icklesham in July 1987 was recovered in El Kalaa, Morocco, 2225 km SSW, in September 1988.   *Dave Smith*

Andy Williams

The chalk cliffs between Seaford and Eastbourne are a major arrival and departure point for summer migrants. They are also the traditional haunt of Sussex Peregrines.

Roger Wilmsh[

The Lower Cuckmere valley, although subject to heavy visitor pressure,
attracts a wide range of species including breeding Shelduck.

Andy Will[

Pulborough Brooks, now in the ownership of the RSPB have benefited from extensive habitat management and now holds good numbers of breeding Snipe, Redshank and Yellow Wagtails. It is also an important wintering area for wildfowl and waders.

Roger Wilmsh

*The South Downs are the county's most prominent physical feature and have
seen great farming changes over the last century. They remain a stronghold
of the Linnet while the Yellowhammer is still a common sight.*

Mike R

Read

*Grey Partridges are becoming an uncommon sight in the county,
even in such formerly ideal habitat as on the Downs above Amberley.*

Wilmshurst

Sussex retains a number of heathlands, the largest being Ashdown Forest, a mosaic of dry, damp and wet heathland with valley mires, streams, scrub and woodland. The recent run of mild winters has helped the breeding population of Dartford Warblers.

Roger Wilmsl

Roger Wilmsl

*There are a number of inland waters throughout the county including
Weir Wood Reservoir. Other than holding breeding Great Crested Grebe
and Kingfishers, migrating Ospreys are sometimes recorded.*

In the ownership of the National Trust, East Head at the entrance to Chichester Harbour is an excellent spot to observe waders. Chichester Harbour holds internationally important concentrations of Dunlin and Black-tailed Godwits.

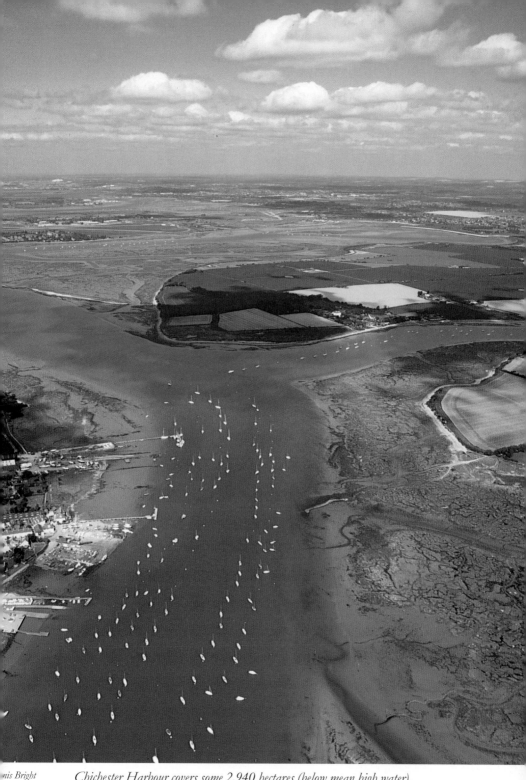

nis Bright

*Chichester Harbour covers some 2,940 hectares (below mean high water).
It is a Grade 1 NCR and Ramsar site. It supports internationally important
numbers of wintering Brent Geese, Ringed and Grey Plovers, Dunlin and
Bar-tailed Godwits plus six species of national importance.*

Ebernoe Common is a fine example of high-forest woodland containing old beech and younger woodland plus an area of scrub. It is owned and managed by the Sussex Wildlife Trust and provides ideal habitat for arboreal birds such as the Nuthatch.

The view from Duncton Hill across the Weald shows that farming remains the dominant land use. The Weald supports healthy populations of Nightingales and Barn Owls.

Dennis Br

Selsey Bill is one of the most popular sea-watching spots in the county and has been watched regularly since 1959.
Although relatively small, Pagham Harbour holds a wide diversity of waders and wildfowl. It is a SPA and Ramsar site.

Dennis Br

Wood Sandpiper   *Tringa glareola*

Status:- A scarce spring and autumn passage migrant; recorded once in winter.

Up to 1937 only nine birds had been recorded in spring but between 1948 and 1961 from one to six (usually only one) were recorded annually at that season, but none in 1952 and 1958 (des Forges & Harber).

Between 1962 and 1993, Wood Sandpipers were recorded in all but seven springs. In most years, up to six were reported but there were exceptional influxes in 1987 and 1990, in which totals of 20 and 14 respectively were recorded. The earliest sightings were for 15 April 1992 at Burton Mill Pond and 19 April 1969 at Crowhurst Marsh but most were seen between late April and early June, with a peak in the latter half of May. It is unusual to see more than two birds together in spring, but six were seen at Rye Harbour on 17 May 1959 and five at Pevensey Bridge Level on 4 May 1990. Birds have very occasionally been noted on sea-watches in the spring. At Beachy Head, one flew north on 13 May 1984, as did singles at Selsey Bill on 26 May 1974 and 2 May 1979.

A number of records for mid-June could refer to either late spring or early autumn migrants, while those at the end of the month presumably refer to the latter. The main autumn passage is from late July until mid-September. As in spring, the annual totals have varied considerably between nine in 1976 and 1979 and 60 in 1972. At this season parties of up to five are not uncommon and sometimes larger groups have been seen, including 15 at the Midrips on 3 September 1956, nine at Rye Harbour on 30 July and 11 August 1972 and at Pett Level on 7 September 1988 and eight there on 8 August 1978. There have been very few records for October and just two for November, comprising singles at Newhaven from 23 October to 3 November 1976 and at Pett Level on 2 November 1987. The annual totals recorded in both spring and autumn are shown in fig. 43.

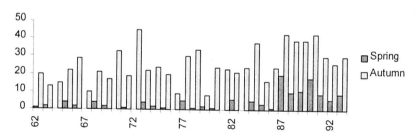

Figure 43. Spring and autumn totals of Wood Sandpipers, 1962 - 93.

One in the Ouse Valley, at Iford on 11 February 1967, is the only winter record for the county, although Hudson (1973) reported this as the earliest spring record for Britain.

The cumulative monthly totals for the periods 1962-76 and 1977-93 shown below indicate the general pattern of occurrence.

	Jan	Feb	Mar	Apr	May	Jun	Jul	Aug	Sep	Oct	Nov	Dec
1962 - 76	-	1	-	4	14	7	66	207	57	5	1	-
1977 - 93	-	-	-	9	80	45	128	291	74	3	1	-
Total	-	1	-	13	94	52	194	498	131	8	2	-

Dave Smith

Terek Sandpiper   *Xenus cinereus*

Status:- A very rare vagrant (two records).

One was recorded prior to 1962, at the Midrips on 30 May 1951 (Betts 1952). It was the first British record.

One in Pagham Harbour, on mud flats near Church Norton, on 10 May 1969 was seen for about 20 minutes feeding and in flight. It was the sixth British record.

There were nearly 40 records of this species in the British Isles during 1962-94. It breeds from southeast Finland across Siberia and winters on the coasts from western Africa to Australia.   *Richard Fairbank*

Common Sandpiper   *Actitis hypoleucos*

Status:- A fairly common passage migrant; a few regularly winter; has bred at least once.

In spring, passage normally commences in April and reaches a peak in the last week of the month and the first half of May. Most records are of single birds or small parties at both coastal and inland sites, the latter including gravel pits, river margins and reservoirs. The largest counts at this time have included 21 at Rye Harbour on 26 May 1970, 20 in the lower Cuckmere Valley on 5-6 May 1978, 17 at Splash Point, Seaford on 12 May 1988, 16 on the shore between Rock-a-Nore and Fairlight on 21 May 1977 and 15 at Arlington Reservoir on 30 April 1972. A few birds linger into June.

A pair bred on the River Arun, just south of Horsham, in 1978, hatching three young, while breeding may also have occurred at Bewl Water the following year.

Return passage starts in mid-June, as shown by a record of eight at Waltham Brooks on 15 June 1980, and peaks in late July and early August and again in mid to late August. Numbers tail off rapidly in September and by October only stragglers remain. The largest numbers have been recorded at coastal sites including 66 in the Rye area on 14 August 1983, 61 in Chichester Harbour on 31 July 1976, 56 there on 13 August 1977 and 50 in Pagham Harbour on 18 August 1968. Other notable concentrations have included a flock of 50 on the banks of the Ouse near Lewes on 3 August 1967, 40 at Arlington Reservoir on 12 August 1975 and on the Ouse near Iford on 8 August 1968, 37 at the Long Pits at Rye Harbour on 8 August 1973 and 35 at Bewl Water on 23 August 1986. The autumn totals for the whole county for the period 1977-93 indicate that numbers have decreased significantly from a peak in 1986 (fig. 44), as in Hampshire where there has been a decline since the late 1980s (Clark & Eyre 1993).

Shrubb stated that it was likely that a few Common Sandpipers always wintered in Sussex and that the numbers involved rarely exceeded five birds, although there were 12 in 1950. This is still very much the situation today for no more than nine were recorded in any winter in the period 1976/77-92/93 and no more than three at any one site (Thorney Island, 16 December 1990). By far the most favoured localities are Chichester Harbour (especially Thorney Island), the Arun Valley between Littlehampton and Offham, the Ouse Valley between Newhaven and Barcombe, and the lower Cuckmere Valley, though birds have been recorded at a large number of other sites, some well inland, such as Bewl Water, Shillinglee Lake and Warnham Mill Pond.

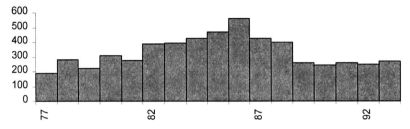

Figure 44. Autumn totals of Common Sandpipers, 1977 - 93.

The pattern of occurrence is clearly shown in the following table of cumulative monthly totals, monthly maxima, minima and means for the period 1980-93.

	Jan	Feb	Mar	Apr	May	Jun	Jul	Aug	Sep	Oct	Nov	Dec
Maximum	5	4	12	51	106	19	215	380	86	16	10	5
Mean	2	2	3	27	78	10	113	172	53	9	3	3
Minimum	0	0	1	13	29	3	51	70	22	3	0	1
Total	33	21	39	382	1097	133	1583	2409	738	122	38	37

Chris Janman

Spotted Sandpiper *Actitis macularia*

Status:- A very rare autumn vagrant (four records involving five or six individuals).

There are two old records, of two, perhaps three, shot on the Crumbles in October 1866 and a female shot at Shoreham-by-Sea on 27 November 1908 (des Forges & Harber). Those in 1866 were the first British records, one of which is in the Booth Museum (either BoMNH 208048 or 208049).

There have been two records since the beginning of 1962:

1974: An adult in summer plumage at Weir Wood Reservoir from 11 to 17 August.
1977: A juvenile at Barcombe Reservoir from 3 to 12 November.

Records have fallen in August, October and November and have not, as yet, included the best watched wader sites. Another is possibly overdue.

There were just over 100 records of this species in the British Isles during 1962-94 which, in the past, has been considered conspecific with Common Sandpiper. It breeds throughout North America and winters from southern USA to central South America. *Richard Fairbank*

Turnstone   *Arenaria interpres*

Status:- **A fairly common winter visitor and passage migrant; scarce in summer.**

Turnstones are coastal waders encountered most frequently in estuaries and on rock strewn sandy shores. In Sussex they are found mainly in Chichester and Pagham Harbours and on the beaches between Pevensey and Rye Harbour.

Autumn migrants arrive in small numbers from about the second week of July, building up rapidly during the following weeks. This is especially evident at Rye Harbour where large concentrations have been recorded on a number of occasions in late July and early August, particularly during the 1980s. Counts have included 205 on 30 July 1985, 251 on 8 August 1983, 342 in mid-August 1984 and 350 on 11 August 1985. In 1984, however, all had gone by 10 September, thus suggesting that the Rye area is more important as a migratory staging post for the species than for its wintering population. A similar autumn build-up occurs in Chichester Harbour where, for example, numbers increased rapidly from 88 on 20 July 1986 to 286 four days later. Other high autumn counts at this site have included 274 on 8 August 1993 and 333 on 12 August 1994.

Although the highest county total of 1227 was recorded in September 1993, the monthly totals shown in table 66 suggest that numbers may continue to increase to reach a peak in October. The totals in the table also suggest that there is a gradual decline in numbers through the winter whereas Shrubb, who analysed counts in Pagham and Chichester Harbours between 1964 and 1974, noted a consistent drop in numbers in December followed by an arrival of further winter visitors in January. Prater (1987) noted that all the peak counts of Turnstones in the 1960s occurred in the autumn whereas in five of the first six years in the 1980s the peaks occurred in the winter.

	69-74	74-79	79-84	84-89	89-94	Peak counts
Chichester Harbour	165	122	193	246	253	384, Nov 1982
Pagham Harbour	176	305	326	362	509	714, Oct 1993
Atherington / Climping	7*	5	19	11*	28	35, Oct 1989
Goring		10*	12	8	9	48, Jan 1989
Langney to Pevensey	57*	123*	194	213	53	345, Dec 1985
Glyne Gap				313	270	393, Oct 1987
Pett Level		132*	270*	152	139	350, Dec 1987
Rye Harbour	64*	95*	50	62	9	276, Feb 1985

Table 65. High tide roost counts of Turnstones:
five year means of maxima and peak counts, 1969/70 - 93/94.

	Sep	Oct	Nov	Dec	Jan	Feb	Mar
Maximum	1227	1134	1084	1122	1056	1123	956
Mean	480	623	620	607	585	579	576
Minimum	52	30	216	182	103	126	100

Table 66. Monthly totals of Turnstones, 1974/75 - 93/94.

The number of Turnstones wintering in Sussex has shown a distinct increase since the late 1960s (table 63). Shrubb referred to a stable wintering population of up to 300 in the two western harbours and estimated the total county wintering population to be of the order of 300 to 600 birds, whereas the peak winter counts for the whole county between 1984/85 and 1993/94 ranged between 561 and 1123, with an average for the period of 920. The increase in the wintering populations in both the western harbours has had a disproportionate impact on the county total and although the numbers wintering in the county as a whole have risen, decreases have occurred at some sites, particularly in East Sussex. A long term decline appears to be occurring in the Pett/Rye Harbour area whereas the wintering population found between Langney Point and Pevensey Bay appears to have declined precipitously during the past five years. Prater (1981) suggested the total British wintering population to be of the order of 25,000 birds; thus Sussex holds about 2.7% of this total.

Large numbers of Turnstones are occasionally recorded at sites not listed in table 65, notably 200 at Littlehampton in January 1983.

In spring, large gatherings were recorded at Rye Harbour in the 1970s and 1980s. A count of 470 at this site on 10 May 1985 remains the highest for the county while more typical counts were those of 260 in May 1977 and 1978, 300 in the first half of May 1984, 310 on 14 May 1986 and 240 during April and May 1987. Since 1987, counts at Rye Harbour have decreased although significant concentrations have been recorded at two other sites in the east of the county, namely Glyne Gap, where there were 250 in early May 1986 and 210 on 4 May 1993 and Pett, where 130 were counted in May 1986 and 230 on 22 April 1990. In recent years the highest spring gatherings have been in Chichester Harbour where a roost on Stakes Island held 400 on 6 May 1989, 300 on both 9 and 13 May 1990 and 275 on 13 May 1991.

Shrubb noted that very few were seen in June and that summering was a rare event. This is no longer the case for summering birds have occurred annually since five were recorded in 1976. Most are recorded in Chichester and Pagham Harbours and at Rye Harbour where the maxima have been 68 in 1986, 30 in 1983 and 25 in 1986 respectively. The county totals exceeded 80 in both 1986 and 1987.

The cumulative monthly totals recorded at Worthing in the period 1978-93, shown in the following table, reveal that moderate numbers of Turnstones pass up-Channel in spring and that some coastal passage may occur in autumn, but on a smaller scale than that in spring.

	Jul	Aug	Sep	Oct	Nov	Dec	Jan	Feb	Mar	Apr	May	Jun
Flying west	8	90	48	65	39	72	12	2	82	56	101	-
Flying east	2	54	28	13	7	22	1	3	39	401	1480	2

As with other species of waders that pass up-Channel in spring, the largest numbers are recorded in periods of settled weather with winds from an easterly direction (Newnham 1985). The total recorded annually varies considerably with that of 386 at Worthing in 1980 the largest for a single site. These figures includes the two largest day totals for the county of 115 flying east on 1 May 1980 and 98 on 3 May. The largest movements which occur in late April or, more usually, in early May, coincide with the peak spring counts at estuarine sites and with the appearance of small numbers of birds at inland localities.

During the spring, flocks are regularly recorded at dusk departing inland from the estuaries in Hampshire in a north to northwest direction (Clark & Eyre 1993). Such behaviour has not been reported in Sussex although a flock of 70 flew north at Combe Haven on 15 May 1985.

Inland records are comparatively rare with about 39 recorded between 1962 and 1993. Following the first for the county at Barcombe Reservoir on 6 May 1967, inland birds were annual until 1977 but thereafter they were recorded in only four years up to 1993. Nearly half were seen at Arlington Reservoir (18) with the remainder at Weir Wood Reservoir (5), Barcombe Reservoir and Bewl Water (4 each), Chichester Gravel Pits (3), Darwell Reservoir (2), and Dragon's Green and Waltham Brooks (1 each). The penultimate bird was found dead under overhead power lines on 10 October 1969. Inland records in spring have all occurred in the period 20 April to 18 May while those in autumn have fallen between 18 July and 9 November. The cumulative monthly totals of inland records are shown below.

Jul	Aug	Sep	Oct	Nov	Dec	Jan	Feb	Mar	Apr	May	Jun
5	11	1	3	1	-	-	-	-	6	12	-

With only 12 Turnstones ringed in Sussex between 1979 and 1993 from which no recoveries have been recorded, ringing has added nothing to our knowledge of this species in Sussex. However, national data show that those wintering in Britain are mostly from the Greenland and Canadian breeding populations while those that occur on passage breed in northern Europe (Prater 1981).   *John Newnham*

Wilson's Phalarope   *Phalaropus tricolor*

Status:- A very rare vagrant (eight recorded).

First recorded in the county in 1971, eight individuals have been seen:

1971:   An adult female at Arlington Reservoir on 25 September, at the Cuckmere Haven oxbows on 26-27 September and then on the 'long pool' near the northwest corner of Pagham Harbour from 28 September to 6 October (*Brit. Birds* 65: plates 50b, 78a and 78b) when it was mindlessly shot.

1978:   An adult along the eastern side of Pagham Harbour on 21 October.

1979:   An adult at Sidlesham Ferry on 26-27 August.

1984:   An adult female at Ternery Pool, Rye Harbour on 30 June and 1 July. An adult at Sidlesham Ferry on 12 October.

1985:   A first-winter at Ternery Pool, Rye Harbour on 9 October.

1987:   A juvenile moulting into first-winter plumage at Sidlesham Ferry from 18 to 26 September (*Brit. Birds* 81: plate 19).

1991:   An adult male at Sidlesham Ferry on 3 June.

All individuals have ended up at either Sidlesham Ferry/Pagham Harbour (6) or Rye Harbour (2). One was seen in late spring (early June), one in mid-summer (June-July) and six in autumn (late August to October).

There were almost 250 records of this engaging wader in the British Isles during 1962-94. This is a massive increase considering the first British record was in 1954, and that there were only four others in the 1950s. It is almost certainly due to an eastwards expansion of its breeding range on the North

American prairies (Hayman, Marchant & Prater 1986). It migrates to the Argentinian pampas and high Andean lakes in southern South America.

Richard Fairbank

Red-necked Phalarope   *Phalaropus lobatus*

Status:- A rare spring and autumn passage migrant.

Up until 1961, a total of about 54 was recorded (des Forges & Harber). Since then, there have been records in 13 years totalling 20 individuals as follows:

1962: A first-winter at Langney Point on 26 August.
1965: A male in summer plumage in a shallow ditch on Amberley Wild Brooks on 12-13 June.
      One at the Wicks on 28 August.
1967: One at Rye Harbour on 25 August.
1968: An adult in summer plumage on Thorney Deeps on 25 May.
1970: One at Rye Harbour from 11 to 16 September.
1974: One at Rye Harbour on 7-8 June.
      One at Chichester Gravel Pits on 27-28 July.
1976: A first-winter at the Severals, Church Norton from 26 to 30 October.
1978: A female at Sidlesham Ferry on 5 June.
1979: A female at Sidlesham Ferry on 7-8 July.
      An adult at Pett Level Pools on 18-19 September.
1981: A first-winter at Pett Level Pools from 27 September to 3 October.
      One at Langney Point on 19 September.
1989: A female at Sidlesham Ferry on 2 June.
      A first-winter at Widewater, Lancing from 1 to 7 September (*Brit. Birds* 83: plate 35).
1990: A first-winter at Rye Harbour from 29 August to 3 September.
      A first-winter at Sidlesham Ferry on 12 September.
1992: A first-winter at Sidlesham Ferry from 26 August to 3 September (*Brit. Birds* 86: plate 110).
      One on the River Ouse near Glynde on 1 or 2 September.

Most spring birds have been in early June or, less frequently, in late May. There is, however, an exceptionally early record of one at Bexhill on 14 April 1906 but this is probably best discounted due to its association with the Hastings Rarities.

In autumn, the vast majority of birds have been in the last week of August and the first three weeks of September. Of the thirteen August to October records after 1961, eleven were in this four week period. The latest Sussex record is of one killed near Lewes during November 1850 (Walpole-Bond).

As might be expected, most records during the period 1962-94 were for coastal localities such as Sidlesham Ferry (5), Rye Harbour (4) and Pett Level Pools (2). Some of these birds were most confiding, allowing very close views, such as those at Widewater in 1989 and Sidlesham Ferry in 1992.

The cumulative monthly totals for the period 1962-94 are shown below.

May	Jun	Jul	Aug	Sep	Oct
1	4	2	5	7	1

The species has a circumpolar breeding distribution, including northern Europe, and winters chiefly at sea in the tropics. In Britain, there is a small breeding population in the Shetland Islands and Outer Hebrides. *Richard Kelly*

Grey Phalarope
Phalaropus fulicarius

Status:- A very scarce autumn and rare winter visitor, usually occurring after gales.

During the 19th century, large numbers occurred on several occasions after severe gales, for example *ca*. 250 in 1866 (des Forges & Harber). More recently, *ca*. 60 were recorded in 1960, part of an exceptional influx into Britain at this time. Between 1962 and 1994, there were records in 29 years totalling approximately 142 birds (fig. 45).

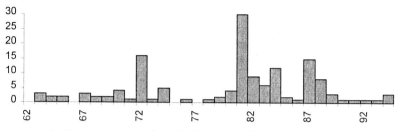

Figure 45. Annual totals of Grey Phalaropes, 1962 - 94.

Of these, 30 were recorded in 1981 following stormy weather in the North Atlantic that displaced birds into the Western Approaches. The first appeared on 22 September at Shoreham Harbour (the day before 200 were recorded off the Isles of Scilly). Six were present in the county on 27 September and 12 on 10 October. Birds were recorded at a number of localities including Chichester Harbour, Bracklesham Bay, Selsey Bill, Pagham Harbour, the lower Cuckmere Valley, Langney Point, Pett Level Pools and Rye Harbour. The last was seen at Shoreham-by-Sea on 17 October. After the storm in October 1987, surprisingly only *ca*. 15 were recorded, compared with 25 in Hampshire (Clark & Eyre 1993). Sometimes flocks of up to 1000 may occur off southwest England after severe gales but the largest number seen together in Sussex in recent years was a party of nine that flew west past Langney Point on 19 November 1972.

The earliest recorded in autumn was on 17 August 1844 followed by one at the Midrips on 25 August 1948 but most have occurred in the period from late September to early November. Stays of one or two days are typical but there have been some longer staying individuals such as those at Rye Harbour from 26 September to 11 October 1981, where two were present from 4 to 8 October, and at Sidlesham Ferry from 15 to 28 October 1983 (two present from 16th). Although the Grey Phalarope is very much an oceanic species outside the breeding season, birds may occur well inland after autumn gales, of which singles at Glynde Levels on 3 November 1967, Ardingly Reservoir on 27 September 1983, Barcombe Reservoir on 23-24 November 1985 and Bewl Water on 17 October 1987 are the most recent.

Few have been seen after mid-November; the latest in winter were at Brighton Marina on 29 January 1986 and at Church Norton on 3 and 9 February 1974.

The only spring record was of one at Rye Harbour on 23 April 1973 and what was almost certainly the same bird at Camber on 25 April.

The cumulative monthly totals of all records for the period 1962-94 are shown below.

Sep	Oct	Nov	Dec	Jan	Feb	Mar	Apr
34	63	31	7	5	1	-	1

The Grey Phalarope has a circumpolar breeding distribution. The main wintering grounds of Western Palearctic birds are at sea off West Africa.

Richard Kelly

Pomarine Skua   *Stercorarius pomarinus*

Status:- A passage migrant, regular in varying numbers in spring but very scarce in autumn; a very rare visitor in winter.

Up until 1961 des Forges & Harber recorded a total of about 66 birds. Of these most were in autumn and, of those observed in spring, all but one occurred in 1961. The five winter records, in December (3), January (1), and February (1), were all before 1924. Since the beginning of 1962, a total of at least seven has been recorded in winter as follows:

1970: One flying west off Goring on 10 March.
1985: One flying east at Selsey Bill on 21 December was seen 30 minutes later at Worthing.
1986: An immature at Selsey Bill on 10 January.
1990: One off Selsey Bill on 30 December.
1991: An adult and two juveniles seen from a fishing boat 14 km off Brighton Marina on 29 December and probably one of the same the following day.

It is in spring, however, that the most marked increase has occurred (fig. 46). This trend, which has also been noted in Kent and Hampshire, appears to be genuine and not just the result of increased sea-watching activity since the early 1960s.

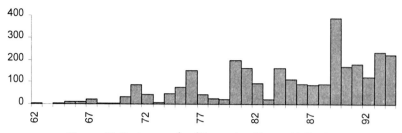

Figure 46. Spring totals of Pomarine Skuas, 1962 - 94.

The earliest recorded on spring passage was one flying east off Seaford on 2 April 1989. Most, however, are seen in the last week of April and the first three weeks of May, the largest movements occurring in anticyclonic weather with winds between south and northeast, but especially from the southeast. Such conditions produced exceptional numbers in 1989, the total of at least 390 for the whole spring being the largest yet recorded in Sussex. In unfavourable winds, it is likely that many birds pass to the west of Britain and Ireland and this would account for the low totals in some years. Since the beginning of 1962 at least 2922 have occurred in April and May, most of which passed up-Channel. The largest movement was of 120 that flew east off Splash Point, Seaford on 5 May 1989, including parties of 26, 25 and 20, while the biggest flocks recorded in the county were those of 51 flying east off Brighton Marina on 14 May 1984 and 47 flying east off Worthing on 29 April 1990. There have been six June records totalling eight birds from 1968 onwards, the latest of which flew east off Seaford on 16 June 1991.

Two were observed from a fishing boat 10 km off Brighton on 16 July 1989 and an adult was seen 8 km off Shoreham-by-Sea on 9 July 1994.

Since the beginning of 1962, a total of about 60 has been recorded in autumn in the period 4 August (1973, off Birling Gap) to 20 November (1994, Pagham Harbour). Of these, 15 were in August, 14 in September, 21 in October and 10 in November, mainly flying west off the main sea-watching localities. The largest movement recorded was of seven flying west off Selsey Bill on 15 October 1963, the day after a large influx of the species into the North Sea.

Although the only inland record for Sussex is of one caught at Rogate in December 1865, there is some evidence to suggest overland movement through the county. This is provided by the presence of two birds on the beach at Cuckmere Haven on 27 April 1991, which later flew off inland in a northerly direction.   *Paul James*

Arctic Skua   *Stercorarius parasiticus*

Status:- A fairly common to scarce spring and autumn passage migrant; very scarce in summer and rare in winter.

A total of about 40 has been recorded in winter, of which 27 were in December, eight in January and five in February. Of those recorded in December, ten were in 1983, including nine flying west at Worthing on 13th, and nine in 1985, comprising totals of five east and two west at Worthing between 21st and 24th and singles west off Langney Point on the 24th and 25th.

As passage migrants, Arctic Skuas are normally recorded from early April to early November. There are, however, a number of records for March and it is possible that a bird that flew east off Worthing on 29 February 1984 was an early spring migrant. The latest date for autumn passage is 25 November 1988 although a dead bird was found at Rye Harbour on 29 November 1970. The numbers recorded annually vary considerably, particularly in the spring when the occurrence of large movements depends on the incidence of fresh to strong southeast to southwest winds, with associated frontal systems or low pressure areas moving eastwards across the country (Newnham 1984a). Between 1962 and 1993, spring totals ranged from 25 to 398 (fig. 47). The reasons for the apparent increase shown by the graph are unclear but it may be significant that the size of colonies of Arctic Skuas in Orkney and Shetland, which hold the main concentrations of this species in Britain, increased between 1969 and 1985 (New Atlas). The growth in sea-watching activity since the 1960s may also be a factor. Autumn totals have ranged from 17 to 135 birds, an average of 73 per autumn for the period 1983-92 compared with 45 for 1962-76, suggesting that an increase may also have occurred at this season.

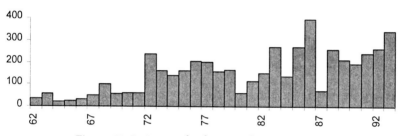

Figure 47. Spring totals of Arctic Skuas, 1962 - 93.

Spring passage regularly extends into early June, but the peak movements normally occur in late April and early May (fig. 48), usually slightly earlier than those of Pomarine Skuas. Movements of 20-30 in a day are frequent and the largest movements so far recorded were of 55 flying east off Birling Gap on 1 May 1972 followed by a further 54 on 7 May. At Seaford, totals of 89 flew east between 24 and 30 April 1991 and 84 between 24 and 26 April 1991.

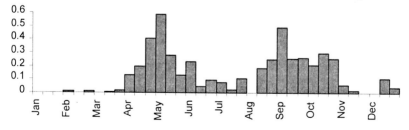

Figure 48. Hourly rates of passage, in 10-day periods,
of Arctic Skuas at Worthing, 1978 - 93.

A few Arctic Skuas, assumed to be non-breeding birds, are seen most summers. Autumn passage may commence as early as the second half of June, for 16 flew west off Selsey Bill between 21 and 30 June 1969 but in most years, returning birds are not seen until late July. Autumn movements are smaller than those in spring and there is often not a clear peak. However, 49 flew west off Langney Point on 14 September 1970, 43 east off Beachy Head on 17 October 1982, and 78 west off Selsey Bill on 6 September 1992, the latter a day of exceptional tern passage at coastal sites. These are the largest autumn movements so far recorded.

Arctic Skuas usually migrate singly or in small parties although there is an exceptional record of 28 flying east together off Selsey Bill on 8 May 1960. With hindsight, however, there must be a strong possibility that these were Pomarine Skuas, given that such a record has not been repeated, despite the increase in sea-watching. A few parties of skuas have been tracked eastwards along the coast, the times at which they passed different sites indicating that they were travelling at 37 to 50 km per hour (Newnham 1984a). Arctic Skuas are dimorphic and both light and dark phases are recorded during the spring. At Selsey Bill, studies during the early 1980s showed the dark phase to be nearly twice as numerous as the light phase and in 1983 a similar proportion was noted at Beachy Head. As the spring progresses, the proportion of light phase skuas increases; an expected phenomenon as Arctic Skua colonies in southern Scandinavia, comprising more than 95% dark phase individuals, are occupied much earlier than colonies further north and east which have up to 90% light phase birds.

A total of 15 birds has been recorded away from the immediate vicinity of the coast. Of these, three were prior to 1900, one in 1955 and 11 between 1962 and 1993. Those recorded in the latter period included a juvenile picked up alive at Burwash on 4 October 1982, two flying southwest over Crowborough on 23 September 1983 and singles at Weir Wood Reservoir on 1 May 1987 and 11 October 1993, Darwell Reservoir on 3 October 1988 and flying south over Pulborough Brooks on 15 November 1993. Of three birds observed flying north over Chichester Harbour in spring 1988, one appeared to continue over the Downs, suggesting the possibility of a small overland movement through Sussex. Further evidence to support this theory is provided by a record of two flying north over Birdham on 11 May 1980. *Paul James*

Long-tailed Skua *Stercorarius longicaudus*

Status:- A rare vagrant (at least 20 records involving 21 individuals).

There were nine records of ten individuals up to 1962, of which only four were since 1900. Of these four, two were obtained in Rye Bay on 9 August 1910, one seen at the Crumbles on 28 September 1916 and an oiled bird shot in the lower Cuckmere Valley on 1 June 1942. The remaining records include a juvenile caught with floating bait off Brighton Chain Pier in November 1844, an adult shot in a flooded meadow near Henfield on 7 October 1862 and an adult, from a small party of skuas, shot beneath the West Pier, Brighton in November 1870. All three are in the Booth Museum (BoMNH 204018, 204015 and 204558 respectively).

In addition to the above, Walpole-Bond and des Forges & Harber include four birds in May, all seen by Booth: two off Brighton in the morning and (presumably the same) off Shoreham-by-Sea in the evening of 17 May 1872 and two off Shoreham-by-Sea in May 1875. These early sight records should be regarded with a high degree of caution and are best disregarded, not least because Walpole-Bond listed only one spring record of Arctic Skua (in 1919).

Eleven have been recorded since the beginning of 1962, all but one since 1981:

1963: An adult flying west past Selsey Bill on 15 October (*SxBR* 16: 22).
1981: A juvenile at Widewater, Lancing Beach on 11 September spent 15 minutes on the beach before departing west.
1984: An adult flying east past Brighton Marina on 16 May.
1985: An adult flying east past Selsey Bill on 8 May.
1987: A juvenile flying west past Cow Gap, Beachy Head on 18 October. A different juvenile flying west past Selsey Bill on 20 October.
1991: An adult flying east past Splash Point, Seaford on 12 May. A juvenile off Cow Gap, Beachy Head on 5 October arrived from the east and departed south.
1992: An adult flying east past Birling Gap on 14 May later passed Dungeness, Kent. It had earlier been seen, but not positively identified, at Shoreham-by-Sea and Brighton Marina.
1993: An adult flying east past Splash Point, Seaford on 12 May. A juvenile on roadside floodwater on the approach to Church Norton on 12 September.

The 1963 individual was seen feeding offshore for 5-6 minutes before departing west. The sighting was towards the end of a memorable sea-watch which also featured seven Pomarine Skuas, 11 Arctic Skuas and one Great Skua.

Records since 1962 have been divided between spring (five in May) and autumn (two in September and four in October). They have been well scattered along the coast with three at Beachy Head and Selsey Bill, two at Splash Point, Seaford and singles at Brighton Marina, Church Norton and Widewater.

Records of this graceful skua have increased significantly in the British Isles in recent years (e.g. 170 individuals recorded during 1958-67, over 300 during 1976-78 and over 2600 during 1986-90) but vary considerably from one year to the next with, for example, 5350 in 1991 but only 161 in 1992 (Fraser & Ryan 1994). Its breeding range is circumpolar, but mainly north of the Arctic Circle, and it migrates to winter at sea south of the Equator. *Richard Fairbank*

Great Skua   *Stercorarius skua*

Status:- A scarce spring and autumn passage migrant; very scarce but increasing in winter.

Between 1937 and 1961 des Forges & Harber recorded just 26 birds, only six of which were in spring. Since 1962, however, increased sea-watching has shown that Great Skuas occur off the Sussex coast in all months with a marked passage up-Channel in April and May.

For the period 1962-76 Shrubb gave eight winter records: two for December, four for January and two for February. Since 1976, a significant increase has occurred in winter with a total of about 51 recorded in these months, of which 26 were in December, 14 in January and 11 in February. Most were recorded in 1982, when totals of four flew east and two west at Worthing between 2 and 30 December, and in December 1991 when there were two off Brighton on 13th and 30th and singles off Bexhill, Worthing and Newhaven.

As passage migrants Great Skuas are normally recorded from early April. March sightings, however, are not unusual and it is possible that some of the February records refer to early migrants, too. Autumn passage may continue into November or even early December in some years, but more usually until late October. The numbers recorded annually vary considerably and are dependent on the occurrence of suitable weather conditions. Newnham (1984a) stated that, as with Arctic Skua, they are more numerous in spring when the wind swings between southeast and southwest as frequent frontal systems move from west to east across the country. In autumn the largest numbers occur after onshore gales. Between 1962 and 1992, totals of birds recorded passing up-Channel in spring varied between none in 1964 and 77 in 1986 (fig. 49), of which 61 were in April. A further feature of spring 1986 was the unusual total of 34 birds that flew west, including 19 at Selsey Bill on 4 May. Autumn totals have ranged from one in 1965 to 25 in 1984 and 1992 and 26 in 1989.

Spring passage regularly extends into early June, birds being recorded in this month annually between 1986 and 1992. The peak movements, however, normally occur in April, often on days of heavy Arctic Skua passage. Return passage may commence as early as late June given that all the June records for the period 1962-76 were for the last eight days of the month, but in most years birds are not seen until August. Autumn movements are generally smaller than those in spring and, like Arctic Skua, there is rarely a clear peak. At Selsey Bill, 11 flew west in just 30 minutes on 11 October 1981, this being the largest autumn movement so far recorded.

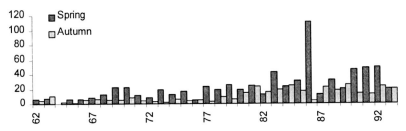

Figure 49. Spring and autumn totals of Great Skuas, 1962 - 93.

Most records of Great Skuas in Sussex are of single birds. Those that have been tracked eastwards along the coast in spring were found to be travelling at speeds between 28 and 43 km per hour (Newnham 1984a).

The only inland record prior to 1980 was of one found dead at Wiston on 18 November 1940. Since then, nine have been seen away from the coast. One flew south over Steyning Round Hill on 10 September 1981 and one was at Bewl Water on 16 September 1983. A bird that flew north over Ashdown

Forest on 7 January 1984 was seen later at Weir Wood Reservoir, where it remained until the following day. Another occurred at Weir Wood on 21 October 1985 and a party of five flew southwest over Bewl Water on 30 September 1988. The latter record is not as surprising as it may at first seem, given that Great Skuas regularly fly into the mouth of the Swale Estuary, Kent in northerly winds and then circle high before appearing to move inland, presumably on overland migration to the south coast.

Two birds ringed as nestlings in Shetland have been recovered in the county. The first, ringed in 1964, was found dead near Portslade in September 1976 while the second, ringed in 1976, was found dead at Cooden Beach in September 1987. *Paul James*

Great Black-headed Gull *Larus ichthyaetus*

Status:- Two old records that are no longer considered to be acceptable.

A winter plumaged adult seen at Telscombe Cliffs on 4 January 1910 and a summer plumaged adult which passed Hove on 9 August 1932 are unconvincingly described in Walpole-Bond. Following a recent review both records have been rejected (*BOURC* 1993a, Vinicombe & Hopkin 1993).

There now remains just one British record of this central Asian species, an adult shot in Devon in May or June 1859. *Richard Fairbank*

Mediterranean Gull *Larus melanocephalus*

Status:- A scarce but regular visitor throughout the year. A few pairs have attempted to breed in recent years.

During the past few decades the world population of this attractive species has increased dramatically. This prosperity has been most marked in regions bordering the Black Sea but there has also been an expansion of its breeding range into the eastern Mediterranean and northwest Europe (BWP). The first breeding record in Britain was in 1968, when a pair nested in a large colony of Black-headed Gulls in Hampshire (Taverner 1970). It was eight years before the species nested successfully again in Britain but since 1979 breeding has been annual, with a maximum of 11 confirmed pairs in 1990, mainly in southeast England (Spencer *et al* 1993). The birds that have colonised Sussex have, as elsewhere, been found in association with other breeding gulls; between 1982 and 1986 pairs were recorded with Black-headed Gulls either at Rye Harbour or on Stakes Island in Chichester Harbour, and with Kittiwakes on the cliffs between Newhaven and Peacehaven. In 1987 two pairs were present at Ternery Pool at Rye Harbour but only one pair, an adult and sub-adult, incubated until late April. The following year a pair 'contemplated' nesting on South Stakes Island and in 1989 two pairs attempted breeding there but were washed out by high tides in June. Pairs were present at both Rye Harbour and South Stakes during the spring and summer of 1990 and 1991 while in 1992 a pair of adults was seen in another colony of Black-headed Gulls at Camber Gravel Pits. Breeding at South Stakes was again thwarted in 1992 by high spring tides which washed away a nest containing three eggs.

303

Thus in a decade of early colonisation, no young Mediterranean Gulls have fledged in Sussex.

In recent years there has been a dramatic increase in Mediterranean Gulls in Sussex (fig. 50) commencing in the early 1980s and coinciding with the first pairs prospecting in the county.

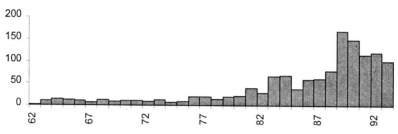

Figure 50. Annual totals of Mediterranean Gulls, 1962 - 93.

An appreciation of the speed with which this species has increased can be gleaned by considering that in Britain there were only four records prior to 1940 yet by 1963 the species had become too common for records to continue to be assessed by *BBRC* (Sharrock 1974). In Sussex, the first acceptable records were of a first-winter at Pagham Harbour on 26 October 1947 and an adult at Shoreham-by-Sea on 24 September 1950. By 1987, the species was removed from the list of those requiring descriptions by the SOS.

Shrubb, as well as noting the obvious increase in records, observed a change in the pattern of occurrence of Mediterranean Gulls. Of 41 birds recorded prior to 1963, most were in spring and autumn, whereas between 1963 and 1976 most occurred in winter and spring. The following table of cumulative monthly totals for the period 1962-93 clearly shows a peak in spring.

Jan	Feb	Mar	Apr	May	Jun	Jul	Aug	Sep	Oct	Nov	Dec
102	93	169	305	263	111	92	93	89	106	86	99

Shrubb tabulated monthly occurrences by 5-year periods and he noted a high proportion of adults. Fig. 51 shows the monthly totals for the 5-year period 1988 to 1992 only and it reveals that adults are more regularly encountered than other ages in most months. In spring, adults and second-year birds peak in April whereas the main passage of first-year birds occurs in May. Outside spring and early summer, first-years are not that often recorded.

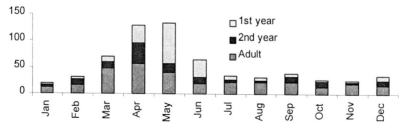

Figure 51. Monthly totals of Mediterranean Gulls by age, 1988 - 92.

Mediterranean Gulls have wintered in Sussex every winter since 1963/64, albeit in small numbers. It is likely that the same individuals have returned in successive years to favoured wintering sites such as Hove, Littlehampton, Shoreham Harbour and the Pagham area, often arriving in November and departing in February or March.

In spring there has been a marked increase in records from sea-watching sites of birds, often apparently paired, passing along the coast. These are presumed to be birds returning to colonies in Netherlands, where there were 125 pairs in 1990 (New Atlas), having wintered elsewhere to the south and west.

Initially records were of single birds but as the species has become more numerous, larger numbers, mainly comprising immatures in spring, have been recorded together. The largest concentration at a single site was in June 1989 when 16 different birds were recorded in Chichester Harbour, including 11 first-summers on Pilsey Sands on 1 June 1989. The other large counts have all occurred since 1986 with records of six at Splash Point, Seaford on 16 April 1988, at Birling Gap on 7 May 1989 and in Chichester Harbour on 30 March 1991 and 19 May 1993, of seven immatures at Rye Harbour on 12 May 1986 and of eight immatures at Worthing on 9 May 1991. The largest group recorded in winter was four that roosted on the playing fields of Dorothy Stringer School, Brighton during December 1988.

Although most are recorded at coastal sites, there were nearly 80 records from 17 different localities away from the coast during the period under review. Birds have been seen at most of the large reservoirs and gravel pits with the exception of Darwell and Powdermill Reservoirs; feeding with other gulls on downland at Poverty Bottom and near Sompting and Steyning; in the river valleys of the Arun, Adur and Ouse; and feeding with other gulls on refuse tips at Small Dole and Sompting. Although there are considerably fewer records, the monthly distribution of inland records, shown in the table, lacks the large spring peak and shows that most are in mid-winter.

Jan	Feb	Mar	Apr	May	Jun	Jul	Aug	Sep	Oct	Nov	Dec
13	9	8	4	1	0	5	5	5	6	7	11

Although only two Mediterranean Gulls have been trapped for ringing in the county, both have proved to be of considerable interest. The first, caught at Hove on 15 January 1977, had been ringed as an adult at Kalmthout, Belgium on 12 April 1972 and an adult ringed at Sompting refuse tip in December 1988 was seen nesting in a colony of Slender-billed Gulls in the French Carmargue, 882 km SSE, in June 1990. Furthermore, a bird marked with a white colour-ring (24H) as a chick in a Dutch colony in June 1992 was sighted on the River Adur at Shoreham-by-Sea in January 1993, from 22 November 1993 to 8 March 1994 and in the winters of 1994/95 and 1995/96.

John Newnham

Laughing Gull   *Larus atricilla*

Status:- A very rare vagrant (two records).

One was recorded before 1962, an adult at the Crumbles from 2 to 9 July 1923 which was the first British record (des Forges 1968).

A highly mobile adult in summer plumage was seen on the River Adur at Shoreham-by-Sea, at Splash Point, Seaford and at Widewater, Lancing Beach during the morning of 6 April 1991. It left the Adur, opposite Shoreham Airport, at *ca.* 09:05 GMT, was seen at Splash Point at 10:00-10:20 GMT and then flew back west past Widewater at 11:00 GMT.

There were just over 60 records of this dark-mantled gull in the British Isles during 1962-94, but only two prior to 1962. It breeds commonly on the eastern seaboard of North America to northern South America, northern birds moving south in winter. *Richard Fairbank*

Franklin's Gull *Larus pipixcan*

Status:- A very rare vagrant (three records involving two individuals).

First recorded in 1970, there have been three records, involving two individuals:

1970: An adult in summer plumage at Arlington Reservoir for 20 minutes on 4 July was the second British record (Rogers 1972).

1990: An adult in winter plumage at Brighton Marina briefly on 29 December before drifting off west.

1991: An adult in winter plumage, presumably that seen at Brighton Marina, in fields near Newhaven Tide Mills on 4 January.

First recorded in the British Isles in 1970, there had been 30 records to the end of 1994. It breeds on the North American prairies, migrating to the Pacific coast from Central America to southern Chile. *Richard Fairbank*

Little Gull *Larus minutus*

Status:- A scarce visitor and passage migrant, most numerous on passage in spring.

This delightful and most elegant of the regularly occurring gulls has, like many other members of its family, increased significantly during the past few decades. This increase, which probably reflects the expansion of the breeding population in areas bordering the Baltic Sea (BWP), is shown clearly in fig. 52.

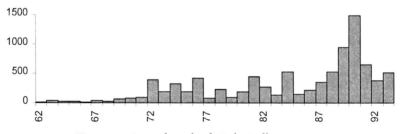

Figure 52. Annual totals of Little Gulls, 1962 - 93.

Little Gulls have never bred in Sussex; indeed only four instances are known of the species nesting in Britain (Spencer *et al* 1991). Apart from isolated instances, small numbers of first-summers have summered regularly in the county, mainly at Rye Harbour, but also in the Chichester area between

1974 and 1979. In most summers only one or two birds are involved but up to nine were present at Rye Harbour in June 1973 and 1985. In neighbouring Kent, summering birds were also first noted in 1972 (Taylor, Davenport & Flegg 1981).

The winter status may also be changing. Shrubb noted that no more than five birds had been seen in any winter (January to early March) between 1948 and 1976 and this was to continue until the early 1980s when parties of eight, all adults, flew east off Worthing on 3 February 1982 and 15 flew west off Selsey Bill on 6 January 1983. A total of nine was recorded in January 1988 and 11 in January 1991, including seven together at West Wittering on 31 January. The most remarkable year, however, was 1990 when seven occurred in January and 78 in February. Birds were recorded at 22 coastal sites and also inland at Chichester Gravel Pits and Pulborough Brooks, with up to four at the latter site between 10 and 14 February. Most were adults, as is typical of birds recorded in Sussex in winter. Little is known of the winter distribution of the species but it is thought that immatures move further south than adults and that the total wintering population scattered off the south and west coasts of Britain may be less than 100 (Winter Atlas).

The exceptional total recorded in February 1990 was perhaps due to an early start to spring passage which, in most years, starts slowly in late March. It is at this season that most Little Gulls are now seen, the variations in numbers from year to year reflecting the incidence of winds from the east and southeast. In 1990, for example, at least 1133 were recorded in April and May whereas in 1983 the same period produced only 57. The following table shows the cumulative monthly totals for the period 1963 to 1993 compared with the figures for the period 1948 to 1962 from Shrubb. This emphasises the marked increase that has occurred, not only throughout the year, but more especially in spring which has now overtaken autumn as the principal season for observing Little Gulls.

	Jan	Feb	Mar	Apr	May	Jun	Jul	Aug	Sep	Oct	Nov	Dec
1948-62	10	8	9	16	14	7	5	28	38	63	69	32
1963-93	77	14	142	3029	2677	121	72	228	842	822	351	151
Total	87	22	151	3045	2691	128	77	256	880	885	420	183

An increase in spring has also occurred in Kent where Taylor, Davenport & Flegg (1981) noted a huge increase in the number of birds flying up-Channel at Dungeness from 1973 onward. In Sussex the largest movements have all occurred since 1974. The following table lists all the days on which more than 100 Little Gulls have been recorded passing a single site in the county. From this it can be seen that the large movements occur in April and early May with most birds passing sites in East Sussex, particularly Splash Point, Seaford.

The absence of 'big' days at Beachy Head in recent years is due to a reduction in sea-watching at this site but this is not the case for the sites in West Sussex where far fewer Little Gulls have been recorded despite similar hours watching. Only on 1 May 1990 was the movement recorded equally along the coast although on 3 May 1974, when 148 were recorded at Beachy Head, 315 passed Hurst Castle, Hampshire (Clark & Eyre 1993) with 355 off

Dungeness the following day (Taylor, Davenport & Flegg 1981). Few birds linger in spring but a gathering of up to 129, mainly adults, at the Crumbles in late April 1989 provided a spectacular sight.

	Selsey Bill	Worthing	Brighton Marina	Splash Point, Seaford	Beachy Head
3 May 1974					148
1 May 1976					115
5 May 1984				224	
16 May 1988				105	
2 Apr 1990				222	
30 Apr 1990				113	
1 May 1990	122	112	127	129	
2 May 1990				113	105
11 Apr 1991				113	
25 Apr 1991				123	
21 Apr 1992				185	

Although movements in spring in West Sussex are not so obvious, fig. 53, which is based on nearly 6000 hours of sea-watching between 1978 and 1993 at Worthing, clearly shows the expected peak in late April and early May. The graph also suggests that autumn passage is more protracted, extending from September until December with peak rates, similar to those in spring, in late October and late November.

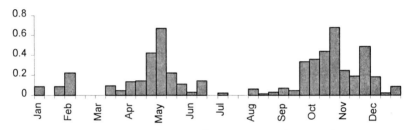

Figure 53. Hourly rates of passage, in 10-day periods, of Little Gulls at Worthing, 1978 - 93.

The autumn movement of a large portion of the Baltic and Russian population is thought to be through the Baltic Sea into the North Sea and English Channel. Between 5000 and 10,000 may occur in the Netherlands during the course of the autumn and it is believed that some of these may then pass down-Channel off the French coast in October and November. For example, at Cap Gris Nez, there were 3400 in the autumn of 1970 and 3300 in 1974 (BWP). In spite of the relative abundance of Little Gulls off the French coast in autumn, no such numbers have been recorded in Sussex. The best autumn was in 1972 when 255 occurred including, at Beachy Head, 40 feeding offshore on 17 September, 70 flying east on 19 September and a further 45 east on 1 October. A sequence of severe gales in October 1987 resulted in another good autumn with a total of 227 reported, including 50 flying west off Selsey Bill on 17 October 1987. Other notable autumn movements have included 53 flying west off Langney Point on 26 September 1981, 35 passing southwest over Rye Harbour on 9 November 1984 and 30 flying west at Selsey Bill on 9 November 1991 but these obviously do not match the peaks recorded in spring. Autumn passage may continue into December but whether the 36 that were seen after severe southeast gales on 20 December 1981 were late migrants or wintering birds forced inshore is debatable.

Although most sightings are from the coast there have been a number of inland records. The species is particularly attracted to gravel pits and reservoirs where small numbers may be recorded on passage. At Weir Wood Reservoir, Mortlock (1992) noted a marked increase during the 1980s with most in autumn, particularly August. It is in spring, however, that the largest flocks have occurred including seven at Weir Wood Reservoir in April 1984, 11 at Bewl Water on 1 May 1984 and 19 at Arlington Reservoir on 29 April 1972. Singles have been noted at other inland sites but there is an exceptional record of a party of 12 adults that flew west over West Chiltington on 12 October 1980.   *John Newnham*

Sabine's Gull   *Larus sabini*

Status:- A rare autumn vagrant (at least 47 individuals recorded).

Prior to 1962 there were 15 records (des Forges & Harber), although one undated record has not been traced. Most were in September (4) and October (7) and include a juvenile found dying at Hove on 21 September 1871 which is in the Booth Museum (BoMNH 208123). The other dated records are one attracted to food put out in a Hove street on 26 January 1932 (Walpole-Bond), a first-summer off Langney Point on 25 August 1951 and one obtained near Brighton (possibly at Portslade) on 18 December 1876. That in January, like most records outside the period late August to December, must leave some room for doubt.

Since the beginning of 1962 at least 32 individuals have been seen, more than half in October 1987 immediately after the great storm:

1967: A juvenile at Newhaven Harbour and Tide Mills on 11-12 October.
1968: One flying west past Selsey Bill on 26 September.
1970: A juvenile flying east past Selsey Bill on 13 September.
A juvenile lingering off Langney Point on 13 September.
A juvenile in Newhaven Harbour from 13 to 18 September. All three were assumed to be different.
1971: A juvenile flying west over Sidlesham Ferry on 27 December, having flown out of Pagham Harbour.
1979: One, presumably a juvenile, flying west past Worthing on 3 January.
1980: A juvenile flying east past Selsey Bill on 2 November.
1983: One, presumably a juvenile, flying west past Worthing on 11 May.
1984: An adult inside Brighton Marina on 28 September departed southwest.
1987: At least 19, and possibly as many as 28 between Chichester Harbour and Cuckmere Haven during 16 to 21 October.
1988: A juvenile at Galley Hill, Bexhill on 9 October from 12:30-13:00 hrs when it drifted off west.
A juvenile, presumably the same, at Shoreham Harbour on 9 October from 14:50-15:10 hrs when it again drifted off west.
1990: A juvenile feeding off Worthing for a few minutes on 3 October before departing west.
1992: A juvenile at Arlington Reservoir on 30-31 August.

Following the great storm in October 1987 at least 19 were seen and possibly as many as 28. That all but one or two were adults is even more remarkable. The storm moved rapidly northeast from the Bay of Biscay on the evening of 15 October, crossing southeast England in the early hours of 16 October when gusts of over 90 mph were recorded (Hume & Christie 1989). Two Sabine's Gulls were recorded at Cuckmere Haven on 16 October with four at Brighton Marina, singles at Worthing and Selsey Bill and 6-8 in Chichester Harbour on 17 October. On 18 October 13 were seen along the coast between Seaford and Chichester Harbour, including three at Brighton Marina and two at both Widewater, Lancing Beach and Littlehampton. There were six more sightings, all in West Sussex, the last being one at Widewater and two at Littlehampton on 21 October. Although an exceptional showing, these were totally overshadowed by up to 125 recorded in Dorset and 120-140 in Hampshire during the same period (Hume & Christie 1989), the latter including 50+ at Hurst Castle on 18 October (Clark & Eyre 1993).

Since 1962 most records have been in September (5) and October (22+) with single occurrences in January, May, August, November and December. Given the distinctive juvenile and adult plumages of this species in autumn, it is surprising that the individual reported in 1968 was not aged. The individuals which flew past Worthing in 1979 and 1983 were both reported to have juvenile body plumage but adult tails, seemingly anomalous characteristics (P J Grant *in litt.*, Grant 1986).

The 1987 occurrences were unprecedented. In more normal years there are usually between 60 and 200 records of this exciting gull in the British Isles (Fraser & Ryan 1994). It breeds around the Arctic, wintering at sea in both the Atlantic and Pacific Oceans. *Richard Fairbank*

Bonaparte's Gull   *Larus philadelphia*

Status:- A very rare vagrant (three records).

Three were recorded before 1962 (des Forges & Harber), a juvenile shot at St Leonards in early November 1870, an adult on the sea to the west of Newhaven Harbour breakwater on 14 November 1948 (Alder & James 1950) and a first-summer feeding off Langney Point on 24 June 1951 (Harber 1952a). These were the fifth, eighth and ninth British records.

A record of a first-summer at Portobello, Brighton on 20 June 1961 has recently been reviewed and is considered to be inadequately documented (Rogers *et al* 1995). An adult at Dungeness on 15 April 1989 (the only Kent record) drifted off west and may have entered the county although it was not seen to do so.

There were just over 70 records of this small gull in the British Isles during 1962-94. It breeds in Canada and winters on the Great Lakes and coastal USA south to Mexico and the Caribbean. *Richard Fairbank*

Black-headed Gull   *Larus ridibundus*

Status:- A common breeding species and abundant winter visitor and passage migrant.

The Black-headed Gull is the most numerous and widespread gull in Sussex. During winter, the largest numbers are found along the coast or roosting on reservoirs, though flocks frequent a wide range of other habitats including flooded water meadows, ploughed fields and pasture, refuse tips, playing fields and even urban parks and gardens. Although there were colonies near Eastbourne and Winchelsea in the first half of the 17th century, it was not until the 1940s that the species effectively recolonised the county. At the Midrips/Wicks, where there was an isolated instance of breeding in 1932, some bred for a few years prior to 1948 including 200 pairs in 1947. The last year, however, when nesting was attempted in this area was 1954, when there were about 12 pairs (des Forges & Harber). Breeding was also recorded during the 1940s at Pett Level (which had been flooded) and it is presumed that these early colonists derived from birds nesting at nearby Dungeness, Kent where about 300 pairs bred in the 1930s and 1940s (Aspinall, Taverner & Wiseman 1993). At Rye Harbour, where 11 pairs nested in 1947, numbers increased gradually throughout the 1950s to 155 pairs in 1958 and 200 pairs in 1960. Further growth of the colony was discouraged, as it occupied the same area as the breeding terns, but between 115 and 350 pairs nested there until further control measures were instigated in 1971. Numbers fell thereafter with none breeding between 1975 and 1977. The colony then re-established itself and grew rapidly to reach 1050 pairs by 1987 but it then decreased precipitously to less than 200 pairs in the early 1990s (fig. 54). Breeding success at this site has been generally good; poorer years have been attributed to predation, control measures or disturbance. Two other colonies have since established themselves on islands left by gravel extraction work in the east of the county. At Scotney Court Gravel Pit, where ten pairs bred in 1979, the colony increased to a peak of 177 nests in 1983. It was, however, deserted in 1985 and, although 25 pairs nested in 1986, there have been no subsequent breeding records for this site. At nearby Camber, a new colony held 60 pairs in 1992 and 30 pairs in 1993.

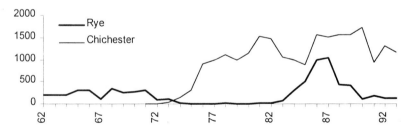

Figure 54. Annual totals of breeding pairs of Black-headed Gulls at Rye Harbour and Chichester Harbour, 1962 - 93.

The growth and history of the colony that exists on Stakes Island in Chichester Harbour is clearly shown in fig. 54. A single pair attempted to breed there in 1964 but there were no further records until 1974 when four pairs bred. The colony has since grown rapidly, reaching 1536 nests by 1981 and thereafter fluctuating between a low of 891 nests in 1985 and a high of 1732 nests in 1990. In years when breeding success has been good, 1000 or more young have fledged from the colony. In other years, however, when inclement weather has coincided with high spring tides, many nests have been submerged. In 1991, for example, 942 nests were counted in May yet only 34 chicks were present in June. The only breeding record for West Sussex away from Chichester Harbour is that of a pair at Pagham Harbour in 1983.

Between April and late June, most of the Black-headed Gulls seen away from the breeding colonies are immature birds. Numbers, which are usually at their lowest in June, build up from July onwards as shown by counts at Worthing Beach in 1981 of 162 immatures on 21 June, 4184 mainly adults on 18 July, 9000 on 29 August and 33,500 on 29 September and by counts in other years of 10,000 on 31 July 1980 and 50,000 on 5 September 1979. Visible movements are rarely recorded in autumn though exceptions have included 6000 flying west at Worthing on 13 November 1969 and 30,000 flying west in just two hours at Goring on 14 October 1982. A peak count of just 682 flying west at Selsey Bill on 1 October 1966 would suggest that this species did not form a significant proportion of the large south-westerly movements of gulls recorded at this site in the 1960s.

The largest numbers of Black-headed Gulls occur in winter when the local population is augmented by the presence of continental birds (Newnham 1986b). An indication of the size of the wintering population in the county is provided by various co-ordinated surveys of roosting gulls carried out in 1977-79 (Porter 1979), 1983 (Newnham 1984b) and 1993 (de Potier & Yates 1994), the results of which are shown in the following table.

Date of count	Total at inland sites	Total at coastal sites	County Total
5 Feb 1977			30,703
28 Jan 1978			14,145
20 Jan 1979			53,377
23 Jan 1983	18,253	66,488	84,741
23 Jan 1993	30,036	54,870	84,906

Although the totals suggest a marked increase between 1979 and 1983, followed by little change in the period 1983-93, they should be treated with caution as counters were asked to identify the species if possible, but otherwise to distinguish between 'large' (Herring, Lesser and Great Black-backed) and 'small' (Black-headed and Common) gulls. From extrapolated totals which included the counts for 'small' gulls, de Potier & Yates (1994) were able to show a reduction in the wintering population of Black-headed Gulls in the county from 129,000 in 1983 to 102,029 in 1993. By the same method they suggested that the approximate population in 1977-79 was 101,500.

Shrubb suggested a minimum wintering population of some 40,000 birds based on a series of very incomplete counts since 1967. Counts of 12,000 at Roedean on 31 January 1972 and 30,000 on the flooded Shoreham airfield on 9 February 1974 were considered to be exceptional at the time. As the winter population has grown, so larger numbers have been reported including an estimated 80,000 feeding in the surf between Goring and Shoreham-by-Sea on 25 December 1981, 40,000 at Rye Harbour on 16 March 1986 and 24,000 roosting at Bewl Water on 23 January 1993. Roosts of 20,000 were also recorded at the latter site between January and early March in 1986, 1988, 1990-91 and 1993.

Spring passage may begin as early as late February but both roost counts and a ringing study near Worthing have shown that many wintering adults remain well into March. The exodus from the Worthing area occurs in the last half of the month and is often associated with periods of south-westerly winds. Most records, thereafter, refer to eastward movements of mainly immature birds along the coast; these tend to be heaviest in light south-westerly winds and often in the evening. Peak movements have included totals of 3000 and 3122 flying east at Worthing on 29 March 1984 and 9 May 1991 respectively and 4500 flying west at Brighton on 1 April 1984. Totals for the whole spring for each of the main sea-watching sites typically fall between 3000 and 8500. The graph below (fig. 55), which is based on nearly 6000 hours of sea-watching at Worthing between 1978 and 1993, shows peaks in late March and early May and infrequent smaller movements during the rest of the year.

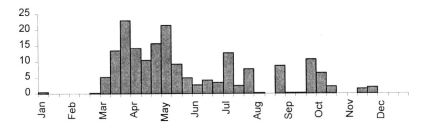

Figure 55. Hourly rates of passage, in 10-day periods,
of Black-headed Gulls at Worthing, 1978 - 93.

This species has been the subject of an intensive ringing study near Worthing and between 1975 and 1993 a total of 20,875 birds were ringed. Newnham (1986b) showed, from a series of maps plotting 610 recoveries up to 1985, that the wintering population in Sussex originates from the Low Countries, the Baltic States and Fenno-Scandinavia and that some birds return to the same area in subsequent winters. Some have been recovered further east, particularly in the former USSR, as demonstrated by the longest recorded movement of an adult ringed at Sompting in January 1980 and found dead near Pechora, 3696 km ENE, in September 1984. By 1988 a total of 100 gulls had been captured which had been ringed elsewhere as nestlings. Of these, 94 were from Europe but only six from colonies in southeast England (Newnham 1988). The number of recoveries of birds ringed in Sussex had increased to 1387 by 1994 (table 67).

Most of the recoveries shown in the table involved birds caught in the cannon-netting study of wintering gulls in the Worthing area. However, the recovery from Portugal and one of the those from Wales involved nestlings ringed at Rye Harbour in 1958 and recovered later the same year. A total of 373 Black-headed Gulls ringed elsewhere have been recovered in Sussex. The pattern of these is similar to that in the table above except for a first-year bird that was ringed in Switzerland in January 1978 and controlled at Lancing, 740 km northwest, in February 1987.

	Jan	Feb	Mar	Apr	May	Jun	Jul	Aug	Sep	Oct	Nov	Dec	Total
Sussex	29	35	33	13	6	3	54	55	18	15	24	25	310
S.England	47	36	33	6	3	9	28	16	7	13	26	25	249
N.England	1	1			1	2	3	5		1			14
Wales											2		2
Ireland										1			1
Finland			1	16	42	47	23	9					138
Norway	1			2	2	2		2					9
Sweden			3	18	14	29	17	2	3	2	1		89
Baltic States			1	11	12	17	7	2	3			1	54
former USSR		1	1	4	8	9	5	6	1	2			37
Poland			3	7	2	3	2	3				1	21
former Czech'kia			1	1		1	3		2				8
Denmark	2		45	32	31	33	17	15	11	9	9	1	205
Germany	1		11	4	39	12	17	4	2	3	1	2	96
Holland	2	3	13	14	22	15	18	6	8	11	4	2	118
Belgium	2		3	1	2	1	2		2		1		14
France / C.I.	3	4	1	1	2			1	1	4	4		21
Portugal												1	1
Total	88	80	149	130	186	183	196	126	58	63	70	58	1387

Table 67. Recoveries of Black-headed Gulls ringed in Sussex.

John Newnham

Slender-billed Gull   *Larus genei*

Status:- A very rare vagrant (two records).

One was recorded before 1962 (des Forges & Harber), a first-summer at Langney Point on 19 and 22 June and 6 and 10 July 1960 (Harber 1962). It was the first British record.

A first-summer seen on gravel pits at Rye Harbour for an hour on 28 April 1963 (Charlwood 1964) was the second British record.

There have only been four records of this attenuated gull in the British Isles, those in Sussex, an adult at Dungeness, Kent (and briefly Minsmere, Suffolk) during the summer of 1971 and a pair in Norfolk in May 1987. It breeds discontinuously from Spain to central and southern Asia. Mainly resident, central Asian birds winter in the Persian Gulf (Dymond, Fraser & Gantlett 1989). *Richard Fairbank*

Ring-billed Gull   *Larus delawarensis*

Status:- A very rare vagrant (six records, all in the mid 1980s).

First recorded in 1984, there were six in four years but, rather surprisingly, there have been none since:

1984:   An adult at Weir Wood Reservoir from 10 to 20 December.
1985:   A first-winter on the River Adur at Shoreham-by-Sea on 11 and 22 January.
        A second-winter at the Crumbles Gravel Pits and Langney Point intermittently between 15 December and 8 February 1986.
1986:   An adult at Weir Wood Reservoir on 3 November.
1987:   An adult at Cuckmere Haven on 1 January.
        A first-summer at the Crumbles Gravel Pits on 6 June.

One has been seen in late spring (June) and the rest in winter (November to February) with two at both Weir Wood Reservoir and the Crumbles. The easterly bias of the coastal records is perhaps surprising for a nearctic species.

First recorded in the British Isles in 1973, there were between 69 and 182 records of this readily overlooked species each year during 1986-92 (Fraser & Ryan 1994). It breeds across North America wintering south to Central America and occasionally northern South America. *Richard Fairbank*

Common Gull *Larus canus*

Status:- A common winter visitor and passage migrant; small numbers summer; bred until 1963.

The Common Gull is a familiar species with a wide distribution throughout the county at all times of the year except in late spring and summer. A small breeding colony was first recorded at the Midrips in 1932 but this apparently never exceeded ten pairs and the last pair bred there in 1963. Although a few Common Gulls nest at Dungeness, Kent (Taylor, Davenport & Flegg 1981) and have recently bred in Hampshire (Clark & Eyre 1993), there have been no further attempts at breeding in Sussex. Apart from sporadic sightings, often in the Black-headed Gull colonies in Chichester Harbour and at Rye Harbour, adults are infrequent between mid-May and early July. An exceptional record exists of up to ten adults that were observed flying south over Patcham, Brighton during several evenings in June 1978 but most Common Gulls seen at this season are immatures, the largest group of which was 80 at Rye Harbour in June 1984.

Autumn passage starts in earnest in July with numbers increasing further during August when high counts have included 2000, mainly adults, at Chichester Gravel Pits on 15 August 1965, 1180 flying south over Findon on 12 August 1971 and 1000 at Rye on 21 August 1971. The highest counts in September have been of birds roosting on the sandy shore between Worthing and Ferring; 10,000 were counted there on 27 September 1979 and 6700 on 29 September 1981. The records suggest that numbers decline in late autumn given that all the coastal counts at this time of year have been of 1000 or less except for 4000 at Bognor Regis on 10 November 1982 and 8050 roosting between Rye Harbour and Camber on 25 November 1991.

The size of the winter population is best assessed from a series of co-ordinated counts of roosting gulls that were carried out in 1977-1979 (Porter 1979), 1983 (Newnham 1984b) and 1993 (de Potier & Yates 1994). The results of these counts are shown in the following table.

Date of count	Total at inland sites	Total at coastal sites	County Total
5 Feb 1977			4879
28 Jan 1978			3269
20 Jan 1979			9699
23 Jan 1983	505	7315	7820
23 Jan 1993	4840	8639	13479

There has been a recent increase in the number of Common Gulls roosting at inland sites in Sussex, a trend that is in line with the results of the national winter gull roost survey (Waters 1994). At Bewl Water, for example, where only two were recorded in 1983, there were 400 on 23 March 1984, 450 on 24 February 1985, 1800 on 20 January 1986, and 4000 on 6 February 1990 and 23 January 1993. Large winter roosts have also been recorded at Arlington Reservoir, where there were 3000 on 6 February 1977 and 7000 on 15 January 1984, and at Darwell Reservoir where 1200 were counted, also on 15 January 1984. At Weir Wood Reservoir, however, the numbers recorded have been much smaller, the maximum for this site being just 250 after storms on 19 January 1971 (Mortlock 1992). Coastal gull roosts have been irregularly counted but large numbers may occur, particularly between Rye Harbour and Camber, where 10,000 roosted during the winter of 1985 and 13,560 were present on 24 February 1992.

Numbers increase from mid-February onwards as spring passage commences. Once again the highest counts recorded at this time of year have been at roosts at Rye Harbour where 10,000 were counted on 15 March 1982, 16 March 1986 and 27 March 1990, 21,600 on 31 March 1992 and 32,000 on 18 March 1991. The latter figure is the highest total for a single site in Sussex. Elsewhere a spring roost of Common Gulls on Southwick Beach reached a peak of 7000 on 19 March 1979 and 3000 were on Worthing Beach on 7 April 1982.

Although 10,000 passed through the Rye area between 10 and 12 April 1971 the numbers recorded in April are normally much smaller. At this time, visible migration is most evident as small numbers of immatures pass up-Channel. In most years the total seen passing any one site seldom exceeds 2000. The small volume of passage, the April peak and the virtual lack of coastal movements at other times of the year is clearly shown in fig. 56 which is based on nearly 6000 hours sea-watching at Worthing between 1978 and 1993.

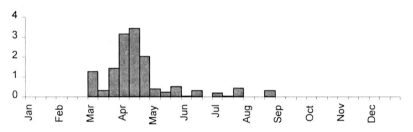

Figure 56. Hourly rates of passage, in 10-day periods, of Common Gulls at Worthing, 1978 - 93.

The largest movements have been at Beachy Head where 3000 flew east on 17 April 1965 and a passage on 15 and 16 April 1967 reached a peak of 150 birds per minute.

During the day most Common Gulls leave their coastal or reservoir roosts to feed inland. Birds may gather on downland pasture or recently tilled land but there are also records of large groups feeding on water meadows and, more recently, scavenging with other gulls on refuse tips. The largest flocks noted on downland have included 1500 near Hove in January 1975, 3000 near Cissbury Ring on 26 October 1989 and 2000 at Steyning on 3 November 1990 and at Devil's Dyke on 27 March 1992 and in this habitat it may be the most regularly encountered gull. The numbers recorded at refuse tips are smaller, of which 250 at Small Dole on 4 April 1983 and 1000 at Pebsham on 3 March 1986 are the most noteworthy.

Between 1975 and 1993 a total of 683 Common Gulls was trapped and ringed on beaches and refuse tips near Worthing. The recoveries generated from this study and plotted by Newnham & Watson (1994), show that most of the Common Gulls wintering in Sussex originate from Scandinavia and Denmark with none from the British breeding strongholds in northern England or Scotland. However, there have been six recoveries further east in Russia. The movements, coupled with measurements of the trapped gulls, suggest that most belong to the nominate race *L.c. canus*. However, one trapped at Sompting refuse tip on 21 January 1987 has been accepted by the British Ornithologists' Union as belonging to the larger eastern race *L.c. heinei* (*BOURC* 1994). *John Newnham*

Lesser Black-backed Gull *Larus fuscus*

Status:- A fairly common passage migrant and winter visitor; small numbers (mainly immatures) summer and a few pairs breed.

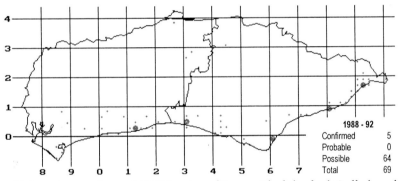

	1988 - 92	
	Confirmed	5
	Probable	0
	Possible	64
	Total	69

Although an estimated 83,500 pairs of Lesser Black-backed Gulls breed in Britain (New Atlas), this species remains one of the scarcest breeding birds in Sussex. Prior to 1962 from one to three pairs nested regularly though there were six pairs in 1946 (des Forges & Harber). A census of breeding seabirds in the county in 1969 found just two pairs while a census in 1983-84 found three pairs in St Leonards, one pair on the sandstone cliffs between Hastings and Cliff End and another pair holding territory on a roof in Worthing (Prater 1985). More recently there has been a change in distribution, as indicated by the Atlas map, which shows the presence of pairs in the coastal towns of Brighton, Eastbourne and Worthing and also at Rye Harbour. Numbers, however, have remained low with a maximum of three pairs at Worthing in the 1990s and no more than two pairs elsewhere.

A few birds, mainly immatures, summer but by late June numbers increase as autumn passage commences. Typically gatherings of up to 100 are recorded but higher counts have included 200 at Chichester Gravel Pits on 29 June 1968

317

and 200 immatures at Rye Harbour on 28 June 1984. Up until 1970, southwesterly movements of Lesser Black-backed Gulls were regularly observed at Selsey Bill in June and July. In June 1968, for example, a total of 720 was recorded while 1300 were seen in just four days in June 1969. In some years passage continued beyond July as shown by a count of 234 on 14 August 1966. Interestingly no comparable coastal movements have been recorded since 1970. Large autumn gatherings of up to 600 birds were regular at a refuse tip at Chichester Gravel Pits during the 1960s but they too no longer occur. Indeed in only four autumns between 1970 and 1993 were counts in excess of 250 recorded, the largest being 1500 at Scotney Court Gravel Pit on 29 September 1989 and 900 at Colgate refuse tip in October 1980.

An indication of the size of the population in winter is provided by a series of co-ordinated counts of roosting gulls that were carried out in 1977-79 (Porter 1979), 1983 (Newnham 1984b) and 1993 (de Potier & Yates 1994). The results of these counts, which show considerable variation between winters, are shown in the following table.

Date of count	Total at inland sites	Total at coastal sites	County Total
5 Feb 1977			1
28 Jan 1978			1140
20 Jan 1979			10
23 Jan 1983	5	110	115
23 Jan 1993	7	742	749

The total recorded in 1978 included 1000 on Shoreham airport while that in 1993 included 715 in Pagham Harbour. These unprecedented counts are by far the largest for the county in winter, far exceeding other notable counts at coastal sites including 240 and 180 at Rye Harbour on 12 November 1977 and 28 February 1978 respectively and 400 at Pagham Harbour on 1 November 1992.

Nationally, the number of Lesser Black-backed Gulls wintering inland has increased steadily since the early 1950s as shown by totals for England and Wales of 165 in 1953 and 44,564 in 1983 (Winter Atlas). In Sussex, however, numbers have not increased to the same extent. A count of 100 near Itchingfield on 26 December 1965 was described in the *Sussex Bird Report* for that year as "quite exceptional" while subsequent gatherings inland have included 190 at Sutton in December 1974, 300 at Itchingfield in 1978 and 216 at Weir Wood Reservoir on 20 January 1989. At Faygate there were 190 on 2 February 1983, 250 on 28 January 1990 and 160 on 29 November 1992. It may be that the increasing tendency for Lesser Black-backed Gulls to winter inland in the southern half of Britain accounts for the lower numbers seen in Sussex on autumn passage.

Spring passage occurs between March and May, mainly at the coast. Numbers are variable but never reach those that have been recorded in some autumns. Large counts have included 600 at Rye Harbour between mid and late March 1970 (with 400 still present on 3 April), 300 flying east there on both 10 April 1971 and 10 March 1973, and 250 at South Heighton on 24 March 1984. After the end of April, counts are much smaller with 130 at Rye Harbour in early May 1972 and 60 at Cuckmere Haven on 23 May 1975 the largest recorded. There is also a small passage up-Channel although it is unusual for more than 100 to be recorded at any one site over a whole spring. The largest movements, which typically occur in April, usually involve less than 50 birds in a day. Exceptional numbers were, however, recorded in 1969 when 105 and 180 flew east at Selsey Bill on 6 and 21 April respectively. The small volume of passage, the peak in April and the virtual lack of coastal movements at other times of the year, with the exception of August, is clearly shown in fig. 57 which is based on the results of nearly 6000 hours of sea-watching at Worthing between 1978 and 1993.

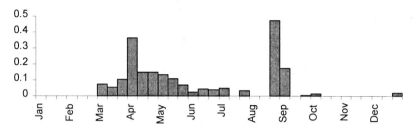

Figure 57. Hourly rates of passage, in 10-day periods,
of Lesser Black-backed Gulls at Worthing, 1978 - 93.

Concentrations of Lesser Black-backed Gulls can be found in association with those of other large gulls at coastal and estuarine sites but birds may also be found scavenging on refuse tips, particularly those inland. Furthermore it is the only large gull to be encountered regularly on farmland away from the coast; most are recorded in the Horsham and Crawley area but small groups have been seen on the Downs including 50 on Burton Down on 8 September 1971, 190 at Sutton in December 1978, and up to 110 at Slindon Park in October of both 1991 and 1992.

Both dark and pale-mantled birds are recorded in the county although there is little available data on their relative abundance. Most recorded in summer are pale-mantled, while observations at Worthing suggest that the majority of individuals seen moving east in spring are dark-mantled.

The racial identification of dark-mantled birds has been considerably complicated by the recognition of the blackish backed *L.f. intermedius* as separate from the jet black backed *L.f. fuscus* (Barth 1975). The latter, from the Baltic and northern Norway, migrates southeast to winter in the Middle East and East Africa, while *intermedius* breeds in southern Scandinavia and, like the pale backed *L.f. graellsii*, winters south to West Africa (Grant 1986).

While *fuscus* may have occurred in the county, it is likely that the vast majority of dark-mantled birds recorded are *intermedius*, a view supported by observations in Kent (Grant 1986) although the possibility of some being *fuscus* is recognised. BWP alludes to only three (ringing?) records of *fuscus* from eastern England.

Ringing in Sussex has provided little information about movements of this species when compared with that for the other more common gulls. The most interesting recovery was of an adult *graellsii* ringed at Sompting on 7 March 1984 and found dead at Sorvay Vagur, Faeroes, 1317 km NNW, on 18 July

1984. Two adults ringed at Seaford on the 15 June 1948 were recovered later that summer in Dumfries and Galloway while a third bird ringed at Seaford on 1 July 1948 was seen, also in Dumfries and Galloway, on 7 July 1948. Three birds ringed as nestlings, two in Suffolk and one in Northumberland, were recovered in Sussex the August after hatching while a nestling ringed in the Netherlands was observed feeding at a refuse tip in the county just three months after ringing.   *John Newnham*

Herring Gull   *Larus argentatus*
Status:- A common breeding resident, passage migrant and winter visitor.

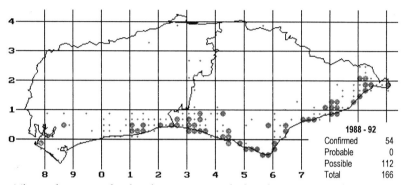

	1988 - 92
Confirmed	54
Probable	0
Possible	112
Total	166

The Atlas map clearly shows a coastal distribution extending eastward from Worthing to Rye and beyond. The map also shows confirmed breeding in two tetrads in the Chichester area and in a number of other tetrads several km inland, the furthest from the sea being at Cuilfail Cliff at Lewes. It does not, however, reveal the change that has occurred in both the size of the breeding population and its distribution in Sussex over the past few decades.

Walpole-Bond noted that during the 1920s the chalk cliffs from Seaford to Beachy Head held about 2000 pairs of Herring Gulls and this was clearly the main nesting area in the county at that time. A breeding distribution map for Herring Gull drawn in Walpole-Bond's era would have been similar to that for Kittiwake today. Between 1935 and the early 1940s the sandstone cliffs near Hastings were colonised and in the 1950s Herring Gulls started to nest on the roof tops of buildings in Hastings and St Leonards-on-Sea. Surveys of nesting Herring Gulls were conducted in 1965 (Porter 1966), in 1969 for Operation Seafarer, in 1976 and in 1983-84 (Prater 1985). The totals recorded by these surveys in each of the main nesting habitats is shown in table 68 reproduced from Prater (1985).

	1965	1969	1976	1983/84
Sandstone cliffs	371	315	nc.	75
Chalk cliffs	394	401	nc.	63
Roofs / Inland	23	106-131	244	675
Low coastal sites	12	39	nc	38
Total	800	861-886	244	851

Table 68. Numbers of and habitat choice of Herring Gulls in Sussex.

The breeding population of Herring Gulls in Britain increased dramatically between the 1940s and early 1970s but more recent census information has shown that it almost halved between 1969 and 1987 (New Atlas). The reduction in the Sussex population by over 50% between the 1920s and 1965 was, therefore, contrary to the national trend as was its stabilisation between 1965 and 1984. More remarkable has been the change that has taken place in preferred breeding sites from the traditional cliffs in favour of roof top sites. Regrettably, there have been no full counts since 1984 but the available records suggest that this withdrawal is continuing given that only three pairs were located on the cliffs between Birling Gap and Cuckmere Haven in 1991.

Natural cliff falls may have initially reduced the availability of stable nesting ledges but the construction of undercliff walks between Brighton and Peacehaven and subsequent cliff-face management has also contributed to the move to roof tops. Roof top nesting started in southwest England in the 1920s and was first noticed in southeast England in the 1930s (Cramp, Bourne & Saunders 1974). Until 1971, roof nesting in Sussex was confined to Hastings and St Leonards but this habit was first noted in Brighton in 1971, Eastbourne in 1972 and Worthing in 1974. The Atlas map reflects this dispersion as it shows all the coastal towns to the east of Worthing now supporting breeding Herring Gulls.

Apart from on cliffs and roof tops, Herring Gulls regularly nest on shingle islands and by gravel pits, mainly in the Rye area. Here the annual counts suggest marked fluctuations in numbers with up to 170 pairs at Rye Harbour in 1970. A small colony at Northpoint Gravel Pit, near Rye, reached 37 pairs in 1989; seven pairs nested at Scotney Court Gravel Pit in 1985 and up to four pairs have nested on shingle islands at Cuckmere Haven.

The size of the winter population is best assessed from a series of co-ordinated counts of roosting gulls that were carried out in 1977-79 (Porter

1979), 1983 (Newnham 1984b) and 1993 (de Potier & Yates 1994). The results of these counts are shown in the following table.

Date of count	Total at inland sites	Total at coastal sites	County Total
5 Feb 1977			1734
28 Jan 1978			3113
20 Jan 1979			2095
23 Jan 1983	505	7315	7820
23 Jan 1993	71	12797	12868

In 1977, 1978 and 1983, 3-4% of all the gulls counted were Herring Gulls whereas in 1978 and 1993 they made up 14% and 11% of the count respectively.

During the period from 1983 to 1993 there was a 70% national increase in the number of Herring Gulls roosting on the coast (Waters 1994) and the figures in the table show that a similar change occurred in Sussex. A count of 7978 in Pagham Harbour on 23 January 1993 represented nearly 62% of the county total for this species and was also the highest count ever recorded at one site in Sussex. Wintering Herring Gulls are found mainly on the coast, particularly on rocky foreshores, in harbours where commercial fishing continues and on rubbish tips. During most winters, maximum counts for individual sites are usually in three-figures but larger gatherings have been recorded at Pebsham refuse tip where there were 5000 on 17 February 1986, 2500 in February 1988 and 2000 in both April 1986 and December 1988. At Brighton Marina 1500 were recorded in January 1982 and the following January 1050 were counted between Brighton and Saltdean. A roost between Rye Harbour and Camber held 1150 in March 1991, 1320 in January 1992 and 1650 in March 1992. Counts at inland sites are generally lower but a total of between 2500 and 3000 at Arlington Reservoir on 29 October 1972 was exceptional.

During the 1960s, sizeable movements were recorded off both Beachy Head and Selsey Bill. Generally these were in an eastward direction between February and May and westward from June onwards. The largest spring movement was in 1969 when the total recorded moving up-Channel was 6930 including a peak of 1000 on 7 April. Some of the largest westward movements have occurred in June including 4890 that passed Selsey Bill over a period of four days at the end of the month in 1969. Other significant westerly movements at this time of the year have included 1315, 70% of which were adults, off Selsey Bill on 7 June 1967, a further 1600 there, mainly immatures, on 2 July 1967 and 2250, mainly adults, off Beachy Head on 31 July-1 August 1965.

The origins and destinations of the birds involved in these movements are unclear, especially as studies of Herring Gulls caught and ringed on beaches and refuse tips near Worthing between 1975 and 1993 suggest that the Herring Gull is the most sedentary of all the gulls found in Sussex. The recoveries generated from this study, and plotted by Newnham (1988), have mainly been in Sussex and in neighbouring coastal counties. There have also been a few recoveries from the Bristol Channel, from northern Britain and from coastal sites bordering the southern North Sea, but only one from southern Norway.

These findings are in stark contrast to those reported for a ringing study of wintering Herring Gulls at inland refuse tips around London (Stanley *et al* 1981) from which there were several recoveries during the breeding season in arctic Norway. Furthermore, mantle colour and biometrics of the Surrey birds suggested that they were of the race *L.a. argentatus* which breeds in Scandinavia and the Baltic. In Kent too, it is normal for up to 10% of adult Herring Gulls in winter to show characteristics of *argentatus* (Sutherland 1983), whereas the wing and bill lengths of those ringed in Sussex conform to the quoted figures for the race *L.a. argenteus* which breeds in Britain and between northwest France and the Netherlands (BWP). In Sussex only 13 birds have been ascribed to *argentatus* although the paucity of records may be due, at least in part, to difficulties in identifying this race in the field. All those recorded have been in the winter, between 4 November and 3 March, and all except for one at Weir Wood Reservoir on 3 February 1990 have been at coastal sites. The first for the county was one at Scotney Court Gravel Pit on 4 November 1987 and the most reported in any one year was seven in 1991.

In recent years, increasing numbers of yellow-legged birds have been recorded. Most show characteristics of the race *L.a. michahellis* which, according to some authorities, should be treated as a separate species, the Yellow-legged Gull *L. cachinnans*. Shrubb made no reference to yellow-legged birds although, in 1970, singles were recorded at Rye Harbour on 14 August and Warnham on 6 November and two at Chichester Gravel Pits on 5 November. Since then they have occurred annually with a dramatic increase during the 1980s (fig. 58). Virtually all the records have been of adults, the harder to identify first and second-year birds probably being overlooked.

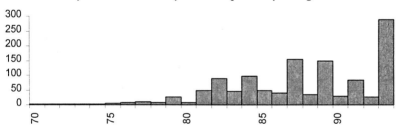

Figure 58. Annual totals of yellow-legged Herring Gulls, 1970 - 93.

Studies in France and Belgium have shown that birds of the race *michahellis*, which nest in the Mediterranean and Iberia, undertake a northerly or northwesterly dispersal after breeding (Grant 1983). This movement has only been observed in the past 20 years and undoubtedly some of these birds reach Sussex as the largest numbers of yellow-legged birds occur between June and October. The cumulative monthly totals for 1970-93 are shown below, confirming the peak in the post-breeding period.

Jan	Feb	Mar	Apr	May	Jun	Jul	Aug	Sep	Oct	Nov	Dec
31	33	27	8	19	112	663	984	457	420	149	25

Although yellow-legged Herring Gulls have occurred at several locations, the largest concentrations have been recorded in the Adur Valley and on the Selsey peninsula. At the former site, the peak counts have been 68 at Shoreham-by-Sea on 29 July 1982 and 63 at Small Dole refuse tip during

August 1984 and these are probably the same birds that have occurred at Washington refuse tip, where a maximum of 60 was seen on 13 September 1989. On the Selsey peninsula the largest counts have been in Pagham Harbour where, in 1993, there were 105 on 17 July, 159 on 21 July, 281 on 1 August, 122 on 13 October and 64 on 2 November. These counts exceeded the peaks for previous years in this area that included 131 at Chichester Gravel Pits on 8 August 1987 and 106 in Pagham Harbour on 2 August 1989.

John Newnham

Iceland Gull   *Larus glaucoides*

Status:- A very scarce rare winter visitor and passage migrant.

In the 33 winters between 1961/62 and 1993/94 a total of about 41 Iceland Gulls was recorded compared to the 26 reported by des Forges & Harber up to 1961. Thus it remains one of the scarcest gulls in the county with no records for 14 of the winters since 1961/62 and a period of absence of eight consecutive winters from 1973/74 to 1980/81. Shrubb in 1979 suggested it was then a declining species in Sussex; an observation supported by fig. 59 which shows a decrease in the number of occurrences in the 1970s.

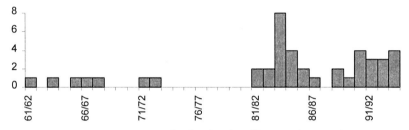

Figure 59. Winter totals of Iceland Gulls, 1961/62 - 93/94.

The graph also confirms that the downward trend has now been reversed with an increase in records in recent years. The best winter was 1983/84 when eight were recorded in Sussex, most between mid-January and early May 1984. These were part of an influx of more than 250 Iceland Gulls into Britain and Ireland following severe northwesterly gales in early 1984 which drove birds from their usual wintering grounds in Iceland (Winter Atlas).

Apart from a third-summer individual in Pagham Harbour on 5 July 1985, the pattern of occurrence is that of a rare winter visitor and spring passage migrant, with spring the most likely season to encounter this species. The monthly cumulative totals for the period 1962-94 are shown below.

Oct	Nov	Dec	Jan	Feb	Mar	Apr	May	Jun	Jul
1	2	3	7	3	6	15	7	1	1

Further analysis of the records since 1961 shows a roughly equal distribution between East and West Sussex with most records coming from the Pagham Harbour and Selsey area in the west of the county and from Beachy Head and Eastbourne in the east. First-year birds clearly outnumbered other age classes as, during the same period, there were eight adults, 11 sub-adults and 22 first-year birds.

All the records have been of single birds, most staying for short periods, except for a remarkable individual which remained at Shoreham-by-Sea from 24 January 1958 to 22 January 1961. All have been seen at coastal sites except for one near Tunbridge Wells in December 1958 and an adult at Chichester Gravel Pits from 17 to 21 January 1984.   *John Newnham*

Glaucous Gull   *Larus hyperboreus*

Status:- A very scarce but regular winter visitor and passage migrant.

Between 1962 and 1994 about 165 Glaucous Gulls were recorded compared with a total of over 50 birds up to 1961 (des Forges & Harber). It would appear, therefore, that there has been an increase in the number of occurrences of this species in Sussex although the number of individuals involved is probably less than the total given above, due to the same birds returning to winter in successive years. Since 1961/62, Glaucous Gulls have been seen in all winters except 1965/66, the totals recorded in each of these varying between one and 25 (fig. 60).

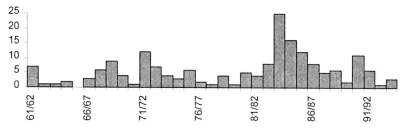

Figure 60. Winter totals of Glaucous Gulls, 1961/62 - 93/94.

The best year, 1984, coincided with the county's record year for Iceland Gulls and a large influx of 'white-winged' gulls into Britain, following severe north westerly gales. Interestingly, a similar large influx in 1980/81, when 500-600 Glaucous Gulls were recorded in Britain and Ireland (Winter Atlas), was not reflected in Sussex. First-winter birds are most frequently reported, comprising 119 of the total recorded since 1961/62. Of the remainder, 26 were aged as second-years and the others as adults. The number of adults recorded has, however, been distorted by two birds which have returned in successive years to winter in the same areas. One, which first appeared at Hove in first-year plumage on 5 July 1967, returned each winter thereafter, and was last seen on 7 February 1976. More recently, one that arrived in first-winter plumage during the large influx in early 1984, has frequented the Selsey/Pagham Harbour area every winter since and was still present in early 1996. In most years they both returned in August but arrivals by 5 July 1967 and 28 July 1988 for the Hove and Selsey birds respectively constitute the earliest autumn dates for the county.

The following table, showing the cumulative monthly totals of all records for 1962-94, includes these and several other long staying individuals. Clearly this species is most likely to be encountered from December to April, either as a winter visitor or as a spring passage migrant.

Jul	Aug	Sep	Oct	Nov	Dec	Jan	Feb	Mar	Apr	May	Jun
5	15	18	23	30	41	64	51	61	42	22	4

Interestingly all the June birds have been seen at the Crumbles or Langney Point; first-years were recorded there from May until 20 June 1982, on 5 June 1983 and on 9 June 1991 and a second-year on 15 June 1991. The 1983 individual was also seen in the Adur Valley between late June and August of that year.

An analysis of the records between 1962 and 1994 suggests that there is little difference in the pattern of occurrence between East and West Sussex with most sightings coming from the Chichester/Pagham area in the west of the county and between Beachy Head and Eastbourne in the east. Most Glaucous Gulls have been recorded at localities typically frequented by other large gulls. Favoured habitats include estuaries, harbours and the open shore, and also gravel pits and lagoons situated near the coast. Birds have been recorded in the lower reaches of river valleys as far inland as Arundel on the River Arun, to Small Dole on the River Adur and to Lewes on the River Ouse. Like other gulls they may forage on refuse tips and this behaviour has been recorded at Chichester Gravel Pits, Pebsham and Small Dole. More unusually, there are two records for further inland, at Hassocks on 8 February 1986 and at Weir Wood Reservoir on 15 January 1989.

Most records of Glaucous Gulls have been of single birds although two or three have occasionally frequented the same area and in January 1984 at least five different birds were seen at Chichester Gravel Pits.

There have been no ringing recoveries to suggest the origins of Glaucous Gulls reaching Sussex although a single hybrid Glaucous x Herring Gull at Fairlight on 31 March 1986 may have come from the extensive hybrid colonies in Iceland. Sutherland (1983) noted more Glaucous x Herring hybrids in Kent than Glaucous Gulls although, elsewhere, most records involve pure Glaucous Gulls thought to originate from East Greenland or the Barents Sea (Dean 1984).   *John Newnham*

Great Black-backed Gull   *Larus marinus*

Status:- A common winter visitor and passage migrant; small numbers summer.

Although Great Black-backed Gulls are present throughout the year and small numbers breed in Hampshire and on the Isle of Wight (New Atlas), none have bred in Sussex. Summering birds are mainly immatures and are most frequently found at Rye Harbour, where up to 300 have occurred, and in Chichester Harbour where 200 is the maximum recorded.

Numbers increase throughout July and August as adult birds return to Sussex. At Rye Harbour, half those roosting there on 14 August 1983 were adults whereas a month earlier they had all been immatures. Numbers continue to build up in autumn as shown by counts of 750 at the Crumbles on 11 September 1988 and 700 at Shoreham-by-Sea on 21 October 1989.

The size of the winter population is difficult to assess as numbers loafing or roosting at favoured sites can change from one day to the next. A series of co-ordinated counts of gulls roosting in winter undertaken in 1977-79 (Porter

1979), 1983 (Newnham 1984b) and 1993 (de Potier & Yates 1994) show the species to be the fourth most numerous gull in the county behind the Black-headed, Common and Herring Gull. The results of these counts, which show that Great Black-backed Gulls make up 1-2% of the gulls wintering in Sussex, are shown below.

Date of count	Total at inland sites	Total at coastal sites	County Total
5 Feb 1977			787
28 Jan 1978			516
20 Jan 1979			680
23 Jan 1983	10	814	824
23 Jan 1993	215	2199	2414

The largest count received for individual sites in each of the winters from 1961/62 to 1992/93 is shown in fig. 61. Although the numbers have fluctuated from year to year, no clear pattern emerges and, unlike the co-ordinated counts described above, they have shown no significant change. The largest gatherings recorded in the county have all been in the Rye area where maxima have included 1400 between Rye Harbour and Bulverhythe in December 1971 and 1210 and 1305 at evening roosts on 9 November 1984 and 25 November 1991 respectively. Large concentrations sometimes occur at Bulverhythe, Cuckmere Haven, Shoreham-by-Sea and in Chichester Harbour.

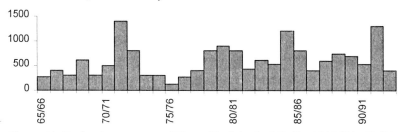

Figure 61. Peak winter counts of Great Black-backed Gulls, 1965/66 - 92/93.

Although the Winter Atlas demonstrated that comparatively large numbers of Great Black-backed Gulls winter inland in England (Winter Atlas), they are the most maritime of the *Larus* gulls and they do not occur inland in Sussex in large numbers. Like other large gulls, they may be found foraging on refuse tips, the highest counts being recorded at those tips nearest the coast, for example 800 at Pebsham on 8 January 1986. Smaller numbers (up to 38) have, however, been recorded on refuse tips well inland near Horsham. Also noted as unusual were counts of 30 at Amberley on 27 January 1963 and at Cowdray Park on 12 December 1982.

Even at the reservoirs, where other gulls may be numerous, the Great Black-backed Gull is recorded in only small numbers. Most have been noted at Darwell Reservoir where the largest counts were 200 flying over on 1 February 1964 and 95 on 15 January 1989. Mortlock (1992) described the species as a regular winter visitor to Weir Wood Reservoir but the total recorded there between 1957 and 1989 was only 257 with a maximum of 44 during 1984.

Visible movements of Great Black-backed Gulls are not well documented. However, a coastal movement up-Channel may occur in late winter and early spring as indicated by totals of up to 40 per hour passing Pevensey Bay on 6 March 1968 and 273 flying east at Newhaven on 8 February 1992. In autumn the few significant movements that have been recorded have all been in a westward direction, the largest being at Beachy Head where the highest counts have been "hundreds" on 15 October 1975, 400 in association with a large Gannet movement on 18 September 1976 and 200 the following day.

Ringing has not provided a vast amount of information although it has given some clues about the origin of Great Black-backed Gulls wintering in Sussex. Most of this information has come from a gull ringing programme conducted near Worthing since 1975 in which 140 Great Black-backed Gulls have been ringed. This study has produced single recoveries between May and early September from Denmark and Sweden and three from coastal Norway, including one at 71 degrees north in arctic Finnmark, 2619 km NNE. Furthermore four nestlings ringed in Norway and one ringed in Estonia have subsequently been found dead in Sussex. These recoveries, coupled with that of a bird found dead at the Midrips in February 1972 which had been ringed at Great Ainov Island, USSR in July 1965 (Shrubb), suggest that wintering Great Black-backed Gulls in Sussex come from Scandinavia and northern Europe rather than from the British breeding population. The only other foreign recovery was from the Netherlands in late September. A number of local recoveries and retraps confirm that birds return to the same site in successive winters.   *John Newnham*

Kittiwake   *Rissa tridactyla*

Status:- A common but localised breeding species; common winter visitor and passage migrant.

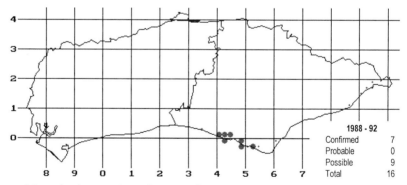

1988 - 92	
Confirmed	7
Probable	0
Possible	9
Total	16

Although three pairs of Kittiwakes were present amongst the Herring Gulls on the sandstone cliffs at Cliff End near Pett on 3 June 1967, breeding was not recorded until 1976 when 4-5 pairs nested on the cliffs near Newhaven. The Atlas map shows the restricted area of chalk cliffs between Peacehaven and Beachy Head where Kittiwakes have colonised and also their absence from the cliffs between Hastings and Pett and from stretches of the coast without cliffs. The early development of the colony between Peacehaven and Newhaven was documented by James (1981). Its continued growth to a peak of 1260 nests in 1990 is shown in fig. 62 although, regrettably, there were no counts in 1986, 1988, 1991 and 1993.

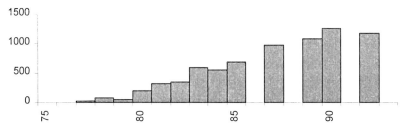

Figure 62. Annual totals of breeding pairs of Kittiwakes at Newhaven, 1975 - 93.

As the Newhaven colony, and the area of cliff it occupies, has increased, other small colonies have become established elsewhere. In 1981 there were 40 pairs at Beachy Head, but by 1984 this figure had decreased to just seven pairs and there have been no records of breeding since. A colony at Splash Point, Seaford held 46 pairs in 1989, 69 pairs in 1990, 24 pairs in 1992 and 300 nests in 1994.

Nationally the Kittiwake population grew by 22% between 1969 and 1985-87 (New Atlas), an expansion which has been continuing for most of this century (Cramp, Bourne & Saunders 1974). Although only a small proportion of the national population breeds in southeast England, the increase here has been more dramatic than in other regions with the Sussex colonies holding more than a quarter of the Kittiwakes nesting between Lincolnshire and Dorset.

Large gatherings of Kittiwakes may occur where there is a local abundance of food or where there are safe roosting sites. Some of the largest concentrations were recorded long before the species nested in the county and most were in East Sussex. The largest was 600 in Newhaven Harbour on 3 November 1969 but there were regular three figure counts from the Rye Harbour area during the summer months in the 1970s with maxima there of 200 in May 1970, 300 in August 1972 and 280 in July 1977. Flocks of 200 or more were recorded feeding offshore at Birling Gap during August and

September of both 1971 and 1973 and, more recently, off Worthing during June 1989. A roost in early autumn at Brighton Marina reaches a peak in September or early October; maximum counts have ranged between 69 in 1986 and 221 on 5 September 1992. There are only a few records of flocks in the winter, of which 112 at Rye Harbour on 25 January 1981 and 65 following a fishing vessel there on 23 January 1983 are the largest.

Large offshore movements of Kittiwakes may occur at any time of year, often in association with those of other seabirds, yet no clear pattern emerges. In winter, birds may be recorded moving both east and west whereas in spring, mainly eastward movements are observed, particularly in East Sussex. The largest movement recorded in the county in spring was that of 2000 east at Newhaven on 25 April 1991, although many may have come from the breeding colony there. In West Sussex there is a more pronounced westward movement in late winter and spring, as has been noted for other seabirds, mainly Gannets, Fulmars and auks (Newnham 1987). In late summer and autumn, most passage is down-Channel yet the county's largest autumn movement of 1080 off Selsey Bill on 19 October 1980 was in an easterly direction. The counts in table 69 give an indication of the scale of the movements recorded and they confirm the lack of a clear pattern.

| | Eastbound | | | Westbound | | |
	Site	Date	Total	Site	Date	Total
January	Hove	26 Jan 1994	367	Selsey	13 Jan 1993	601
February	Selsey	1 Feb 1981	315	Pett	2 Feb 1985	200
March	Brighton	13 Mar 1983	629	Selsey	23 Mar 1981	116
April	Newhaven	25 Apr 1991	2000	Worthing	8 Apr 1970	71
May	Beachy Head	7 May 1992	310	Worthing	22 May 1984	63
June	Brighton	19 Jun 1986	156	Selsey	21 Jun 1969	982*
July	Pett	5 Jul 1977	200	Selsey	4 Jul 1970	82
August	Brighton	10 Aug 1983	200	Southwick	2 Aug 1978	21
September	Brighton	13 Sep 1993	137	Beachy Head	2 Sep 1968	550
October	Selsey	19 Oct. 1980	1080	Selsey	26 Oct 1980	628
November	Worthing	4 Nov 1985	505	Worthing	5 Nov 1989	365
December	Worthing	20 Dec 1981	296	Worthing	29 Dec 1990	190

* total of 2 or 3 days movement

Table 69. Peak monthly movements of Kittiwakes.

As with other seabirds, movements recorded at one site are not always observed at other watched sites, as on 7 May 1972, when 310 Kittiwakes passed Beachy Head but only 15 were noted at Selsey Bill. However, on 25 March 1979 a marked easterly passage occurred along the entire coast with 394 recorded at Selsey Bill and 349 at Birling Gap. In autumn, too, numbers may vary considerably despite similar watching effort at different sites. A good example of this is provided by counts of 167 and 522 at Selsey Bill on 18 and 22 October 1984, on which dates the totals at Worthing were 574 and 327 respectively.

Most large passages of Kittiwakes have been recorded in fresh to strong onshore winds but up-Channel movements of 200 at Brighton on 10 August 1983 and 354 at Worthing on 15 January 1987 occurred in strong northeast winds.

Shrubb noted that the Kittiwake was comparatively uncommon in the winter months and, nationally, winter numbers are less than 1% of those expected in the summer (Winter Atlas). The above table clearly shows, however, that large numbers may occur off Sussex in winter and an analysis of Kittiwake movements at Worthing (based on over 6000 hours of sea-watching) shows more Kittiwake movement offshore in late autumn and winter than at other seasons (fig. 63).

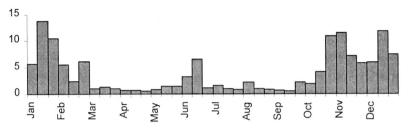

Figure 63. Hourly rates of passage, in 10-day periods, of Kittiwakes at Worthing, 1978 - 93.

Kittiwakes are the most maritime of our gulls and they are, therefore, rarely recorded inland. Between 1962 and 1993 there were sporadic inland records, mainly from reservoirs, in 20 different years and in all months except June. After severe gales larger numbers have been recorded and these include 100 at Arlington Reservoir on 13 November 1972, 35 at Ardingly Reservoir on 29 April 1981 and 65 at Weir Wood Reservoir on 25 January 1993.

Only a few Kittiwakes have been ringed in Sussex and none have been recovered. There are, however, seven records of birds ringed elsewhere, mostly as nestlings, and subsequently found dead in the county. These recoveries form three distinct groups. The only movement from overseas was of a nestling ringed in Finisterre, France in July 1981 and found dead at Bognor, 415 km northeast, on 9 March 1985. Two nestlings ringed at Langdon Bay, Dover were found dead on the shore in East Sussex in late summer, one seven years later, and four birds ringed on the northeast coast in Northumberland or Tyne and Wear were recovered, probably having died off the Sussex coast during the winter. *John Newnham*

Ivory Gull   *Pagophila eburnea*

Status:- Seven or eight old records, all of questionable identity.

des Forges & Harber give about ten records up to 1960, although two or three have not been traced. Seven or eight records have been found, five or six relating to specimens reported to have been obtained during the 1800s. Two were at Brighton and one at St Leonards prior to 1849, one at Worthing *ca.* 1845, one at Rye in winter 1848 and one at Hastings in August 1848 (a very unusual date), although this may have been the individual obtained at St Leonards (Walpole-Bond). Single adults were also reported from the mouth of the River Rother at Rye Harbour on 6 January 1931 (Williams 1931) and at Cuckmere Haven on 19 November 1954 (Harber 1955b and *SxBR* 7: 15), the latter departing north up the Cuckmere Valley. Published accounts of both these adults are unconvincing and as none of the earlier specimens survive or appear to have been aged, they too must be regarded as somewhat suspect. None of the above records are recognised as valid by Evans (1994a).

A record of an adult at Portobello, Brighton on 19 November 1961 has recently been reviewed and is considered to be inadequately documented (M J Rogers *in litt.*).

Although this species has undoubtedly become rarer in recent times, the occurrence of adults as far south as southern England is very considerably less likely than first-winters. While first-winters can be readily identified, there is a very real danger that albinos of other gull species, or even Iceland or Mediterranean Gulls, have been mistaken for adult Ivory Gulls in the passed. The species continued place on the county list is, at best, decidedly tenuous.

There were nearly 40 records of this superb Arctic gull in the British Isles during 1962-94, compared with nearly 80 before 1962. It winters primarily in the Arctic Ocean. *Richard Fairbank*

Gull-billed Tern *Gelochelidon nilotica*

Status:- A rare vagrant (62 records of *ca.* 81 individuals).

Forty-eight were recorded prior to 1962, seven up to 1855 and 41 during 1950-61. These include the first British record at Rye Harbour in 1802 (where a further two were collected up to 1813), one shot at Selsey Bill on 31 March 1852 (an exceptionally early date), six feeding off Langney Point for some hours on 26 June 1952 (Harber 1952b) and one flying over fields and mud banks at Shoreham-by-Sea on 17 September 1950 (the latest county record). A record total of ten was reported in 1960, five singles flying east past Selsey Bill between 23 April and 15 May, one flying west past Langney Point on 2 July, one flying west past Selsey Bill on 3 July, with two west there on 13 July and one on 24 August.

Since the beginning of 1962 approximately 33 have been recorded:

1962: One flying east past Selsey Bill on 26 April.
1963: Singles flying past Selsey Bill on 26 and 29 August were possibly the same.
1964: Singles flying past Selsey Bill on 19 April, 21 and 24 May and, probably the same, in Pagham Harbour on 25 May.
1965: One flying past Selsey Bill on 29 May, with two on 12 June and one again on 13 June.
    Singles flying past Langney Point on 1 and 5 July, with two on 13 July and one flying past Holywell, Eastbourne on 20 August.
1966: One flying east past Selsey Bill on 7 May.
1967: Singles flying east past Selsey Bill on 30 April and 5 May.
1974: One at Pagham Harbour on 11 May.
    One, possibly the same, at Pett Level on 12 May.
1975: One over the Long Pit, Rye Harbour on 24 August.
1978: One at Rye Harbour on 27 August was feeding and resting on a sand bar west of the mouth of the River Rother.
1981: An adult in summer plumage at Ternery Pool, Rye Harbour during the evening of 19 May.
1982: Flocks of four and three flying east past Birling Gap on 13 May (at 06:20 and 06:40 GMT respectively).
1984: One flying east past Ferring on 26 April.

1987:   One flying east past Langney Point on 20 June.
        An adult in summer plumage flying west past Langney Point on 15 August.
1988:   An adult at Pett Level Pools on 15 August.

The decline in number of records since the late 1960s is most pronounced (fig. 64), and would be more so if it were not for the seven at Birling Gap in May 1982. The pattern of occurrences has also changed significantly with (more debatable) flypasts accounting for most of those reported during the 1960s but less than half the subsequent records. The adult flying past Langney Point in August 1987 was most probably that seen on the River Plym, Devon between 22 August and 11 September.

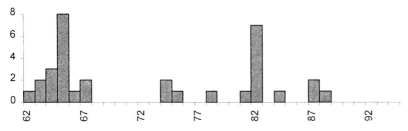

Figure 64. Annual totals of Gull-billed Terns, 1962 - 94.

The cumulative monthly totals below show that recent records (since 1970) have fallen in April, May, June and August while there are earlier records for all months between March and September with most in May, June and July.

	Mar	Apr	May	Jun	Jul	Aug	Sep
Before 1970	1	6	16	14	16	5	3
1970-94	-	1	10	1	-	4	-

The decline of north European breeding colonies is undoubtedly reflected in these records. In Denmark 229 pairs in the 1950s had fallen to 106 in 1960s and 30-37 during 1970s (BWP) with 0-2 pairs in 1991 (Tucker & Heath 1994). However, if those in spring during the 1950s and 1960s were heading for the Danish colonies (as was supposed at the time) why were they almost without exception doing so alone and over such a wide time period? Average Sussex spring flock sizes are significantly less than those recorded (in BWP) in Holland and Denmark at similar times of the year. Selsey Bill, which was 'the' site for the species, has not recorded one since 1967 (though 22 were reported there during 1960-67). This decline is even more apparent when contrasted with the fortunes of other sea-passage species which have increased, in part at least, in line with observer coverage (e.g. skuas). All records along the English south coast in the early and mid 1960s are currently under review by *BBRC*, its inital view being that "few if any would be acceptable by today's standards (but that is true for many other perfectly good records of several other species for that era)" (*Brit. Birds* 88: 379). To date only one, past Selsey Bill on 4 May 1960, is considered to be inadequately documented (M J Rogers *in litt.*). It is excluded from all the above totals.

There were nearly 170 records of this challenging tern in the British Isles during 1962-94 but occurrences are currently (since 1983) averaging between two and three a year. It breeds discontinuously from Iberia to China and in North America migrating south (some as far as Australia). European individuals winter in West Africa (BWP). *Richard Fairbank*

Caspian Tern *Sterna caspia*

Status:- A rare vagrant (twelve records).

Although two were recorded before 1962 (des Forges & Harber), only one record, flying west past Langney Point on 14 July 1961, is now considered to be acceptable (see below).

Eleven have been recorded since the beginning of 1962:

1962:   One on a sand bar in Pagham Harbour on 28 July.
1964:   One on gravel pits at Rye Harbour on 19 July.
        One flying west past Langney Point on 13 September.
1966:   One at Chichester Gravel Pits on 11 to 13 and 31 July.
1967:   One on Winner Bank, Chichester Harbour on 11 September.
1971:   One flying past Selsey Bill on 31 May.
1975:   One at Cuckmere Haven on 26 June came in from the sea and flew north up the valley
1981:   One at sea 10 km south of Shoreham-by-Sea on 28 July.
1984:   One at Ternery Pool, Rye Harbour on 9-10 July arrived shortly after the departure of the Sooty Tern.
1990:   One flying east past Hastings Pier on 31 March.
        One at Weir Wood Reservoir for five minutes on 19 August before departing to the southwest.

The run of records in the 1960s has unfortunately not been repeated, possibly reflecting the decline of the Baltic population (Tucker & Heath 1994). Most records have been between late June and mid-August with single occurrences in March and May and two in September. Most have been recorded from the coast, but two were inland, at Chichester Gravel Pits and Weir Wood Reservoir.

Records of individuals flying east past Selsey Bill on 6 May 1960 (*SxBR* 13: 13) and east past Worthing on 30 April 1969 and 16 May 1971 have recently been reviewed by *BBRC* and are considered to be inadequately documented (M J Rogers *in litt.*).

There were 190 records of this huge tern in the British Isles during 1962-94. It breeds discontinuously throughout much of the world, excluding western Europe and South America. The closest breeding population is in the Baltic. These birds, from which vagrants here most likely derive, winter in West Africa (BWP). *Richard Fairbank*

Lesser Crested Tern *Sterna bengalensis*

Status:- A very rare vagrant (two records, probably relating to the same individual).

First recorded in 1986, there have been two records:

1986:   An adult at Ternery Pool, Rye Harbour from 14:45 to 16:45 hrs on 13 May.
1989:   An adult flying east past Splash Point, Seaford at 14:10 hrs and east past Birling Gap at 14:30 hrs on 6 May later flew east past Dungeness, Kent at 17:40 hrs.

These records almost certainly relate to an adult female, colloquially known as 'LC' or 'Elsie', which has returned to summer on the Farne Islands, Northumberland annually since 1984, often pairing with a Sandwich Tern. She wasted no time journeying north appearing on the Farnes on 14 May 1986 and 7 May 1989, the very next day after being seen in Sussex in both years.

Although only four individuals have been recorded in the British Isles, the first in 1982, it is currently annual, mainly due to the return each year of 'Elsie'. This bright-billed tern breeds in Libya and from the Red Sea to Australia. Libyan birds winter off West Africa (BWP) and it is likely that British individuals failed to turn east at the entrance to the Mediterranean.

Richard Fairbank

Sandwich Tern   *Sterna sandvicensis*

Status:- A scarce breeding summer visitor and common passage migrant; rarely recorded in winter.

The changing fortune of this species is a success story for conservation in Sussex. It is interesting to note that in the 1963 *Sussex Bird Report* mention was made of "up to four seen together along the coast in June". There has been a steady increase since and breeding was first noted in Chichester Harbour in 1975 (Prater 1985). Numbers increased rapidly thereafter, reaching a peak of 105 pairs in 1977. At Rye Harbour, nesting was first recorded in 1984 and this colony is considered to be associated with that at Dungeness, Kent. The number of pairs at both Sussex colonies since their colonisation is shown in table 70.

	Chichester Harbour	Rye Harbour
1975	20	-
1976	35	-
1977	105	-
1978	54	-
1979	66	-
1980	70	-
1981	98	-
1982	42	-
1983	36	-
1984	18	2
1985	15	-
1986	12	40
1987	22	150
1988	-	-
1989	14	3
1990	?	25
1991	5	2
1992	27	8
1993	?	90

Table 70. Totals of breeding pairs of Sandwich Terns, 1975 - 93.

This species is vulnerable to disturbance and both colonies are on islands where there is some measure of control of visitors. The colonisation of the county took place at a time of national increase. In 1985-87, the British and Irish population was *ca.* 18,400 pairs (Lloyd, Tasker and Partridge 1991), an increase of 50% since 1969-70 (New Atlas). However, 80% of the population of this species in Britain is usually confined to just six breeding sites (Batten *et al* 1990). In Sussex, breeding success is variable. In 1993, for example, 120 young were raised at Rye Harbour, but in other years no young have fledged due to such factors as predation by foxes, flooding of nests by spring tides and inclement weather. From the figures in table 68, it is clear how erratic this species can be, but at Rye Harbour, at least, the species nests in years when there are good numbers of nesting Black-headed Gulls from which they derive some protection (Veen 1977).

Prior to 1962 the only record for December-January was of one at Winchelsea on 19 December 1953. However, since the beginning of 1962 eight have been recorded as follows:

1972: One at Southwick on 20 December.
1974: One at Southwick on 1 and 19 January.
1975: One at Hove Lagoon on 18 December.
1977: One at Southwick on 30 January.
1978: One at Pagham Harbour on 2 January.
1981: One at Camber on 8 January and at Rye Harbour from 11 January to 20 February.
1982: One at Shoreham-by-Sea from 23 to 31 January.
1989: One off Marker Point, Thorney Island on 2 December.

A further seven have occurred in February, but some of these (e.g. singles off Brighton on 25 February 1983 and off Selsey Bill on 10 February 1990) may refer to very early spring passage. The first returning birds are usually noted in mid-March, and in April and to a lesser extent May there is an eastward coastal passage which may involve several hundred birds a day (fig. 65). It is likely that these have wintered off West Africa and are returning to their breeding colonies adjoining the North Sea. The numbers recorded each spring are very variable and are dependent on the incidence of south-easterly winds in which more birds pass close to the shore. The largest total so far recorded was in 1983 when at least 7054 birds passed up-Channel including peaks of 1248 off Worthing and 1015 off Brighton on 10 April and a further 1000 at the latter site on 22 April (Newnham 1984a). The movement at Worthing exceeded the previous highest day total for the county of 1080 off Beachy Head on 18 April 1968.

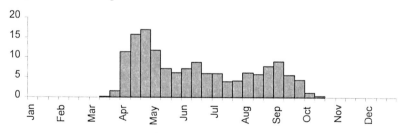

Figure 65. Hourly rates of passage, in 10-day periods, of Sandwich Terns at Worthing, 1978 - 93.

The autumn passage down-Channel is less pronounced than in spring although movements of up to 300 in a day are noted, as are occasional flocks of up to 1000 feeding offshore, such as that in Seaford Bay on 27 August 1968. By the end of September the species is scarce and, in the period 1965 to 1993, the last departing birds were noted between 3 October and 20 November.

Inland records are regular, with one to five reports in most years of small numbers at reservoirs, mainly in the autumn. There are, however, a number of records that further suggest that there is a small but regular overland movement through the county. These include, on 23 September 1983, parties of 32 and 40 that flew south over Arlington and Weir Wood Reservoirs respectively, and 50 that flew west, also at Arlington, on 27 August 1977.

Five colour-ringed birds seen on passage at Rye Harbour originated from colonies on the Farne Islands, Northumberland and the Sands of Forvie, Grampian.   *Dr B J Yates*

Roseate Tern   *Sterna dougallii*
Status:- A very scarce passage migrant and non-breeding summer visitor.

Up until 1961 about 44 were recorded, all but four them after 1950 (des Forges & Harber). Between 1962 and 1994 about 258 were reported with records in every year except for 1976 (fig. 66). Ironically, this was the year in which Roseate Terns were proved to breed for the first time just over the county boundary at Dungeness, Kent (Taylor, Davenport & Flegg 1981).

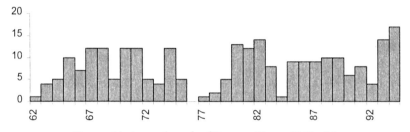

Figure 66. Annual totals of Roseate Terns, 1962 - 94.

The first are normally recorded in early May, but the earliest ever were singles at Beachy Head on 17 and 19 April 1968. Most spring records are of birds passing up-Channel, especially at Selsey Bill, Worthing and Beachy Head. The most seen in a day was a flock of seven at Selsey Bill on 14 May 1967 while the best years, as shown in fig. 66, were 1982 (14), 1993 (14) and 1994 (17).

During June and July, the principal locality for Roseate Terns in Sussex is Rye Harbour, where up to five birds have been recorded together at Ternery Pool. There is, however, no firm evidence that they have ever bred there and it is likely that many of the records refer to wandering adults from the large Common Tern colony at Dungeness or to unpaired individuals. Juveniles there from 2 to 8 August 1980 and on 22 July 1991, the former accompanied by two adults, probably also originated from Dungeness.

As the cumulative monthly totals for the period 1962-94 show, far fewer have been recorded in autumn than spring. The latest ever were singles at Brighton Marina from 21 to 25 September 1987 and at Langney Point on 30

September 1965. One at Arlington Reservoir on 9 September 1974 is the only inland record for the county.

Apr	May	Jun	Jul	Aug	Sep
13	116	52	46	21	9

The origins of colour-ringed adults at Pett Level Pools on 21-22 July 1989 and at Rye Harbour from 4 to 6 June 1991 have not been traced although a bird seen in Hampshire in August 1990 had been ringed as a chick at an Irish Sea colony in 1988 (Clark & Eyre 1993).   *Tim Toohig*

Common Tern   *Sterna hirundo*

Status:- A scarce breeding summer visitor and common passage migrant.

This species is the least maritime of the *Sterna* terns and it is likely to be encountered along rivers and at reservoirs, as well as on the coast. There are only three regular colonies in the county (Chichester Gravel Pits, Chichester Harbour and Rye Harbour), although birds may occasionally breed elsewhere (table 71). The provision of rafts at Chichester Gravel Pits and the management of suitable islands for nesting at Rye Harbour show just how dependent this species is upon positive conservation management.

	1960s	1970s	1980s	1990s
Arundel WWT	0	0	0	0-1
Bewl Water	0	0	0	0-1
Chichester GP	1	1-9	9-17	10-20
Chichester Harbour	0-36	36-88	14-73	17-22
Midrips / Wicks	1-3	0	0	0
Northpoint GP	40	0-118	0	0
Pagham Harbour	0-1	0-2	0	0
Rye Harbour	47-118	0-40	60-95	45-90
Scotney Court GP	0	0	0-1	0
Waltham Brooks	0	0	0	0-1

Table 71. Totals of breeding pairs of Common Terns, 1962 - 93.

Breeding success is generally good, but dramatic failures occasionally occur. At Rye Harbour, for example, no young were raised in 1989 when foxes were able to get out to the islands and, in 1992, the colony on the rafts

338

at Chichester Gravel Pits deserted after predation of eggs by Magpies. In Chichester Harbour there is the risk of high spring tides washing nests away.

For the purposes of discussing the numbers on passage, all records of unidentified Common/Arctic Terns are included under this species.

In the 1970s, the first birds were usually seen in the second week of April but in each of the years 1989-93 the first arrivals were in the last week of March. The earliest ever was one at Beachy Head on 21 March 1981 and three at Roedean on 25 March 1972, on which date one also passed Beachy Head. Regular sea-watching has shown that large numbers pass up-Channel in spring, the biggest movements being most frequent in early May, rather later than those of Sandwich Terns (Newnham 1984a). Movements of 500 to 1000 in a day are of almost annual occurrence but larger numbers are sometimes seen, including at Beachy Head, 5306 on 8 May 1981, 4180 on 1 May 1965 and 3365 on 5 May 1976. The totals recorded each spring are very variable. Cooper (1976a) reported that the totals for Beachy Head in the early 1970s varied between 10,691 in 1975 and 2620 in 1971 while more recent totals at Splash Point, Seaford have varied between 12,898 in 1989 and only 1119 in 1987. The figures reflect the incidence of south-easterly winds in each of these springs. Passage is heaviest in late April and early May (fig. 67) though in some years movements continue into June, as in 1984 when 996 flew east off Worthing on 1st and 913 on 3rd, and in 1977 when an exceptional 338 flew east at Church Norton on 18th. On days of heavy coastal passage, birds may occur at inland waters. Up to 200 were present at Arlington Reservoir on 29 April 1972 and 270 at Bewl Water on 20 April 1983.

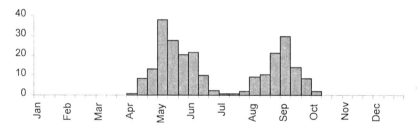

Figure 67. Hourly rates of passage of Common/Arctic Terns, in 10-day periods, at Worthing, 1978 - 93.

Autumn passage is typically less well marked than in spring with few obvious peaks. There have, however, been occasional large movements, including 3115 that flew west at Selsey Bill between 31 August and 3 September 1990 and 1100, also flying west, at Langney Point on 6 September 1992, a day also of exceptional Black Tern passage. In contrast to the spring, more are recorded inland. On 30 August 1992, for example, there were 100 at Chichester Gravel Pits, 78 at Barcombe Reservoir, 70 at Arlington Reservoir, 61 at Bewl Water and 36 at Weir Wood Reservoir. Visible movements in recent years have included, at Weir Wood Reservoir, 108 on 15 August 1982 and 110 on 29 August 1982 and 20 August 1989, all flying south or southwest.

In most years a few remain into October. In 1975, 36 flew west off Selsey Bill on 4th and in 1978 there were 50 off Worthing, also on 4th. Later records have included a Common Tern at Bewl Water from 13 to 26 November 1986 and single birds not specifically identified at Selsey Bill on 23 November 1963 and in Chichester Harbour on 19 November 1983.

A large number of Common Terns have been ringed in the county, almost all as chicks. Of the 17 birds recovered outside southern England, six were in France, two each in the Netherlands, Morocco, Senegal and Ghana and the remainder in Spain, Portugal and Sierra Leone. Most of these had been ringed at Rye Harbour in the 1950s. One ringed as a chick at Chichester Gravel Pits in 1986 was found nesting near Oxford in 1993.   *Dr B J Yates & Paul James*

Arctic Tern   *Sterna paradisaea*

Status:- Uncertain, but probably a fairly common spring and autumn passage migrant.

The status of this species in the county remains unclear due to difficulty in separating it from Common Tern in the field. Between 1965 and 1977 the *Sussex Bird Report* did not give a separate account for this species and, although there is now a better understanding of the relevant identification criteria (Hume 1993), the number of records has not increased significantly.

It is likely that the large up-Channel movements of Common/Arctic Terns in spring contain a proportion of Arctic Terns, given that a flock of 49 flew east off Splash Point, Seaford on 6 May 1983 and that a total of 173 did likewise at Hove on 18 April 1978. Passage may continue into early June as in 1984 when 24 flew east at Lancing on 2nd.

A first-summer bird was recorded at Rye Harbour on 18, 19 and 27 June 1987 while other reports for the period between late May and early August include up to three in Chichester Harbour from 3 to 11 July 1991 and six in Pagham Harbour on 18 July 1993.

In autumn, most are seen in September, particularly after gales, when birds may occur at inland waters, as well as on the coast. Numbers are typically small although 16 were recorded at Brighton Marina on 13 September 1993 and an exceptional flock of 34 flew south over Pulborough Brooks on 3 September 1992. Few are seen after mid-October, the latest being singles at Pett Level on 5 November 1977 and in Chichester Harbour on 12 and 15 November 1977 while one at Pagham Harbour on 30-31 December 1966 was thought to be this species.

The cumulative monthly totals of all dated records published in the *Sussex Bird Report* for the period 1977-93 are shown below.

Apr	May	Jun	Jul	Aug	Sep	Oct	Nov
230	140	28	20	12	104	21	2

Dr B J Yates & Paul James

Bridled Tern   *Sterna anaethetus*

Status:- A very rare vagrant (one record).

An adult at Ternery Pool, Rye Harbour during the evening of 16 May 1993 roosted overnight and was seen early the following morning before flying strongly out to sea (*Brit. Birds* 87: plates 138 and 139).

There were 16 records of this species in the British Isles during 1962-94. It occurs in all tropical oceans, dispersing offshore when not breeding.

Richard Fairbank

Sooty Tern   *Sterna fuscata*

Status:- A very rare vagrant (two records).

One was recorded before 1962, an adult female picked up exhausted on the shore at Black Rock, Brighton on 24 April 1911 (Griffith 1911). It is on display in the Booth Museum (BoMNH 207623) and was the seventh British record.

An adult at Ternery Pool, Rye Harbour during the afternoon of 9 July 1984 (*Brit. Birds* 78: plate 265) had been seen at Dungeness, Kent earlier that day.

This oceanic tern has become much less frequent in the British Isles with only eight of the 26 recorded up to 1994 being since 1962, and only one, the Rye individual, since 1980. It occurs throughout the tropics, breeding on islands and dispersing far out to sea when not breeding.   *Richard Fairbank*

Little Tern   *Sterna albifrons*

Status:- A scarce breeding summer visitor and fairly common passage migrant.

The Little Tern is of high conservation priority in Britain because it breeds in internationally important numbers and is concentrated into relatively few sites (Batten *et al* 1990). It is one of the most vulnerable breeding species in the county due to its preference for sand and shingle beaches, where it is particularly vulnerable to human disturbance. There are now few suitable undisturbed areas remaining in Sussex and, without the protection given to Little Terns within nature reserves over the last 20 years, it is likely that this species would no longer breed regularly in the county. This protection takes the form of voluntary wardening schemes, fences to exclude the public, control of predators and, at Rye Harbour LNR, the use of extensive electric fencing to reduce the impact of foxes on the population. However, concentrating the species within these protected areas may enable long-lived predators to specialise on Little Terns. Birds may be subjected to enormous pressure from predators such as foxes, Kestrels and Little Owls. This usually involves the loss of eggs or young, but in some years incubating adults are taken, especially by Little Owls. If all this were not enough, there is an additional hazard, in some years, of high tides coinciding with bad weather, resulting in the flooding of nesting areas. As a result there are few years in which the productivity of the breeding birds has exceeded 0.5 young per pair, the suggested level for replacement to maintain the population.

Shrubb referred to breeding colonies at four localities and annual totals for the whole county of up to 150 pairs. In addition a pair summered at Chichester Gravel Pits in 1965, 1967 and 1969-71 and four pairs bred at the Crumbles in 1970. A survey of breeding seabirds carried out in 1983-84 by the SOS revealed a total of 93 pairs, all in wardened nature reserves at Chichester,

Pagham and Rye Harbours (Prater 1985). The minimum and maximum totals of pairs at each of the sites in the county where Little Terns are known to have bred in the period 1962-92 is shown in the following table:

	1960s	1970s	1980s	1990s
Chichester Harbour	1-52	25-100	3-45	6-11
Pagham Harbour	6-44	20-75	0-68	0-15
Crumbles	?	0-4	0	0
Midrips	5-23	0-26	0	0
Northpoint Gravel Pit	?	0-2	0	0
Rye Harbour	5-55	2-29	30-76	35-50

Little Terns are typically the last of the breeding terns to arrive and the first to depart. During 1970-92, first dates varied between 3 and 16 April with the average 10 April. That at Worthing on 3 April 1985 is the earliest ever for the county. As with other terns, there is a marked passage up-Channel in spring. The numbers each year are variable but 971 were recorded at Selsey Bill between 12 April and 31 May 1981, 989 in 253 hours of sea-watching at Worthing in April-May 1990 and 949 in 404 hours at Selsey Bill in April-May 1991. Passage is heaviest in the last week of April and the first week of May, invariably in light east or south-easterly winds. Peak movements have included 220 off Selsey Bill on 4 May 1981 and, off Worthing, 749 between 1 and 6 May 1990 and 193 on 24-25 April 1991.

Following the breeding season, large gatherings may form in Chichester Harbour where there were 220 on 10 August 1986 and 371 on 24 July 1993. Passage at coastal sites is, however, poorly marked compared with the spring although 200 were seen off Ferring on 24 August 1975 and 70 flew west off Langney Point on 6 September 1992. The latest ever was one off Selsey Bill on 4 November 1991 although in some other years the last birds have be seen as early as late September.

Between 1962 and 1993 there were 24 inland records (excluding the summering pairs at Chichester Gravel Pits) totalling 47 birds, the cumulative monthly totals of which are shown below.

Apr	May	Jun	Jul	Aug	Sep	Oct
3	-	2	2	22	17	1

Most were recorded at Weir Wood Reservoir (23), Bewl Water (12) and Arlington Reservoir (6) with the remainder at Chichester Gravel Pits (2) and Barcombe Mills Reservoir, Bodiam, Burton Mill Pond and Darwell Reservoir. Further evidence of a small overland passage through the county is provided by a record of a party of seven that flew north up the lower Cuckmere Valley on 7 May 1988.

In contrast to Common Tern, and even though many fewer are ringed in Sussex, there is only one recovery of this species outside southern England. This was a bird trapped as an adult in June 1939 at Rye Harbour and killed in August 1948 in Loire-Atlantique, France, 472 km SSW.   *Dr B J Yates*

Least Tern   *Sterna (albifrons) antillarum*

Status:- One record, under consideration
A male exhibiting the characteristics of Least Tern was present at Rye
Harbour between late May and mid-July in successive years from 1983 to
1992, although it was seen (and heard) more regularly in some years than
others. It consorted with Little Terns and was occasionally seen attempting to
mate with them. It was most frequently encountered at the Little Tern colony
southwest of Ternery Pool, high tides often being best, and here its voice was
recorded providing a valuable clue to its identity (Yates & Taffs 1990). This
record is currently under consideration by *BOURC*, a major concern being
the elimination of the little known West African race of Little Tern *S.a.
guineae* (A Knox *pers. comm.*).

If accepted, this will be the first record for Europe, although whether it is
recognised as a full species (distinct from Little Tern) remains open to debate.
It differs from our Little Tern mainly in its vocalisations and concolourous
grey back, rump and tail (Chandler & Wilds 1994) and breeds on the coast and
along the largest waterways in the USA, wintering from central America
south to Brazil and Peru.   *Richard Fairbank*

Whiskered Tern   *Chlidonias hybridus*

Status:- A very rare vagrant (nine records involving ten individuals).
Ten have been seen, the first in 1963:

1963:   An adult in winter plumage at Darwell Reservoir on 3 September
        (*SxBR* 16: 24).
1967:   An adult in summer plumage on Winner Bank, Chichester Harbour on
        11 September.
1970:   One in summer plumage at Ivy Lake, Chichester from 14 to 21 May.
1979:   Two, probably a pair, in summer plumage at Rye Harbour from 31 May to
        4 June were most frequently seen at Ternery Pool.
1984:   One in summer plumage flying east past Church Norton on 2 June.
1985:   One in summer plumage flying east past Worthing on 25 May.
1988:   One in summer plumage at Ternery Pool, Rye Harbour on 28-29 May.
1994:   One in summer plumage at Sidlesham Ferry on 2 May departed east over
        Pagham Harbour.
        One, possibly the same, in summer plumage at Rye Harbour on 7-8 May.

The 1994 individual at Rye Harbour commuted between Ternery Pool
and the Long and Narrow Pits and had also been seen, and photographed, at
Dungeness, Kent on 5-6 May (*Birding World* 7: 179).

Seven were found in May, one in early June and two in September. While
most were from the coast (including flypasts reported in 1984 and 1985), two
were inland, at Darwell Reservoir and Chichester Gravel Pits. That in 1967
was amazingly seen with a Caspian Tern although it is currently under
review.

There were just over 90 records of this species in the British Isles during
1962-94. It breeds discontinuously throughout Europe, Africa, Asia and
Australia. West European birds winter in tropical West Africa (BWP).
                    Richard Fairbank

Black Tern
Chlidonias niger

Status:- A fairly common passage migrant.

The first Black Terns typically occur in mid to late April, although the earliest ever was one at Chichester Gravel Pits on 4 April 1957. The main passage takes place in the first three weeks of May but the totals recorded each spring are very variable, having ranged from 40 to 900 in recent years, with an average of 180. The largest numbers are generally seen flying up-Channel from the main sea-watching localities of Selsey Bill, Worthing, Seaford and Beachy Head. Normally only 10-25 birds are recorded in a day but occasional larger movements have included 342 off Selsey Bill on 1 May 1965 and 320 off Beachy Head on 9 May 1989 and at Seaford, 340 on 4-5 May 1990 and 389 on 10 May 1993. Small numbers may occur in spring on inland waters but, in years of heavy coastal passage, many more may be recorded, as on 1 May 1965 when there were 300 at Chichester Gravel Pits and 27 at Burton Mill Pond and on 10 May 1993, when there were 57 at Arlington Reservoir, 23 at Chichester Gravel Pits and 19 at Weir Wood Reservoir. Spring passage may continue well into June, as in 1977, when an exceptional total of 20 flew east off Church Norton on 18-19th with a further 20 offshore at Selsey Bill and five flying east at Rye Harbour on the latter date. Records of birds later in the month are thought to relate to non-breeding summer wanderers, most of which have been seen in Chichester Harbour and at Rye Harbour.

Autumn passage starts in early July and will often continue to mid or late October, but may also cease as early as mid-September. There is not such a clear peak as in spring and the numbers recorded are typically smaller, having averaged 100 birds per autumn in the period 1962-93. There have, however, been a few exceptions, particularly during or after strong onshore winds. Following such conditions, 70 were present on the Adur at Shoreham-by-Sea on 24 August 1977, up to 100 at Chichester Gravel Pits and Pagham Harbour two days later and 150 at Arlington Reservoir on 30 August 1985. There was a remarkable coastal movement on 6 September 1992, on which date at least 1800 flew west at Langney Point and 1026 at Selsey Bill. These totals were unprecedented for Sussex, but a far larger movement of 10,215 birds, mainly adults, was recorded at Dungeness, Kent on the same day (Nightingale & Allsop 1993).

The latest ever recorded in the county was one in the Cuckmere Valley from 13 to 21 November 1954 although there have been five other records for the month, comprising singles at Chichester Gravel Pits on 5 November 1967, Thorney Island on 10 November 1967, Glynde Levels on 12 November 1967, Weir Wood Reservoir on 4 November 1980 and in Chichester Harbour from 8 to 16 November 1986. *Tim Toohig*

White-winged Black Tern
Chlidonias leucopterus

Status:- A rare vagrant (43 records of 41 individuals).

Twelve were recorded before 1962 including three in 1959 and two in 1960. Six were in May (including two at the Midrips on 30 May 1891) and two were undated (one at Warnham Mill Pond many years prior to 1905). The remaining records were of adults in summer plumage flying east past Selsey Bill on 18 April 1959 (the earliest British record to date and currently under review due to plumage inconsistencies) and 27 April 1960 (also under review) and flying west past Hove on 15 June 1956 (Sutton 1958) and a juvenile west off Langney Point on 23 September 1960.

Twenty-nine have been seen since the beginning of 1962, records being fairly constant averaging just over one each year although there may have been a slight decline since the mid-1980s. Four were recorded in 1977 and three in 1984 (fig. 68).

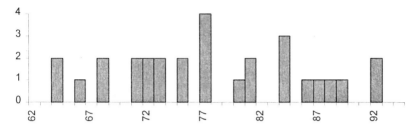

Figure 68. Annual totals of White-winged Black Terns, 1962 - 94.

The cumulative monthly totals of all dated records are shown below. Up to 1962 all but one of the records were in spring, with autumn occurrences surely overlooked. This contrasts strongly with more recent occurrences, where more have been seen in autumn than spring with almost as many have being found in August as in all other months combined. The earliest occurrence since the beginning of 1962 is of one at Bewl Water on 3 May 1981 while one at Ivy Lake, Chichester from 3 to 10 October 1984 is the latest.

	Apr	May	Jun	Jul	Aug	Sep	Oct
Before 1962	2	6	1	-	-	1	-
1962-94	-	6	4	2	13	3	1

Since 1962 over half the records have come from Chichester Gravel Pits (7), Rye Harbour/Northpoint Gravel Pit (6) and Pett Level Pools (4). Three have been seen at Pagham Harbour/Sidlesham Ferry and two at the Crumbles Gravel Pits (in 1964). Other more notable occurrences have been summer plumaged adults at Bewl Water on 3 May 1981, Barcombe Reservoir on 19 May 1984 (*Brit. Birds* 78: plate 268) and flying east past Brighton Marina on 21 June 1986 while a juvenile was at Arlington Reservoir on 24 August 1971. The remaining records were from Chichester Harbour (a first or second-summer usually at Cobnor Point from 15 July to 3 August 1988), the lower Cuckmere Valley (a juvenile from 16 to 28 August 1984), Scotney Court Gravel Pit (a juvenile on 3-4 September 1989) and two at Thorney (adults moulting into winter plumage at the Great Deep on 11 August 1973 and in summer plumage at Pilsey Island on 14-15 May 1992). The individual at Cobnor Point in 1988 was first seen at Sidlesham Ferry while one at Pett Level Pools in August 1992 moved to Northpoint Gravel Pit, Rye.

Most records have been of single individuals although a juvenile at Pett Level Pools from 27 August to 10 September 1977 was joined by a second on

2-3 September while an adult at the Crumbles Gravel Pits on 12-13 August 1964 overlapped with a juvenile there on 13-14 August.

There were nearly 600 records of this marsh tern in the British Isles during 1962-94. It breeds from eastern Europe to China. European birds winter in sub-Saharan Africa while central and east Asian populations winter as far south as Australia. *Richard Fairbank*

Guillemot *Uria aalge*

Status:- A fairly common winter visitor and passage migrant; formerly bred.

Guillemots once bred on the chalk cliffs at Beachy Head, Crowlink and Seaford Head and on the sandstone cliffs at Fairlight (Walpole-Bond). Cliff falls destroyed the nesting ledges at Beachy Head in 1853 and, although an egg shell was found in 1872, the species had disappeared by 1879. A pair was said to have laid at Saltdean in 1897 and three pairs did so at Beachy Head in 1904 but there have been no subsequent breeding records for the county.

The monthly totals for the period 1980-93, shown below, indicate that Guillemots are far more numerous than Razorbills in the winter months but that they may be scarcer in spring, when passage of both species occurs.

Jan	Feb	Mar	Apr	May	Jun	Jul	Aug	Sep	Oct	Nov	Dec
2082	304	119	31	109	19	18	9	34	70	312	736

The largest movement recorded was that of 1200 flying east at Pett in 1.5 hours on 9 January 1982. It is likely, however, given the relative abundance of this species in winter compared with Razorbills, that the large movements of unidentified auks recorded in some winters comprise mainly Guillemots. Such movements, discussed by Newnham (1987), included 737 flying east and 544 flying west at Brighton Marina on 26 January 1985 and 19 January 1986 respectively, 621 (including 81 definite Guillemots) flying east at Worthing on 4 November 1985 and 600 flying west at Langney Point on 2 February 1985. The absence of large movements from the extreme west of the county lends support to Shrubb's suggestion that Guillemots may be more numerous off East Sussex than West Sussex in winter.

Ringing recoveries confirm that birds from a wide area visit Sussex. Of 41 that had originated from outside the county, 20 were from Scotland, ten from Ireland, six from northern England and five from Wales. A few birds have been ringed in Sussex after being cleansed of oil. Of those recovered, none travelled more than 100 km except for one released at Fairlight in January 1981 and found dead only days later on the Dutch coast, 302 km ENE.

There are no inland records for the county. *Paul James*

Razorbill *Alca torda*

Status:- A scarce winter visitor and passage migrant; formerly bred.

Razorbills bred until 1878 at the very latest on the chalk cliffs at Beachy Head and possibly also at Seaford Head and the Seven Sisters (Walpole-Bond).

Although many of the auks observed in Sussex are not specifically identified, it is clear from the records available that Razorbills are less common in the county than Guillemots. The cumulative monthly totals for the period 1980-93, shown below, indicate that small numbers are present during the winter months and that some passage occurs in April-May and October-November.

Jan	Feb	Mar	Apr	May	Jun	Jul	Aug	Sep	Oct	Nov	Dec
88	53	28	53	166	13	2	13	34	109	100	65

Shrubb stated that, in winter, Razorbills were probably less common than Guillemots, and that of 520 auks picked up oiled along the Sussex coast between 1968 and 1972, only 26% were Razorbills. It is clear from the information available that this is still the trend, given that only 88 Razorbills were recorded in January in 1980-93 compared with over 2000 Guillemots. Of 648 auks picked up dead and/or oiled during this period, just under 10% were Razorbills, suggesting that a decrease has occurred since the early 1970s.

The origin of Sussex birds is indicated by recoveries of 18 individuals from Wales, 12 from Scotland and five from Ireland. Ringing has also shown that Razorbills do not fare well after be cleansed of oil. Of those recovered in Sussex, none had travelled further than 50 km or survived for more than a few days.

There are no inland records for the county. *Paul James*

Black Guillemot *Cepphus grylle*

Status:- A rare vagrant (14 records involving 12 individuals).

Prior to 1962 there were nine records (des Forges & Harber): four during 1882-98, one in 1950 and four in 1961. A juvenile was shot off St Leonards on 12 October 1882, and three were obtained off Langney Point, being adults on 3 August 1890 and 19 December 1892 and a juvenile in autumn or winter 1898. One in winter plumage was seen off Langney Point on 8 November 1950 (*SxBR* 3: 26). In 1961 singles were recorded off Selsey Bill on 11 August, 3 and 16 September and 1 October, although it is likely that only two individuals were involved. That seen in August was in summer plumage, those on 3 September and 1 October in winter plumage and the other in transitional plumage.

Five have been recorded since the beginning of 1962 with two in 1969, but only two since 1970:

1965: An oiled bird off Selsey Bill on 20 April.
1969: An adult in summer plumage off Beachy Head on 5 July.
A juvenile or winter plumaged adult flying west past Beachy Head on 26 August.
1982: One in winter plumage off Portslade-by-Sea on 7 January.
1985: A first-winter off East Head on 26 October.

There have been sightings in all months between July and January with an isolated record for April. Most have been seen in August (3), September (2) or October (4).

Very rare in southeast England, there is just one record of this distinctive coastal auk from Hampshire (Clark & Eyre 1993) and 16 in Kent, mostly along the Channel coast (J Cantello & T Hodge *in litt.*). It has an almost circumpolar distribution, the nearest breeding areas being in southern Ireland and Anglesey to the west and northeast Scotland, Denmark and southern Scandinavia to the east.   *Richard Fairbank*

Little Auk   *Alle alle*

Status:- A very scarce but increasingly regular autumn passage migrant and winter visitor.

Between 1948 and 1961 about 53 were recorded, including 17 in 1959. Since 1961, a total of at least 182 has occurred in 24 of the 33 years up to 1994 (fig. 69).

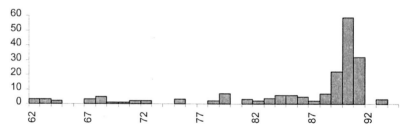

Figure 69. Annual totals of Little Auks, 1962 - 94.

The extreme dates for live birds were 12 October at Steyning in 1987 and 23 February at Worthing in 1983 but corpses were found at Rye Harbour on 1 March 1969 and at Climping on 4 April 1979. The latter was considered to be about a month old. The approximate cumulative monthly totals for the period 1962-94 are shown below.

Oct	Nov	Dec	Jan	Feb	Mar	Apr
10	91	67	12	4	1	(1)

Up until 1988 no more than 17 had been recorded in any one year, the annual average for the period 1962-88 being between two and three. Since then, a marked increase has occurred with 22 recorded in 1989, all in

November, an absolute minimum of 59 in November-December 1990 and at least 29 in October-December 1991. There were, however, none in 1992 and 1994 and only three in 1993. The 1990 total included an exceptional passage at Selsey Bill, where 39 flew west on 29-30 December, the largest ever movement recorded in the county. The reasons for this increase are unclear but there has been a recent tendency for birds to appear along the Sussex coast a day or two after influxes into the North Sea, following periods of strong northerly winds.

It is likely that many of the birds that reach us are in a weakened condition as shown by one at Brighton Marina on 16 October 1993 that was found dead the following day. Most are seen in flight passing along the coast but there have been 12 inland records since the beginning of 1962. These were at Bewl Water (2), East Chiltington, Finchdean, Fontwell, Glynde, Hunston, Lodsworth, Partridge Green, Sedgewick, Steyning and Westbourne. Of these, five were dead when found and most others died soon after recovery.

Little Auks breed in abundance in western Greenland and on islands from Spitsbergen to Siberia. They winter in the North Atlantic.   *Paul James*

Puffin   *Fratercula arctica*

Status:- A very scarce visitor, most frequently recorded in spring.

Between 1946 and 1961 a total of 16 was recorded in the period 18 July to 9 May. Of these, six were dead or dying.

Since the beginning of 1962, a total of 58 has been recorded (fig. 70).

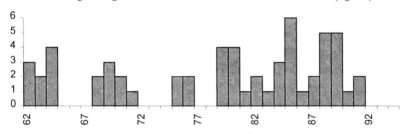

Figure 70. Annual totals of Puffins, 1962 - 94.

The cumulative monthly totals for the period 1962-94 are shown below.

Oct	Nov	Dec	Jan	Feb	Mar	Apr	May	Jun
4	2	2	3	3	5	7	26	5

A total of 12 was found dead or oiled, all between December and April and all on the coast, with the exception of one found dead near Kingley Vale (see below). A further two were picked up exhausted, both inland, the first an immature on the Downs near Sompting on 29 November 1962 and the other at Black Down, near Fernhurst on 14 October 1971. The remaining birds were all on the coast at Beachy Head (22), Selsey Bill (8), Brighton (5), Pett (3), Worthing (3) and Bexhill, Lancing and Langney Point (1 each).

There is some evidence to suggest a small but regular passage in April and May. At Beachy Head, for example, a total of 17 flew east in six of the ten springs between 1980 and 1989, including six on 6 May 1985. There have, however, been no records for this locality since 1989 although this is perhaps

349

attributable to a reduction in sea-watching at this site rather than a genuine decrease.

Two ringing recoveries affect Sussex. The first was caught as a chick at Skokholm, Wales in August 1951 and found dead five years later at Brighton. The second, ringed in Northumberland in June 1970, was found dead inland near Kingley Vale in 1972.

The nearest breeding colonies of Puffins to Sussex are in Dorset, the Channel Islands and the Isles of Scilly.   *Paul James*

Pallas's Sandgrouse   *Syrrhaptes paradoxus*

Status:- Formerly a rare vagrant (at least 120 recorded during the irruptions of 1863 and 1888).

Ten were recorded during the 1863 irruption. One which hit telegraph wires near Pevensey on 29 May was presumably from a party of seven or eight seen there the previous day while one was shot at Balcombe on 5 June and one at Camber in July (Walpole-Bond).

The irruption of 1888 was on a much larger scale involving at least 100 individuals although, pleasingly, only four were 'brought to bag' (Walpole-Bond). Five or six were seen at Filsham Farm on 26 May, *ca.* 30 around Jury's Gap in late May, a small covey frequented the shore between Shoreham-by-Sea and Lancing in May and June, 20-30 flew over Warnham Court Park on 31 May, *ca.* 30 commuted between the Downs and shore at Brighton in June and may have included eight to ten seen at Patcham (one of which was shot) on 4 June and two shot at Falmer on 20 June. One was found dead at Sedlescombe on 20 June and up to nine were present at Camber in June and July, where one pair may have bred. Finally one was shot at Shoreham-by-Sea on 8 November and one died at Itchenor in February 1889 (Walpole-Bond).

There have been no more recent records.

There were seven records of this almost mythical central Asian species in the British Isles during 1962-94 but only one of those has been since 1975, on Shetland in May and early June 1990.   *Richard Fairbank*

Feral Pigeon   *Columba livia*

Status:- A common resident.

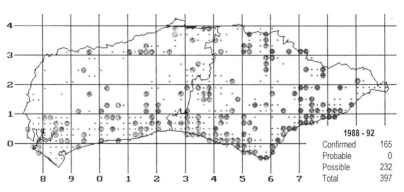

1988 - 92	
Confirmed	165
Probable	0
Possible	232
Total	397

Although one of our most familiar birds, few records of Feral Pigeons are ever submitted. Reference has only been made to the species in the *Sussex Bird Report* since 1992 and little is currently known of its status or population trends within the county, except that it has obviously increased significantly in recent years.

The Atlas map shows the Feral Pigeon to be widespread, especially in urban areas and on the cliffs between Brighton and Eastbourne. It is, however, absent from large areas of the interior of the county, reflecting the lack of suitable habitat for nesting away from the towns and sea cliffs. The Atlas map when compared with that published in the 68-72 BTO Atlas suggests that there may have been an expansion in range over the past 20 years. In the most recent survey, breeding was confirmed in 39 10-km squares compared with only 28 in 1968-72, perhaps reflecting the increased urbanisation of Sussex over this period.

Although the Rock Dove, the wild form of the Feral Pigeon, still inhabits coastal cliffs in Scotland and Ireland, there is no evidence that it has ever occurred in the county. The issue is, however, slightly confused by Stock Doves being "found in abundance" on the cliffs between Beachy Head and Seaford (in 1875 by Meade Waldo) and being locally called 'Rock Doves' or 'Blue Rocks' (Walpole-Bond). *Derek Crawley*

Stock Dove *Columba oenas*

Status:- A common resident and possible winter visitor.

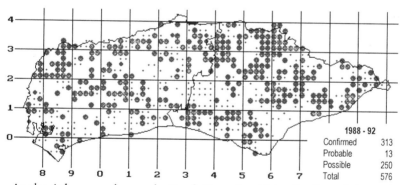

1988 - 92	
Confirmed	313
Probable	13
Possible	250
Total	576

As the Atlas map shows, the Stock Dove is widely distributed throughout the county, more especially to the north of the Downs. It nests mostly in holes in trees, showing a preference for areas of old scattered timber, including parkland. It will also utilise buildings, cliffs and quarries and occasionally rabbit-holes and the old nests of other species. Its absence from some parts of the county, such as Pevensey Levels and the heavily built-up coastal plain, undoubtedly reflects the lack of suitable timber in these areas.

The Stock Dove was badly affected by the use of organochlorine seed dressings in the 1950s. des Forges & Harber referred to flocks of about 200 birds but, between 1965 and 1970, only four flocks of 100 or more were reported in Sussex, the largest being that of 175 birds at Rye Harbour in

January 1965 (Shrubb). When the use of these pesticides was restricted in the 1960s, a slow but steady recovery took place and, as the 1970s progressed, the flocks that gathered in autumn increased in size and regularity. Flocks of 200 to 400 occurred in several areas. As noted in Shrubb, it is the size and number of the feeding flocks that assemble in winter that is the best indicator of status of the Stock Dove in the county. A number of recent counts of 200 or more, including 400 at Pagham in February 1992 and Sidlesham Ferry in November 1993, suggest that the species is currently doing well, a trend supported by national CBC results that indicate that current population levels are double those at the time of the 68-72 BTO Atlas (New Atlas). Factors militating against a return to the numbers of the earlier part of the 20th century include extensive use of weed-killers, changes in the sowing patterns of cereal crops, destruction of hedgerows, destruction of old buildings and tree loss due to Dutch elm disease (Marchant et al 1990).

In Sussex, population densities are likely to be highest in areas of semi-natural broadleaved woodland. Bealey & Sutherland (1983) in a survey of 40 such woodlands in West Sussex found an average density of 4.7 pairs per km², a figure higher than that of 1.75 pairs per km² reported by Prater (1983b) for farmland at Plumpton. Applying these densities to the 566 tetrads in which Stock Doves were recorded during the Atlas Survey indicates a county population of 4000-8000 pairs.

It is not clear to what extent the species visits the county in winter. des Forges & Harber referred to a number of records of birds flying in from the sea during hard weather on the Continent and also to the arrival of Stock Doves on the East Sussex coast in October and early November, together with large numbers of Woodpigeons. During 1962-93 there were virtually no published records indicative of immigration, except in 1978 when the *Sussex Bird Report* for that year referred to unusual numbers in autumn, including feeding flocks of 103 at Pett Level, 150-200 at Rye Harbour, 150 at Piddinghoe and 60 at Thorney Deeps, all between 8 and 19 November. On the latter date, 50 flew southwest over Rye.   *Derek Crawley*

Woodpigeon   *Columba palumbus*

Status:- An abundant resident and winter visitor.

The Woodpigeon was originally a bird of deciduous woodland, but is now typically found on arable farmland where it nests in small copses and isolated trees and bushes. It is also increasingly found in parks and town centres. Woodpigeons are a major avian pest and control is common in cultivated areas, although its success or otherwise is the subject of controversy. Shooting is probably more effective when winter food is plentiful otherwise it can simply replace starvation as the cause of mortality, leaving the remaining birds to survive on the available food (Marchant et al 1990). Nationally there was a decline in numbers during the 1970s brought about by changing agricultural practices, including the extensive use of herbicides, reducing the availability of winter feed. The sowing of oil-seed rape during the 1980s on a much larger scale than hitherto provided a plentiful winter food supply and there was a subsequent recovery in numbers where this crop was extensively grown

(Marchant *et al* 1990). Recently there has been a reduction in the production of oil-seed rape but there is no evidence, as yet, to suggest a change in the size of the breeding population.

During the Atlas Survey, there were records in 989 (98%) tetrads with breeding confirmed in 861 and possible in 128. By combining the results of a number of censuses of breeding birds in defined areas carried out since the early 1980s, an average density of 17.9 pairs per km² is obtained. This figure is rather lower than Bealey & Sutherland's (1983) estimate of 29.0 pairs per km², based on their survey of semi-natural broadleaved woodlands in West Sussex. Applying these densities to the tetrads in which the species was recorded during the Atlas Survey indicates a county population of 70,000-115,000 pairs.

Ringing has shown that the local breeding population is essentially sedentary. Numbers in autumn are, however, boosted by migrants. Diurnal movements are noted almost annually in October and November, though numbers vary considerably from year to year. In 1975 there was an unprecedented south-easterly movement involving *ca.* 70,000 birds at Beachy Head between 19 October and 5 November, including 30,000 on 2 November (Shrubb). This movement was also obvious in Kent where 55,000 flew southeast at Dungeness between 4 October and 21 November (Taylor, Davenport & Flegg 1981). Movements may also be recorded in autumn at inland localities. At Weir Wood Reservoir, for example, 5700 flew west on 5 November and 7000 did likewise on 8-9 November 1990. At West Chiltington, three flocks totalling 8000 flew over on 7, 23 and 25 November 1991.

Spring passage is far less regular and marked but flocks have occasionally been observed arriving and departing at coastal sites. In 1962, a total of 400 flew out to sea at Selsey Bill between 17 March and 20 May and 50 arrived there on 23 April. At Beachy Head, 600 flew east on 5 April 1974 and, at Shoreham-by-Sea, 1750 flew northwest from over the sea on 2 March 1986.

Feeding and roosting flocks of up to 4000 birds are recorded regularly during the winter months. Movements of Woodpigeons may occur during periods of hard weather, as in early 1963, when 1000 flew west at Littlehampton on 3 January, thousands flew east at Brighton on 6 January and 4000 did likewise at Selsey Bill on 11 January. In early 1986, 1500-2000 flew north at Pagham on 9 February.   *Derek Crawley & Paul James*

Collared Dove   *Streptopelia decaocto*

Status:- A very common resident.

The Collared Dove is closely associated with human habitation. It is found nesting in most suburban areas, where there are large gardens with ornamental conifers for nest-sites, and also in the vicinity of farms where there is a plentiful supply of grain. It does, however, avoid open expanses of countryside unbroken by farm buildings (New Atlas), perhaps explaining its absence from some areas of the county, as shown by the Atlas map.

	1988 - 92
Confirmed	565
Probable	0
Possible	183
Total	748

In 1958, three years after its initial colonisation of Britain, the Collared Dove arrived in Sussex. In that year, birds were present at East and West Wittering and breeding may have taken place, though this was not proved. Birds were again present in this area in 1959 but it was not until 1960 that breeding was proved, in which year a pair bred at Selsey raising two young and 10-12 birds were reported breeding at St Leonards (Porter 1967). Colonisation of the whole county was comparatively rapid. By 1966, the population had increased to some 1400 birds and by 1969, a further increase of the order of 380% had occurred, resulting in a minimum county population of 5300 birds (Porter 1970). Numbers continued to increase between 1970 and 1982 when national CBC data showed that the population peaked (Marchant *et al* 1990). For such a familiar species, there is surprisingly little information available on breeding densities in the county. Prater (1983b) reported a density of 2.75 pairs per km² on farmland at Plumpton, a figure which, if applied to the 748 tetrads in which the species was recorded during the Atlas Survey, indicates a county population of 8000 pairs. This may, however, be an underestimate given that a density of 35 pairs per km² was reported for East Grinstead in 1983.

During the autumn months, flocks gather wherever suitable food is to be found, especially in the form of maize stubble and grain spilt from barns and silos. A gathering of 800 at one Sussex farm, that was estimated to be consuming 50 kg of grain a day (O'Connor & Shrubb 1986), appears to be the largest flock recorded in the county. A flock of 400 was noted at Southwick in early 1986 but, more recently, the largest counts have been at Rye Harbour, where up to 220 have been noted.

Occasional records of birds coming in off the sea, such as that of 17 that flew north at Selsey Bill on 17 April 1986, suggest there may still be a small degree of colonisation taking place. One ringed in Belgium on 19 October 1968 was caught at Seaford on 1 June 1969.   *Derek Crawley*

Turtle Dove   *Streptopelia turtur*

Status:- A common, but probably declining, summer visitor and passage migrant. Very rare in winter.

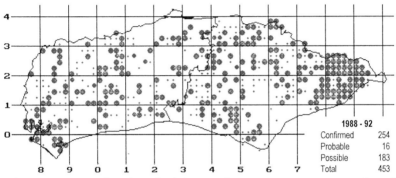

	1988 - 92
Confirmed	254
Probable	16
Possible	183
Total	453

des Forges & Harber described the Turtle Dove as "common as a breeding species in suitable localities throughout the county". The Atlas map shows that it is still widely distributed, particularly in the extreme east of the county, a distribution that reflects the southeast bias shown by the abundance map in the New Atlas. In West Sussex, however, the general impression is one of increasing scarcity although there is insufficient information available with which to substantiate this claim.

Arrival usually begins in mid-April and continues into May or even early June, as in 1985, when a total of 14 flew north at St Leonards on 3rd. The earliest ever were singles at Plumpton on 22 March 1966 and Rye Harbour on 26 March 1970 but in other years during 1965-93 first dates varied between 29 March and 1 May with the average 14 April. Numbers recorded on passage are usually low, counts of 46 flying east at Pett in 30 minutes on 10 May 1981, 46 at Beachy Head on 14 May 1973 and 40 at West Chiltington on 27 May 1966 being exceptional.

During the 1980s, a number of censuses of breeding birds in defined areas were carried out, covering a wide range of downland, farmland and woodland habitats. Combining the results gives an average of 3.2 pairs per km², a figure similar to Bealey & Sutherland's (1983) estimate of 2.6 pairs per km², based on their survey of semi-natural broadleaved woodlands in the West Sussex Weald.

Applying these densities to the 270 tetrads in which breeding was confirmed or probable during the Atlas Survey indicates a county population of 2800-3500 pairs. The British population in 1989 was estimated at 75,000 pairs (New Atlas).

In the 1960s and 1970s flocks of up to 50 and sometimes more were regularly seen in autumn. Larger concentrations included 100 at Earnley on 17 September 1974, 120 at Beachy Head on 15 September 1974, 110 at Cissbury on 30 August 1976 and separate flocks of 200-300 and 180 on the Selsey peninsula on 26 and 27 August 1979 respectively. In the 1980s, the only three-figure flocks reported were 100 at Sidlesham on 23 September 1980 and 100+ at Rye Harbour on 24 August 1986, while in the period 1987-93 no count exceeded 30.

Autumn movements begin in July but after early October only stragglers remain. Between 1965 and 1993, the last dates fell in the period 9 October and 12 November (1978, Pagham) with the average 27 October.

At least seven have been recorded in winter as follows:

1847: One at Denton prior to 10 February.
1898: One at Horsham on 8 February.
1969: One with Collared Doves at Patcham, Brighton on 5 and 8 February.
       One with Collared Doves at Bexhill in December.
1980: One with Collared Doves at Shoreham-by-Sea on 25 March and presumably the same there on 11 November and 2 December.
1990: One at Rye Harbour on 2, 4 and 5 December and a second bird there from 3 to 18 December.
1991: One at Rye Harbour from 28 February to 12 March was presumably one of the birds recorded there in December 1990. It was found dead on 19 March.

Derek Crawley & Paul James

Ring-necked Parakeet   *Psittacula krameri*

Status:- A very scarce introduced breeding resident.

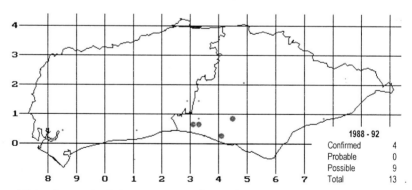

	1988 - 92	
Confirmed	4
Probable	0
Possible	9
Total	13 .

The Ring-necked (or Rose-ringed) Parakeet is a native of much of the Oriental and northern Afrotropical regions (Forshaw 1980). In Sussex, there is a feral population in Brighton where 1-3 pairs have bred most years since at least 1977. Their offspring have maintained a small colony which reached a maximum of 11 in 1992. The following year, however, it was drastically cut to four when a small group of 'travellers' were thought to have shot at or trapped some of the birds. Birds believed to be from this colony (in Hollingbury Woods) have, over the years, been recorded at several sites between Ovingdean and Shoreham-by-Sea, while roosting has been noted on a number of occasions in Hove Park.

For nesting, Ring-necked Parakeets use tree holes in gardens, parks and orchards, where they compete with several native hole-nesting species (New Atlas). They may also be a serious pest to gardeners with their preference for fruit. Up until the storm in October 1987, the Brighton birds fed largely on natural resources, including beech nuts, but more recently they have become regular visitors to bird tables and nut feeders. They have also been observed raiding allotments for beans and peas.

Ring-necked Parakeets first appeared in the wild in Britain in 1969 (Hudson 1974), and were admitted to Category C of the British and Irish List in 1983. Earlier, they had been mentioned only briefly in the *Sussex Bird Report* and, because of the obvious escape possibility, documentation of records was somewhat lacking. Most Sussex sightings would seem to be of odd roving birds or escapes, although a pair accompanied by a food begging juvenile was observed at Littlehampton Golf Course on 12 August 1985 (A S Cook *in litt.*). A number of sightings from the Selsey peninsula in the late 1970s and early 1980s may also indicate the possibility that a pair bred in that area. Apart from the Brighton colony, less than a dozen are recorded from scattered localities each year. unusual records were those of seven at Orlton's Copse, Rusper on 17 June 1990 and four flying west at Beachy Head on 24 September 1983.   *Peter Whitcomb*

Great-spotted Cuckoo   *Clamator glandarius*

Status:- A very rare vagrant (two records).
First recorded in 1967, there have been two records:

1967:   One picked up dead at Shripney, near Bognor Regis, on 4 August was the 11th British record.
1990:   An adult found immediately to the north of Shoreham Airport on 4 April remained to 1 May (Fairbank 1991b, Millington 1990, *Brit. Birds* 83: plate 297).

The 1990 individual was found by a passing lorry driver stopped at traffic lights, its long stay being greatly appreciated by those who flocked to see it. It was usually to be found feeding on caterpillars (or sitting quietly digesting them) in the hedges immediately to the west of Ricardo Consulting Engineers and along the northeastern perimeter of Shoreham Airport, although it ranged more widely on occasion. It is likely that it left the area when caterpillars became harder to find (Fairbank 1991b).

There were 29 records of this stunning cuckoo in the British Isles during 1962-94, just under one a year on average. It breeds from Spain to the Middle East and in Africa, European birds migrating just into sub-Saharan Africa (Moreau 1972).   *Richard Fairbank*

Cuckoo   *Cuculus canorus*

Status:- A fairly common summer visitor.

The Atlas map shows the Cuckoo widely distributed in Sussex although absent from heavily built-up areas such as the coastal strip from Littlehampton to Brighton. It is unlikely that many birds were missed during the Atlas Survey as the male's distinctive song is heard from late April until the end of June. The Cuckoo occurs commonly throughout Britain and Ireland, occupying most habitats. In southern and central England the main host is the Dunnock while other hosts may include Meadow Pipit and Reed Warbler. Assuming a density of one pair per tetrad in which birds were recorded during the Atlas Survey indicates a county population of about 750 pairs. The British total was estimated at 13,000-26,000 pairs in 1988-91 (New Atlas).

	1988 - 92
Confirmed	374
Probable	17
Possible	344
Total	735

The first Cuckoos are normally heard in early April. During 1971-93 first dates varied between 21 March and 16 April with the average 7 April. The earliest ever was on 15 March 1936 at Fairlight Cove followed by others on 21 March 1993 at Rye and 23 March at Harting and Pagham in 1967 and 1992 respectively. The main influx occurs in late April and early May but birds may continue to arrive into early June, at least in some years. Large 'falls' do not occur; for example, the largest day total at Beachy Head to date is seven on both 17 May 1968 and 16 May 1975.

Autumn departure of adults is noted in July and August while juveniles are quite usual up until the end of September. Shrubb stated that there were six records for October and, more recently, birds have occurred during that month in eight of the years in the period 1977-93, including three at Beachy Head on 5 October 1978. There are three November records for the county, the latest of which was at Goodwood on 11 November 1928.

Females of the rare rufous morph have been recorded very occasionally, the only ones in recent years being at Pett Level on 31 July 1977 and 19 August 1979, at Horse Eye Level on 1 June 1982 and in the lower Cuckmere Valley on 8 August 1987. A variant bird at Possingworth Park on 26 July was described as "uniformly very dark slate, almost black, with white belly and undertail-coverts heavily barred blackish".

Peter Whitcomb

Yellow-billed Cuckoo *Coccyzus americanus*

Status:- A very rare vagrant (two records, both found dead).

Two were recorded before 1962 (des Forges & Harber). Both were picked up dead, one in Furness Road, Eastbourne on 4 November 1952 and the other at Middleton-on-Sea on 14 December 1960. The former was thought to have collided with a brick wall (Simms 1953) while the latter, an adult female, appeared to have died of starvation and was thought to have been dead for about five days.

There were nearly 40 records of this slim cuckoo in the British Isles during 1962-94, many of which were dead or dying. Along with the similar Black-billed Cuckoo *C. erythrophthalmus* it has one of the worst survival records of any vagrant to Britain due to its specialised diet (mainly caterpillars). It breeds mostly in the USA wintering throughout South America. *Richard Fairbank*

Barn Owl *Tyto alba*

Status:- A scarce breeding resident.

The breeding population of Barn Owls in Sussex has continued to fluctuate markedly although, nationally, there has been a major decline since the early part of this century (New Atlas). Prestt (1965) reported a moderate decline in the county between 1953 and 1963 while Shrubb considered there was evidence to suggest some recovery from 1964. From that year to 1975, the average number of pairs proved to breed in Sussex per year was seven and the average number of pairs or birds present during the breeding season, but without proof of breeding, was 15. During the period 1976-92 both these averages dropped to five. This decline seems to have occurred evenly across the county. Records for 1976-87 showed confirmed breeding in 34 different 10-km squares compared with 26 in the period 1988-92. The cause of the decline is almost certainly the intensification of agriculture and consequent loss of suitable habitat. The loss of areas of rough grassland, which provide cover for small mammals, has proved detrimental to the species, as has the intensive cultivation of field boundaries. The demolition of farm buildings, the conversion of barns into homes and the loss of trees due to Dutch elm disease have also contributed. However, Barn Owls are undoubtedly under-recorded and reports of a "catastrophic decline" in Sussex can be discounted.

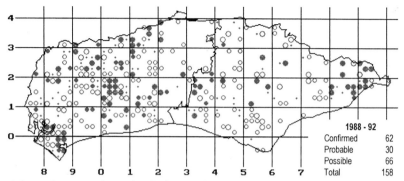

1988 - 92	
Confirmed	62
Probable	30
Possible	66
Total	158

The Atlas map shows both the results of the 1988-92 Atlas Survey and also those tetrads (as open circles) where Barn Owls were recorded in the period 1976-87 but not in 1988-92. During the 12 years between 1976 and 1987, birds were recorded in 236 tetrads, while during the five years between 1988 and 1992, they were recorded in 158 tetrads, a reduction of about 33%. The number of tetrads in which breeding was confirmed also fell from 75 in 1976-87 to 62 in 1988-92, a decline of 17%. However, it is interesting to note that, during the Atlas Survey, the species was recorded in 33 tetrads where birds had not been reported between 1976 and 1987. Many, but not all, of these new registrations were in tetrads adjacent to those where the species had been recorded in 1976-87. Sandison (1981), in his detailed review of Barn Owl records in the period 1968-79, concluded that the Sussex breeding population was between 100 and 150 pairs; the results of the recent Atlas Survey suggest a similar number today.

Barn Owls occur more widely in some parts of Sussex than others, particularly the Selsey peninsula, the far east of the county and an area extending northwards from the upper Arun valley. This reflects their preference for farmland below 300 m with hedges and rough fields for hunting. Heavily wooded areas and dense thickets are shunned, as shown by the paucity of registrations in the High Weald between Horsham and Battle. Barn Owls are also very scarce on the Downs, although disused chalk pits may be utilised for nesting and roosting, and are largely absent from urban areas, where ground supporting sufficiently high densities of small rodents is lacking.

The number of young reported annually varies considerably although this is dependent on visits being made to known nest-sites. In the period 1976-92 an average of only nine fledged young per year was reported though in 1989 at least 28 were known. The number of young fledged per nest has, however, remained more constant, with an average of three over the same period. Nest-sites are typically in old barns and other ruined buildings (where strategically placed nest boxes may be used) but trees (live and dead), a chimney, a church tower, a disused water tank and a hide set up to watch the birds have also been used.

Barn Owls are fond of hunting roadside verges and, unfortunately, road casualties are all too frequent. Sandison (1981), who examined the cause of Barn Owl deaths in Sussex, reported a total of 31 road casualties between 1968 and 1979; 32 more were reported between 1980 and 1993 and, as the cumulative monthly totals for the period 1968-93 show, distinctly fewer road casualties were found during the months with shorter nights.

Jan	Feb	Mar	Apr	May	Jun	Jul	Aug	Sep	Oct	Nov	Dec
4	6	10	3	4	2	3	1	5	12	7	6

Barn Owls also appear to suffer badly in very cold weather, when emaciated corpses have been found. Both Walpole-Bond and des Forges & Harber recorded an influx of birds in the winter, which was more marked in some years. There is no evidence of this today.

A report of a pair shot by a gamekeeper in 1980 has, thankfully, not been repeated.

An analysis of 40 Barn Owl pellets from a regularly occupied farm roosting site at Arlington showed the following contents: field vole (37), house mouse (23), pigmy shrew (9), wood mouse (7), sparrow-sized birds (6) and smaller birds (4). Mice and voles are the main prey items and Barn Owl numbers are thought to fluctuate in response to variations in the populations of these small mammals (BWP).

Captive-bred Barn Owls have regularly been released in Sussex and records must inevitably include some of these birds.

British Barn Owls belong to the race *T.a. alba;* there are, however, several references in the Society's files to birds with particularly dark breasts. des Forges & Harber noted the occurrence of nine individuals showing the characteristics of the central eastern European race *T.a. guttata,* the most recent of which were two at the Midrips from 3 December 1938 to mid-February 1939. More recently, one found moribund in a garden on Shoreham Beach on 14 October 1975 was considered to be an *alba/guttata* intergrade of the type found in Belgium and Northern France. A dark-breasted individual, presumed to be *guttata,* but of unknown origin, was present at Thorney Deeps in January 1994.

Ringing data have highlighted the sedentary nature of this species. Of 82 ringed in Sussex and subsequently recovered, only two had moved further than 100 km. One ringed as a nestling at Westfield in July 1987 was found dead at Huntingdon, Cambridgeshire, 166 km NNW, in March 1988. The other, also ringed as a nestling, at Northchapel in June 1988 was found at Old Sodbury, Avon, 130 km WNW, in February 1989. Twelve ringed elsewhere in Britain have been recovered in the county but only one had moved any distance. This individual, from a nest near Lulworth, Dorset in June 1976, was found dead near Hastings, 202 km ENE, in December 1977.

Sarah J Patton & Roy Sandison

Eagle Owl
Bubo bubo

Status:- A very rare vagrant (one very old record).

One was shot at Herstmonceux on either 29 December 1782 or sometime in 1784.

One shot near Cuckfield on 13 January 1939 was thought to have been an escape and one at Chichester Cathedral from November 1988 to March 1989, when it was recaptured, definitely was.

There have been about 20 records of this powerful owl in the British Isles but it has not been recorded since 1883. It is mainly resident, breeding across Europe to China and the Himalayas. Populations in southern Asia and in North Africa are sometimes considered separate species (Howard & Moore 1991).
Richard Fairbank

Snowy Owl
Nyctea scandiaca

Status:- A very rare vagrant (two or three records, all probably of suspect origin).

One seen near Littlehampton in November 1926 and the same, or another, on a farm at Colworth, Chichester at the end of that month were assumed to have escaped from a passing ship. The latter remained for about three weeks feeding principally on Moorhens and allowed approach to within five yards (Walpole-Bond). A number had been noted on ships in the North Atlantic prior to this, with many being captured and brought ashore (Witherby 1927).

One seen to fly north up the Cuckmere Valley from Seaford Head on 8 November 1968 was possibly an escape from captivity. The record is currently under review.

Although there were about 110 British records of during 1962-94, only three were in southeast England, both the others in early 1965, in Kent in January (J Cantello & T Hodge *in litt.*) and in Hampshire and, presumably the same, on the Isle of Wight in March (Clark & Eyre 1993). It was thought at the time that those in 1965 may have been escapes following the importation of large numbers into Britain (Harber *et al* 1966). This large feline owl breeds right around the Arctic occasionally erupting southwards.
Richard Fairbank

Little Owl
Athene noctua

Status:- A fairly common resident.

The Little Owl is not native to Britain. Birds were first released in Yorkshire in 1842, but the experiment failed. Further introductions followed and, by the end of the 19th century, breeding was regularly established in Kent, Bedfordshire, Northamptonshire and Rutland (68-72 BTO Atlas). It is not known exactly when Little Owls were first introduced into Sussex, but Walpole-Bond recorded that two pairs were released at Knepp in 1876. By 1904 the species was well established in the Horsham area and by 1938, following a population explosion during 1910-30, it was described as abundant and generally distributed in the county. Thereafter, it spread more slowly, with local decreases in some areas. A more general decline in southern counties from 1955 into the early 1960s was most likely the result of pesticide poisoning although cold winters during this period may also have taken their toll. des Forges & Harber noted that "it was no longer the commonest owl" and Shrubb was of the opinion that a decline had been apparent since 1963.

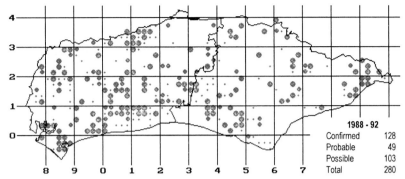

1988 - 92	
Confirmed	128
Probable	49
Possible	103
Total	280

The Atlas map shows the Little Owl to be widely distributed across Sussex, but more common in the west of the county. The species has an affinity for open country with hedgerows, copses and small woods and in Sussex is found predominantly in agricultural areas. Most nests are in hollow deciduous trees, but they have also been found in rabbit burrows, barns, sea-cliffs and even under the roots of an oak tree.

In recent years, the number of pairs confirmed as breeding has varied between 52 in 1983 and just five in 1991. It is clear, however, that the species is significantly under-recorded given densities of four pairs on 60 ha at West Chiltington in 1986 and seven pairs on 130 ha at Icklesham in 1987. Even applying a conservative estimate of 5-10 pairs per occupied 10-km square (New Atlas) suggests a county population of 220-440 pairs.

In the early 1980s, Little Owls started to predate the Little Tern colony at Rye Harbour, killing 20 adults and 30 young in 1981 and 12 adults and 30 young in 1983.

Of nine birds ringed in the county and subsequently recovered, five had dispersed by more than 10 km but even the furthest of these had travelled just 34 km from Peasmarsh to Brabourne, Kent in 1932. Birds ringed outside the county seem equally sedentary, the longest movement recorded being one of 25 km from Edenbridge, Kent to Haywards Heath in 1926.   *Sarah J Patton*

Tawny Owl   *Strix aluco*

Status:- A fairly common resident.

The Tawny Owl is Britain's most numerous owl. As the Atlas map shows, it is widely distributed in Sussex, particularly in the more wooded central and western parts of the county where mainly broad-leaved trees flourish. Favouring tree cavities for both nesting and roosting, it also inhabits parkland, old orchards, gardens and farmland embracing suitable habitat. It is not averse to coniferous plantations and has steadily established itself in built-up areas, such as Chichester, Worthing, Eastbourne and Hastings, where additional food sources such as bird roosts and small rodents are available. It also readily takes to nest boxes.

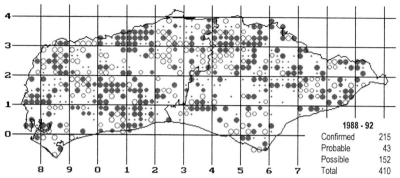

Tawny Owls are widespread throughout Sussex although there are a number of areas where it is scarce or absent. The dearth of records from the levels in the vicinity of Pevensey and Rye and from the large tracts of treeless country on the chalk downland east of the Adur Valley and on parts of the coastal plain near Chichester is understandable. Less clear, however, is an explanation of why this species was only patchily recorded in a fairly broad corridor of Wealden Sussex extending from Billingshurst to Uckfield.

The Atlas map shows both the results of the 1988-92 Atlas Survey and also those tetrads (as open circles) where Tawny Owls were recorded in the period 1976-87 but not in 1988-92. Between 1976 and 1987, birds were recorded in 358 tetrads, while between 1988 and 1992 there were records in 410 tetrads, a total of 568 tetrads for the entire period 1976-92. Breeding was confirmed in 215 tetrads during the Atlas Survey and in 208 tetrads during 1976-87, thus indicating that the species is normally under-recorded. Further evidence that the species is under-recorded is provided by the results of the BTO Tawny Owl survey carried out in 1989. In six randomly selected 'key' 10-km squares there was an average of 6.5 occupied tetrads compared with an average of four occupied tetrads per 10-km square in other parts of the county.

A comparison of the results of the New Atlas with those of the 68-72 BTO Atlas suggests that the population has not changed significantly in the past 30 years. The 68-72 BTO Atlas estimated a population of 50,000-100,000 pairs of Tawny Owls in Britain but from the results of the New Atlas and the Tawny Owl survey, a figure of 20,000 pairs was considered more realistic. An assumed average density of ten pairs per occupied 10-km square (Percival 1990) extrapolates to a county population of about 400 pairs. It is likely, however, that the density of Tawny Owls is very much higher in the more heavily-wooded parts of the county. Shrubb reported densities as high as 3.0 pairs per tetrad near Horsham and 2.3 pairs per tetrad near Blackdown while Bealey & Sutherland (1983) reported an average density of 2.4 pairs per km² (9.6 pairs per tetrad) based on their survey of semi-natural broadleaved woodlands in West Sussex. Applying the latter figure to the 29,300 ha of woodland of this type in the county suggests that this habitat alone could support in excess of 700 pairs, indicating a county population of between

1000-2000 pairs, a figure comparable with that estimated for neighbouring Hampshire (Clark & Eyre 1993).

Road casualties are less frequent than in other owl species but the effect on populations by Dutch elm disease and the storms of 1987 and 1990 has not been properly studied.

The winter and summer ranges overlap considerably as Tawny Owls are strongly territorial and highly sedentary. Of 15 recovered in the county, all had been ringed in Sussex and only four had moved more than 10 km from the ringing site. *Sarah J Patton & Roy Sandison*

Long-eared Owl *Asio otus*

Status:- A rare resident and very scarce passage migrant and winter visitor.

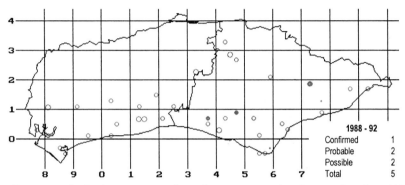

Long-eared Owls were moderately common in Sussex in the 1930s (Walpole-Bond), mostly in mature conifers, and were sufficiently numerous for a few pairs to be present in mature hedges on Pevensey Levels. Records since 1947 have shown that the breeding population has declined, disappearing from sites such as Friston Forest and the Downs behind Brighton during the 1950s. Between 1962 and 1976, breeding was proved at only six sites and suspected at eight more (Shrubb). One or two pairs bred annually from 1976 to 1979 but the only pairs known to have subsequently bred were in 1983, 1988 and 1993. The Atlas map includes all the available records since 1976. It is likely, however, that some pairs have been overlooked and that others have not been reported to the SOS. Breeding has occurred in a variety of habitats since 1962 including downland scrub, conifer plantations, thorn thickets and a yew forest.

During the winter, Long-eared Owls form roosts in dense scrub and thickets and overgrown hedgerows. These may occur on the Downs and coastal plain and in the river valleys. Since 1976, an average of 12 birds per winter has been recorded but in 1975/76 and 1986/87 there were 22 and 27 respectively. The influx in 1975/76 was part of an invasion into Britain of several thousand owls, thought to be due to a crash in the number of rodents on the Continental breeding grounds (Winter Atlas). A roost of nine on the Downs near Steyning in early 1976 was the largest recorded in recent years, matched only by another roost of nine in the Ouse Valley in February-March 1992. The behaviour of Long-eared Owls at a downland roosting site near Lewes was studied by Leverton & Haskell (1985). Birds were present between late October-early November and late March-early April, roosting by day in a thicket of elder and hawthorn. The same thicket, and even the same tree, was chosen for roosting every year, though the owls were not necessarily the same individuals. Hunting did not begin until well into dusk. Analysis of about 100 pellets showed that short-tailed voles (43%), bank voles (17%), wood mice (15%) and birds (20%) made up the bulk of the diet.

Walpole-Bond indicated that Long-eared Owls were once quite numerous, at least in some years, either on passage or as a winter visitor, and that flocks of 15-20 had been recorded on occasions. Since the beginning of 1962, a total of about 41 migrants has been reported, mainly at coastal sites, including 14 at Beachy Head. The extreme dates were 4 September and 2 December in autumn and 7 March and 23 May in spring. The cumulative monthly totals of migrants recorded in the period 1962-94 are shown below.

Sep	Oct	Nov	Dec	Jan	Feb	Mar	Apr	May
9	12	5	2	-	-	5	10	5

Reports of two birds with broken legs in 1980 aroused suspicions that illegal pole-trapping may have been taking place. Thankfully, such reports have not been repeated.

An adult trapped near Romney, Kent in July 1966 was found dead near Rye in February 1967. *Sarah J Patton*

Short-eared Owl *Asio flammeus*

Status:- A scarce winter visitor and passage migrant. Has bred.

In Sussex, wintering Short-eared Owls are found mainly on the coastal plain, especially around Chichester and Pagham Harbours, on Pevensey Levels and at Rye Harbour. They also occur in smaller numbers on the

Downs and in the river valleys of the Adur, Arun and Ouse. Numbers fluctuate widely from winter to winter and are likely to be affected by a crash in the vole populations in Europe or by severe weather, such conditions forcing birds to move into Britain to hunt. In the period 1962-76, between 15 and 80 birds were recorded per year (Shrubb). Totals of at least 37 and 36 were reported in the winters of 1988/89 and 1992/93 respectively, but the total for 1990/91 was only ten. Counts rarely reach double figures at any one site although up to 13 were recorded at Pulborough Brooks in the winter of 1988/89 and 15 at two roosts on Thorney Island on 8 February 1992.

Although one was found dead at Rye Harbour on 29 July 1982 and others were recorded at Chichester Harbour on 23 July 1993, on Pevensey Levels on 8 August 1956 and at Church Norton on 16-17 August 1993, most autumn migrants arrive from September onwards, but especially in October and early November. Birds are sometimes observed flying in off the sea and, at Beachy Head, where the species is regularly recorded in autumn, a total of 11 roosted on 9 October 1982, with six there the following day. At traditional wintering sites, birds are occasionally present from September but more typically from October until March or April, with some late individuals remaining into May. Spring passage is less well marked than in autumn and totals of known migrants rarely reach double figures in any year. A number have been recorded flying in off the sea and one such bird, at Birling Gap on 25 May 1991, is among the latest to have occurred in the county. Others include singles at Pagham on 24 May 1992 and Pilsey Island on 7 June 1989.

The cumulative monthly totals for the periods 1961/62-1975/76 and 1976/77-1992/93 are shown below:

	Jul	Aug	Sep	Oct	Nov	Dec	Jan	Feb	Mar	Apr	May	Jun
1961/62-75/76	2	6	60	275	271	275	285	243	217	204	56	6
1976/77-92/93	-	6	37	137	161	172	153	150	142	59	13	-
Total	2	12	97	412	432	447	438	393	359	263	69	6

Although small numbers of Short-eared Owls breed in Kent and East Anglia, the species has only nested twice in Sussex. In 1921, ten pairs bred on Pevensey Levels as did one pair in the same area in 1922. One summered near Piddinghoe in 1979.

A bird trapped and ringed at Dungeness, Kent in October 1984 and found dead near Rye in May 1985 had presumably wintered in the area.

Sarah J Patton

Nightjar   *Caprimulgus europaeus*

Status:- A fairly common summer visitor rarely seen on migration.

The Nightjar has long been associated with Sussex, the county being one of its major strongholds in Britain. The species was the subject of surveys in 1977, 1979, 1981 and 1991-92 (Hughes, Houghton & Blake 1978, Houghton 1980, 1982, Halls 1993). These showed a marked correlation between the distribution of the Nightjar and that of sandy or chalk soils, both of which provide free-draining ground for the nest site. The main habitats are heathland and plantations, the latter in the first few years after planting and again after clear felling. The Atlas map, which shows both the results of the Atlas Survey and also those tetrads (as open circles) where Nightjars were recorded in the period 1976-87 but not in 1988-92, reflects the availability of suitable habitat and reveals that the species is largely confined to four distinct areas of the county. In West Sussex, there is a small population on the forest ridges in the extreme north of the county but most occupied territories are to be found in the woodlands and on the heaths and commons on the Greensand. In East Sussex, Ashdown Forest, an area of open heathland with scattered Scots pine, typically holds 20% of the county's Nightjars while in the southeast of the county there is a fourth population in the central Weald to the northwest of Bexhill and Hastings. Downland sites which previously held the species, rarely hold Nightjars nowadays.

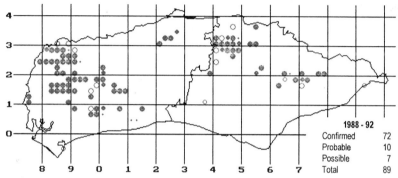

The Sussex population was found to comprise 180 territories in 1977, 155 in 1981 and 145 in 1991 with a further 18 at sites in 1992 which were not surveyed in 1991. To put this figure into perspective, the county population in 1946 was estimated to have been 1000-2000 occupied territories. This compares with over 3000 churring males located nationally in the 1992 RSPB/BTO Nightjar survey. Clearly there has been a substantial decline in both the national and county population but, fortunately, the most recent survey shows that this has now been halted.

Nightjars are rarely seen on migration although there have been occasional reports of birds arriving over the sea during spring sea-watches. The earliest date for the county is 8 April 1912 at Pulborough and the latest is 5 November 1961 at Worthing. With the current state of the national population, such dates seem extreme and few now appear before mid-May or remain after early September. An interesting record concerns that of a bird which sat on a garden fence in Bexhill for 13 hours on 9 September 1991 before eventually flying off in the evening.   *Mike Scott-Ham*

Swift   *Apus apus*

Status:- A common summer visitor and passage migrant.

The Atlas map shows the Swift to be widely distributed in the county, particularly in the main urban areas. The only quantitative data available to help in an estimation of the county population is that given by Hughes (1971), based on a survey carried out by members of the SOS in the years 1968-70. The results of counts received for 219 areas (amounting to at least 85% coverage of the towns and villages in the county) revealed a population in June 1970 of *ca.* 4000 birds. The total county population was therefore estimated to be in the order of 4500. The largest counts were not unexpectedly in the main urban areas of Bexhill, Brighton and Hove, Eastbourne, Horsham and Worthing. There were, however, no counts for East Grinstead or for some other parts of the northeast of the county and it was also thought that in some areas birds were under-recorded. Nearly 200 towns and villages held breeding Swifts while there were negative results for about sixty locations. The most important counts were:

Bexhill	210	Midhurst	140
Brighton	240	Lewes	65
Chichester	74	Lindfield	135
Crawley	92	Littlehampton	60
Eastbourne	160	Petworth	65
Hastings	60*	Rye	65
Horsham / Roffey	318	Uckfield	80
Hove	235	Worthing	206

* incomplete coverage suspected

It was estimated in the 68-72 BTO Atlas that there might be 100,000 breeding pairs in Britain and Ireland and given that there is no good evidence that numbers have changed significantly since then (New Atlas), it seems reasonable to suggest that the county population remains in the region of 4500 birds.

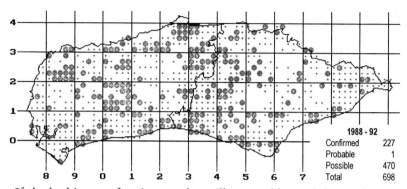

1988 - 92	
Confirmed	227
Probable	1
Possible	470
Total	698

If the harbingers of spring are the Willow Warbler and the Cuckoo, then one of the sounds of summer must be the 'screaming' of Swifts, following their arrival from their wintering grounds in central and southern Africa. The first birds are usually seen in late April but the main arrival generally occurs during the middle two weeks of May (des Forges & Harber) when large numbers may be recorded coming in off the sea. During 1970-93 first dates varied between 10 April and 30 April with the average 22 April. The earliest ever recorded were singles in the lower Cuckmere Valley on 10 April 1989 and at Seaford Head on 13 April 1990. Hudson (1973) refers to a record of one at Telscombe on 14 February 1896 or 1897 which although "seen by a competent observer" was not included by des Forges & Harber.

In May it is not unusual to record flocks of 300 or more at favoured sites such as Bewl Water, Chichester Gravel Pits and Weir Wood Reservoir. Large concentrations may occur over water during inclement weather when birds are forced to feed at low levels. These include, for example, 2000 at Chichester Gravel Pits from 5 to 8 May 1984 and on 9 May 1992 and 1500 at Arlington Reservoir on 16 May 1975. Later in the year, even before the commencement of obvious return passage takes place, larger numbers have been recorded such as 2500 feeding over the gravel pits at Rye Harbour on 6 June 1981, 2000 there at dusk on 1 June 1989 and 1500 over Friston Forest on 13 June 1982. Mid-summer movements are well documented but they have not been fully explained. These have been mainly at coastal sites, for example, 270 that flew west at Goring on 19 June 1987 and 150 that flew southwest from Langney Point and Selsey Bill in June 1965. These may have been early departing birds, although in a normal year eggs do not hatch until 10 June (New Atlas), or they may have been on long distance feeding movements.

Autumn departure begins in July and by mid-August most birds have left the county. Very large movements may occur in early August and these have included, at Beachy Head, an estimated 10,000 flying south on 10 August 1985, 5000 flying west on 6 August 1972 and 3000 moving out to sea on 10

August 1968. Other large concentrations at this time of the year have included 2000 over Pulborough Brooks on 8 August 1971 and a coastal movement of 1700 east at Climping in early July 1991. Small numbers are recorded regularly up until mid-September. During 1970-93 last dates varied between 20 September and 13 November with the average 8 October. There are seven November records for the county, of which singles at Selsey on 13 November 1988 and Church Norton on 22 November 1994 are the latest.

Ringing recoveries of this species away from nesting areas are few. There have been just five recoveries of Sussex-ringed Swifts, one of which was an adult ringed at Kirdford in July 1981 and found dead at the same location nearly eight years later. There are no records of any Sussex-ringed individuals being found overseas. Of birds ringed outside the county, the only one found that had moved very far was an adult ringed at Glossop, Derbyshire in July 1980 and found dead at Hastings, 337 km SSE, in June 1984.   *Peter Whitcomb*

Alpine Swift   *Apus melba*

Status:- A rare vagrant (29 records).

Two were recorded before 1962: singles over Isfield on 4 September 1904 and Hove on 23 June 1925 (des Forges & Harber).

Since the beginning of 1962 there have been 27 records, all involving lone individuals.

Records peaked in the early 1980s with eight seen in the four years 1981-84 (fig. 71), although the three records in 1981 may have involved only two individuals as one east over Beachy Head on 8 May and one west at Portobello on 9 May were perhaps the same. Assuming these two were different, none have been seen on more than one date and, as might be expected, most sightings involve a direct fly-over.

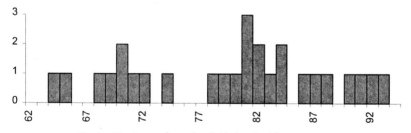

Figure 71. Annual totals of Alpine Swifts, 1962 - 94.

The cumulative monthly totals of all records are shown below. The earliest were at the Crumbles Gravel Pits on 25 March 1990 and over Beachy Head on 27 March 1988 while the latest were over Hollingbury Camp on 11 October 1964 and over Church Norton on 30 October 1972.

Mar	Apr	May	Jun	Jul	Aug	Sep	Oct
2	4	9	2	1	6	3	2

Thirteen have been seen over Beachy Head and two over the nearby Crumbles Gravel Pits, making up just over half the county total, but, perhaps rather surprisingly, only one has been recorded at Selsey Bill (on 5 May 1984).

Other records have been from Rye Harbour (3), Church Norton (2), and singles over Chichester (25 September 1979), Isfield, Litlington (16 May 1970) and Sompting (1 August 1993). Four have been recorded in the Brighton area: over Hove, Hollingbury Camp, Portobello and Brighton sea front.

There were nearly 350 records of this large swift in the British Isles during 1962-94 which currently averages 16 records per year (Evans 1995). It breeds across Europe to India and in eastern and southern Africa, most wintering in sub-Saharan Africa.   *Richard Fairbank*

Kingfisher   *Alcedo atthis*

Status:- A fairly common resident and probable winter visitor.

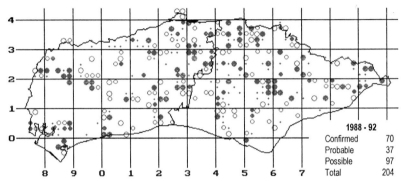

	1988 - 92
Confirmed	70
Probable	37
Possible	97
Total	204

The distribution of the Kingfisher in Sussex correlates well with the main drainage network of the county. However, few pairs are found along the main rivers, possibly due to pollution and, as Shrubb stated, most are now found on the many mill and hammer ponds throughout the Weald and the streams that serve them. The Atlas map, which shows both the results of the Atlas Survey and also those tetrads (as open circles) where Kingfishers were recorded in the period 1976-87 but not in 1988-92, reveals a loss of breeding sites along the Adur, Ouse and Cuckmere, in particular. The main concentrations are now along the Rother, the lower reaches of the Arun and the mid-reaches of the Adur in West Sussex and along the upper reaches of the Ouse, the Medway and the streams which drain south from Heathfield in East Sussex. Although usually absent from the coast in summer, the Atlas map shows confirmed breeding at Pagham Harbour, Atherington and the lower Cuckmere Valley.

There have been a number of appeals for records of Kingfishers and, in the 13 years from 1972 to 1984, an average of 31 pairs per year was reported. However, in the eight years from 1985 to 1992, this average fell to only 15, a halving of the population. This is difficult to reconcile with the results of Atlas Survey in which breeding was confirmed in 69 tetrads and probable in another 33, suggesting a population of perhaps 90-150 pairs over the period 1988-92. The number of pairs reported annually over the period 1963-93 (based on records of confirmed breeding and of birds at potential sites in the breeding season) is shown in fig. 72.

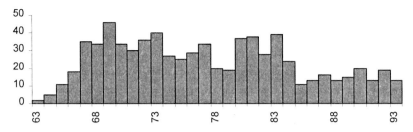

Figure 72. Annual totals of breeding pairs of Kingfishers, 1963 - 93.

Kingfishers are very vulnerable to cold winters, those of greatest severity being 1962/63, 1978/79, 1981/82, 1984/85 and 1985/86. Only two pairs were reported after the prolonged winter of 1962/63 but, as the graph shows, numbers recovered well following this and the 1978/79 winter. There has, however, been only a slight recovery following the winters of 1984/85 and 1985/86, despite a run of recent comparatively mild winters. This suggests another factor may be depressing the Sussex population. Certainly some pairs are fecund and in 1984 one pair produced three broods totalling 15 young.

In winter, many Kingfishers move to the coast, particularly in cold weather. In late 1981, a total of 53 was reported at 13 coastal and 25 inland localities but, following a spell of severe weather, only six were recorded at two inland and four coastal localities in February 1982.

There have been 17 recoveries involving Sussex-ringed birds, of which 16 had moved less than 10 km. Of those ringed outside Sussex and recovered in the county, the most notable was a first-year bird ringed on 27 May 1988 at Ashurst, Hampshire and controlled at Shoreham-by-Sea, 87 km away, on the 22 June of the same year. There has been one recovery of a foreign-ringed bird, which was ringed in Belgium on 28 July 1974 and found dead at Buxted on 2 April 1975. Perhaps it had wintered here?   *Robert D M Edgar*

Bee-eater   *Merops apiaster*

Status:- A rare vagrant (29 records involving 54 individuals; three pairs bred in 1955).

There were 11 records before 1962 involving 23 individuals (des Forges & Harber). Three pairs nested in a sand pit at Streat in 1955; one nest was destroyed (by sand excavations) but the other two pairs raised seven young. The young of one brood left their nest on 20, 21, 25 and 27 August, of the other on 1, 2 and 3 September, all returning regularly for a few days to roost in the holes. This was the first, and so far only, British breeding record. Despite not being publicised, the site was probably visited by over 1000 people, including 140 on one day (Kimmins 1955). Once fledged, all 13 were seen together, remaining in the area up to 24 September, although nine seen between Ringmer and Laughton, eight miles away, on 17 September were almost certainly some of the same. A female summered at Streat in 1957 (des Forges & Harber). The remaining records involved single individuals in April, May (3), June (2), summer, August and September. These include both the earliest and latest county records; the former arrived at Selsey Bill from the south on 30 April 1949, returning south an hour later (Joy 1949) and the latter flew over north Lancing on 19 September 1958.

There have been 18 records, involving 31 individuals, since the beginning of 1962:

1969:   One southeast over Hodcombe, Beachy Head on 5 June.
1981:   One over the wood at Rye Harbour on 25 May.
        One, possibly the same, circled Hodcombe, Beachy Head in poor visibility on 26 May before departing west.
1983:   A party of four at Whitbread Hollow, Beachy Head from 26 to 28 June.
1984:   One at Birling Gap, Beachy Head on 25 May remained for much of the day.
        One at Sidlesham Ferry on 19 August.
1986:   One flying west over Belle Tout, Beachy Head on 26 May.
1987:   One flying east over Hodcombe, Beachy Head on 25 May.
1988:   An adult at Belle Tout, Beachy Head during the early morning of 1 August (where it may have roosted) later flew east over Cow Gap, Beachy Head.
1989:   One flying east over Cow Gap, Beachy Head on 28 May.
        A party of six at Whitbread Hollow, Beachy Head later on 28 May arrived from the south and departed to the east after a few minutes.
1990:   One over the Coastguard Cottages, Pett and later Icklesham on 20 May.
1991:   Five flying northeast over Hodcombe, Beachy Head on 22 May.
        One at Rye Harbour on 3 July was seen on an electric fence near Ternery Pool before departing east.
        One, possibly the same, flying east over Littlehampton West Beach on 4 July.
1992:   One flying east over Shooters Bottom, Beachy Head on 22 May.
1993:   One on the cliffs at Belle Tout, Beachy Head on 22 May was also seen flying west over Hodcombe.
1994:   Two flying west over Shooters Bottom, Beachy Head on 5 June.

The recent (post 1980) increase in records is most pronounced with annual occurrences since 1986 and seven individuals seen in 1989 and 1991 (fig. 73).

Eleven records since 1962 have been in May (all from 20th and seven during 25-28th), with three in June and two in both July and August (latest 19th). Thirteen were from Beachy Head with three in the Rye/Pett area and just two in West Sussex (at Littlehampton and Sidlesham).

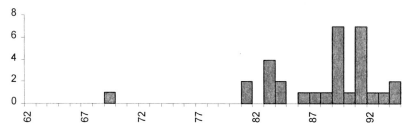

Figure 73. Annual totals of Bee-eaters, 1962 - 94.

There were between 14 and 66 records of this colourful aerial feeder in the British Isles each year during 1962-94 (Fraser & Ryan 1994). It breeds from Spain to western India and in South Africa and winters in sub-Saharan Africa.

Richard Fairbank

Roller   *Coracias garrulus*

Status:- A rare vagrant (16 records).

Thirteen were recorded before 1962. Of those dated, one was in May, three in both June and July and two in both August and September (des Forges & Harber). The earliest record was of one killed at Nutley on 29 May 1849 and the latest of one shot and caught alive at Crowhurst on 22 September 1790. Records since 1900 are of individuals killed near Colgate in St Leonard's Forest on 31 July 1907 (Millais 1907) and at Framfield in June 1910, one flying south over Wish Park, West Hove on 11 September 1924 (Walpole-Bond) and one flying over Clayton Downs on 15 August 1949 (Alder 1950). The brief published details of the last two could be more convincing. A male killed at Isfield on 12 June 1870 is in the Booth Museum (BoMNH 208194).

There have been three records since the beginning of 1962:

1970: One at Neylands Farm, immediately to the west of Weir Wood Reservoir from 28 June to 4 July.
1976: One at Charleston Bottom, Friston Forest on 12 July.
1977: One at Upwaltham Down from 19 to 22 June.

These records would seem to be typical, occurring away from the coast in June or July.

One reported from a fast moving car about a mile north of Gatwick Airport on 29 May 1978 is excluded as it was, in all probability, in Surrey. It is also currently under review by *BBRC*.

There were just over 80 records of this conspicuous species in the British Isles during 1962-94 but nearly 150 prior to 1962. It breeds from Spain to western Asia and winters in sub-Saharan Africa. The decrease in records may reflect its decline in much of Europe (Tucker & Heath 1994) and sustained persecution in Italy (Fry, Fry & Harris 1992).

Richard Fairbank

Hoopoe

Upupa epops

Status:- A very scarce spring and autumn passage migrant; has bred.

The Hoopoe with its striking plumage pattern, particularly in flight, is a spectacular species that regularly 'overshoots' in spring. It may occur at well watched coastal localities, such as Beachy Head, but it also shows a preference for garden lawns and, for this reason, it is likely that a significant number of sightings are not reported.

Up until 1960 des Forges & Harber recorded about 385 birds, 125 of them between 1947 and 1960, of which almost half were in April. Four were recorded in 1961 and between 1962 and 1994 about another 281 were seen (fig. 74).

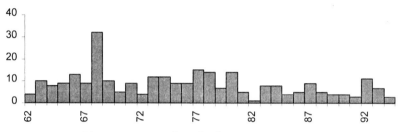

Figure 74. Annual totals of Hoopoes, 1962 - 94.

A comparison of the totals for the periods 1962-71 (110 recorded), 1972-81 (100) and 1982-91 (52) shows that there has been a decline in the number of occurrences in recent years, although there may be both 'good' and 'poor' years for the species. For example, 1968 was a record year with 32 birds reported but in 1982 just one was seen. Other good years were 1977 (15 recorded), and 1978 and 1980 (14 in each).

More Hoopoes are seen in spring than autumn as shown by the approximate monthly totals (excluding known breeding birds) for the period 1962-94:

Mar	Apr	May	Jun	Jul	Aug	Sep	Oct	Nov	Dec
10	131	76	13	4	16	17	7	5	1

There are three old records for early March including one at St Leonards for two or three mornings about 1 March 1932 (Walpole-Bond), the earliest county record. In recent years the earliest have been at Camber on 14 March 1983, Sidlesham Ferry on 20 March 1989, Slinfold from 21 March to 31 July 1980 and at Poverty Bottom from 23 to 28 March 1992. The latest recorded between 1962 and 1993 were in a Nutley garden on 7 November 1992, at Wilmington from 11 to 13 November 1968 and at Climping from 21 November to 6 December 1970. The latter is the latest for the county except for one at Hartfield on 14 December 1897.

Hoopoes have been proved to breed in Sussex seven times as follows: Park End, Chichester (1835), Southwick Square (a few years prior to 1849), Oving, near Chichester (1868 or 1869), near Eastbourne (1895), Asham, near Iford (before 1908), Bignor Park (1976) and Rackham Woods (1977). One young was raised in 1976 and two young in 1977 but the latter birds and one of the adults were reported as having been killed, probably by a fox. Two birds summered at Storrington in 1921 and at Uckfield in 1932, of which the latter may have attempted to breed. Single birds summered at Robertsbridge in 1968 and Slinfold in 1980.

An analysis of the sightings since 1976 reveals that half of those recorded have been at widely scattered inland sites, of which only Kingley Vale has held more than one. Favoured areas on or near the coast include Beachy Head, the Selsey peninsula, between Hastings and Camber and the Downs near Brighton. Apart from the breeding pairs in 1976 and 1977, most records have been of single birds although two have been recorded together on ten occasions since the beginning of 1962. Three were seen together at Lancing College on 15 April 1966. *Peter Whitcomb*

Wryneck *Jynx torquilla*

Status:- A very scarce passage migrant; has bred.

The Wryneck ceased to be a regular breeding species in Sussex in about 1920 and it last bred in 1944 in the Hastings area. There have, however, been a number of records of single birds being seen during the summer, of which those at Alfriston from 21 June to 11 September 1976 and at Weir Wood Reservoir on 19-20 July 1991 are the most recent.

Between 1962 and 1994, numbers of spring migrants showed little change, with no more than three recorded in any one year and none in seven years (fig. 75). Most arrived in April (27) with slightly fewer in May (19). The earliest for the county were singles at Pulborough on both 9 March 1908 and 10 March 1918 (Hudson 1973). One at Battle on 22 March 1990 was the earliest during 1962-94.

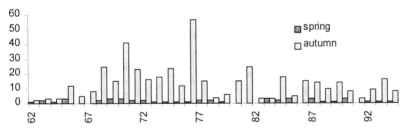

*Figure 75. Spring and autumn totals of Wrynecks
(excluding summering birds), 1962 - 94.*

In autumn, most migrants occur from mid-August to mid-October although the actual number recorded each year is probably dependent on the incidence of easterly winds, in which birds may 'drift' across the North Sea reaching eastern Britain. In some years only a handful occur, in marked contrast to other years such as 1970 and 1976, when totals of 41 and 56 were recorded. Of these, 34 were seen at Beachy Head in 1970 and 40 in 1976. The latter figure includes 14 that were trapped, none of which were retrapped. Most sightings are of single birds or occasionally twos. Totals of five at Beachy Head on 25 August 1970 and eight at the same site on 27 August 1977 were, therefore, quite exceptional. Analysis shows that the Beachy Head area is the most frequented site in Sussex, accounting for 31% of the birds recorded in recent autumns. Other favoured areas include the Selsey peninsula (17%) and then Rye Harbour/Pett (6%), the Downs near Brighton (6%), the lower Cuckmere Valley/Seaford (5.5%) and Climping (5%). Inland records account for 17% of the total reported. The latest recorded in recent years was one that was found freshly dead at Hurstpierpoint on 2 November 1990. The only other record for the month was on 5 November 1947 at the Crumbles.

There have been two recoveries of Wrynecks ringed in Sussex. The first bird, ringed at Beachy Head in August 1974, was controlled in Kassel, Germany, 639 km east, in June 1975 while the second, ringed at Icklesham on 5 September 1989, hit a window and died at Marlborough, Wiltshire, 176 km WNW, just six days later. *Peter Whitcomb*

Green Woodpecker *Picus viridis*

Status:- A fairly common resident.

The habitat requirements of the Green Woodpecker include mature broad-leaved trees for nesting and open ground for feeding, ants being the staple diet. In Sussex, it frequents a variety of habitat types including deciduous woodland, parkland, commons, heathland, well-timbered farmland and large gardens. Suitable habitats, such as these, occur across much of the county. However, notable gaps in the species distribution, as shown by the Atlas map, include the levels in the vicinity of Pevensey and Rye and also large urban areas where there are few mature trees and little pasture.

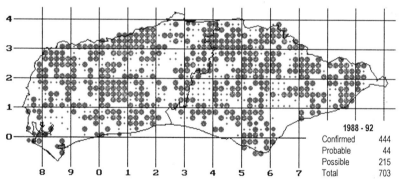

1988 - 92	
Confirmed	444
Probable	44
Possible	215
Total	703

The Atlas map for the Green Woodpecker shows a remarkable similarity to that of the Great Spotted Woodpecker, both occurring widely across the county. It is difficult to determine which is the commoner species. Shrubb considered the Great Spotted Woodpecker to be the most numerous woodpecker in Sussex, although as late as 1961 des Forges & Harber believed it to be less common than the Green Woodpecker.

There is only limited data available to estimate the size of the population in Sussex. A systematic search of tetrads in the Horam area during 1980 indicated a density of one pair per 250 ha but ringing studies on the Downs near Lewes point to a larger territory size of 400-600 ha. Records received

378

over the 10-year period 1983-92 suggest breeding densities of 1-3 pairs at Cattlestone Farm, West Chiltington (60 ha), 3-8 pairs at Pippingford Park (200 ha) and 4-5 pairs along the 8 km length of the Bluebell Railway. A survey of semi-natural broadleaved woodlands in West Sussex in 1982 found the species in 27 of 40 woods examined at a mean density of 2.5 pairs per km² (Bealey & Sutherland 1983). This figure, if applied to the 29,300 ha of woodland of this type in Sussex, extrapolates to a county population of over 700 pairs.

Severe winters can cause marked changes in status and distribution. Numbers were considerably reduced during the hard winter of 1962/63. Recovery took many years, particularly on the coastal plain where in 1971 it was still noted as absent from some formerly occupied areas.

Ringing recoveries suggest that the species is largely sedentary. Birds ringed in Sussex have produced a total of 12 recoveries, only one of which has moved more than 10 km. However, there is some evidence of spring and autumn movement or dispersal. For example, on 23 April 1981 one arrived from the south at Brighton Marina and landed on the clifftop.   *Graham Roberts*

Great Spotted Woodpecker   *Dendrocopos major*

Status:- A common resident.

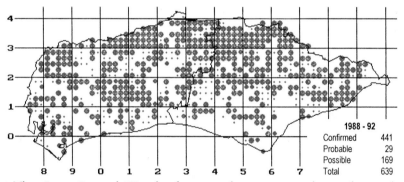

	1988 - 92
Confirmed	441
Probable	29
Possible	169
Total	639

The Great Spotted Woodpecker may be encountered anywhere where there are trees. Sussex is particularly well-wooded and it is hardly surprising that the Atlas map shows the species to be widely distributed across the county. It does, however, occur in greater abundance in the heavily wooded Weald and on the western South Downs than elsewhere on the Downs and the relatively treeless coastal plain.

A survey in 1980 of six well-wooded areas in northwest Sussex (*SxBR* 33: 42) showed the species to be widespread with densities varying between 0.25-0.43 pairs per km². It is likely, however, that this survey underestimated true population levels given that a survey of semi-natural broadleaved woodlands in West Sussex in 1982 found the species in 38 of 40 woods examined, at a mean density of 5.1 pairs per km² (Bealey & Sutherland 1983). This density, if applied to the 29,300 ha of woodland of this type in Sussex, extrapolates to a county population of 1500 pairs.

A record of a pair that bred successfully in a tit nestbox at Bewl Water in 1987 is of interest.

The species regularly penetrates into suburban areas to visit garden feeding stations, particularly during winter. It is normally attracted to fat and suet but in 1985, birds were reported feeding from nut baskets at Ansty, High Salvington and Sharpthorne in every month, except May and June.

Most years a few birds are reported some distance from typical habitat. Such sightings usually occur between August and November; many suggest local dispersal, though some, especially those from coastal localities, are thought to be immigrants. Recent records indicative of immigration include, at Seaford Head, one that flew west over the sea on 25 October 1985 and one that arrived there with thrushes on 12 October 1991 and, at Glyne Gap, singles that arrived from the direction of the sea on 8 August and 23 October 1993.

There are a number of ringing recoveries involving local movements of less than 10 km. However, there is an unusual record of a female shot dead at Chailey, near Lewes on 13 July 1914 which had been ringed as a nestling near Godalming, Surrey, some 54 km away, on 10 June 1913.   *Graham Roberts*

Lesser Spotted Woodpecker   *Dendrocopos minor*

Status:- A fairly common resident.

The Lesser Spotted Woodpecker is an inconspicuous species which is easily overlooked and as a consequence very much under-recorded. However, it is undoubtedly the least numerous of the three woodpeckers. It occurs in various types of broad-leaved woodland but appears especially attracted to open woodland, particularly if damp. It does, however, appear to avoid conifers and very dense stands of other tree species.

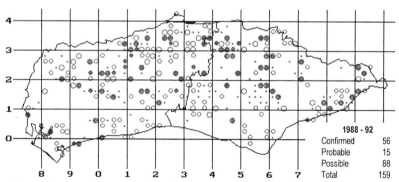

1988 - 92	
Confirmed	56
Probable	15
Possible	88
Total	159

The Atlas map shows both the results of the Atlas Survey and also those tetrads (as open circles) where the species was recorded in the period 1976-87 but not in 1988-92. The breeding records on the coastal plain are of interest. It is thought that the species may have expanded its range there in recent decades. Shrubb was aware of an increase in records on the coastal plain in West Sussex in 1975-76, which he attributed to the species' exploitation of the abundant dead and dying wood resulting from Dutch elm disease.

Dougharty & Hughes (1990) undertook a thorough review of all information relating to this species collected over the 25-year period, 1964-88. They estimated the Sussex population at 300-500 pairs, a figure that may constitute approximately 6-10% of the British population.

It is generally accepted that the species is not prone to anything more than very local movements (Winter Atlas). However, in the Society's records there is some evidence that in winter the species may leave the immediate vicinity of its breeding area and wander locally to feed in scrub and reeds (where it may be more conspicuous). Unlike the Great Spotted Woodpecker, it is only rarely seen at garden feeding stations in the county.   *Graham Roberts*

White-winged Lark   *Melanocorypha leucoptera*

Status:- A very rare vagrant (one old record).

A female netted with *ca.* 24 Snow Buntings near Brighton on 22 November 1869 was the first British record and is in the Booth Museum (BoMNH 208047) where it shares a display case with two others of 'Hastings Rarity' origin (see *Brit. Birds* 88: plate 101).

Two other sight records, of three along West Hove sea front on 15 November 1917 and one between Rye and Camber on 19 August 1933 (Walpole-Bond), have recently been reviewed and their identification is no longer regarded as proven (*BOURC* 1993b).

There remains only one other acceptable record of this little-known lark in Britain, near Kings Lynn in October 1981. It breeds on the central Asian steppes wintering as far west as the Black Sea.   *Richard Fairbank*

Short-toed Lark   *Calandrella brachydactyla*

Status:- A rare vagrant (seven records involving 11 individuals).

Five were recorded before 1962 (des Forges & Harber). One caught near Brighton on 26 September 1854 and kept alive in an aviary for "some time" was the second British record, while one caught at Amberley on 18 July 1888 was seen alive in captivity on 27 July (Walpole-Bond). A female caught at Hollingbury Hill, Brighton on 16 November 1909 (Langton 1910) is in the Booth Museum (BoMNH 207824). Two were seen in a meadow adjacent to Pagham Harbour on 29 April 1951 (Metcalfe 1952).

Since the beginning of 1962 there have been three records:

1972: Four flew northeast from Birling Gap into a stubble field near Cornish Farm, Beachy Head on 2 October.
1991: One in the dunes at East Head, West Wittering between 26 June and 4 July.
1994: One in a seeded field at Birling Gap on 7-8 May.

Appearances conform to no clear pattern with single records in each month from April to July and September to November. The flock of four in 1972 was, at the time, the largest group recorded in Britain, although similar sized parties have occurred since, on the Isles of Scilly in early October 1975 and mid-October 1977.

There were over 400 records of this unobtrusive small lark in the British Isles during 1962-94. It breeds from northwest Africa and Iberia to Mongolia, western populations wintering in the Sahel. *Richard Fairbank*

Crested Lark *Galerida cristata*

Status:- A very rare vagrant (four old records).

There are four old records from well before 1962 (des Forges & Harber). These are: one shot at Littlehampton prior to 1845 (the first British record), one netted at Shoreham-by-Sea on 20 October 1863, one shot near Worthing in spring 1879 and an adult male caught at Portslade-by-Sea on 10 October 1881. The two caught in October are in the Booth Museum (BoMNH 208073 and 208072 respectively).

There were just five records of this large-billed lark in the British Isles during 1962-94, one in June 1982 being the most recent. This contrasts with 14 records prior to 1962. It breeds as close as Dieppe and throughout much of continental Europe although it is generally decreasing in the northern part of its range (BWP). European birds are mainly resident. Other races occur across northern Africa and the Middle East to India and Korea. *Richard Fairbank*

Woodlark *Lullula arborea*

Status:- A very scarce resident and passage migrant.

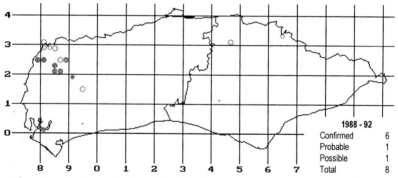

1988 - 92	
Confirmed	6
Probable	1
Possible	1
Total	8

The Woodlark, with its delightfully evocative song, is associated with heathlands bearing scattered trees to act as songposts. It nests where ground cover is sparse, often as a result of a fire within the last few years. Although the species has colonised areas of young and cleared conifer plantations in East Anglia, this does not appear to be the case in Sussex. There are currently few breeding sites in the county and, as the Atlas map shows, these are all in West Sussex close to the borders of Hampshire and Surrey. In East Sussex, Ashdown Forest has long been abandoned as a regular haunt although occasional records, such as the presence of a singing male in May-June 1984, suggest that it may not be too long before Woodlarks return to the area. The available historical information on the breeding status of the Woodlark in

Sussex has been summarised by Hughes (1970). He gave estimates for the county of *ca.* 50 pairs in the late 1930s and 50-100 pairs in the immediate post-war years. Evidence of a subsequent decline was provided by the results of a survey during 1967-69 that found about ten pairs annually in this period. None were found breeding from 1972 to 1976 but in 1977 birds were present at three suitable localities in the county. There were further records of birds in breeding habitat in each of the years 1978-81 and 1983-86 but nesting was not proved until 1987. There has been a gradual recovery since, an incomplete survey in 1994 revealing the presence of 11 territories, all in the northwest of the county (D Burges *in litt.*). The Atlas map shows both the results of the Atlas Survey and also those tetrads (as open circles) where the species was recorded in the period 1976-87 but not in 1988-92.

Woodlarks are only rarely recorded on spring passage and, since 1976, there have been just five reports of single birds, all between 15 March and 3 May. More are noted on autumn passage and arrivals are frequently associated with winds from an easterly direction. Since 1976, a total of *ca.* 61 has been recorded, all between 18 September and 27 November. Of these, 23 were in 1992 and 18 in 1993. Although birds have appeared at a number of coastal sites between Selsey Bill and Fairlight, most have been at Beachy Head where *ca.* 22 have been recorded since 1976. The upsurge in the number of autumn migrants may be linked to the recent increase in the Woodlark in East Anglia. This sub-population, unlike those in Hampshire/Surrey and southwest England, is migratory, deserting its breeding sites in winter, probably due to lower winter temperatures (Sitters 1986).

In Sussex, the breeding population is generally sedentary and birds may sometimes be found throughout the winter at their breeding sites. Occasional flocks, such as one of 14 feeding in a cereal field in the northwest of the county on 21-22 November 1981, probably comprise birds from Hampshire or Surrey. Small numbers may be recorded at coastal sites in very cold weather. Shrubb noted the occurrence of at least 35 along the coast between Seaford and Eastbourne in January 1966. More recently, there have been five such records, totalling eight birds, including one at Sidlesham Ferry and three at Pagham in February 1991. The origin of such birds is uncertain, although the Winter Atlas states that they are probably from the continent.

Mike Scott-Ham

Skylark   *Alauda arvensis*

Status:- A common resident, passage migrant and winter visitor.

The Skylark is still commonplace in Sussex, particularly on the Downs and the levels in the far east of the county although, as the Atlas map shows, its distribution is somewhat patchy. It is largely absent from urban and heavily wooded areas. Recent national trends have shown the species to be undergoing a marked decline. Indeed the New Atlas suggested that numbers may have fallen to half their former level since about 1980. The limited survey data available for the county supports this trend, as shown by a decrease in the number of pairs on a 55 ha CBC plot on the Adur Levels from 32 in 1983 to 22 in 1986.

Recent information on breeding densities in the county is lacking. Shrubb, however, quoted densities of up to 17.5 pairs per km² on the coastal plain, 3.5-10 pairs per km² on the Downs, 6 pairs per km² in the permanent grassland of the river valleys and 8.5 pairs per km² on Wealden grassland. Combining the results of a number of censuses of breeding birds in defined areas during the 1980s, in which densities varied between 1.4 pairs per km² (at Kingley Vale) and 58 pairs per km² (on the Adur Levels) gives an average of 5.8 pairs per km², a figure which if applied to the 627 tetrads in which breeding was confirmed during the Atlas Survey indicates a county population of about 14,000 pairs, rising to about 18,000 pairs if all records are considered. However, this estimate may be too high, given the recent loss of temporary grassland which is the favoured habitat (O'Connor & Shrubb 1986) and the widely varying breeding densities in different habitats. This has been offset to some extent by the provision of set-aside land under the Common Agricultural Policy, although the cutting of such areas in May 1993, in the middle of the breeding season, was disastrous for Skylarks (Mead & Wilson 1993).

1988 - 92	
Confirmed	627
Probable	0
Possible	165
Total	792

In autumn, diurnal movements of Skylarks occur, especially at coastal sites, where passage is principally to the west. These are recorded from mid-September through to early December, but mostly in October and November. Passage may be observed anywhere along the coast, though in recent years the highest counts have been at Seaford Head where totals of 1475, 500, 460 and 300 were recorded on 17 October 1992, 8 October 1993, 12 October 1991 and 5 October 1991 respectively, all flying west. At Pagham Harbour, there were 700 west in one hour on 20 October 1983. Movements at inland localities in autumn have included 358 northwest at Maynards Green on 12 October 1980 and 200 north at Plumpton on 8 November 1986. Shrubb referred to the build-up in autumn of "some very large flocks involving several thousand birds", particularly at Beachy Head though none of this magnitude have been noted since 2000 were recorded there on 30 November 1969.

Large numbers of Skylarks often arrive in the county following the onset of severe weather in winter. Spectacular cold weather movements may be induced by heavy snowfall, as in January 1966, when 10,000 flew west at Brighton in three hours on 15th and 2000 north at Selsey Bill the following day. A large movement in the harsh winter of 1978/79 began on 31 December when "huge numbers" moved west or northwest from "first light until late afternoon". Up to 1500 per hour were recorded at Hove and 3000 at Worthing in 1.25 hours. The movement continued the following day with 1200 recorded at Chichester in 0.5 hours and 2500 at Shoreham in 2.25 hours. Another influx started on or about 24 January when 2000 flew west over the Downs near Lewes in two hours. Movement on such a large scale was not recorded again until February 1991 when at least 5000 flew west at Rye Harbour on 8th and 422 at Brighton Marina in ten minutes on 13th. Skylarks may also be grounded in severe weather. A number of very large concentrations in early 1979 included 6000 at Church Norton on 28 January, an estimated 10,000 in the Sidlesham area the following day and "uncountable" thousands in the Ouse Valley on 18 February. In February 1991, the largest flocks recorded were 1000 at Climping on 10th and 3000 at Lewes Brooks and 1000 at Shoreham on 14th. Birds may also appear in less favoured habitats such as gardens and along tidelines during spells of cold weather. The size of the 'normal' county wintering population is not known but, since the late 1980s, there have been few reports of flocks in excess of 100 birds (except in February 1991). There were, however, 700 at Pagham Harbour on 11 December 1991 and 450 at Seaford Head in early 1993.

Although Shrubb stated that most spring passage was in March and that both immigration and emigration had been noted, there have been no recent reports of significant diurnal movements at this time of the year.

Of interest are two records of albino birds, one at Chichester Harbour in January 1979 and one at Rye on 6 December 1981, both during periods of snow, and a leucistic bird at Mile Oak, Portslade in early 1993.

Few Skylarks have been ringed in Sussex and, as yet, there is no evidence of movement beyond the county. The furthest travelled bird from outside the county was ringed at Dungeness, Kent in September 1961 and found dead at West Wittering, 131 km west, in May 1963.   *Mike Scott-Ham*

Shore Lark   *Eremophila alpestris*

Status:- A rare winter visitor.

des Forges & Harber recorded a total of over 100 up until 1960 with birds annual in the periods 1946-50 and 1955-60. Since then, there have been records in 13 winters totalling a minimum of 55 individuals (fig. 76).

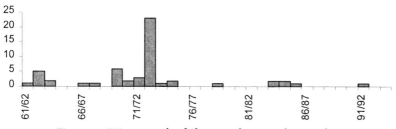

Figure 76 Winter totals of Shore Larks, 1961/62 - 93/94.

Prior to 1962 most occurrences were of single birds, but parties of up to five were sometimes recorded. In the period 1962-94, there were only five

385

occasions when three or more were seen together comprising three at the Midrips from 13 January to 13 March 1963, five at Crowlink from 31 January to 16 April 1970, five at Beachy Head on 14 October 1972 increasing to 11 the following day, four at Sidlesham Ferry on 23 November 1972 and six at Cuckmere Haven on 10 December 1972.

In Britain, most Shore Larks are seen on the east coast, especially between the Humber and Thames estuaries. In a normal winter, about 300 are recorded (Winter Atlas) but in recent years there has been a marked decline, a feature evident in the graph above. Following an exceptional influx in the autumn and early winter of 1972, when a minimum of 22 occurred, only eight were recorded in the period 1973/74-85/86 and just one since, at Atherington from 8 to 13 December 1991 and again from 26 December to 23 March 1992.

Up to 1937 most birds were seen in the east of the county but since 1974 only two (at Bexhill on 19 January 1985) have occurred east of Worthing. The localities favoured by wintering birds in recent years (Atherington, East Head and Pagham Harbour) reflect the species' preference, in winter, for coastal dunes, saltmarshes and beaches (BWP). One at Chichester Gravel Pits from 1 to 17 January 1984 is the only truly inland sighting for the county although there is an old record for Piddinghoe (des Forges & Harber).

The cumulative monthly totals for the period 1962-94 are shown below:

Oct	Nov	Dec	Jan	Feb	Mar	Apr
14	13	14	19	14	12	5

Shore Larks breed mainly in the Arctic zone and the birds that winter in Britain are thought to come from a population in northern Eurasia (Winter Atlas). The first typically arrive in mid-October and departures occur during March. However, the earliest recorded in Sussex in autumn were two at Sidlesham Ferry on 28 September 1946 and the latest in spring was one shot at Rye on 22 April 1885 (Walpole-Bond).   *Richard Kelly*

Sand Martin
Riparia riparia

Status:- A fairly common summer visitor and very common passage migrant.

The Sand Martin is constrained by its requirement for suitable sites in which to excavate nesting burrows. Although a variety of sites have been used, the only large colonies are found in sand quarries. The permanence of these depends very much on the extraction industry and, in recent years, a number have been filled in with refuse. No detailed co-ordinated survey of nesting burrows has been undertaken since 1985-86 when a countywide survey revealed only about 150 in each of those years. A total of eight sites was occupied in West Sussex and three in East Sussex (Edgar 1987), the former holding about 86% of the breeding population. The results of this survey indicated a decrease of 95% since the mid-1960s when the county population may have been as high as just under 4000 pairs (Shrubb). The 1985-86 survey was probably undertaken when the county population was at its lowest ebb. During the Atlas period, about 11 sites were again used but not necessarily all in any one year. Taking the maximum count for each of these colonies in the period 1988-92 indicates a total of 700-750 occupied burrows, almost all of which were in West Sussex. In the 1985-86 survey the largest colony was of only 60 occupied burrows whereas the largest more recent count was of 150 in 1989 at Stedham. Although nearly all the colonies currently in existence are in sand pits, about 50 different sites have been used in the county at some time. One of the East Sussex colonies, occupied in 1986-87, was in a steep bank of a drainage channel. Historical nesting sites have included chalk pits, coastal cliffs, holes in masonry and, on one occasion, a pile of salt stored for cold weather road treatment (Shrubb).

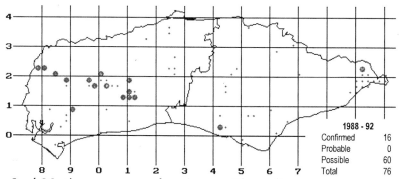

	1988 - 92
Confirmed	16
Probable	0
Possible	60
Total	76

Sand Martins are very early migrants. The earliest ever was one on 5 March at Chichester Gravel Pits in 1994 and singles on 6 March in the lower Cuckmere Valley in 1977 and at Pevensey Bridge Level in 1992. During 1966-93 first dates varied between 6 March and 3 April with the average 21 March. The majority arrive between mid-April and early May during which time feeding flocks may be found over open water, typically in cold or wet weather. Numbers tend to be fairly low although there were 500 at Chichester Gravel Pits on 12 May 1992 and 400 at Weir Wood Reservoir on 12 May 1968 and Rye Harbour on 17 April 1980.

Return passage commences in July and is on a very much larger scale than that in spring, as shown by counts of 15,500 at Rye Harbour on 18 August 1972, 14,000 there on 22 August 1990 and 6000 at Beachy Head and Chichester Gravel Pits on 22 September 1980 and 11 August 1993 respectively. Large movements include 3700 flying south, 3680 flying west and 4290 flying south at Selsey Bill on 23 August 1964, 28 August 1965 and 31 August-1 September 1969 respectively and 4000 flying west at Beachy Head on 3 September 1966 and 17 September 1978.

Spectacular reedbed roosts may form during the autumn, the largest of which were 50,000 at Chichester Gravel Pits in the 1960s and at Icklesham in August 1989. From ringing recoveries it is known that the birds that form such roosts have bred over a huge area extending at least as far as the west coast of Ireland and the Highlands of Scotland. Work at the Chichester roost in 1962-68 showed that a high proportion of birds came from south of a line from the Mersey to the Thames Estuary, indicating a south-easterly migratory direction (Mead, Boddy & Watson 1964, Mead & Harrison 1979). At Icklesham a total of 24,200 Sand Martins was ringed in the autumn of 1990. Between 1990 and 1992 over 180 birds that had been ringed at this site were controlled in Senegal between 17 November and as late as 19 April. Singles were also recovered in Mali in 1989 and the Canary Islands in 1990, the latter in an Eleonora's Falcon's nest. One ringed at Drum, Tayside on 17 August 1989 was controlled at Icklesham just two days later, a distance of 687 km.

During 1974-93 last dates fell between 28 September and 24 November with the average 29 October. The latest date for the county is 5 December 1911 while other late records include three at Rye Harbour on 24 November 1982, one at Beachy Head on 19 November 1966 and singles on 16 November at Church Norton in 1975 and Rye Harbour in 1993.

In 1977 two albino Sand Martins were recorded: one flying west at Pett Level on 17 September and another, possibly the same, at Chichester Gravel Pits on 25 September.   *Robert D M Edgar*

Crag Martin   *Ptyonoprogne rupestris*
Status:- A very rare vagrant (one record).

One seen at Cow Gap, Beachy Head for about 30 minutes during the morning of 9 July 1988 was the second British record, the first being in Cornwall 17 days earlier (Higson & Urquhart 1990, Urquhart 1990).

There have been three records of this stocky hirundine in Britain up to 1994. It breeds from northwest Africa and Iberia to the Himalayas and eastern China. European populations winter mainly around the Mediterranean.
Richard Fairbank

Swallow   *Hirundo rustica*
Status:- A common summer visitor and abundant passage migrant.

The Swallow's main habitat is lowland farmland and, as the Atlas map shows, it is well distributed throughout most of the county, except in urban areas where there is a shortage of suitable buildings for nest-sites. Information on breeding densities or population trends in the county is very limited.

However, Prater (1983b) in his study of farmland bird communities at Plumpton reported a density of 1.5 pairs per km², a figure which if applied to the 711 tetrads in which breeding was confirmed during the Atlas Survey indicates a county population of over 4000 pairs compared with a British population estimated at 570,000 pairs (New Atlas). Although a comparison of the map published in the New Atlas with that in the 68-72 BTO Atlas shows little change in distribution, there does seem to have been a general decline in numbers, especially in southern and eastern England. This is thought to be the result of droughts during the last decade in southern Africa where the species winters. Changes in farming practices in Britain have probably also had an effect. The modernisation of farm buildings may have reduced the availability of suitable nest-sites while the development of cleaner, more hygienic farms and the use of pesticides may have reduced insect prey.

1988 - 92	
Confirmed	711
Probable	0
Possible	198
Total	909

The first Swallows are normally recorded in late March. During 1965-93 first dates varied between 3 March and 10 April with the average 22 March. One at Langney Point on 4 February 1967 may possibly have overwintered as may one recorded at Playden, Rye on 12 February 1914. The next earliest was one at Pebsham on 3 March 1969 followed by singles at Rottingdean on 5 March 1972 and Ashburnham on 6 March 1960. An early influx occurred in 1977, with one at Shoreham-by-Sea on 7-8 March, three at Pett Level on 11th, further singles there on 12th, 18th and 19th and at Pagham Harbour on 20th. On 27th, 11 were recorded at Arlington Reservoir, an early date for numbers of this order. In most years, however, the main arrival starts in late April and usually peaks in early May. Few large movements have been recorded in spring but 1000 were noted at Beachy Head on 2 May 1972, 500 there on 11 May 1975 and 665 at Selsey Bill on 12 May 1992. In bad weather, large gatherings may occur at inland waters, for example, 3000 at Bewl Water on 24 April 1989 and 1000 at Chichester Gravel Pits on 12 May 1992.

Emigration usually begins in late August and continues until early October. Communal roosts may form in reedbeds during this period, the largest of which have included 13,000 and 6000 at Combe Haven on 5 September and 1 October 1988 respectively, 6000-7000 at Litlington on 2 October 1971 and 5000 at Pett Level on 7 September 1988. Four-figure counts have also been made at Thorney Deeps where there were 4000 on 28 August 1985 and 3000 on 11 September 1985.

Movements of 10,000 or more in a day are frequently recorded in mid-September. Larger counts, all at Beachy Head, have included an exceptional 55,000 on 13-14 September 1971, 35,000 mostly flying south on 14 September 1975, 30,000 flying east on 27 September 1965, 20 September 1986 and 16 September 1987 and 30,000 flying west on 12 September 1965. A total of 30,000 passed Worthing Beach in just three hours on 24 September 1989.

A few remain in late October and November, although about 123 were recorded in the latter month in 1987, 111 in 1988 (including 70 flying southeast at Cuckmere Haven on 5th) and 114 in 1989 (including 53 in the lower Cuckmere Valley on 12th). During 1966-93 last dates fell between 12 November and 28 December with the average 2 December. An unusual number of records in December 1974 included three at Church Norton on 22nd, two there on 27th and one on 28th, the latter the latest county record. Other late records include singles at Pagham on 26 December 1960, Eastbourne on 25 December 1966, Chichester on 23 December 1894 and Plumpton on 20 December 1977.

Records of albinos include singles at Mill Hill, Shoreham in October 1969, Rottingdean on 9 September 1976, Pett Level on 30 September 1979 and at Brooklands, Worthing on 18 October 1987.

Of 167 recoveries/controls of Sussex-ringed birds during the period 1979-92, 140 were in Britain and Ireland and 27 abroad. Recoveries in South Africa (4), Zaire (3) and Namibia (1) indicate the wintering areas of birds ringed in the county while recoveries in Morocco (5), Algeria (2) and Nigeria (1) indicate the route taken to and from their winter quarters. The most distant recovery was of an adult ringed at Shoreham-by-Sea on 16 July 1958 and found dead in Queenstown, South Africa, 9576 km SSE, on 22 January 1959.

One controlled at Icklesham on 27 September 1990 had been ringed as a nestling in Orkney, 930 km NNW, on 5 July.   *Tim Parmenter*

Red-rumped Swallow   *Hirundo daurica*

Status:- A rare vagrant.

First recorded in 1967, thirteen have been seen, ten during 1985-94:

1967: One at Whitbread Hollow, Beachy Head for two hours on 23 April.
1970: One flying west over Belle Tout, Beachy Head on 18 April.
1971: One flying north over Charleston Reedbed on 4 May.
1985: One feeding over a field behind the Severals, Church Norton for 20 minutes on 29 May.
1987: One flying east over Pett Level Pools on 17 April.
One at Cow Gap, Beachy Head on 12, 15 and 17 May.
One around Watch Cottages, Rye Harbour on 26 May.
1989: One at Sidlesham Ferry on 22 April, remaining in the area for several hours.
1990: One flying east over Selsey Bill on 29 April.
1992: One at the Severals, Church Norton during the late afternoon of 3 May.
1993: One flying east over Cow Gap, Beachy Head on 2 May.
1994: One at Cow Gap, Beachy Head for 20 minutes on 3 May.
One at Cuckmere Haven during the evening of 19 May moved off north.

All records have fallen between 17 April and 29 May, five in the former month and eight in the latter, four during the three day period 2 to 4 May.

Five have been seen at Beachy Head, three at Pagham Harbour, two in the lower Cuckmere Valley and singles at Pett Level Pools, Rye Harbour and Selsey Bill.

There were over 250 records of this distinctive southern swallow in the British Isles during 1962-94, but only eight before. It has a wide distribution across southern Europe and Asia, being rather more patchy in sub-Saharan Africa where European birds winter. The increase in records in Britain coincides with a northwards range expansion in France and Spain (Dymond, Fraser & Gantlett 1989). *Richard Fairbank*

House Martin *Delichon urbica*

Status:- A common summer visitor and abundant passage migrant.

The Atlas map shows that the distribution of the House Martin is broadly similar to the Swallow's except that they occur more widely in urban areas, such as Crawley and the heavily developed coastal strip, where they have probably benefited from the growth of housing and industrial development. By contrast, they appear to be less widespread in agricultural areas where there is a lack of suitable buildings for nesting.

1988 - 92	
Confirmed	552
Probable	0
Possible	238
Total	790

It is generally accepted that the national population is stable or showing a slow long-term decline (Parslow 1973, Marchant *et al* 1990), though good evidence of this lacking (New Atlas). Recent counts of colonies in Sussex are conflicting but the general trend seems to be downward. Assuming a density of 100-200 pairs per occupied 10-km square (68-72 BTO Atlas) indicates a county population of up to 7600 pairs.

In most years the first birds are recorded in late March or early April. Excluding two very early records of single birds at Petworth on 1 February 1975 and Brighton on 3 March 1988 (which may possibly have overwintered), first dates during 1965-93 fell between 11 March and 15 April with the average 30 March. The earliest certain migrants were four at Cuckmere Haven on 11 March 1989 and singles on 13 March at Chichester Gravel Pits in 1966 and at Pett in 1985. In 1992, the first spring record was of 12 at Warnham Mill Pond on 18 March, an unusually high number for such an early date. In most years, the main passage is in early May. The largest movements recorded were of 400 flying east at Rye Harbour on 14 May 1971 and 300 flying north at Beachy

Head on 19 May 1968 though counts at the latter site have included 1000 on 2 May 1972 and 590 on 11 May 1975. In bad weather, large numbers may be recorded at inland waters, for example, 1500 and 750 at Barcombe Reservoir on 8 May 1985 and 28 May 1984 respectively, 1200 at Weir Wood Reservoir on 5 May 1985 and 700 at Bewl Water on 2 May 1983.

An incomplete census between 1967 and 1972, which recorded a total of 2700 nests at 53 localities (Shrubb), regrettably provided little comparative data due to inconsistent coverage of sites from year to year. Some of the largest colonies recorded during this period included 119 at Nyewood in 1967, 182 on a farmhouse at Icklesham and 240 at Plumpton Agricultural College in 1971 and 93 at Rye in 1972. Cliff nesting has been reported on five occasions since 1962, most recently by two pairs at Brighton Marina in 1978 and single pairs at Peacehaven in 1984 and between Birling Gap and Beachy Head in 1987. Perhaps the most unusual breeding record involved the building of nests on the cross-channel ferry MV Senlac when the ship was berthed at Newhaven. Three nests were built in 1973 and one in 1974. The adults did not accompany the ship to Dieppe but waited for its return nine hours later.

Emigration usually begins in August but the main autumn passage takes place in mid to late September. The largest single movement so far recorded took place on 16 September 1987 when an estimated 45,000 flew east at Beachy Head. Heavy passage was also noted on 20 September 1986, when a large easterly movement was recorded at several coastal localities including 33,000 at Goring, 30,000 at Beachy and 10,000 at Saltdean. A large southerly movement was noted on 19 September 1970 with 25,000 recorded at Selsey Bill and 20,000 at Beachy Head. An estimated 45,000 were present at Beachy Head on 13-14 September 1971 and 36,000 on 14 September 1974. Few are normally seen after late October although a total of about 463 was recorded in November 1988, made up largely of an exceptional movement of 411 flying east at Cuckmere Haven on 6th. House Martins were recorded in December in ten of the 17 years between 1966 and 1982, including about 46 in 1974, but none have since been seen in this month. During 1965-93 last dates fell between 16 November and 16 December with the average 28 November. The latest ever were three at Fishbourne on 22 December 1894 followed by three at St Leonards on 21 December 1938 and singles on 18 December 1994 at Bexhill and on 16 December at Camber in 1972, Arundel in 1974 and Seaford in 1979.

Records of albinos include singles seen at Burgess Hill on 1 October 1969, Midhurst on 12 September 1970 and Northease the following day, at Goring on 20 September 1986 and Brooklands, Worthing on 28 September 1993. A partial albino was at Icklesham on 21 September 1992.

Of 75 recoveries/controls of Sussex-ringed birds during the period 1979-92, 63 were in Britain and Ireland and 12 abroad (nine in France and singles in the Netherlands, Spain and Morocco). The major wintering area of birds from Britain is not yet known other than it is in Africa, south of the Sahara.

Tim Parmenter

Richard's Pipit   *Anthus novaeseelandiae*

Status:- A rare vagrant (64 individuals recorded, nearly all in autumn).

Thirty-three were recorded before 1962: mostly in autumn (September to November) with three or four in December and January and one in March (des Forges & Harber). The last, caught at Clayton Hill on 12 March 1869 is in the Booth Museum as is one caught at Hangleton on 20 January 1865 and four others from Brighton and Shoreham-by-Sea during 1867-69 (six of BoMNH 207800-6). One was at Hove Lagoon from 25 to 29 January 1956 (*SxBR* 9: 25).

Since the beginning of 1962 there have been 26 records involving 31 individuals. Records peaked in the late 1960s with five seen in 1967 and 1968 and four in 1970. There was a minor resurgence in the late 1970s but there have only been six records during 1982-94 (fig. 77).

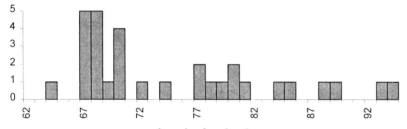

Figure 77. Annual totals of Richard's Pipits, 1962 - 94.

All recent records have been in autumn with the exception of one near Hodcombe, Beachy Head on 26 March 1974. The earliest autumn records were one at Combe Haven on 12 September 1988 and two at Rye Harbour on 22 September 1970 while the latest were singles between Church Norton and Sidlesham Ferry on 3 November 1993 and at Cuckmere Haven on 7-8 November 1978. Since 1962 eight have been seen in September, 19 arrived in October and three in November. This species tends to appear later in autumn than the similar Tawny Pipit (fig. 78) and is clearly much less regular.

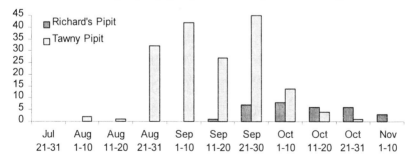

Figure 78. Cumulative 'autumn' arrival dates of Richard's and Tawny Pipits, 1962 - 94.

Most records have been of single individuals but four were seen at Horse Eye, Pevensey Levels on 22 October 1967 (with up to three present to 2

November), two near Belle Tout, Beachy Head on 19 October 1968 and two at Rye Harbour on 22 September 1970. Although seven have been recorded at Beachy Head since 1962, the most recent was at Hodcombe on 2 November 1979. The Bexhill and Hastings area has also accounted for seven records since 1962, including six since the beginning of 1980. One in a stubble field at Falmer from 8 to 11 October 1964 is the furthest recent record away from the coast although two have been seen at Sidlesham (on 4 October 1967 and 21 October 1968). Other records not already mentioned, but including the three most recent sightings, were from Church Norton (3 November 1993), the Crumbles (5 October 1977), East Head (30 September 1984), Littlehampton Golf Course (26-27 September 1977), Pett Level (8-9 October 1989) and Selsey Bill (29 September 1968 and 1 October 1994).

There were between 40 and 151 records of this large, upright pipit in the British Isles each year during 1986-92 (Fraser & Ryan 1994), the vast majority being in late September and October (Dymond, Fraser & Gantlett 1989). Its rare spring occurrences are invariably earlier than for Tawny Pipit and most in autumn are later and more frequently in longer or rougher grass (Fairbank 1987). It breeds from western Siberia to Mongolia wintering in the Indian subcontinent and South East Asia. Other races occur in Africa, eastern and southern Asia and Australasia.   *Richard Fairbank*

Blyth's Pipit   *Anthus godlewskii*

Status:- A very rare vagrant (one old record).

One obtained near Brighton on 23 October 1882 was recorded as a Tawny Pipit (Walpole-Bond) until it was discovered by Williamson when researching large pipit identification in the early 1960s (Shrubb 1979b, Williamson 1977). The skin is in the Natural History Museum (Tring).

There is only one other accepted record of this enigmatic large pipit for Britain (Landguard, Suffolk in November 1994) although six other recent October-November records (during 1988-94) are currently under consideration (Rogers *et al* 1995), possibly as a result of the field identification of the species becoming better understood. It breeds from Mongolia and adjacent Russia south to Tibet and winters in the Indian Subcontinent.
                                                     Richard Fairbank

Tawny Pipit   *Anthus campestris*

Status:- A very scarce visitor (235 individuals recorded, most in autumn).

des Forges & Harber recorded about fifty before 1962, although this total included the Blyth's Pipit of October 1882 which was only 'discovered' in the early 1960s. Of those that were dated, five were in August, about 40 in September, eight in October and one, netted near Eastbourne, on 8 November 1874. They included the first and second British records, obtained at Shoreham Harbour on 17 August 1858 and near Rottingdean on 24 September 1862 and one procured inland at Ditchling on 29 September 1876 (Walpole-Bond). One netted between Brighton and Rottingdean on 30 September 1864, one of two shot near Rottingdean on 6 September 1869 (the other was "blasted beyond repair") and one caught in a net near Brighton in October 1871 are in the Booth Museum (BoMNH 208132, 208134 and 208133 respectively).

During 1962-94 176 individuals were recorded, an average of over five per year. Annual occurrences have varied from none in 1962 and one in 1978 to 13 in 1980 and 14 in 1977 and 1985 (fig. 79). These records do not obviously reflect the decline over most of Europe since 1970 (Tucker & Heath 1994), which is perhaps counteracted by increased observer coverage.

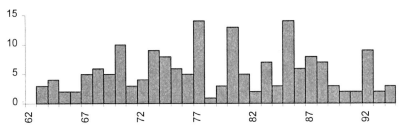

Figure 79. Annual totals of Tawny Pipits, 1962 - 94.

Seven have been recorded in spring, with both the earliest and latest at Beachy Head, flying west towards Hodcombe on 29 April 1978 and at Whitbread Hollow on 24 May 1969. Other spring records are of single individuals at Horse Eye, Pevensey Levels on 30 April 1975, west over Birling Gap on 4 May 1980, at Icklesham on 14 May 1988, Littlehampton Golf Course on 14 May 1992 and in a set-aside field at Birling Gap on 23 May 1994.

Early autumn birds were seen at Arlington Reservoir on 6 August 1973, Saltdean on 10 August 1968 and Birling Gap on 16 August 1980. A further 33 have occurred in August (26 during 27th-31st), 114 arrived in September and 19 in October (but only five after the 7th). The latest records were at Hodcombe, Beachy Head on 13 October 1972 and from 15 to 17 October 1973, and reported over Crowlink on 28 October 1973 (a very late date). Autumn arrivals are usually earlier than for the similar Richard's Pipit (fig. 78).

Six were found at Beachy Head (a party of five near Cornish Farm and a single at Hodcombe) amongst an impressive fall of common migrants on 21 September 1980. Two were also seen near Cissbury Ring and one at Littlehampton Golf Course on the same day. Of these, four at Cornish Farm and the two near Cissbury Ring were still present on 22 September. Parties of four have been recorded at Beachy Head twice, at Hodcombe from 7 to 10 October 1973 (three being trapped) and at Cornish Farm on 24 September 1983 while three were together at Beachy Head on 17 September 1975, 27 August 1977 (with another nearby earlier that day) and 13 September 1992. Three were also seen at Selsey Bill on 18 September 1960, Langney Point on 19 September 1960 and flying east over Newmarket Hill, Woodingdean on 27 September 1985. Two have been recorded together on 14 occasions since 1962.

During 1962-94 just over half the total recorded have been seen at Beachy Head or Birling Gap (91 individuals) with a further 11 at Langney Point and the Crumbles. Littlehampton Golf Course has hosted 13 records (all but one since the beginning of 1980) with ten at Pagham Harbour and five at Selsey Bill. In the east of the county there have been records from the Bexhill and Hastings area (7), Camber and the Midrips (3), Icklesham and Pett Level (3) and Rye Harbour (6). Those at Bexhill included two at Pebsham on both 7 September 1969 and 4 September 1984. Other records are from Arlington Reservoir (6 August 1973 and 4 September 1976), the Brighton area (10), Cissbury (five, including two at Tenants Hill on 27 August 1970), Cuckmere Haven (two on 29 September 1977, one remaining to 1 October), Darwell Reservoir (6 October 1965), Newhaven (23 September 1989), Pevensey Levels (30 April 1975), Pilsey Island (two on 7 September 1988) and Seaford (1963, 1967 and 1991).

In most years there are usually between 30 and 60 records of this large pale pipit in the British Isles, mostly between late August and early October (Dymond, Fraser & Gantlett. 1989, Fraser & Ryan 1994). It occurs later in spring and is usually earlier in autumn than Richard's Pipit and generally prefers shorter grass or stubble (Fairbank 1987). It breeds from northwestern Africa and Iberia to Mongolia wintering from the Sahel to India. Its range in western Europe is patchy and has decreased (BWP).   *Richard Fairbank*

Olive-backed Pipit   *Anthus hodgsoni*

Status:- A very rare vagrant (one record).

One at Hodcombe, Beachy Head on 11 October 1987 is the only record. It was present for three hours before departing east.

There were just over 190 records of this secretive pipit in the British Isles during 1962-94, but only one earlier occurrence. Even by the end of 1979 there had only been 14 British records, whereas 48 were recorded in 1990 alone (mostly in October). It breeds across Siberia from the Urals to Japan, with a separate population in the Himalayas and southern China, and winters in India and South East Asia.   *Richard Fairbank*

Tree Pipit   *Anthus trivialis*

Status:- A fairly common but local summer visitor and passage migrant.

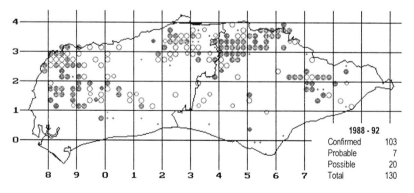

	1988 - 92
Confirmed	103
Probable	7
Possible	20
Total	130

The Tree Pipit is traditionally associated with heathland in Sussex. However, with the advent of the planting of conifers in large expanses, the species has readily moved into such plantations in the first few years of growth and again when the mature trees have been felled. Comparison between the Atlas map and the results of a survey carried out in the years 1967-70 (Hughes 1972) shows little change in distribution apart from more occupied tetrads in three 10-km squares, TQ62, TQ71 and TQ72, all in the southeast of the county. About 70% of the county was surveyed during the period 1967-70 and an estimated 449 territories were located. On this basis, it was suggested that the whole of Sussex might support more than 600 territories. Although no survey has been carried out since, it is unlikely that the current population is more than half of this figure, based upon casual reports submitted annually. The New Atlas suggests that the cause of the decline, which has also occurred nationally, may be the loss of conifer plantations as they become too old and overgrown. However, in Sussex many such plantations have now been felled making them again suitable, but with no corresponding increase in the number of breeding territories. Walpole-Bond described the Sussex strongholds of the Tree Pipit as Ashdown Forest and some of the commons around Midhurst. The former site still supports the bulk of the county population, holding perhaps 100 pairs, but at other sites there have been no recent counts in excess of 15 pairs.

The earliest ever were singles near Bexhill on 17 March 1922 and at Hastings on 21 March 1897 (Hudson 1973), two singles at Beachy Head on 25 March 1990 and one there on 26 March 1984. In other years during 1977-93, first dates fell between 27 March and 13 April with the average 2 April. The number of birds observed on spring passage is small, rarely exceeding 30 in total, and the highest day count for any site in recent years remains that of 15-20 at Beachy Head on 21 April 1968 (Shrubb).

Tree Pipits are more numerous on autumn passage. The largest numbers occur from mid-August onwards at both coastal and downland sites, especially Beachy Head, and on the Downs behind Worthing. In a typical autumn, 200-300 are reported but in 1980 and 1993 the totals were over 500 and 675 respectively, the latter figure including a total of 182 at Lancing Clump in

August. Shrubb reported that counts of 50-100 in a day at Beachy Head were frequent in the second half of August and that 250 there on 18 August 1968 was the maximum recorded. That there has been a significant decline since is evident from more recent maxima for this site, for example 115 on 21 August 1977 and 100 on 16 August 1980, but just 50 on 19 August 1989 and 16 on 31 August 1992. One at Bexhill on 9 November 1980 is the latest record for the county.

One ringed near Sidlesham in August 1970 was killed in Beira Litoral, Portugal, 1250 km SSW, in March 1972. *Mike Scott-Ham*

Meadow Pipit *Anthus pratensis*

Status:- A locally common resident, very common passage migrant, winter visitor.

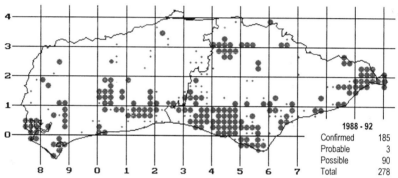

1988 - 92	
Confirmed	185
Probable	3
Possible	90
Total	278

Unfortunately the Meadow Pipit has a reputation for being an uninteresting species and, as relatively few records are received, its status in the county is hard to assess. The Atlas map reveals five main areas of distribution, comprising Chichester and Pagham Harbours, the South Downs, the major river valleys, Ashdown Forest, and the extreme east of the county around Rye. It also confirms the species' absence from the clay soils of the interior. This distribution reflects the variety of habitats which Meadow Pipits favour including saltmarshes, flood meadows, chalk grassland, and lowland heath (New Atlas).

Information on breeding densities is limited. Shrubb referred to densities of 4-6 pairs per km² in the Arun Valley in 1967 and 1970, and on the Rother Levels in 1966. He also quoted densities as high as 20 pairs per km² in very favourable areas such as Beachy Head but as low as 1.3 pairs per km² in predominantly farmland regions. Combining the results of a number of censuses of breeding birds in defined areas carried out during the 1980s, in which densities varied between 0.5 pairs per km² and 30 pairs per km², gives an average of 3.5 pairs per km², a figure which if applied to the 185 tetrads in which breeding was confirmed during the Atlas Survey indicates a county population of about 2500 pairs rising to about 4000 pairs if all records for Meadow Pipits are included. However, this range should be treated with caution as breeding densities vary considerably from one part of the county to another and from year to year. On the Adur Levels, for example, the number of pairs recorded in a 55 ha CBC plot decreased from 31 in 1981 to 12 in 1985 but recovered slightly to 18 in 1986.

In late March and early April, large numbers of Meadow Pipits may be seen flying north over the coast, particularly in light northerly winds. Counts of up to 400 in a day are not unusual but occasionally larger numbers are recorded, for example, 1340 at Selsey Bill on 1 April 1962, 3000 at Beachy Head on 4 April 1962, 1400 at Selsey Bill on 28 March 1970, totals of 1299, 1046 and *ca*. 1000 at Selsey Bill, Brighton Marina and Worthing respectively on 31 March 1984, and 2500 at Selsey Bill in 3.5 hours on 12 April 1990. Movements of 800-1000 northeast over Pett Level and 402 north over Pevensey Levels on 8 March 1978 were unusual in that they occurred earlier than those above and in a strong westerly wind.

Passage of Meadow Pipits is heavier in the autumn when large diurnal movements, usually to the west, may be observed at coastal sites between mid-September and mid-October. Although it is impossible to give a precise total for a whole autumn, some indication of the number of birds involved may be obtained from counts in 1989 of 200 at Beachy Head and 453 in the lower Cuckmere Valley on 23 September, 1000 at Beachy Head and 150 at Hollingbury Camp on 24 September, 1500 flying east at Pagham Harbour on 27 September and 1000 at Beachy Head on 28 September. What is not clear, however, is whether those at Beachy Head each day were new arrivals or birds remaining from previous days. Similarly, counts for 1993 included 1550 at Church Norton and 400 at Selsey Bill on 22 September, 2000 flying west at Seaford Head on 25 September, a further 800 west there the following day and 1150 west on 8 October, and 2000 at Beachy Head on 25 October. An estimated 5000 were present at Beachy Head on 26 September 1991.

Little is known of the species' status in winter other than that flocks may occur in a variety of habitats similar to those favoured for breeding. These rarely exceed 50 but larger numbers may gather to roost as shown by counts of 226 at Chailey Common in December 1992 and 141 at Iping Common in January 1984. Numbers may increase in severe weather, probably as birds are forced to move from elsewhere by snow covering their feeding areas. A flock of 250 was recorded on arable land at Cissbury in December 1981 and another of over 300 at Ferring in January 1985.

Records of interest include a leucistic bird at Beachy Head on 6 October 1984 and a partly albino bird in the Brighton area in November-December 1985.

A number of recoveries in the county of birds from outside Sussex include one ringed at Spurn Point, Humberside in September 1990 and found at Worthing, 531 km south, in April 1991. *Mike Scott-Ham*

Red-throated Pipit *Anthus cervinus*

Status:- A very rare vagrant.

First recorded in 1969, five have been seen:

1969:   One in a cattlefield above Whitbread Hollow, Beachy Head on 19-20 October.
1970:   One at Arlington Reservoir from 13 to 15 October.

1973: One northeast over Belle Tout, Beachy Head on 6 October.
1984: One at Combe Haven on 28 October was present for most of the day, although only seen in flight.
1991: A summer plumaged male in song beside the Cuckmere Haven oxbows, just south of Exceat Bridge, from 28 May to 1 June (*Brit. Birds* 84: plate 303).

Four have been in October and one in May-June. All were in East Sussex, two being at Beachy Head and singles at Arlington Reservoir, Combe Haven and Cuckmere Haven.

There were nearly 280 records of this species in the British Isles during 1962-94. It breeds across the arctic tundra from eastern Norway east to western Alaska, wintering in sub-Saharan Africa and South East Asia.

Richard Fairbank

Rock Pipit   *Anthus petrosus*

Status:- A very scarce resident, fairly common passage migrant and winter visitor. Rare away from the coast.

Rock Pipits bred regularly in Sussex until 1891. There were no further breeding records until 1932, after which colonisation of the chalk cliffs took place with an estimated 30 pairs there by 1938. (Walpole-Bond).

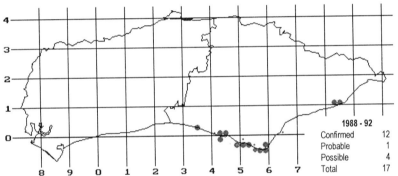

	1988 - 92	
Confirmed	12
Probable	1
Possible	4
Total	17

Although the Rock Pipit remains a regular breeder in the county, the Atlas map shows its range restricted to the chalk cliffs between Brighton and Eastbourne and the sand and clay cliffs between Hastings and Pett. As a breeding bird it is under-recorded, reflecting the inaccessibility of the rocky foreshore where it nests. It is likely that the county population is currently around ten pairs although the presence of seven pairs between Birling Gap and Cow Gap in 1992 suggests that a full census might reveal more. A county survey as long ago as 1965 located 42 males holding territory (Porter 1966), including 23 between Birling Gap and Holywell and three between Hastings and Pett, the latter apparently the first breeding birds ever found there (Shrubb). The former count covered much the same stretch of cliffs as that where seven pairs were found in 1992, suggesting that a significant decrease has occurred, the reasons for which are not apparent. Birds are occasionally recorded away from the cliffs during the summer, for example singles at Northpoint Gravel Pit on 3 June 1987 and at Littlehampton West Beach on 4 June 1988.

In winter, Rock Pipits are widely distributed along the coast. Wintering birds usually arrive in late September or early October although earlier arrivals sometimes occur, as indicated by the presence of singles at Pett Level on 16 August 1979 and at Widewater, Lancing on 25 August 1983. Shrubb referred to concentrations of up to 50 at Thorney Island/Chidham in 1965/66 and 30 between Bracklesham and Church Norton in 1968/69 but, more recently, the largest numbers have occurred at Rye Harbour (up to 40) and between Seaford and Cuckmere Haven (max. 23 on 1 January 1993). Other large counts in recent winters have included 23 at Pagham Harbour on 19 October 1993 and 20 on Worthing Beach on 20 January 1990.

Although Shrubb stated that "some movement has been recorded into November" and that there is "quite a marked return passage in March and early April", the extent of this is not clear as the species tends to congregate at favoured wintering sites on the coast, so masking birds which are passing through. Most inland records have been for passage periods. One was recorded at Arlington Reservoir on 5 August 1974 while in the period 1976-93 there were records totalling eight birds between 23 September and early November. These were at Arlington Reservoir (3), Weir Wood Reservoir (2) and Arundel WWT, Barcombe Reservoir and Bewl Water. Fewer have been noted in spring, the only recent reports being of singles at Weir Wood on 12 March 1990 and Bewl Water on 1 April 1981 and 30 March 1983. Outside the passage periods, the only inland birds have been one at Arlington Reservoir on 7 December 1980 and three there on 30 December 1982.

A taxonomic review of the Rock/Water Pipit complex in 1986 resulted in the recognition of three distinct species, the two aforementioned and the Buff-bellied Pipit *A. rubescens* of North America and eastern Asia (Knox 1988).

The vast majority of Rock Pipits recorded in the county belong to the nominate race (from Britain and western France) while the Fenno-Scandinavian race *A.p. littoralis* (colloquially known as Scandinavian Rock Pipit) is a rare winter visitor and/or early spring migrant. It is probably overlooked, particularly in winter when its identification in the field is virtually impossible.

Walpole-Bond considered Scandinavian Rock Pipits to occur annually between the latter half of February (earliest 18th) and late April (latest 30th) although he personally never saw more than about half a dozen together. He also refers to one captured at Shoreham-by-Sea in August 1868.

Perhaps surprisingly there were only three records during 1948-61, all in March (des Forges & Harber) and including five at Hove Lagoon on 7 March 1948. Between 1962 and 1994, a total of about 45 was reported, all at coastal localities apart from two at Arlington Reservoir on 17 March 1975 (one remaining to 19th) and one at Litlington on 5 December 1976. Most records were of single birds though, exceptionally, ten (considered to be migrants) were seen at Shoreham Fort on 27 February 1994. The cumulative monthly totals for the period 1962-94 show that most birds are recorded in early spring, although they are probably overlooked in winter.

Sep	Oct	Nov	Dec	Jan	Feb	Mar	Apr
1	1	1	2	-	12	26	6

Mike Scott-Ham

Water Pipit

Anthus spinoletta

Status:- A scarce winter visitor and passage migrant.

The Water Pipit only gained full species status in 1986 following a review of its taxonomy (*BOURC* 1986). Prior to this, the Water and Rock Pipits were generally regarded as one polytypic species of Holarctic distribution (Knox 1988).

Water Pipits are typically found in freshwater habitats, particularly on wet grassland adjacent to Chichester and Pagham Harbours and at Combe Haven (table 72), although the numbers vary greatly from year to year.

	Sep	Oct	Nov	Dec	Jan	Feb	Mar	Apr
Combe Haven	1	8	10	13	20	24	21	12
Fishbourne			4		1	1	1	
Pagham Harbour		3	4	3	1	3	2	2
Thorney Island	1		2	2	4	2	6	6

Table 72. Monthly maxima of Water Pipits, 1962 - 94.

The only other sites where counts have exceeded two during the winter months are the Adur Levels (four on 30 December 1983) and Barcombe Reservoir (up to four in early 1983).

The first birds normally reappear in October, although there have been several earlier records including those of singles at Atherington on 1 September 1986 and at Combe Haven on 2 September 1985. There is little evidence of an autumn passage but in spring, passage is indicated by increases at wintering sites in late March and early April. Migrants also appear at this time, especially at coastal sites such as Pett Level, where there were six on 16 April 1978, one of which stayed until 27 April, and two in April 1993, one of which stayed until 18 May, a late date. Unusually, six were recorded in atypical habitat on Pilsey Island on 1 April 1993, one remaining until 13th. A single at Beachy Head on 28 May 1967 is the latest to be reported in spring.

It is thought that the Water Pipits wintering in Britain originate from the mountains of central and southern Europe, but there are no ringing recoveries to confirm this.　　　　　　　　　　　　　　　　　　　　　*Mike Scott-Ham*

Yellow Wagtail

Motacilla flava

Status:- A fairly common but localised summer visitor and common passage migrant.

des Forges & Harber noted that the Yellow Wagtail had been in decline since about 1939, coinciding with the greatly increased drainage of levels. A breeding survey in each of the years 1965 to 1967 recorded between 150 and 270 pairs (Shrubb 1968), mainly on the permanent grassland of the river valleys and levels. Over half the population was then found in the Arun Valley above Amberley while other favoured areas were the Adur Levels, Pevensey Levels, the Rother Levels and Rye Harbour with a few pairs round Chichester Harbour. Breeding densities varied between 0.65 pairs per km² and 4.3 pairs per km² and, not surprisingly, the highest concentrations were on the levels. A further survey in 1980-81 located a total of 432 pairs (Mitchell

1982), thus pointing to an increase since the 1967 survey. However, numbers at individual sites can vary widely from year to year and it is likely that coverage was more thorough in the 1980-81 survey. A total of 222 pairs was found on the Rother Levels while other important areas were Pevensey Levels (54 pairs), the Arun Valley between Amberley and Pulborough (40 pairs), Brede Levels (28 pairs), Rye Harbour (26 pairs), the Ouse Valley (19 pairs) and Pett Level (11 pairs). Breeding densities varied between 2.8 pairs per km² and 7.8 pairs per km² with an average of 5.7 pairs per km². The Atlas map, shows that the breeding population, as in 1980-81, remains concentrated in East Sussex. The tetrads which held Yellow Wagtails during 1976-87 but not during 1988-92 are shown as open circles.

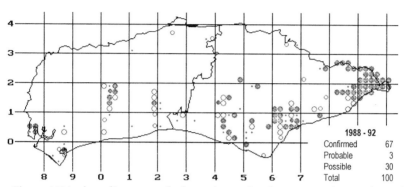

1988 - 92	
Confirmed	67
Probable	3
Possible	30
Total	100

Since 1981, breeding records have been far from complete. They do, however, indicate that a steady decline has occurred at some sites but an increase at others. At Amberley Wild Brooks, for example, no more than five pairs were recorded in any one year between 1983 and 1993, but at Pevensey Levels 170 territories were located in 1986 and 119 in 1987 (Hitchings 1988), a huge increase compared with the results of the 1980-81 survey. The decline in the breeding population at the former site has been offset, at least partly, by the restoration of wetland habitat at Pulborough Brooks following its acquisition by the RSPB. By 1988, the population there was down to 5-6 pairs, but by 1991 it had recovered to 16 pairs. A total of 19 pairs was present in 1992 but only six pairs in 1993. Counts of breeding pairs at Rye Harbour during 1982-93, shown below, demonstrate the considerable annual fluctuations that occur in this species. Interestingly, only 11 pairs were present at this site in 1972.

1982	1983	1984	1985	1986	1987	1988	1989	1990	1991	1992	1993
30	30	15	16	28	46	38	59	66	38	30	25

The first birds usually arrive in late March or early April. The earliest ever were singles at Sidlesham Ferry on 12 March 1990 and at Rye Harbour on 18 March of the same year. Over the period 1965-93 first dates fell between 12 March and 7 April with the average 30 March. Spring passage peaks in late April, as in 1989, when a total of 272 was recorded at six sites on 23rd-24th (including 171 at Barcombe Reservoir), and then tails off rapidly into May. Shrubb, however, referred to arrivals as late as 8 June though there has been no evidence of this in recent years. Other large counts have included totals of 43, 40 and 26 at Rye Harbour on 8 April 1993, 16 April 1979 and 16 April 1984 respectively, 27 at Seaford Head on 19 April 1992 and 24 at Selsey Bill on 18 May 1991 (a late date for this number).

The first autumn migrants may appear in late July but the main movement occurs between mid-August and late September. The largest numbers are recorded at or near the coast, especially in favoured areas such as the Selsey peninsula, Seaford Head and the lower Cuckmere Valley, Beachy Head and Rye Harbour. High counts include 750 at Beachy Head on 21 September 1980, 500 at Rye Harbour on 27 August 1992, 410 flying west at Seaford Head on 29 August 1992 and 390 flying east there on 28 August 1993. Roosts may form in reedbeds during the autumn. Between 500 and 1000 were recorded at Combe Haven in late August-early September 1984 and 376 at Thorney Deeps on 3 September 1990. Larger roosts have occurred in the past, for example, 2000 at Camber on 1 September 1949 (des Forges & Harber).

Most have departed by early October though 20 were recorded at Selsey Bill on 2nd in 1983 and six at Beachy Head on 15th in 1991. A total of 88 in October 1993 included 17 at Brooklands, Worthing on 2nd, 14 near Shoreham on 3rd and 11 at Seaford Head on 8th. During 1974-93, last dates fell between 3 October and 20 November with the average 25 October. The latest in the period were two at Amberley Wild Brooks on 15 November 1986, one at Church Norton on 16 November 1985, one at West Wittering on 19 November 1964 and one with two Snow Buntings at Pett Level on 19-20 November 1978 though the latest ever was one at Hove on 21 November 1926. Singles were recorded at West Wittering on 19 January 1947, Sidlesham Ferry from 11 December 1960 to 14 January 1961, in the lower Cuckmere Valley on 12 February 1967 and at Glynde on 7 and 13 January 1973.

A few birds showing the characteristics of the continental race *M.f. flava* are recorded annually. Most pass through in spring but males bred with *flavissima* females on six occasions between 1976 and 1993 and pure pairs bred in the Ouse Valley in 1983 and at Pevensey Bridge Level in 1989. The approximate cumulative monthly totals for the period 1962-93 are shown below.

Apr	May	Jun	Jul	Aug	Sep	Oct
49	52	11	11	9	10	1

There was one record of a male showing the characteristics of the Scandinavian race *M.f. thunbergi*, the Grey-headed Wagtail, prior to 1962 relating to a bird shot near Lancing on either 28 May 1869 or 24 April 1870. Since the beginning of 1962, six other males have been recorded as follows:

1970: One at Pagham Harbour on 4 June.
1978: One at Sidlesham Ferry on 10 September.
1980: One at Langney Point on 3 May.
1984: One at Sidlesham Ferry on 8 May.
      One at Mile Oak on 17 May.
1993: One at Arlington Reservoir on 11-12 May.

There have been four records of males showing the characteristics of the Italian and northwest Yugoslavian race *M.f. cinereocapilla*, the Ashy-headed Wagtail, all since the beginning of 1968, as follows:

1968: One at Beachy Head on 28 April.
1982: One at Pett Level on 7 and 20 May.
1987: One at Pevensey Bridge Level on 12 May.
1989: One at Icklesham on 31 May.

One, at Selsey Bill on 18 September 1960, was perhaps of the Grey-headed or Ashy-headed races while two males showing the characteristics of the western Siberian race *M.f. beema*, Sykes Wagtail, were recorded at Langney Point on 1 May 1983. However, des Forges & Harber reported that pairs with males of this type had been found breeding in the county on some 12 occasions and that males, not quite typical with the above, but differing somewhat from typical male Blue-headed Wagtails had also been recorded. There is a possibility, therefore, that some, if not all, were hybrids, particularly as BWP states that all British records of *beema* and the majority of those of *flava* refer to variants or hybrids of *flavissima*.

The sole county record of the race *M.f. feldegg*, the Black-headed Wagtail, at Thorney Island on 23 July 1974, is no longer considered acceptable following a review (Rogers *et al* 1995).

Few Yellow Wagtails have been ringed in the county but, even so, several of these have been recovered elsewhere. Among them was a young male ringed at Chichester in September 1963 killed in Beira Alta, Portugal, 1243 km SSW, in October 1965; an adult ringed near Sidlesham in August 1968 controlled in Landes, France, 801 km south, two weeks later; and a young bird ringed near Battle in September 1973 reported from Morocco, 2175 km SSW, in April 1975. A young female ringed in Landes, France in August 1975 was controlled at Pett Level one year later.   *Dave Smith*

Grey Wagtail   *Motacilla cinerea*
Status:- A fairly common resident, passage migrant and winter visitor.

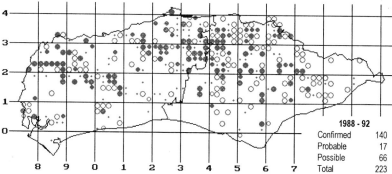

1988 - 92	
Confirmed	140
Probable	17
Possible	66
Total	223

Ticehurst (1907) considered that the Grey Wagtail was mainly a passage migrant in Sussex, breeding only rarely. By 1938 it had become a "tolerably familiar bird in Sussex between autumn and early spring", according to Walpole-Bond, who suggested that the average annual breeding population was 60-70 pairs. There was a general increase in the population in southern England in the first half of the century, with a more rapid expansion in the

1950s (Parslow 1973). The hard winter of 1962/63 undoubtedly had a disastrous effect on the Sussex population and there were no reports of breeding in the following summer. By 1966, however, some recovery had occurred with reports for the breeding season totalling 28 pairs. The extensive fieldwork for the Society's survey in 1967-69 (Merritt, Greenhalf & Bonham 1970) revealed a total of 193 occupied territories with single birds present at an additional 33 sites. In a second county survey in 1993 and 1994 (Manns 1996), breeding was confirmed or probable at 161 sites with single birds present at a further 54 sites. This represented a 16.6% reduction in the number of pairs compared with the results of the 1967-69 survey. A comparison of site data from the second survey against archived records suggested a considerable shift of territories over a long period, although often only to nearby localities. The map shows the tetrads which were occupied in 1993-94 as solid circles, with additional pre-1993 and Atlas Survey records as open circles.

The results of the two surveys indicate the importance of the county's rivers to the distribution of the species, especially the Western Rother/Arun and Ouse/Medway (Crawley to Crowborough) systems, and also the influence of the surface geological strata. The highest population densities were found on the greensands in the northwest of the county and the sandstones in the northeast. Table 73 summarises the number of pairs recorded within each river system or geographical area in both the 1967-69 and 1993-94 surveys.

River System or Geographical Area	1967-69 Confirmed or probable breeding	1993-94 Confirmed or probable breeding	1993-94 Single birds	1993-94 Total
Chichester	7	6	4	10
Wey	1	1	2	3
Rother (Western)	40	30	4	34
Arun	24	23	4	27
Adur	13	3	4	7
Mole	5	8	5	13
Eden	1	1	-	1
Ouse	50	31	9	40
Medway	30	35	19	54
Cuckmere	3	9	1	10
Ashburnham	3	3	-	3
Asten	3	1	-	1
Rother (Eastern)	13	10	2	12
Totals	193	161	54	215

Table 73. The distribution of Grey Wagtails by river system.

Data on habitat features were collected for 177 sites in the 1993-94 survey (table 74). A preference was shown for sites with running water, especially where it was shallow (95 records). Waterways with muddy beds (51 records) were used nearly as often as those with gravel (56 records), a preference which may reflect availability rather than choice. Sites with a fall of water, both natural and man-made, were much favoured (91 records), as were those on rivers and streams which were tree-lined (87 records), factors possibly linked to the potential invertebrate food supply.

Primary feature	Number of sites	Secondary feature	Number of sites
Pond or lake	80	Natural waterfall	10
Reservoir	5	Outfall from pond or lake	50
River more than 2 m wide	69	Sluice gate	12
Stream or ditch up to 2 m wide	62	Weir	26
Water mill	13	Bridge	68
Industrial site	30	Mill pool	19
Water works	1	Mill stream	26
Sewage works	4	Boat house	4
Garden	12	Adjacent buildings	28
Park	1		
Other	4		

Table 74. Habitat features of Grey Wagtail territories, 1993 - 94.

The breeding population appears to be largely sedentary, based on the findings of the 1967-69 survey in which 84% of all breeding sites were less than 3 km from the nearest known wintering site. Diurnal movements are, however, recorded annually at coastal sites between late August and late October, with a peak in mid-September. Day totals are usually in single figures but notable exceptions have included 37 at Littlehampton on 12 September 1989 and 46 at Sompting on 26 September 1991. Most passage is along the coast, but there have been some reports of emigration, the majority from Beachy Head and Selsey Bill where autumn totals of up to 32 and 20 respectively were recorded in the 1960s.

During the 1967-69 survey, Grey Wagtails were found wintering at 147 sites, in a wide range of both natural and man-made habitats, such as reservoirs, lakes, ponds, rivers, streams, marshes and sewage works. During 1980-93, there were records from up to 28 and 26 inland sites and 26 and 21 coastal sites in November-December and January-February respectively.

Spring passage, which extends from late March to early May, is always small, the majority of records being of single birds at coastal sites. As in autumn, most movements are along the coast, but there were reports of birds arriving off the sea at Selsey Bill in March 1969 and May 1989.

There is some ringing evidence to show the dispersal of birds from Sussex. Three birds, all ringed as nestlings at Friars Gate between 1983 and 1986, were subsequently recovered at localities to the northwest, the furthest reaching Hatfield, Hertfordshire, 81 km NNW. One ringed as a nestling near Horsham in May 1970 was found dead in the New Forest, Hampshire, 84 km west, in December 1971. One ringed at Icklesham in September 1988 was controlled three months later near Sevenoaks, Kent, 41 km WNW. Of those ringed outside Sussex and recovered within the county, several had ventured some distance. One ringed at Cuddesdon, Oxfordshire in July 1958 was controlled at Wartling, 142 km southeast, in September 1959; one ringed at Lyndhurst, Hampshire in July 1981 was found at Swanborough Sewage Farm, 112 km east, in December 1983; and one ringed at Crickhowell, Powys in April 1990 was found dead at Gatwick Airport, 218 km ESE, the following December. All had been ringed as nestlings. *Leonard Manns*

Pied Wagtail *Motacilla alba*

Status:- A common resident, passage migrant and winter visitor.

1988 - 92	
Confirmed	409
Probable	5
Possible	252
Total	666

The Atlas map reveals that the Pied Wagtail is more widespread in central and northern parts of the county. It is patchily distributed on the Downs and coastal plain and is largely absent from the Selsey peninsula and Pevensey Levels, perhaps reflecting an absence of suitable buildings and other man-made structures for nest sites in these areas. Favoured sites include farm buildings and large houses with well kept lawns while more bizarre nest sites have included a derelict car dashboard in Worthing, a pile of old tyres at Plumpton, and under the steering column of a motor boat at Bewl Water; the young were parted from their parents every time the boat was used.

des Forges & Harber stated that the species bred commonly throughout the county but Shrubb, quoting H A R Cawkell in Parslow (1973), noted that nesting numbers had declined by about half in East Sussex in 30 years. During the Atlas Survey, there were records in 666 (66%) tetrads with breeding confirmed in 409 and probable or possible in the remainder. The low proportion of confirmed breeding records suggests that the density of breeding Pied Wagtails in Sussex is not high with perhaps just one or two pairs per occupied tetrad thus indicating a county population of no more than 1500 pairs. The abundance map in the New Atlas suggests that Pied Wagtails are present at lower densities in Sussex than in neighbouring Hampshire. The Atlas Survey in that county in 1986-91 found the species in 90% of tetrads with confirmed breeding in more than 60% (Clark & Eyre 1993). The New Atlas estimated the breeding population in Britain at 300,000 pairs.

Diurnal passage is well marked in autumn, usually peaking in the last week of September and first three weeks of October. Movements at coastal localities are predominantly to the east, and include 125 at Beachy Head on 13 October 1985, 160 at Climping on 12 October 1986 and 540 at Worthing on 16 October 1988 though westerly movements also occur, e.g. 250 at Beachy Head on 29 September 1988, 90 at Shoreham on 11 October 1989 and 56 at Seaford Head on 17 October 1992. Counts of birds on the ground include 500 at Shoreham airport in October 1980 and 250 on the beach at Church Norton on 25 September 1993. Roosts may form in autumn and large counts have included 100 at Horam in October 1980, 300 at Striven's Reedbed, Steyning in September-October 1984, 200-300 at Shoreham in August-September 1985 and 200 at Gatwick in September 1988.

Communal roosts also form in winter and some sites may be occupied over a period of several years, though they are not necessarily counted annually. Certainly the species is opportunistic and will readily move 'en masse' to a more suitable site. Table 75 lists details of roosts known to have held more than 100 birds at any one time since 1975.

Year	Total	Site	Months	Habitat
1975	1000	Thakeham	January - February	Glasshouses
1976	200	Worthing	November	
	200	High Hurstwood	January - February	
1978	250-300	Rotherfield	December	Sewerage plant
	700	Shoreham	November - December	Reedbed
1979	150	Eastbourne	January	Town centre tree
1981	120	Arundel WWT	February	Reedbed
1982	140	Southease	December	Reedbed
1983	477	Framfield	January - February	Reedbed
1984	120-150	Combe Haven	November	
1985	up to 150	Combe Haven	November	
1986	200+	Gatwick	November	Bushes on roundabout
1988	132	Bognor Regis	November - December	Reedbed
1989	250	Eastbourne	November - December	Town centre trees
1991	600	Horsham	December	Acacia tree
1992	112	St John's Park, Burgess Hill	February	
	200	Eastbourne	January	Town centre trees

Table 75. Roost counts of Pied Wagtails, 1975 - 93.

As can be seen from the table, many roosts are in reedbeds. Others roost sites used in recent years, but not listed above, include a disused barge, fish cages (at Bewl Water), golf links, roof tops and the hot air ducts of large buildings. Feeding flocks of 40-80 birds are regular at a wide variety of both coastal and inland localities in winter while larger concentrations have included 147 on a playing field at Crowborough on 26 December 1987 and 150 at Lancing on 1 November 1991.

Spring passage, which may possibly commence as early as February, is less obvious than in autumn. Between mid-March and May, flocks of up to 50 occur at both coastal and inland localities. Diurnal movements may also be noted, e.g. ten flying north at Selsey Bill on 23 March 1976 and 25 flying north at Seaford Head on 5 April 1992, and roosts occasionally form, for example 60 at Striven's Reedbed on 12 May 1989.

Few concentrations have been recorded in summer but one of 100, mainly young birds, at Rotherfield sewerage plant on 30 June 1979 was noteworthy.

Of 21 Sussex-ringed birds recovered outside the county, nine were in southern England, five in northern England, three in Scotland and one in Wales. The remainder comprised one ringed at Pett in June 1910 which was killed in Beira Alta, Portugal, 1319 km SSW, the following December, one also from Pett that was ringed in June 1912 and found dead in Gironde, France, 648 km south, in October of that year, and a more recent bird, ringed at Chichester in August 1962, and found dead in Eure, France, 241 km southeast, in December 1962. Of those birds ringed outside the county and recovered in Sussex, 27 were from southern England, five from northern England and four from Scotland.

Two races of this species occur in Sussex. The breeding population is of the British and Irish race *M.a. yarelli* but birds showing the characteristics of the nominate continental race *M.a. alba* are recorded annually and have bred. Most records of the latter race are of 1-3 birds at coastal localities in spring though there were eight together at Seaford Head on 17 March 1992 and eight at Icklesham on 28 October 1993. Breeding was recorded near the Devil's Dyke in 1904 and near Coldwaltham in 1926 (des Forges & Harber) while in 1974, a 'pure' pair bred successfully in the Cuckmere Valley. A female *yarelli* bred with a male *alba* at South Stoke in 1966 and a male *alba* paired with a female *yarelli* were seen feeding young in the Cuckmere Valley in July 1986. A male *alba* present at the latter site in June-July 1988 probably bred, as it was accompanied by two young towards the end of its stay.   *Dave Smith*

Waxwing   *Bombycilla garrulus*

Status:- A very scarce winter visitor.

In most years, Waxwings are scarce winter visitors to Britain, but there are occasional eruptions from their breeding grounds in Fenno-Scandinavia which may result in the appearance of large numbers of birds in this country. While most flocks occur on the East Coast from Norfolk to Shetland, a few may reach Sussex when diminishing supplies of berries encourage birds to move southwards and westwards.

The most recent irruptions into Sussex were in the winters of 1965/66 and 1970/71, each of which is dealt with separately below.

1965/66

Birds started to arrive in Britain in mid-October, and by the end of the month large numbers were present on the East Coast. There were several hundred in Scotland and one flock of 230 in Norfolk (BWP). The first to occur in Sussex were six at Beachy Head on 14 November and the first large flock was ca. 55 at Pett Level on 21 November, increasing to 80 by the end of the month. Flocks totalling *ca.* 130 were recorded at Groombridge on 10 December. In the period 10 to 26 December, when numbers were at their peak, it is likely that at least 200 were present in the county.

Numbers fell after 26 December with the onset of cold weather and in the first three months of 1966 approximately 100 birds remained in the county at about 15 localities. The largest flocks during this period were 12 at Hailsham on 16 January, 22 at Horsham on 13 February and 20 at Haywards Heath on 6 March. The last recorded were two at Bexhill on 5 April. While the numbers in Sussex were impressive, it is estimated that there were 10,000 in Scotland at the peak of the irruption (Everett 1967).

1970/71

This irruption was on a smaller scale than that in 1965/66. The first recorded in Sussex was one at Horsham on 30 November where numbers peaked at 10-15 on 14 December. In December, birds were also seen at Gossops Green (6), Lewes (6), Milland (4) and Fernhurst (1). In early 1971, most were seen in the Crawley area. The highest counts were 30 at Ifield from 6 to 9 January and 20 at Three Bridges on 21 February. At Furnace Green there were still 12 on 5 April. While it is possible that only 30 birds were involved in this influx, a figure of at least 50 is probably more realistic.

In the remaining winters 1961/62-93/94, a total of about 50 was recorded, including ten in 1976/77 (see below), six in 1991/92 and five in both 1971/72 and 1974/75.

The only record prior to November was of ten at Rushlake Green on 1 October 1976. In both 1965/66 and 1970/71 the last birds were seen on 5 April but the latest record for the county was that of a party of 20 on the Downs near Bramber on 20 April 1941.   *Richard Kelly*

Dipper   *Cinclus cinclus*

Status:- A very rare vagrant (six records of seven individuals).

Prior to 1962 there were five records: one shot at the mouth of the River Ouse at Newhaven prior to 1821, two shot near Eastbourne *ca.* 1870, one obtained near Rye prior to October 1871, one killed on the 'salts' at St Leonards on 13 September 1884 and one at the Crumbles on 11 November 1944 (des Forges & Harber). The latter was seen in a small stream, sitting on an empty petrol can (Arnold 1945).

Since the beginning of 1962 only one has been recorded, by a pool close to the headwater of the River Dudwell, near Old Tottingworth Farm, Broad Oak on 29 December 1962.

Only the two shot near Eastbourne were racially identified, as *C.c. gularis*, the mainland British race. Despite breeding in Hampshire in 1930s and in 1991-92 (Clark & Eyre 1993) and there being 25 records in Kent, including 12 during 1960-93 (J Cantello & T Hodge *in litt.*), this delightful species remains very rare in Sussex. All the recent Kent records are of the continental 'Black-bellied' race *C.c. cinclus* which breeds as close as southern Belgium, although those seen in eastern Britain are more likely to originate from the more migratory Scandinavian populations (BWP).   *Richard Fairbank*

Wren
Troglodytes troglodytes

Status:- An abundant resident.

Despite its secretive nature, the Wren was found to be very widely distributed in the county with records during the Atlas Survey in all but 21 of the county's tetrads. Breeding was confirmed in 922 tetrads and probable or possible in 65. As the species is very vocal, with both the call and song demanding attention, birds are unlikely to be overlooked.

Wrens breed wherever there is available cover, preferring fairly dense undergrowth, but when the population is high they will readily occupy more marginal habitats. The main factor affecting the size of the population is undoubtedly the severity of the preceding winter, with those occupying the more exposed sites, such as on the Downs, showing the greatest decrease following a cold winter. For example, at Lullington Heath NNR where a CBC was carried out in each of the years 1964-65, 1971-73 and 1979-88 (Bowley 1994), no pairs were present in 1964-65, following the severe winter of 1962/63. In 1973, there were 43 pairs but in 1979, following another severe winter, there was only one pair. Numbers recovered to 51 pairs in 1981 but then crashed again to just nine pairs in 1982. There was a subsequent recovery to 38 pairs in 1984 but only 12 pairs were present in 1985 and six in 1986, following further hard winters.

Information on breeding densities for other sites in the county is limited. Shrubb reported a density of 14 pairs per km² on farmland while survey work by Bealey & Sutherland (1983) in 40 semi-natural broadleaved woodlands in West Sussex found an average density as high as 55 pairs per km². Combining the results of a number of surveys of breeding birds in defined areas carried out in the 1980s gives an average of 39 pairs per km², a figure which if applied to the whole county, indicates a population of about 150,000 pairs.

There have been no reports of increased numbers on or near the coast in spring, thus indicating that the breeding population in Britain is largely sedentary. However, numbers may increase at coastal sites in autumn, particularly Beachy Head and Selsey Bill, but despite many birds having been ringed in the county, none have been recovered abroad. The increase in the autumn is almost certainly due, therefore, to the increased population levels following the breeding season, possibly augmented by some local post-breeding dispersal.

A habitat seemingly favoured during the winter months is reedbeds as shown by counts of 200-300 at Filsham. During spells of severe weather, Wrens are well known for roosting communally. A good example of this is provided by a count of 31 birds using a House Martin nest-box at Waldron in January 1980.

All the recoveries of birds ringed in Sussex have been either within the county or elsewhere in southern England. One ringed near Battle in October 1975, was found dead in Warwickshire, 230 km northwest, and three others moved distances in excess of 100 km to Hampshire, Wiltshire and Suffolk. Of those birds ringed outside the county and recovered in Sussex, six had moved distances greater than 150 km from Cambridgeshire, Suffolk, Lincolnshire (2), Lancashire and Cumbria.   *Mike Scott-Ham*

Dunnock   *Prunella modularis*

Status:- An abundant resident.

The Dunnock is a widely distributed bird of a generally fairly secretive nature. During the Atlas Survey, it was found in 947 (94%) tetrads with breeding confirmed in 860 of these. The species' presence is betrayed by its characteristic song which is typically at its height in late winter and early spring. It is likely, therefore, that pairs were overlooked in some tetrads. Information on breeding density is limited, particularly in suburban areas. The situation is further complicated by the species' complex social system, which has been summarised in the New Atlas, and which can lead to underestimation of the population. Bealey & Sutherland (1983) in their survey of semi-natural broadleaved woodlands in West Sussex found a mean density of 5.3 pairs per km² whereas studies of farmland at the Brinsbury Estate and at Plumpton by Prater (1982, 1983b) found densities of 19 pairs and 6.2 pairs per km² respectively. Combining the results of a number of surveys of breeding birds in defined areas carried out in the 1980s gives an average of 10 pairs per km², a figure which if applied to the 947 tetrads in which the species was recorded during the Atlas Survey, indicates a county population of about 38,000 pairs compared with a national total of 2.0 million pairs (New Atlas). However, the population is probably dynamic due to its susceptibility to cold winters, as shown by a reduction in the number of occupied territories at Lullington Heath NNR from 21 in 1984 to 12 in 1985 (Bowley 1994), following the hard winter of 1984/85.

Walpole-Bond and des Forges & Harber stated that the Dunnock is a passage migrant in Sussex but ringing data suggest that the breeding population is largely sedentary. Of 145 recoveries of Sussex-ringed Dunnocks, only ten had moved more than 10 km and only three were outside the county. A record of one ringed in Vest-Agder, Norway in September 1991 and controlled at Icklesham less than one month later provides some evidence of movement into the county.   *Mike Scott-Ham*

Alpine Accentor
Prunella collaris

Status:- A very rare vagrant (four records of five individuals).

There have been four records, all prior to 1962, in March, April (2) and December (des Forges & Harber). Two were shot on the Downs near Lewes on, or immediately before, 26 December 1857. Single individuals were seen on the beach below Seaford Head between 7 and 20 April 1921, at Rottingdean on 16 March 1922 and on the cliff face at Telscombe, being viewed from the top of a low cliff, on 24 April 1955 (James & James 1955). The Seaford individual was seen on 7, 18 and 21 April and a full account is given by Walpole-Bond, who also had the good fortune to be the observer of the individual at Rottingdean the following year, although this bird is not described (Walpole-Bond).

There were just nine records of this large montane dunnock in the British Isles during 1962-94 compared with 30 before 1962. It breeds in mountains from North Africa and central Europe eastwards to Japan. Most populations are subject to local altitudinal movements, descending below the snowline in winter.
Richard Fairbank

Rufous Bush Robin
Cercotrichas galactotes

Status:- A very rare vagrant (two autumn records).

Two have been recorded, both before 1962. A male shot at Plumpton Bostall on 16 September 1854 was the first British record. It was assigned to the paler western race *C.g. galactotes* (Nichol 1908). One seen on the Kent/Sussex border at the Wicks on 12 September 1951 was the sixth British record (Milne, Palmer & Pilcher 1955).

There are just 11 records of this terrestrial chat in Britain of which only four were during 1962-94. It breeds around the western Mediterranean, from Greece to Pakistan and central Asia and in sub-Saharan Africa north of the Equator, where most winter.
Richard Fairbank

Robin
Erithacus rubecula

Status:- An abundant resident, passage migrant and winter visitor.

The Robin is one of the most familiar British birds. During the Atlas Survey, it was found in 987 tetrads, with breeding confirmed in 922 of these. Information on breeding densities is limited so making an accurate assessment of the species' status in the county difficult. However, combining the results of a number of surveys of breeding birds in defined areas carried out during the 1980s gives an average density of 48 pairs per km², a figure which if applied to the whole county, indicates a population of the order of 190,000 pairs. With a widespread distribution it is not surprising that very few tetrads lack Robins. The species can suffer from cold winters, particularly in the more exposed sites, as shown by the decrease in breeding pairs at Lullington Heath NNR from 16 in 1984 to two in 1985 (Bowley 1994), following the preceding severe winter.

Although the local breeding population is largely sedentary, ringing has shown that Robins move both into and out of the county in the autumn. Although the majority of the 250 recoveries of Sussex-ringed birds have been within the county or in southern England, others have been found in France and the Channel Islands (12), Spain (5), Portugal and Denmark (3 each), and Belgium, Finland, Morocco and the Netherlands (1 each). There are far fewer records of foreign-ringed Robins recovered in Sussex, but of these, two originated from each of the Netherlands, Poland and Sweden and singles from Belgium and Finland.

In autumn, there are frequent influxes at sites on or near the coast, with the largest numbers typically reported from Beachy Head. Day totals do not normally exceed 100 although there were 150 at Pagham Harbour on 3 October 1992 and 127 at Lancing Clump on 25 September 1993. Ringing on the Downs at Ashcombe Bottom has suggested that birds of continental origin arrive from late September onwards and continue to do so until early November. However, those caught prior to late September were judged on coloration and weight to be British-bred.   *Mike Scott-Ham*

Thrush Nightingale   *Luscinia luscinia*

Status:- A very rare vagrant (one record).

A first-year trapped at Whitbread Hollow, Beachy Head on 26-27 August and 1 September 1984 is the only record. It had been ringed in Vestfold, Norway, 1099 km northeast, on 14 August. It weighed 20.8 grams when first caught, increasing by 36% to 27.9 grams on 1 September.

There were 110 records of this earthy eastern nightingale in the British Isles during 1962-94, but just three before 1962 and only nine prior to 1970. It breeds from Denmark and extreme southern Norway to central Siberia, wintering in sub-Saharan Africa. An increase in the western part of its range is reflected by the upsurge of British records since 1970 (Dymond, Fraser & Gantlett 1989).   *Richard Fairbank*

Nightingale   *Luscinia megarhynchos*

Status:- A fairly common summer visitor and infrequently seen passage migrant.

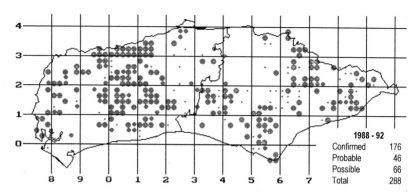

1988 - 92	
Confirmed	176
Probable	46
Possible	66
Total	288

The breeding distribution and population of the Nightingale in Sussex has been well studied with full surveys conducted between 1974 and 1977 (Merritt 1979) and in 1980 (Newnham 1981). The preferred breeding habitat was discussed by Merritt who found a common factor in all the sites in the county to be the presence of thick scrub preferably in damp, lowland areas. Downland scrub, too, is regularly used and the Atlas map shows scattered records in tetrads on the South Downs.

The Atlas Survey showed Nightingales to be present in 288 tetrads compared with 259 tetrads in 1980 and 330 tetrads in 1974-77. The Atlas figures therefore suggest that the number of tetrads supporting Nightingales has remained fairly constant since the 1970s. Analysis of the records gathered from surveys prior to the Atlas has revealed that singing male Nightingales have been recorded in 523 of the county's 1008 tetrads, of which 290 were in West Sussex and 233 in East Sussex. Only one new tetrad was added during the Atlas Survey.

The distribution of the occupied tetrads was remarkably similar to that of the two previous surveys. Although Nightingales were widespread across the county, there were three areas where they were most frequently encountered. In West Sussex the best area was west and south of Horsham embracing Loxwood, Plaistow and Wisborough Green and extending southward through the Arun Valley towards Arundel. In East Sussex, tetrads bordering the Cuckmere Valley and between Hastings, Battle and the Kent border held most Nightingales. There were three 10-km squares in which no birds were recorded: SZ89 (Selsey peninsula), TQ60 (Pevensey Levels) and TQ91 (Winchelsea). All these lack suitable breeding habitat.

The population of Nightingales in Sussex is impossible to extrapolate from either the Atlas work or from the annual records submitted to the Society. In the years 1968 to 1990 between 55 and 124 singing males were recorded annually with no change observed during the years of the Atlas fieldwork. However, during the Nightingale surveys far higher numbers were reported with 664 in 1976 and 858 in 1980. In both these survey years Sussex held about 20% of the national Nightingale population and was second only to Kent in the numbers present (Davis 1982).

The Nightingale is not often observed on passage, thus in most springs the first birds are heard at breeding sites where the range of first recorded dates is 2 April (1966, Milton Hide) until late April; the average during 1962-93 being 13 April. Annually small numbers are recorded on spring passage at coastal sites and these have included the earliest county records at Littlehampton and Church Norton on 21 March and 29 March 1988 respectively.

During the autumn the species is infrequently recorded and it is probably overlooked because of its skulking habits. Most have occurred at Beachy Head where the small numbers recorded peak during August and the highest count was eight on 13 August 1976. A small autumn passage has been demonstrated by ringing at Elms Farm, Icklesham where the largest daily count was seven in both August 1991 and 1993. The latest records are of two at Beachy Head on 1 October 1972, and singles there on 7 October 1985, at Handcross on 10 October 1947 and at North Bersted on 19 October 1943, the latter listed by Hudson (1973).

Ringing has shown that some birds return to the same site in successive springs but has added little else. Although several hundred Nightingales have been ringed in Sussex, there are only three recoveries from outside the county, two in Hampshire and one in Berkshire. A bird ringed at Bedford in May 1981 was found freshly dead at Crawley on 14 April 1984 and a juvenile ringed in Somerset on 6 August 1976 was found dead in Sussex a week later on 13 August.

John Newnham

Bluethroat   *Luscinia svecica*

Status:- A very scarce spring and autumn visitor (113 individuals recorded).

Thirty-four were recorded prior to 1962, six in spring and 28 in autumn (des Forges & Harber). Four in spring were in 1958; three (including two males) at Pett between 1 and 13 April and a male at Church Norton on 21 April, all being the 'white-spotted' race *L.s. cyanecula*. The other spring records, an adult female obtained in Worthing in April 1853 and a male at the Midrips from 7 to 9 April 1953, were of the 'red-spotted' race *L.s. svecica*. Autumn records were between 31 August (at Langney Fort in 1922) and 14 October (Pagham Harbour North Wall in 1959), with most in September (including two at Shoreham-by-Sea rubbish dump in 1959). One killed by a cat at St Leonards on 22 September 1912 (Ticehurst 1912) and a male by the western sea wall at Thorney Island on 4 September 1950 were *cyanecula*, all others racially identified being attributable to *svecica*. An adult male on the Downs between Stanmer Park and Brighton was "knocked down by a boy with a stick" on 1 October 1862 and is in the Booth Museum (BoMNH 208199). One at Ditchling Beacon on 3 September 1961 was the first inland record for the county.

Seventy-nine have been seen since the beginning of 1962, with a pronounced peak in the late 1960s but only 13 during 1978-94 (fig. 80).

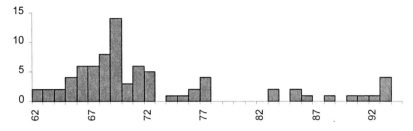

Figure 80. Annual totals of Bluethroats, 1962 - 94.

Since the beginning of 1962 the earliest in spring were a male at Chichester Gravel Pits on 4 April 1965, and females at Cow Gap, Beachy Head on 23 April 1966 and Cuckmere Haven on 30 April 1971. The latest spring records are females at Seaford Head on 25 May 1991, Icklesham on 26 May 1988 and in a garden adjoining Hove Cemetery on 27 May 1971. Whereas less than 5% of the 1960s records were in spring, nearly 20% of those during the 1970s and 31% of subsequent records have been, but this is due mainly to a dramatic decrease in autumn records (fig. 81). One trapped at Ivy Lake, Chichester on 24 August 1970 is the earliest autumn arrival, with eight others since 1962 arriving in late August (from 27th), 49 in September, six in the first week of October, three in mid-October (including one at Icklesham in 1992 between the 18th and 30th), one at Glyne Gap on 28 October 1969 and one at Ham Farm, Sidlesham on 2-3 November 1968.

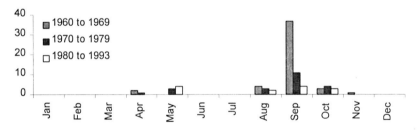

Figure 81. Cumulative monthly arrivals of Bluethroats, 1962 - 94.

Twenty-four have been recorded at Beachy Head since the beginning of 1962 (the most recent in May 1985), ten at Pagham Harbour/Sidlesham, nine at Chichester, seven at Icklesham and Pett (six of which were during 1988-93), six in the Brighton area, and five around Bexhill and Hastings (all in 1969). Three were recorded at the Crumbles (during 1962-64), in the lower Cuckmere Valley (two in 1971 and one in 1977) and at the Midrips (during 1967-69) with two in the Rye area (14 September 1965 and 16-17 September 1967) and at Seaford Head (5 October 1968 and 25 May 1991). Other records not referred to above are from Arlington Reservoir (20 September 1972), Cissbury Ring (28 August 1965), Selsey (11 September 1960), Thorney (20 September 1963) and more interestingly south of Chantry Hill (29 August 1962) and at Cowbeach (29-30 August 1966). Most occurrences have been of single individuals but six were found at Beachy Head on 20 September 1969, including three together east of Belle Tout Wood, with two trapped at Ivy Lake, Chichester on 12 September 1967, two seen at Sidlesham Ferry on 7-8 September 1968 and two at Beachy Head on 10 September 1968.

Although most recent records were indeterminate, both 'red-spotted' and 'white-spotted' races have been recorded in the county since 1962. Males at Beachy Head in 1975 and Belle Tout, Beachy Head in 1985 (coincidentally both on 18 May) and at Woodingdean on 17 May 1985 (sadly dead, having collided with a window) showed characteristics of *svecica* while summer plumaged males at Pagham Harbour North Wall on 7 September 1964 and Rye Harbour on 14 September 1965 showed characteristics of *cyanecula*, as did the two at Sidlesham in September 1968 referred to above.

Variable numbers of this species are recorded in Britain each year, with between 40 and 251 annually during 1986-92 (Fraser & Ryan 1994). While numbers in spring have generally increased (including an unprecedented 590 in 1985), autumn records have declined since the 1960s (Dymond, Fraser & Gantlett 1989). The race *svecica* breeds from Norway across Siberia to western Alaska wintering from the western Sahel to South East Asia while *cyanecula* breeds from Spain to central and eastern Europe mostly wintering in the Sahel, although some over winter in the Mediterranean basin (BWP).

Richard Fairbank

Black Redstart   *Phoenicurus ochruros*

Status:- A rare resident, fairly common passage migrant and scarce winter visitor.

The Black Redstart is one of a number of species to have colonised Britain in recent times. Although isolated instances had occurred previously, it was first proved to breed regularly in this country on the cliffs between Hastings and Fairlight Glen, where one or two pairs nested annually during 1923-25 (Calvert, Fitter & Hale 1944). The 1930s was a period of sporadic breeding in Sussex and it was not until the early 1940s that the species appeared to establish itself firmly. Since that time, the majority of breeding records have been in the coastal towns between Worthing and Hastings, although single pairs bred at Gatwick and Ifield in 1986 and at Crawley in 1987. The Atlas map shows both the results of the Atlas Survey and also those tetrads (as open circles) where the species was recorded in the period 1976-87 but not in 1988-92.

The largest numbers occurred in the immediate post-war years, for example seven pairs in 1947 and ten pairs plus an additional nine singing males in 1948. A BTO survey in 1977 located two successful pairs, two unmated singing males in the Brighton area and another possible pair on the cliffs to the east of Hastings (Porter 1978). More recently, the population has fluctuated at a level below five pairs, with no proof of breeding since 1989. This may merely reflect the fact that pairs are easily overlooked in coastal towns, where the male's song may be lost in background traffic noise. Alternatively, it may be part of apparent thinning of the nucleus population in London and the southeast counties which has coincided with a strengthening of Black Redstart numbers in the Midlands and East Anglia (New Atlas).

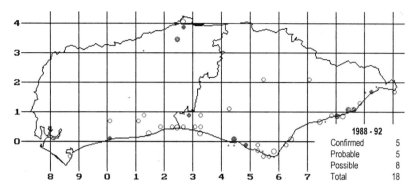

During the autumn, birds are noted from July onwards but few are recorded until mid-October. Most sightings are on the coast, with Beachy Head a favoured haunt. Counts at this site of 25 on 19 October 1960 and 27 on 19 October 1986 are the largest day totals for the county. In most years, the total for October is less than 50, but 168 were recorded in 1984 and 105 in 1988. Passage continues into November when typically about 20 are recorded, although there were 70 in 1984 and 68 in 1982.

Black Redstarts are regularly recorded during December-February, again mainly at coastal sites such as Selsey Bill, Shoreham Harbour, Brighton Marina and Newhaven. Recently, numbers in January and February have been low, with frequently less than five reported, although there seems to have been something of an upsurge in the mid-1980s with double figure counts in several years, including a maximum of 19 in January 1985.

Spring passage is generally evident from mid-March to early May but its commencement is sometimes obscured by the presence of overwintering birds. Most reports are of ones and twos at coastal sites but larger numbers may occur, especially at Beachy Head, where there were 18 on 25 March 1972 and 12 on 4 April 1971 and 14 April 1973.

Few Black Redstarts have been ringed in Sussex but three of these have been recovered outside the county. A nestling ringed at Pett in July 1947 was subsequently found to be a male and breeding at Dover, Kent in June 1952. One bird ringed at Hodcombe, Beachy Head in October 1985 was found dead eight days later 475 km west on St Marys, Isles of Scilly, and one ringed near Beachy Head in April 1974 was found dead 667 km southeast in Berne, Switzerland two months later. *Mike Scott-Ham*

Redstart *Phoenicurus phoenicurus*

Status:- A scarce summer visitor and fairly common passage migrant.

The Redstart has been the subject of two county surveys. The first survey, which was never fully documented, took place between 1967-69 and located between 40 and 60 pairs in 1967 and 1968. The population, however, appeared to crash in 1969, at the same time as that of the Whitethroat, and only 22 pairs were found. A more comprehensive survey in 1982 located 62 pairs with a distribution similar to that of the earlier survey (Houghton 1983). The Atlas map shows that the bulk of the population is centred on Ashdown Forest and records suggest the presence of up to 90 pairs in the area. Elsewhere, there may be ten pairs in the extreme northeast of the county, close to the border of Kent, and a mere handful of pairs on the commons of West Sussex. The map also shows, as open circles, tetrads where Redstarts were recorded breeding during 1976-87 but not during the Atlas Survey. The total county population is currently probably no more than 110 pairs, very similar to the 100 pairs estimated by Houghton. Redstarts are clearly vulnerable to disasters on their African wintering grounds as reflected in the substantial decline in 1969. More recently, however, the county population appears to have remained fairly stable although there is much suitable habitat for expansion, should numbers increase.

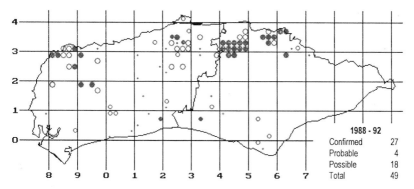

	1988 - 92	
	Confirmed	27
	Probable	4
	Possible	18
	Total	49

The preferred habitat is old open parkland with scattered large beech, Scots pine or silver birch with an understorey of bracken, heather and bilberry. Redstarts begin to arrive on territory from early to mid-April and peak counts suggest that most males have arrived by early May. The species nests mainly in holes in old trees, although since the storm in 1987 several nest sites have been found in the root systems of uprooted trees. Redstarts also readily take to nest-boxes in suitable areas and pairs are occasionally double-brooded. In Sussex, the species is loosely colonial with each pair tending to be within earshot of the next, although a few isolated pairs may also be found. The males of isolated pairs sing less frequently and it is possible that a few may have been overlooked in the surveys. Males sing primarily from high song posts, normally in the top canopy, and the song although not strong can carry a surprising distance.

Redstarts are fairly common passage migrants, particularly in the autumn. The earliest ever recorded in spring were singles at Bognor on 13 March 1993, Pulborough Brooks on 17 March 1992 and at Church Norton on 18 March 1972. During 1970-93 first dates fell between 13 March and 14 April with the average 3 April. The total number recorded in the spring is normally less than 100, although occasional influxes may occur such as the 88 reported between

23-25 April 1989. Few are recorded at the coast after mid-May so the singles at Fairlight and Pett on 19 June 1992 either represented very late arrivals or early post-breeding dispersal.

Many more are seen on autumn passage which normally commences towards the end of July. Peak counts occur from mid-August to mid-September, particularly during spells of easterly winds, and in a typical autumn 200-300 are reported. The highest day count is 85 at Beachy Head on 12 September 1965 and 406 in 1992 is the highest total for the whole autumn. During 1972-93 last dates for departure fell between 8 October and 29 November with the average 2 November. Singles at Chailey Common on 27 November 1982, Sidlesham on 28 November 1980 and Pett Level on 29 November 1989 are the latest county records.

Of the 13 recoveries of Sussex-ringed birds, two were found in southern England, two in northern England, three went to Spain, two each to Portugal and Morocco, and singles to France and Germany. One ringed as a nestling at Marley Common in June 1978 was found at Azemmour, Morocco, 2067 km SSW, the following April. There have been only four recoveries in the county of Redstarts ringed elsewhere, of which two came from Scotland, one from Essex and one from Kent. One recent breeding study in Sussex showed that three adults retrapped in their nesting territories had been originally ringed as nestlings in the same general area, indicating a degree of natal site fidelity in the Sussex stock.   *Mike Scott-Ham*

Whinchat   *Saxicola rubetra*

Status:- A rare summer visitor and fairly common passage migrant.

Although Walpole-Bond reported some regular breeding sites on the south slope of the Downs between Worthing and Eastbourne, on rough ground near Chichester, and in Ashdown Forest, the species has long ceased to nest regularly in the county. Indeed, during the period of the Atlas Survey only one pair was confirmed breeding, at Amberley Wild Brooks in 1991. This was the first breeding record since 1980 when a pair probably bred on Brede Levels. Although a single pair could easily be missed, it is unlikely that Whinchats breed in the county on anything more than the odd occasion. This decline, that has occurred nationally, has been attributed to loss of habitat resulting from new farming practices (New Atlas). However, in Sussex there are still plenty of apparently suitable areas for nesting, particularly the bracken covered parts of the commons in the northwest of the county and on Ashdown Forest.

Despite being only an occasional breeder, the species is a regular passage migrant both in the spring and more especially in the autumn. During 1970-93, first dates in spring varied between 24 March and 1 May with the average 12 April. One at Weir Wood Reservoir on 17 March 1968 is the earliest county record. Numbers reported on spring passage are typically in double-figures but in May 1991 an exceptional 250 were noted in the county, including 32 at Selsey Bill on 18 May. Large numbers have been recorded in other springs (e.g. in 1948, 1965 and 1972) but with the decline in the British population, the totals recorded on spring passage are generally falling. Late migrants may occur into early June.

Return passage may start in late June but generally it peaks in late August to mid-September. The largest fall recorded was on 21 September 1980 when, after a night of southeast winds and rain, between 500 and 1000 were at Beachy Head and 100 at both Pett Level and Seaford Head with 130 seen at Sidlesham Ferry on the following day. In other years the high counts were 250 and 300 reported from Beachy Head on 30 August 1970 and 17 August 1971 respectively, *ca.* 100 also at Beachy Head on 10 September 1982 and 89 at Sompting Brooks on 5 September 1991. Although there has been a marked decline in the number of Whinchats since Shrubb, the following table of 3-year moving averages for autumn records suggest a recent increase in autumn numbers.

82-84	83-85	84-86	85-87	86-88	87-89	88-90	89-91	90-92	91-93
493	417	492	647	697	648	592	687	912	1244

During 1970-93, last dates for departure fell between 14 October and 2 December with the average 29 October. Singles at Pagham Harbour on 28 November 1974 and Shoreham on 2 December 1981 are the latest county records.

Recoveries of Sussex-ringed Whinchats refer entirely to birds that had been caught in the autumn on passage. These include one ringed near Beachy Head in August 1968 that was killed in Cadiz, Spain, 1637 km SSW, in October 1969; another from near Beachy Head in August 1970 that was found dead near Stirling, 667 km NNW, in June 1973; one ringed at Ashcombe in September 1982 that was found dead in Yon, France, 405 km southeast, in April 1983; and one trapped at Icklesham in September 1987 that was controlled in North Yorkshire, 410 km NNW, in May 1989. *Mike Scott-Ham*

Stonechat   *Saxicola torquata*

Status:- A scarce resident and partial migrant.

The Stonechat was the subject of breeding surveys in 1962, 1963, 1964, 1969 and 1971 and in these years efforts were made to obtain coverage of all known and likely breeding sites in the county. In the years 1967, 1968 and 1970, selected breeding areas only were surveyed (Hughes & Shrubb 1974). There has been no survey since but, as numbers fluctuate widely from year to year, depending on the severity of the previous winter, a full county survey on an occasional basis is unlikely to be a reliable indicator of trends within the Sussex population. More meaningful data would be obtained by censusing the main breeding areas within the county. The species is widely reported during the year and many breeding records are submitted. Annual totals of occupied territories for the period 1962 to 1993 are given in fig. 82. These have varied between 85 in 1983 and just 15 in 1986 but as the species can be triple-brooded, the breeding population has the potential to rapidly recover from setbacks. Shrubb's prediction of a long-term decline does not appear to have materialised; indeed the number of pairs that he quotes for Ashdown Forest (27) has been exceeded on several occasions since, for example in 1990 when 44 pairs were present.

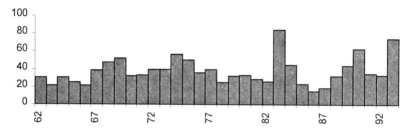

Figure 82. Annual totals of occupied Stonechat territories, 1962 - 93.

The Atlas map overestimates the distribution of breeding pairs in any one year, as it incorporates all records for 1988-92 and, as open circles, additional tetrads with breeding records for 1976-87. It does, however, reflect the availability of suitable habitat within the county. This is principally heathland with scattered clumps of gorse, as in Ashdown Forest, the species' stronghold in the county. Pairs may also breed in a wide variety of other habitats such as young conifer plantations and gorse brakes on the Downs, as at Beachy Head, the species' other main stronghold in Sussex.

Post-breeding dispersal may commence in early July, as shown by records of a male at Chichester Harbour on 4 July 1979 and a female the same day at Cissbury. From mid-September to mid-October there is a marked autumn passage, normally involving between 100 and 200 birds, the majority of which occur at coastal localities. The largest numbers recorded in recent years have included 43 at Beachy Head on 8 October 1978, 28 at Selsey on 10 October 1993, 27 at Thorney Island on 3 October 1993 and 16 at Seaford Head on 2 October 1992, while inland, there were 14 between Cissbury and Chanctonbury Ring on 14 October 1977 and 16 at Pulborough Brooks on 24

October 1991. Varying numbers remain to winter, depending upon the severity of the weather. In 1984/85, for example, totals of 114 and 74 were recorded in November and December respectively, but only 46 in January and ten in February, following a cold spell early in the New Year. By contrast, numbers remained remarkably constant in 1992/93 with 73 recorded in November, 77 in December, 78 in January and 71 in February. Traditional wintering areas that may hold double-figure numbers of Stonechats are Combe Haven, Pevensey Levels and Thorney Island. However, pairs and singles regularly winter along the whole of the county's coastline. If the season remains mild, then several may stay on inland heaths with males singing and defending a territory as early as January.

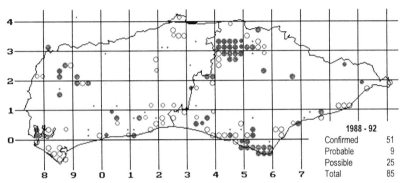

1988 - 92	
Confirmed	51
Probable	9
Possible	25
Total	85

There appears to be no obvious spring passage of Stonechats in Sussex, but this may be masked by the appearance of migrants in coastal areas where pairs have already established territories.

Among the recoveries of Sussex-ringed Stonechats are several that give some indication of the species' wintering area. Four were killed in Spain and one reported from Algeria, all between late October and January. One of those, found near Barcelona, Spain, had been ringed as a nestling near Midhurst in July 1971.

A female or first-winter showing the characters of one or other of the eastern races *S.t. maura* or *stejnegeri* was recorded at Selsey Bill on 8-9 October 1994.   *Mike Scott-Ham*

Wheatear   *Oenanthe oenanthe*

Status:- A very scarce summer visitor and common passage migrant.

In Sussex the Wheatear has declined catastrophically since 1938 when Walpole-Bond described it as one of the typical summer birds of the Downs and quite widely distributed along the coast. A survey in 1962-64 found just 11 pairs on the Downs, about 20 on the shingle areas from Rye Harbour to the Midrips, four on the Crumbles and single pairs at Shoreham Beach and Newhaven Tide Mills (Shrubb 1965). The Atlas map, which shows the tetrads in which Wheatears were recorded during the Atlas Survey and also those (as open circles) in which birds were found during 1976-87 but not during 1988-92, confirms that this decline has continued. Habitat loss is most likely to blame, resulting from an increase in development and disturbance of coastal areas and from a decline in sheep and rabbit grazing on the Downs. Now breeding only takes place regularly at Rye Harbour LNR, where most pairs nest in artificial burrows and benefit from protection provided for breeding Little Terns. Here the population has fluctuated between three and 17 pairs over the period 1970-93.

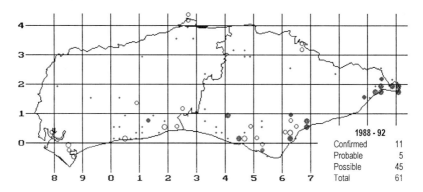

	1988 - 92
Confirmed	11
Probable	5
Possible	45
Total	61

The Wheatear is one of the first summer visitors to arrive and for many birdwatchers it is the herald of spring. During 1962-93, the earliest recorded were singles at Beeding Brooks on 21 February 1971 and at West Wittering on 28 February 1977, although the earliest ever was one at the Midrips on 13 February 1934. The average arrival date during 1962-93 was 11 March, but since the late 1980s there has been a tendency for the first arrivals to be a few days earlier during the first week of March. Each spring there are days on which large numbers of Wheatears occur, when birds may be found scattered along the whole coastline. Such arrivals, which have been noted as early as 9 March, may occur at any time through to early May. The largest so far recorded were 261 on 26 April 1977, 207 on 2 April 1986 and 151 on 10 April 1984. Counts of up to 40 at favoured localities are typical but larger falls have included 130 in the Pagham Harbour area on 26 April 1977, 86 at Ferring on 12 April 1984 and, at Beachy Head, 120 on 26 April 1977 and 30 April 1988 and 100 on 15 April 1973. Few are normally reported inland during spring, so counts of seven at Ifield Mill Pond and 11 at Gatwick Airport on 2 April 1986 were noteworthy. Passage may continue throughout May and into early June. Some of these later birds have shown the characteristics of the larger and brighter Greenland race *O.o. leucorhoa,* the occurrence of which is confirmed by measurements of singles trapped near Lewes on 7 May 1976 and on 10 September 1977.

A few juveniles may be recorded from early July onwards but the main return passage starts at the end of that month or in early August. The largest numbers occur between mid-August and late September, especially at Beachy Head, where counts have included an exceptional 500 on 17 August 1971 and 21 September 1980 (c.f. Whinchat), 250 on 30 August 1970 and 23 August 1971 and 240 on 29 August 1992 (when there were also 120 at Church Norton, 104 at Littlehampton West Beach and 81 at Seaford Head).

Elsewhere, there were 120 at Selsey Bill on 28 August 1982, 118 at Sompting on 5 September 1991 and 115 at Cissbury on 20 August 1984.

Last departure dates are in late October or more typically in the first two weeks of November, the average during 1965-93 being 10 November. Singles were seen on the Downs on 6 January 1912 and at Cuckmere Haven on 26 December 1948 and one wintered at Northpoint, Rye Harbour in 1960/61. More recently, there have been nine records for December-January as follows:

1962: One at Black Rock, Brighton on 8 and 10 December.
1963: One at Portobello on 7-8 December.
1969: One at East Head, West Wittering on 22 January.
       One at North Stoke on 30 December.
1978: One at Pagham Harbour on 17 December.
1982: One at Littlehampton on 2 December.
       One at Shoreham Fort from 27 November to 2 February 1983.
1983: One at New Salts Farm, Lancing on 3 December.
1987: One at Littlehampton Golf Course from 26 to 31 December.

Few Wheatears are ringed annually in Sussex but of seven recoveries to date, three have been overseas. One ringed near Eastbourne in 1970 was killed in Logrono, Spain, 969 km south, two weeks later; a long-lived individual trapped at Beachy Head in August 1971 was reported killed in Navarra, Spain, 981 km south, in January 1981 and a nestling ringed at Rye Harbour in May 1991 was found dead at Amellago, Morocco, 2156 km SSW, the following March. One ringed on Fair Isle in July 1956 was recovered at Beachy Head, 985 km south, in September of that year.   *Dr B J Yates & Paul James*

Pied Wheatear   *Oenanthe pleschanka*

Status:- A very rare vagrant (one record).
    A male present on the beach immediately west of Newhaven Harbour from 7 to 9 July 1990 (*Birding World* 3: 230, *Brit. Birds* 84: plates 98-99, Parmenter 1992, Watson 1992) appeared during unseasonal weather (strong, cold southerly winds and occasional mist).

There were just over 30 records of this dark eastern wheatear in the British Isles during 1962-94 but this is the only record for July. It is the eastern counterpart of the Black-eared Wheatear, breeding from south-eastern Europe to Mongolia and wintering in East Africa. *Richard Fairbank*

Black-eared Wheatear   *Oenanthe hispanica*

Status:- A very rare vagrant (two spring records).
First recorded in 1987, one was also seen in 1988:

1987: A female opposite Hodcombe, Beachy Head on 31 May.
1988: A male on the dam at Bewl Water on 5 May (Baines 1988) was seen in both Sussex and Kent.

The Bewl Water individual was ascribed to the buffier western Mediterranean race *O.h. hispanica*. One day stays in spring are the norm for this species.
There were just under 40 records of this slim, pale wheatear in the British Isles during 1962-94. It breeds from northwest Africa and Iberia east to Iran and winters in the Sahel. *Richard Fairbank*

Desert Wheatear   *Oenanthe deserti*

Status:- A very rare vagrant (three records).
One was recorded before 1962 (des Forges & Harber), a female at Selsey Bill from 28 October to 8 November 1960. It was visibly weaker at the end of its stay (*SxBR* 13: 18*)*.
Two have been recorded since 1962:

1966: A male on the beach below Cow Gap, Beachy Head from 17 to 21 April.
1989: A first-winter or female at Selsey Bill from 1 to 6 November.

The individual at Beachy Head appeared to be in poor condition with rather dishevelled plumage (Quinn & Clement 1972), while that in 1989 was immaculate (*Brit. Birds* 83: plate 197).
There were 35 records of this black-tailed wheatear in the British Isles during 1962-94. It breeds from northwest Africa to Mongolia, wintering around the Sahara, in Arabia and Pakistan. *Richard Fairbank*

Blue Rock Thrush   *Monticola solitarius*

Status:- One record, presumed to be of an escape from captivity.
A male by the sea wall at Rye Harbour on 10 August 1977 is the only record. It has not been accepted as a wild bird due to the high possibility of escape at the time, a fate not shared by two more recent records in Britain, in June 1985 and June 1987, which have been formally accepted (*BOURC* 1993a).
It breeds from northwest Africa and Iberia to Japan. Mediterranean populations are partially migratory, although those in Asia winter south to Indonesia. *Richard Fairbank*

White's Thrush   *Zoothera dauma*

Status:- A very rare vagrant (one old record).

An immature male found dead in the garden of 27 Wilbury Road, Hove on 26 September 1898 is in the Booth Museum (BoMNH 208077). It was reported to have been present on and off for the previous two or three weeks (Walpole-Bond).

There were 17 records of this strikingly patterned, but skulking, large thrush in the British Isles during 1962-94 compared with 31 before 1962. It breeds across Siberia wintering in South East Asia. There are other races in the Himalayas, southern India, Japan and Indonesia (the latter sometimes considered specifically distinct).   *Richard Fairbank*

Ring Ouzel   *Turdus torquatus*

Status:- A passage migrant, scarce in spring, often fairly common but local in autumn.

Ring Ouzels from both the British and Scandinavian populations regularly occur on passage in lowland England, where the species does not breed. Gilbert White (1789) was the first to refer to Ring Ouzels on the sheep downs of Hampshire and Sussex. Nowadays, more are recorded in Sussex than in any other county in southern England, most being found on the chalk of the eastern South Downs (Leverton 1990, 1993).

Excluding singles at Mannings Heath on 2 February 1905, Exceat on 9 February 1986 and Hastings on 16 February 1948, the earliest spring migrant for the county was at Beachy Head on 5 March 1967. Normally, it is the end of that month before the first are seen. During 1970-93, first dates in spring varied between 9 February and 15 April with the average 25 March. In some years there are no records until well into April, and numbers are often highest in the second half of the month, tailing off into May. As nesting by the British population is well underway by that time (Appleyard 1994) these later migrants are probably bound for Scandinavia. Two in a Hove park from 26 to 29 May 1984 were latest of all, apart from a pair on Graffham Down on 5 June 1971, recalling old breeding records from lowland England.

Over the period 1962-93, spring passage averaged 20 birds a year, ranging from five in 1982 to an exceptional 67 in 1989. Up to ten were seen together in that year, whereas most spring records are of one or two birds.

The earliest in autumn was on 16 August 1964, at Beachy Head. Usually, the first are seen from early to mid-September, and there is often a smaller peak towards the end of that month. However, by far the largest falls (almost certainly of Scandinavian birds) occur in October. On 9 October 1966, a remarkable 200 were seen at Beachy Head. Other major falls took place on and after 12 October 1988, with over 400 birds reported during the next few days, and between 11 and 14 October 1991, with over 250 birds including 80 at Beachy Head. A few are seen until early November in most years, with occasional singles later in the month. Of seven stragglers in December, the last was at Wilmington on 26 December 1992, but overwintering has not been noted.

During 1962-93, autumn passage averaged 138 birds annually, with extremes of 20 in 1978 and almost 500 in 1988. No other English county can rival such figures, and it seems likely that the South Downs are used as a staging area by Ring Ouzels of both the British and Scandinavian populations, though numbers of the latter are strongly influenced by weather conditions such as easterly winds.

An analysis of Sussex records (Leverton 1990) found that 75% of spring records and 87% of autumn ones were from the Downs, and almost all the remainder were from the coastal plain. Records of flocks are no longer predominantly from Beachy Head as was noted by Shrubb, perhaps because of wider coverage and also the spread of berry-bearing scrub since the 1960s.

Ring Ouzels frequently stop over for several days in favoured areas. At one such site near Lewes, habitat selection, behaviour, sex ratio and weights of trapped birds were studied (Leverton 1993). A nestling ringed in Gwent, South Wales, was controlled in September at the Lewes site, and a male from a flock of ten ringed on 23 October 1987 was found next breeding season in Norway. Birds ringed at Beachy Head have been recovered in France, Spain and Morocco.   *Roy Leverton*

Blackbird   *Turdus merula*

Status:- An abundant resident and winter visitor; perhaps a passage migrant.

This is the most ubiquitous, and perhaps the most numerous, breeding bird in Sussex. Deciduous woodland and suburban gardens suit it best, but it thrives in town centres, and also in farmland, provided there are a few hedges and copses. Even treeless high downland supports a few pairs, which nest almost on the ground in stunted gorse or on ledges in farm outbuildings. During the Atlas Survey, the species was found in 997 (99%) tetrads, with breeding confirmed in 952 and possible in 45.

Shrubb suggested that the average breeding density of Blackbirds in Sussex farmland was about 35 pairs per km², based on the limited information then available. During the 1980s, some excellent censuses of breeding birds in defined areas were carried out by the Society's members, covering a wide range of woodland, downland and agricultural habitats. Combining the results gives an average of 34 pairs of Blackbirds per km², a density almost identical to Shrubb's figure. Applying this over the whole County would give a population estimate of around 135,000 pairs, rounded up to 150,000 to allow for higher densities in suburban areas. As Blackbirds are less affected than other thrushes by hard winters, the Sussex population is relatively stable, with no present evidence for any long-term trends or noticeable fluctuations.

Sussex resident Blackbirds are very sedentary, hardly ever moving more than 5 km from where they were ringed. They may, however, make local seasonal movements. Near the Downs, many leave suburban gardens in autumn to feast on the berry crop in downland scrub; in hard weather the more exposed territories may be abandoned in favour of lower and more sheltered ground, including orchards with windfalls.

In winter, the resident population is augmented by immigrants from the Continent. Arrivals begin in early October, continuing well into November and even December in some years. Immigration tends to be unspectacular. Peak numbers at migration sites on the coast or Downs are between 40-80 birds a day in most years, and rarely exceed 100. By contrast, arrivals in Kent may reach ten times these figures (Taylor, Davenport & Flegg 1981).

Ringing shows that most immigrants originate from similar latitudes in western Germany, Belgium and the Netherlands, with fewer from Denmark and southern Sweden. Norwegian and Finnish birds reach Sussex more rarely. On downland in the Lewes area, foreign immigrants were estimated to comprise roughly a third of all Blackbirds present in autumn and winter. Most were first-year birds of either sex. They were indistinguishable from the local residents in plumage and behaviour mixing freely with them when feeding or roosting. Numbers of immigrants declined rapidly at the end of February (Leverton 1986).

Although wintering immigrants doubtless spread out after arriving, there is little evidence that the Blackbird is a passage migrant in the strict sense to Sussex. Whereas ringing clearly reveals a strong through passage and onward movement the same winter by Song Thrushes, Redwings and Fieldfares, nothing similar has been recorded for Blackbirds. Nor do they participate much in the cold weather movements undertaken by other thrush species.

Roy Leverton

Black-throated Thrush   *Turdus ruficollis*

Status:- A very rare vagrant (one old record).

A male shot near Lewes on 23 December 1868 was the first British record (Walpole-Bond) and is in the Booth Museum (BoMNH 208005).

There were 30 records of this greyish thrush in the British Isles during 1962-94 and three before. All but one were of the more northern and western black-throated race *T.r. atrogularis* although an individual of the nominate red-throated race was seen in Essex in autumn 1994. The species breeds in central Siberia wintering mainly from Iraq to Burma.   *Richard Fairbank*

Fieldfare
Turdus pilaris

Status:- A common passage migrant and winter visitor.

The first Fieldfares normally arrive in Sussex in mid to late September or occasionally in early October. During 1970-93, first dates varied between 6 August and 8 October with the average 15 September. An adult watched feeding all day at Beachy Head on 6 August 1983 was by far the earliest autumn record. However, in many years a lone Fieldfare or small party of up to seven arrives in Sussex at any time from late August onwards. There is almost invariably a gap, sometimes of several weeks, between such wandering birds and the start of passage proper.

The main arrivals do not begin until mid or late October, and continue throughout November. After this there is no clear pattern, as large flocks of Fieldfares may come or go at any time of the winter. Both the numbers present in Sussex, and their distribution, vary from year to year, and during the course of the same winter. The Downs are favoured in some autumns with an abundant crop of haws, but after these have been eaten the birds move on. Tall sheltered downland scrub, as in Ashcombe Bottom, may be used for roosting by birds which have spent the day elsewhere.

Especially in mid-winter, the greatest numbers are reported from the river levels. Sites such as Pulborough Brooks, Waltham Brooks, Amberley Wild Brooks, the Adur Levels, Glynde Reach and Pevensey Levels regularly hold up to 1000 Fieldfares or more. Although observers tend to report only the largest flocks, this distribution pattern is probably accurate. At a guess, the wintering population at any one time may range from 5000-30,000 birds.

Between December and February, large movements of Fieldfares may occur during cold weather, especially when anticyclonic conditions affect most of southern England and adjacent parts of the Continent. The most spectacular was on 16 February 1969, when 15,000 moved west in a snowstorm at Beachy Head; more recent examples include 1380 west in one hour at Selsey on 11 February 1991, this being the usual direction. Ringing has shown that, even in mid-winter, Fieldfares often leave Sussex and cross the Channel into northwest France to escape harsh weather.

Like Redwings, they may winter in very different areas from one year to the next, as shown by a bird ringed at Burgess Hill on 12 January 1963, which was shot almost exactly one year later in Bulgaria. Breeding season recoveries have come from Norway (3) and Finland (2).

Shrubb considered return passage in spring to be less than well-documented in Sussex. Rather, it seems to be ill-defined. As flocks gradually move northwards and eastwards towards the end of winter, Fieldfare numbers in Sussex often rise in late February and March. The highest reported roost count was of 2000 at Hastings on 25 February 1984. Flocks of 500 are not unusual in March, and in some years good numbers are still present until mid-April, although 800 in St Leonard's Forest on 8 April 1984 was exceptional. During 1965-93, last dates varied between 28 March and 5 June with the average 2 May. The latest county records are those of one at East Head on 31 May 1992 and three at Sompting on 5 June 1977. *Roy Leverton*

Song Thrush

Turdus philomelos

Status:- An abundant resident and partial migrant; abundant passage migrant and very common winter visitor.

Because the Song Thrush breeds in almost every Sussex tetrad, the Atlas map is of little help at showing local variations in density. Renowned for its ability to smash snail shells, and so exploit a source of food denied to other thrushes, ought not the Song Thrush to be commonest on the Downs, where such molluscs are most numerous? Feeding studies have shown, however, that snails only become an important part of their diet outside the breeding season, in late summer and winter (New Atlas) and, in fact, Song Thrush densities are highest in the Weald. Unlike Blackbirds, they are relatively scarce breeders in open downland even where there is scrub. The similarity of their Sussex distribution to that of Mistle Thrushes, as shown by the abundance maps in the New Atlas, is striking.

In the mid-1970s, Shrubb considered that Song Thrush numbers were increasing. Since then, a steady national decline has been reflected in Sussex. Whereas Shrubb estimated an average of 24 pairs per km² in Sussex farmland, censuses in various habitats during the 1980s gave a combined average of less than 9 pairs per km². Song Thrushes were outnumbered by Blackbirds by 1:4. Assuming these figures apply to the whole County, the Sussex breeding population can be estimated at 35,000 pairs. This is likely to fluctuate in response to mild or severe winters.

Whether Song Thrushes will continue to decline, or stabilise at a lower level, in uncertain, as the reason for their decrease is not known. Probably a combination of adverse factors is involved, including changes in farming methods. As Song Thrushes are a favourite prey of Sparrowhawks, being of a size attractive to both sexes, the resurgence of this predator in Sussex since the 1960s cannot have helped.

Song Thrushes in Britain are partial migrants. The percentage of Sussex breeding birds which emigrates for the winter is not known, and indeed may vary. In addition, Song Thrushes from the Continent pass through Sussex in autumn, particularly along the Downs and at the coast. Movements begin in late September, and reach a peak during October. The highest recent count was of 150 at Church Norton on 3 October 1992, but as the birds form loose associations concealed over wide areas of berry-bearing scrub or gorse, true numbers are easily underestimated. Many of the migrants are less warmly-coloured than local breeders and belong to the nominate race (Leverton 1986).

Passage and emigration continue well into November. Both route and destination are clearly shown by ringing recoveries: across the Channel, down the Atlantic coast of France, and into western Spain and Portugal, where many are shot. The origin of the migrants is less clear. The very grey-green Song Thrushes which often arrive in October at the same time as Ring Ouzels may be from Norway. Others ringed on passage or in winter have moved to or from the Low Countries, Germany and Denmark; one caught near Lewes on 8 February 1986 had been ringed in Estonia. Surprisingly, there is no evidence that Song Thrushes from northern Britain ever visit Sussex, but there is a strong pattern of basically east/west movements within southern England, as far as Suffolk, Essex and Devon.

In some years, the end of autumn passage merges with cold weather movements. Song Thrushes are badly affected by severe weather, as in early 1985, when they were seen flying west at the rate of 200 an hour at Saltdean on 7 January. In a second cold spell the same year, 59 flew west at Brighton on 10 February, when 100 were counted on the shoreline at Thorney Island. Significantly, none bred on 156 ha at Lullington Heath that summer, compared with seven pairs the previous year.

Avoidance of open country is less marked outside the breeding season. The berry crop of downland scrub attracts both migrants and residents in autumn. Even after this is depleted, many Song Thrushes overwinter on the Downs, as the Winter Atlas map suggests. Perhaps it is at this time of the year that snails are important to them.

Return passage in spring is rarely noticeable, but (as in autumn) Song Thrushes are sometimes heard at night, travelling with Redwing flocks.

Roy Leverton

Redwing   *Turdus iliacus*

Status:- An abundant passage migrant and very common winter visitor

Although des Forges & Harber mention a record for 5 September 1933 at Brede, the earliest autumn arrival in recent years was on 7 September 1984 at Woodingdean. However, the first Redwings normally arrive in Sussex in late September. During 1970-93, first dates varied between 7 September and 12 October with the average 24 September. Large numbers are rarely seen until the second week in October. Arrivals at this time are often from the southeast rather than the north, for example, a flock of 300 flew up the Ouse Valley from Newhaven on 12 October 1981.

Wind direction, weather and food supplies, both here and elsewhere, presumably influence the numbers of Redwings which reach Sussex in autumn, and determine how long they stay. Night passage is often heard, as many Redwings overfly Sussex, but when a good passage coincides with an abundant haw crop, flocks of several hundred or more may be found on the Downs and elsewhere. They stay until the berry crop is depleted, or the weather turns cold towards the end of the year.

Wide annual fluctuations, and their mobility, make it hard to estimate how many Redwings actually winter in Sussex in an average year. Inevitably, observers tend to submit only those records which involve exceptional numbers or dates, ignoring the commonplace. Thus (as with Fieldfare) concentrations of up to 1000 Redwings are reported in mid-winter from the river levels, where they are easily seen and counted. Yet it is likely that the normal pattern consists of numerous small flocks of 20-50 birds, scattered throughout the county, especially in the sheltered wooded farmland of the Weald. One such flock per tetrad would add up to about 30,000 wintering Redwings, perhaps a tenth of the numbers which visit Sussex on passage or during cold weather movements.

Spectacular daytime movements are observed in response to severe winter weather, the largest being of 40,000 Redwings flying west in a snowstorm at

Beachy Head on 16 February 1969. Westwards is the usual direction, but they are sometimes noted flying east, together with other thrushes, as on 6 February 1986 when 200 birds per hour passed over Brighton. In a less common response to freezing conditions, 500 fed on the shoreline at Thorney Island from 9-10 January 1985. After these two consecutive hard winters, Redwing numbers were low in Sussex for the next three years.

Redwings are known to change their wintering areas, and birds ringed in Sussex one winter have been found in France, Spain, Portugal and Italy during a subsequent one. In a more extreme instance, a Redwing ringed at Falmer in February 1976 was found in late December 1978 in Georgia, USSR. However, there have been three recoveries in the Lewes area of birds ringed there in a previous winter, suggesting that some may be site faithful. Clues as to origin are provided by three recoveries involving Finland.

In spring, returning Redwings usually overfly Sussex, judging by the volume of night passage heard in March, especially when poor visibility makes the birds fly low. Vast numbers must be involved, but (as in autumn) there may be few if any grounded Redwings the next day. An exception was 1984, with 500-1000 at several Wealden sites in March following heavy night passage heard at the coast. Often, the last Redwings are seen in mid-April. Stragglers or injured birds extend into May in some years, but there has never been any suggestion of breeding or summering. During 1965-93, last dates varied between 21 March and 20 May with the average 21 April. The latest county record is that of one seen at Rye Harbour on 24 May 1959 although des Forges & Harber refer to "birds described as recently dead having twice been found in June".

A bird showing the characteristics of the Icelandic race *T.m. coburni* was shot at Stonegate on 21 December 1940 (des Forges & Harber). *Roy Leverton*

Mistle Thrush *Turdus viscivorus*

Status:- A very common resident and partial migrant.

1988 - 92	
Confirmed	649
Probable	1
Possible	147
Total	797

In Britain, Mistle Thrush territories are large, for reasons not well understood, the average density in woodland being about 5 pairs per km². This figure is reached or slightly exceeded in Sussex in parts of the Weald, and also around Moulsecoomb and Stanmer Park, where mature trees adjoin extensive areas of short grazed or mown turf. Territories are larger, up to 1 km², in more open farmland and on the Downs, scrub by itself not being a favoured habitat. The Atlas map hints at this higher density in the wooded Weald; it is shown more clearly in the abundance map in the New Atlas.

Combining breeding surveys from a variety of Sussex habitats, the average density during the 1980s was about 3.5 pairs per km², which would give a county population of 14,000 pairs. This seems excessive. Agreeing with Shrubb that the wide-ranging behaviour of this species even when nesting can lead to the number of territories being overestimated, and allowing for floating non-breeders (New Atlas) and some movement by failed breeders trying again elsewhere, the true Sussex breeding population may be nearer 7000 actual nesting pairs.

For most of the year, individual Mistle Thrushes or mated pairs are determinedly solitary and territorial. However, soon after the breeding season, they form flocks made up of moulting adults and partially-independent juveniles, and may wander widely to feed on the short grassland of the Downs or river levels. In Sussex, such flocks commonly consist of 20-40 birds, less frequently up to 75; in recent years none has approached the 250 reported at Cissbury on 28 August 1965. As the area from which the birds are drawn is unknown, the flocks give little clue to local densities. They break up at or before the approach of winter, although in severe weather Mistle Thrushes may gather at orchard windfalls and occasionally on river levels. Actual cold weather movements seem not to have been noted.

Many first-year Mistle Thrushes are thought to emigrate from Britain to winter in France. Two nestlings ringed in Sussex are known to have done so, one in 1912 and one in 1935. Shrubb gives apparently convincing evidence of regular movements at the coast, especially at Beachy Head, involving up to 100 birds a day in October and sometimes November. Curiously, nothing approaching this scale has been reported in the past two decades or more, indeed the Mistle Thrush is described as "now rare" at Whitbread Hollow, Beachy Head, where two on 26 September was the only autumn record in 1992. Such a discrepancy is hard to explain, there having been no major population decline. Perhaps the large numbers seen in the 1960s were simply attracted to the coastal downland habitat as it then was, and this is no longer suitable. If so, it shows the danger of assuming that all birds seen at a coastal migration site are necessarily on passage.

The few instances of movement at the coast still reported probably reflect the emigration of Sussex-bred Mistle Thrushes and their return in spring. Thus there is no clear evidence that those from elsewhere pass through Sussex in numbers, or join the wintering population of perhaps 5000-10,000 birds. At a downland site near Lewes where passage or immigration was noted annually for the five other thrush species from 1974 to 1989, it was never once suspected for Mistle Thrush.   *Roy Leverton*

Cetti's Warbler   *Cettia cetti*

Status:- A very scarce resident, passage migrant and winter visitor.

The first Cetti's Warbler to be recorded in Sussex was trapped at the Crumbles on 9 October 1962. At the time, it was only the second for Britain, the first having occurred in neighbouring Hampshire the previous year. The next in Sussex (the sixth for Britain) was not until 1968 when one was trapped at Beachy Head on 25 September.

There were no further records until 1973 when there were two in the Cuckmere Valley near Westdean from 5 May to the end of July. These may have bred. Cetti's Warblers have been recorded every year since, breeding being confirmed for the first time in 1975 when a pair nested at Edburton.

One was recorded at Runcton on three dates between 12 and 25 December 1976 but the first bird to definitely overwinter in the county was one at Arundel WWT from 31 October 1976 to 3 April 1977. Up to two birds were recorded at this site in the winter of 1977/78 and two each at Church Norton and Pett Level, the choice of localities reflecting the species' preference for reedbeds during the winter months. Despite this increase in the wintering population and the presence of birds in the summer in a number of subsequent years, there was no further indication of breeding until 1988 when two birds were observed chasing each other at Thorney Deeps. Cetti's Warblers are known to show polygyny (Bibby 1982) and in 1989, a single male paired with two females at Thorney, both of which were seen with three young. A pair raised two young and another male held territory at this site in 1990 while in 1991, seven young fledged from three broods. Two singing males were again present in 1992 and six young fledged. At other localities, however, the number of birds has declined somewhat so that the species' hold in the county remains tenuous.

Immigration into the county takes place in autumn and in October 1990 at least seven birds were recorded at coastal sites, recalling the late 1970s when the species was rapidly increasing. Some returning individuals are clearly site faithful. A female ringed on 13 November 1983 was retrapped at the same site on 14 October and 13 November the following year. Between 1979 and 1993 21 Cetti's Warblers were ringed in Sussex but no recoveries have been reported. *Robert D M Edgar*

Grasshopper Warbler   *Locustella naevia*

Status:- A very scarce and declining summer visitor and fairly common passage migrant.

Walpole-Bond listed five main breeding habitats for the Grasshopper Warbler but gave no indication of the number of pairs found in each. These were downland scrub, osier beds and rough marshland, woodland edge, overgrown hedges and ditches, and gorse commons and heathland, in declining order of frequency. By the start of a breeding survey of the species that covered the period 1977-80 (Parmenter 1982), habitat preference had changed. Forty-five percent of the Grasshopper Warblers located during the survey were in young plantations (mainly conifer), 42% in downland scrub, 6% on gorse commons and heathland and 4% in osier beds and rough marshland. None were in woodland edge or overgrown hedges and ditches. Shrubb, comparing modern records with Walpole-Bond's account, suggested that the species was more numerous than in 1938, because of its preference for young conifer plantations, but Parmenter found no evidence for this, the results of the 1977-80 survey confirming that there had been a steep decline in breeding numbers since 1970 when the population was at a peak (fig. 83).

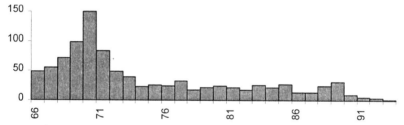

Figure 83. Annual totals of breeding pairs of Grasshopper Warblers, 1966 - 93.

The first year of the 1977-80 survey located a total of 32-35 pairs in 15 tetrads. However, in 1978 numbers fell quite dramatically to only 17-18 pairs, rising again in 1979 and 1980 to 20-22 and 24-26 pairs respectively. Adding the highest figure for each occupied tetrad over the 4-year period indicated a minimum total of 54 pairs in 31 tetrads. As the Atlas map shows, there were records in only 62 tetrads during 1988-92, with breeding confirmed in 31, probable in 13 and possible in 18. Assuming that the birds in the 'possible' category may have been on passage and that each occupied tetrad held a single pair, suggests a total of 31-44 pairs over the 5-year period. Although there was some recovery in 1977 and 1981, the Grasshopper Warbler seems to be heading towards extinction as a breeding species in the county. Reasons for the decrease are unclear though the peak in the early 1970s followed by a steep decline mirrors the trend elsewhere in the country. The contraction in range was greatest in the Weald and on the Downs in the west of the county as revealed by the Atlas map, which shows the tetrads in which the species was recorded during the Atlas Survey and also those (as open circles) in which it was found during 1976-87 but not during 1988-92. It may be that the conifer plantations occupied in the 1960s and 1970s are no longer suitable though other habitats in the county apparently still are, suggesting that adverse factors may be operating in the African wintering quarters.

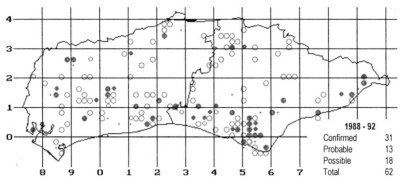

1988 - 92	
Confirmed	31
Probable	13
Possible	18
Total	62

Being a notoriously secretive bird when not singing, it is hardly surprising that records of migrants are relatively few. The first birds usually arrive in mid-April, although the earliest were on 4 April at Beachy Head in 1965 and at the Devil's Dyke in 1972. During the period 1965-93, first dates varied between 4 and 22 April with the average 14 April. Arrival continues into mid-May. The highest spring count was of 30 at Beachy Head on 30 April 1970. Numbers of this magnitude seem improbable in comparison with recent trends but pale into insignificance when compared with the 600 recorded in a 32 ha (80 acre) patch of scrub near Newhaven on 21 April 1922 (Walpole-Bond). Autumn passage occurs from late August to mid-September with a few birds lingering into early October. During 1965-93, last dates varied between 18 September and 1 November with the average 10 October. The latest ever were singles at Combe Haven on 25 October 1987 and Beachy Head on 1 November 1969. Despite the alarming decline in the breeding population, a considerable number must still pass through (or over) the county. Tape-luring (for ringing purposes) at Icklesham by the Rye Bay Ringing Group resulted in totals of 140, 251, 381 and 326 being caught in 1989, 1990, 1992 and 1993 respectively. At other sites, 1-5 in a day is now notable.

Between 1979 and 1993, 1510 Grasshopper Warblers were ringed in Sussex, the vast majority at Icklesham. One ringed at Beachy Head in August 1969 was recovered in April 1970 in Couture d'Argenson, Deux Sevres, France, 523 km south, on its return journey north. At the time, this was only the third foreign recovery of this species. A most interesting control, of a bird ringed at Icklesham on 18 August 1992 and caught in Djoudj, Senegal, 4123 km SSW, on 14 January 1993, was the first British-ringed Grasshopper Warbler recovered south of the Sahara. One ringed in Pembrokeshire (now Dyfed) on 17 April 1968 was found dead near Arundel on 3 May 1972. This was surprisingly far east if it was returning to Wales, as Grasshopper Warblers tend to enter the country to the west of Sussex.

Robert D M Edgar

Savi's Warbler
Locustella luscinioides

Status:- A rare vagrant.

The only record prior to 1962 was of one in song at Selsey Bill on 10-11 and 17-18 April 1961.

Since the beginning of 1962, there have been 12 published records comprising 13 individuals as follows:

1968: One at the Devil's Dyke on 26 April.
1972: One in song at Whitbread Hollow, Beachy Head from 7 to 10 May.
1979: One at Hodcombe, Beachy Head on 1 September.
1980: A first-winter trapped at Whitbread Hollow, Beachy Head on 19 September.
1988: One at Icklesham from 23 to 25 October was trapped.
1989: One in bushes adjoining the Adur Recreation Ground, Shoreham-by-Sea on the morning of 6 September.
1991: One in song at Pett Level Pools on 2-3 June.
1992: One trapped at Icklesham on 15 June.
1993: A juvenile trapped at Icklesham on 23 July.
       One trapped at Icklesham on 2 August.
       Two (one a first-winter) trapped at Icklesham on 8 August.
       One trapped at Icklesham on 14 August.

In addition to the above records, there have been a number of reports (not all fully substantiated) of singing males at a reedbed site in the east of the county in recent springs. It is not known whether these were mated or not but it is considered that breeding probably occurred in 1987 and was attempted in 1988.

Savi's Warblers breed locally from southeast England, the Low Countries, Germany, Poland and central Russia, south to the Mediterranean, the Black Sea and the Caspian Region (New Atlas). *Paul James*

Moustached Warbler
Acrocephalus melanopogon

Status:- A very rare vagrant (one record).

One in a garden in Ham Manor Close, Angmering on 18 August 1979 was the tenth to be seen in Britain although it is currently under review.

There are five records of this dark-crowned warbler in Britain, including a pair seen feeding three young in Cambridgeshire. Only two were during 1962-94, the other being trapped in Buckinghamshire in July 1965. It exhibits one of the most unusual vagrancy patterns of all species on the British List with occurrences at seemingly unlikely locations rather than at the coastal observatories or reedbeds where intensive ringing activity occurs. It breeds around the northern Mediterranean, in Austria and to the Ukraine and Kazakhstan. Eastern birds winter to northwestern India but most in Europe are sedentary or only migrate short distances. *Richard Fairbank*

Aquatic Warbler
Acrocephalus paludicola

Status:- A very scarce autumn visitor (95 individuals recorded).

Eleven were recorded prior to 1962: two in August, six in September and three in October (des Forges & Harber). The earliest to be recorded was at Pagham Harbour North Wall on 29 August in 1959 and the latest an adult shot in a Hove brick pit on 19 October in 1853. Four of the others were recorded at the Crumbles, being singles shot on 7 October 1908 (Arnold 1908) and seen from 1 to 7 October 1949 (Harber 1950) and on single dates in September 1957 and 1959. The individual from Hove is in the Booth Museum (BoMNH 207570) and was the second British record.

Since the beginning of 1962 there have been 84 records (fig. 84), at least 63 relating to birds that were trapped. Full details of eight birds trapped at Filsham Reedbed, four in 1973 and four in 1975, were not submitted to *BBRC* (who assessed all records of this species at that time), although they have been included in the totals here.

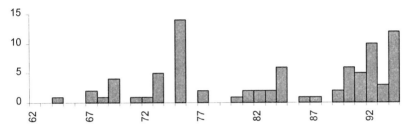

Figure 84. Annual totals of Aquatic Warblers, 1962 - 94.

The significant variations in the number of records each year reflects changing ringing efforts at Ivy Lake, Chichester (five trapped during 1967-72), Filsham Reedbed (four trapped in 1973, 13 in 1975 and two in 1984) and particularly Icklesham (32 juveniles trapped during 1989-94). The recent increase, due to records from Icklesham, sadly does not reflect the status of the species which has declined to the point where it is now considered globally threatened (Tucker & Heath 1994).

Most records have been of single individuals but at Filsham Reedbed in August 1975 three were trapped on 10th, two on 11th, two on 17th and one on 18th, with two trapped there on 18 September 1975 and two on 17 August 1984. At Icklesham two were trapped on 13 August 1991, while in August 1992 two were trapped there on 15th, three on 16th and two on 19th.

All records have been in autumn, in July (1), August (61), September (28) and October (5). The earliest to be recorded were a juvenile at Icklesham on 30 July 1994, an adult at Church Norton on 4-5 August 1990, a juvenile trapped at Icklesham on 5 August 1992 and one at Charleston Reedbed on 7 August 1969. The latest were the three recorded in October prior to 1962 and juveniles trapped at Filsham Reedbed on 4-5 October 1975 and at Icklesham on 5 October 1991. Most records have been in mid to late August with a second, smaller, peak in mid-September (fig. 85).

Since 1962 most records have come from Icklesham (32) and Filsham Reedbed (26), with eight at Charleston Reedbed or the Cuckmere and five at Ivy Lake, Chichester and four at Pagham Harbour. Three have been seen at Thorney Deeps (12 September 1981, September 1992 and 7 August 1994), with two at Littlehampton West Beach (10 August 1981 and 17 September 1983) and singles at Denton (15 August 1980) and Rye Harbour (18 August 1986). Perhaps rather surprisingly only two have been recorded at Beachy

Head (trapped at Whitbread Hollow on 11 August 1968 and seen in scrub above the lighthouse on 13 September 1989) and none at Selsey Bill, emphasising the lack of damp habitat at these premier migration sites.

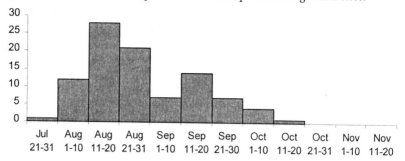

Figure 85. Cumulative arrival dates of Aquatic Warblers (all records).

More widely seen individuals in recent times were between Ternery Pool and the caravan site at Rye Harbour on 18 August 1986, at Church Norton on 4-5 August 1990 (*Brit. Birds* 84: plate 102), at the western end of Thorney Little Deep on 20 and 22 September 1992 and in a ditch in the lower Cuckmere Valley, just south of Exceat, on 24-25 September 1994 (*Birding World* 7: 346). Most favoured *Juncus.*

There were between 14 and 56 records of this secretive warbler in the British Isles each year during 1986-92, all during July to October (Fraser & Ryan 1994). It breeds from eastern Germany (where it is almost extinct) to the Urals wintering, as far as is known, in West Africa (BWP). *Richard Fairbank*

Sedge Warbler   *Acrocephalus schoenobaenus*

Status:- A fairly common summer visitor and very common passage migrant.

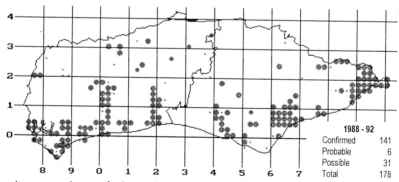

A comparison of the Atlas map for this species with that for Reed Warbler, shows a very similar distribution with the main concentrations found in an area from Pagham Harbour and Chichester Gravel Pits west to the county boundary, in the Arun, Adur, Ouse and Cuckmere Valleys, on

Pevensey Levels, at Combe Haven and in the Rye area. A breeding survey carried out in 1986-87 found that very few pairs were in pure stands of reed and that the majority were in *Phragmites* with scattered hawthorn, blackthorn or other bushes. Some chose dykes with dense growths of *Carex* or *Scirpus* but very few were in cropped fields. Only five territories were located in oil seed rape and one in winter cereal (Prater 1988). The results of the 1986-87 survey (with adjustment for some additional areas visited in 1988) indicated a total county population of about 840 pairs with over 300 pairs in West Sussex and over 500 pairs in East Sussex. Knox (1845) described the Sedge Warbler as "common everywhere" with the Reed Warbler "everywhere less common than the Sedge Warbler". The long term decrease in the Sedge Warbler population has been attributed, in part, to habitat deterioration or loss associated with drainage of wetlands and intensification of agricultural methods (New Atlas). Numbers ringed at Beachy Head have declined markedly. In the 1960s, more Sedge Warblers were ringed at this site than Reed Warblers but the proportion dropped to one-third of the number of the latter species in 1983 and one-quarter in 1985 (Edgar 1986). Shrubb referred to a catastrophic decline in the Arun Valley between 1966, when 165 singing males were counted between Burpham and Houghton Bridge, and 1974 when just seven were found. A total of 15 singing males was located in the same area in the 1986-87 survey, indicating an increase since 1974, but an overall decrease in the breeding population in that area of over 90% since 1966.

Sedge Warblers normally begin to arrive in early April. During 1964-93, first dates varied between 27 March and 17 April with the average 7 April. The earliest ever were singles on 27 March 1977 at Arundel Park and on 29 March at Chichester Gravel Pits in 1968 and 1981 and at Church Norton and

Rye Harbour in 1989. Arrival is heaviest in late April and early May. One at Brighton on 25 June 1984 was indicative of either very late spring arrival or early post-breeding dispersal.

Autumn passage commences in late July and continues into early October, with the main departure in August and early September. During 1965-93, latest dates fell between 4 and 26 October with the average 13 October. The latest ever was one at Pett Level on 29 October 1961. At Beachy Head, counts of 30-50 were recorded on five dates between 1968 and 1976 but, since 1980, day totals there have not exceeded 20, except in 1989 when there were 50 at Whitbread Hollow on 28 August and 30 on 1 September. However, much larger numbers have been recorded in reedbeds near the coast including at least 400 at Combe Haven on 6 August 1977. At a small reedbed at Ivy Lake, Chichester Gravel Pits, more than 1000 were ringed in six of the autumns in the period 1963-72. Ringing evidence shows that birds originating from a wide area of Britain and Ireland use reedbeds in the county as a migratory staging post. Controls in Sussex have included 65 from northern England, 58 from central Scotland, 15 from Wales and no less than 18 from Ireland. At Icklesham, no less than 12,412 Sedge Warblers were ringed in autumn 1992, demonstrating the importance of reedbeds for the species' conservation. From this one site, there were 161 recoveries between 1986 and 1990.

Foreign recoveries of Sussex-ringed birds include 50 in France, 11 in Belgium, seven in Spain, one each in Portugal and Algeria and over 20 in Senegal. The distribution of these recoveries suggest that the Sedge Warblers travel from Sussex to southwest France or northern Spain in one flight and thence on to Africa. Special ringing expeditions have been responsible for the controls in Senegal, of which 16 were in 1992 alone. A bird ringed at Filsham on 6 September 1975 and controlled at Djoudj, Senegal on 19 January 1976 was the first African control of a Sussex-ringed Sedge Warbler. Particularly rapid movements were shown by one ringed at Hollesley, Suffolk on 3 September 1987 and controlled at Chichester, 195 km southwest, the following day, and singles ringed at Icklesham on 24 and 26 August 1991 that were controlled at Poole Harbour, 195 km west, on 25 and 27 August respectively. Also of note was a bird ringed at Chichester on 16 September 1968 and found dead at Anglet in the French Pyrenees three days later. Sedge Warblers typically weigh about 11 grams in summer but, when ringed at 07.00 hrs, this bird weighed 19.5 grams. By the time it left Sussex at dusk, it may well have weighed 20 grams. The weight increase represents fat stored for the flight south. *Robert D M Edgar*

Paddyfield Warbler *Acrocephalus agricola*

Status:- A very rare vagrant.

One trapped at Icklesham on 13 and 18 October 1992 is the only record. It was not seen in the field.

There were over 30 records of this short-winged warbler in the British Isles during 1962-94, two-thirds of them since 1985. It breeds from the western Black Sea to Mongolia and Afghanistan wintering in the Indian subcontinent.

Richard Fairbank

Marsh Warbler
Acrocephalus palustris

Status:- A rare summer visitor and passage migrant.

Marsh Warblers inhabit dense stands of willowherb, nettles, meadowsweet and other tall herbs, with adjacent willow or hawthorn bushes. This habitat, although scarce, is found in most of the river valleys and on the levels adjacent to the coast. Despite its loud advertising song, this species is difficult to census since different localities are occupied from year to year and the habitat is transient. Certainly not all suitable breeding sites are visited each year. From 1920 to 1939, between one and 20 pairs nested annually (des Forges & Harber), spasmodically thereafter and none after 1947 until 1966 when four pairs were found in the Arun Valley between Burpham and South Stoke, two of which raised young. Single pairs were recorded in the same area in 1967 and 1969, of which the former may have raised young. The only more recent records of confirmed breeding, all in East Sussex, were in 1977, 1978, 1986 and 1993, all involving single pairs. In addition to these breeding records, there have been a number of reports of singing males, apparently unpaired, in suitable nesting habitat. A maximum of five males (at four localities) was recorded in 1987 but in most years, only one or two have been reported (table 76).

Year	No. of singing males	No. of pairs	Year	No. of singing males	No. of pairs
1962			1979	1	
1963			1980	1	
1964	1		1981	1	
1965			1982		
1966		4	1983		
1967		1	1984	2-3	
1968		1	1985	2	
1969		1	1986	4	1
1970			1987	5	
1971		1	1988	3	
1972	2		1989	1	
1973	1		1990	1	
1974			1991		
1975	1		1992		
1976	1		1993	1	1
1977	2	1	1994	1	
1978		1			

Table 76. Breeding records of Marsh Warblers, 1962 - 94.

The Marsh Warbler is one of our latest summer visitors to arrive. des Forges & Harber mentioned an old record for 8 May 1923 but stated that arrival did not normally take place before about 19 May. The earliest arrival date during 1962-93 was 24 May but migrants occur well into June, as shown by records of single birds at Fairlight on 18-19 June 1970 and Woodingdean on 21 June 1971.

Few autumn migrants have been recorded although an unprecedented 13 were trapped at Icklesham between 3 July and 15 August 1993. Only nine others have been recorded as follows:

1983:   One at Church Norton on 19 September (*Brit. Birds* 80: plate 59).
1990:   One photographed at Weir Wood Reservoir on 11 September.

1991:   One trapped at Icklesham on 25 August.
        One at Seaford Head on 5-6 October.
1992:   Singles trapped at Icklesham on 26 and 29 July.
1994   Singles trapped at Icklesham on 19 July, 1 and 5-6 August.

There have been no recoveries of ringed birds.   *Rober D M Edgar*

Reed Warbler   *Acrocephalus scirpaceus*

Status:- A common summer visitor and very common passage migrant.

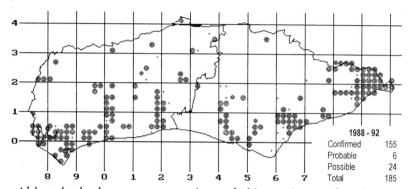

	1988 - 92	
	Confirmed	155
	Probable	6
	Possible	24
	Total	185

Although the largest concentrations of this species are found in more extensive reedbeds, this habitat is relatively scarce in Sussex and mainly confined to the vicinity of the coast. Most Reed Warblers in the county are found in reed-filled ditches on the levels and along stretches of river fringed with reed. However, some birds in the east of the county have been found singing in oil seed rape and a few in winter cereals. A pair at Weir Wood Reservoir used reed canary grass. The Atlas map shows a very similar distribution to that of the Sedge Warbler with the main concentrations found in the vicinity of Chichester and Pagham Harbours, in the Arun, Adur, Ouse and Cuckmere Valleys, on Pevensey Levels, at Combe Haven and in an area extending from Pett to the Midrips and along the Rother Valley. Very few birds were found in the north of the county. A breeding survey carried out in 1986-87 (with adjustment for some additional areas visited in 1988) indicated a total county population of about 2836 pairs, of which 1045 pairs were in West Sussex and 1791 pairs in East Sussex (Prater 1988). The results, when compared with a survey in West Sussex in 1975 and 1976 (by G C Evans) indicated an increase in the breeding population. However, numbers of Reed Warblers fluctuate markedly, as shown by an increase on a 55 ha CBC plot on grazing marsh in the upper Adur Levels from 15 pairs in 1980 to 37 pairs in 1982. Numbers fell to 25 pairs in 1983 but increased further to 39 pairs in 1984 and 44 pairs in 1986. These variations were almost entirely due to the timing of vegetation clearance from the dykes which sometimes occurred during the breeding season.

The earliest ever recorded in spring were singles on 9 April at Selsey Bill in 1966 and at Chichester Gravel Pits in 1981. In other years during 1965-93, first dates fell between 10 April and 2 May with the average 19 April. At many sites the first birds are not recorded until late April or the first week of May although arrival can continue throughout May. Indeed, it is not unusual for migrants to be found at localities totally unsuitable for breeding in the second week of June and, in 1986, a breeding pair was first recorded at one site on 29 June.

Migrants at Beachy Head have been noted from 26 July. Passage occurs throughout August and September but few are normally recorded after early October. In 1991, however, there were 30 at Whitbread Hollow on 14 October while in 1993, 63 were trapped at Icklesham on 8 October, 21 on 9th and 35 on 10th. During 1964-93, latest dates fell between 8 October and 8 November, with the average 22 October. The latest ever were singles at Icklesham on 7 November 1993, Thorney Island on 8 November 1987 and Beachy Head on 13 November 1994.

Numbers away from reedbeds are usually low although 100 were recorded at Beachy Head on 24 August 1977 and 20 September 1980, demonstrating the importance of downland scrub as a habitat for this species on passage. Maxima of up to 30-40 are more typical at this site.

The Reed Warbler is the second most ringed warbler in Sussex (after the Sedge Warbler). Between 1979 and 1993, about 37,000 birds were trapped in the county including, at Icklesham, over 5000 in the autumns of 1990 and 1991, 6978 in 1992 and 6209 in 1993. There have been 285 recoveries of Sussex-ringed birds, of which 63 were abroad, and 414 recoveries in Sussex of birds from outside the county. Only seven had been ringed abroad but these included only the second Norwegian Reed Warbler trapped in Britain. It had been ringed at Skrakilen, Ostfold on 20 August 1993 and was controlled at Icklesham, 1130 km away, 17 days later on 6 September. A juvenile ringed near Gdansk, Poland on 17 August 1977 was controlled at Chichester Gravel Pits on 25 and 27 September 1977. One ringed as a first-year at Icklesham on 2 October 1993 and controlled at Hovvig, Jylland, Denmark, 736 km northeast, on 4 August 1994 was, very probably, the first Danish control of a British-ringed Reed Warbler.

There have been a number of recoveries of birds moving between feeding sites on the south coast in autumn including one ringed at Church Norton on 23 September 1989 and controlled at Icklesham the following day and one ringed at Titchfield Haven, Hampshire on 27 September 1992 that was also controlled at Icklesham the following day. Ringing indicates that the autumn migration of Reed Warblers through western Europe is undertaken in short stages as shown by recoveries of Sussex-ringed birds in France (20), Spain (5), Portugal (10) and Morocco (6). Four Reed Warblers ringed at Icklesham between 14 August and 1 September 1991 arrived in the Charente-Maritime department of France an average of eight days after ringing (Crawley 1992). This area is just over 600 km due south of Icklesham.

There have also been eight recoveries of Reed Warblers in Senegal. Most of these relate to birds controlled in March and April on their return northwards from wintering areas further south. However, a bird ringed at Charleston Reedbed on 2 September 1984 was still in Senegal on 23 May 1987. Similarly, a bird ringed as a breeding adult at Chichester on 26 May 1968 was still in Morocco in late May 1973.

An apparent case of "reverse" migration is provided by a bird ringed at Icklesham on 17 September 1992 and found dead near Eye, Suffolk, 158 km NNE, later in the month. Most recoveries of Reed Warblers in Sussex have been of birds from elsewhere in southern England, reflecting the relatively southerly breeding distribution of the species in Britain. However, one ringed at Frodsham, Cheshire on 20 August 1978 was found in Rottingdean, 333 km southeast, six days later. Longevity is shown by a bird ringed at Church Norton on 19 August 1979 in its first-year and found breeding there on 16 June 1986, nearly seven years later. *Robert D M Edgar*

Great Reed Warbler *Acrocephalus arundinaceus*

Status:- A rare vagrant (13 records involving 14 individuals).

There were two records before 1962 (des Forges & Harber). A male at the Royal Military Canal, Rye between 24 May and 28 July 1951 was in song up to 14 June with a second individual heard on 10 June, when both were singing about 70 m apart (Reynolds 1952, *SxBR* 4: 9). A singing male was also at Selsey Bill on 16 May 1960.

Since the beginning of 1962 there have been 11 records:

1964: One trapped at Sidlesham on 25 June.
1965: One at Selsey Bill on 6 June.
1969: One trapped at Glyne Gap, Bexhill on 11 May.
       One beside Runcton Gravel Pit, Chichester on 4 June.
1970: One trapped at Belle Tout Wood, Beachy Head on 11 May.
1978: A singing male at the Narrow Pits, Rye Harbour from 23 to 30 May.
1979: A singing male at Ivy Lake, Chichester on 2 and 3 June.
1980: One at Filsham Reedbed on 15 August.
1984: A singing male at Filsham Reedbed on 17 and 18 May.
1985: A singing male at Filsham Reedbed on 20 May.
1989: A singing male at Thorney Deeps on 19 May.

In total eight have been seen in May (one remaining to late July), five in June and one in August. Three were seen at Filsham and one at nearby Glyne Gap. There are two records each from Chichester Gravel Pits and Selsey Bill and one each for Beachy Head, Rye, Rye Harbour, Sidlesham and Thorney Deeps. On still evenings the song of the 1978 individual at Rye carried across the breadth of the reserve and could be heard from Ternery Pool.

There were nearly 150 records of this large, noisy, warbler in the British Isles during 1962-94. It breeds from northwestern Africa and Iberia to southern Sweden and Japan, wintering in sub-Saharan Africa and South East Asia, although those breeding from Mongolia east are often considered a separate species, Oriental Great Reed Warbler *A. orientalis* (Howard & Moore 1991). *Richard Fairbank*

Booted Warbler *Hippolais caligata*

Status:- A very rare vagrant (two records).

First recorded in 1993, another was seen in 1994:

1993: One trapped at Icklesham on 19 September was photographed in the hand, but not seen in the field.

1994:   One singing at Cow Gap, Beachy Head between 07:20 and 07:35 hrs on 5 June was not seen subsequently. It was the fourth spring record in Britain.

There were 55 records of this small, pale warbler in the British Isles during 1962-94, including a record 14 in 1993. It breeds from northwestern Russia to Mongolia and Iran wintering in the Indian subcontinent. All British records to date are of the northern race *H.c. caligata.*   *Richard Fairbank*

Icterine Warbler   *Hippolais icterina*

Status:- A rare vagrant (32 records, mainly in autumn).
First recorded at Whitbread Hollow, Beachy Head on 5 September 1965 (*SxBR* 18: 41), 32 have been seen in the county including three in 1977, 1983 and 1990. There were, however, none during 1979-82 (fig. 86).

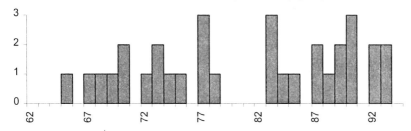

Figure 86. Annual totals of Icterine Warblers (all records).

All records have been of single individuals although two were seen at Beachy Head on 24 August 1970, one at Hodcombe and one in the Beachy Head Hotel garden. Very surprisingly none have stayed for more than a day.

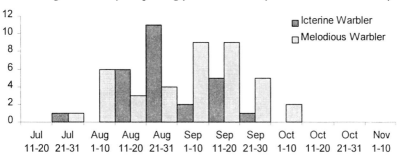

*Figure 87. Cumulative 'autumn' arrival dates of
Icterine and Melodious Warblers (all records).*

Records are for May (5), June (1), July (1), August (17) and September (8). There is an isolated report from Church Norton on 7 May 1968 while all others in spring were individuals in song between 21 May (at Steyning in 1992) and 4 June (at Rye Harbour in 1987), the intervening records being at Hodcombe, Beachy Head on 23 May 1989, near Church Norton on 24 May 1993 and at Whitbread Hollow, Beachy Head on 28 May 1967. A male was trapped at Icklesham on 21 July 1990, all other autumn records being between

11 August (at Hodcombe, Beachy Head in 1983) and 18 September (trapped at Charleston Reedbed in 1988) apart from one at Combe Haven on 28 September 1985. Most arrived in late August contrasting with a slightly later arrival for the very similar Melodious Warbler (fig. 87).

More than half the records have been from Beachy Head (17) with three seen at Church Norton, two at Seaford Head and singles at Charleston Reedbed (18 September 1988), Combe Haven, East Grinstead (Harwood's Lane on 19 August 1989), Littlehampton West Beach (13 September 1983), Icklesham (21 July 1990), Pett (trapped on 23 August 1977), Rye Harbour (4 June 1987) Steyning (21 May 1992), Selsey Bill (14 September 1974) and Woods Mill (21 August 1983). Those inland are of particular note.

There were between 54 and 112 records of this long-winged warbler in the British Isles each year during 1986-91 with 240, including 165 in late spring, in 1992 (Fraser & Ryan 1994). It breeds from northern France to Norway, western Siberia and northern Iran wintering in Africa south of the Equator.

Richard Fairbank

Melodious Warbler *Hippolais polyglotta*

Status:- A very scarce visitor (43 records, mainly in autumn).

Three were recorded before 1962 (des Forges & Harber): at the Crumbles on 25 September 1957 (*SxBR* 10: 20), trapped at Holywell, Beachy Head on 17 August 1958 (*SxBR* 11: 19) and at Selsey Bill on 12 August 1961 (published by des Forges & Harber as 8th).

Since the beginning of 1962 a total of 40 has been recorded including three in 1962, 1982 and 1984 and five in 1994 (fig. 88).

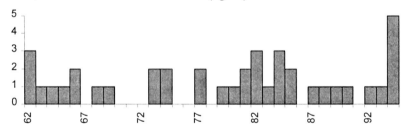

Figure 88. Annual totals of Melodious Warblers, 1962 - 94.

All records have been of single individuals in May (3), June (1), July (1), August (13), September (23) and October (2). Those in spring were in song at Belle Tout Wood, Beachy Head on 10 May 1981, near Belle Tout Wood on 22 May 1994, at Whitbread Hollow, Beachy Head on 27-28 May 1968 and at Icklesham on 12 June 1977. Earliest in autumn were singles trapped at Icklesham on 28 July 1987 and two seen on 1 August, at Hodcombe, Beachy Head in 1973 and Rye Harbour in 1988. Latest records were at Selsey Bill between 27 and 30 September 1962 and west of Belle Tout, Beachy Head on 2-3 October 1982 and 4 October 1969. Most in autumn were in early to mid-September with a smaller peak in early August (fig. 87).

Records of this species have shown much less of an easterly bias than those of Icterine Warbler (Fairbank 1987) and although a similar number have been recorded at Beachy Head (18), this is less than half the county total. There have been seven at Selsey Bill (although only one since 1966), six at Church Norton (from 1980 onwards) and two at the Crumbles (1957 and 8 August 1963), Icklesham (June 1977 and July 1987) and Sidlesham (10 August 1982 and 13 September 1994). Single individuals have been recorded at Crowlink (9 September 1973), Littlehampton Golf Course (7 and 8 August 1993), Pett (trapped at Chick Hill on 10 August 1977), Rye Harbour (1 August 1988), Shoreham-by-Sea (21 September 1994) and inland at Weir Wood Reservoir (9 September 1990). The record of one at Selsey Bill on 3 September 1961, at the time the fourth county record, is no longer considered to be acceptable.

There were between 24 and 43 records in the British Isles each year during 1986-92 (Fraser & Ryan 1994). It is the western counterpart of the Icterine Warbler, breeding from Morocco to Italy and the Netherlands (where it first bred in 1990) and wintering in West Africa (BWP).   *Richard Fairbank*

Dartford Warbler   *Sylvia undata*
Status:- A scarce resident and partial migrant.

This "denizen of the gorse", as the Dartford Warbler was aptly referred to by Walpole-Bond, is enjoying something of a boom in Sussex since its reappearance as a regular breeding species in 1989. It is susceptible to severe weather, resulting in periodic crashes between periods of recovery and expansion and it is likely, therefore, that the number of pairs breeding in the county in any one year is controlled by the weather in the preceding winter. A series of hard winters and loss of habitat by agricultural improvements in the 1940s exterminated the breeding population and none were found between 1947 and 1960, when breeding was established in one area and suspected in another (des Forges & Harber). In 1961 breeding occurred in both these areas, four pairs being involved. This population survived the severe winter of 1962/63, and by 1973 a total of about 23 pairs was nesting at four localities in the county (Shrubb). A gradual decline followed and, although there were three pairs at one locality in 1981, none could be found in 1982, following another cold winter in 1981/82. Although isolated singing males were present in 1984 and 1987, it was not until 1989, when four pairs were proved to have bred successfully, that the county was effectively recolonised.

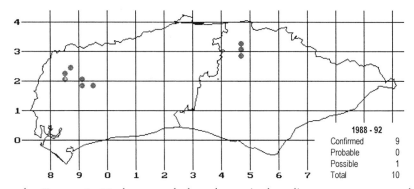

des Forges & Harber stated that the main breeding areas were on the Downs in East Sussex, a situation that prevailed until the late 1970s, when Dartford Warblers ceased to breed at Beachy Head and Lullington Heath. As yet, these sites have not been recolonised and all recent breeding records have been for the commons in the northwest of the county and for Ashdown Forest. The colonisation of the latter area has been well monitored and it was here that one pair bred in 1989. Up to 1992, no more than two pairs were present (and none in 1991). In 1993, however, there were at least 12 pairs and in 1994, more than 26 pairs. The recent spell of mild winters is undoubtedly the reason for this spectacular increase together with an ideal development of gorse and heather, following large fires in the mid-1980s. The ability to rear two, or sometimes even three, broods in good summers (New Atlas) may also be a contributory factor. However, this population has been particularly susceptible to cold winters in the past and it may only take one such winter to severely reduce or even wipe it out.

Although some Dartford Warblers are faithful to their territories throughout the year, there is a tendency for birds to appear on the coast and at non-breeding inland localities during the autumn, especially when population levels are high. Despite the lack of evidence from ringing recoveries, it is tempting to speculate that these movements represent dispersal of locally-bred birds, particularly as the growth in the breeding population in Sussex since 1989 has been accompanied by an increase in the number of autumn sightings. The approximate cumulative monthly totals of such records for 1962-94 are shown below.

Aug	Sep	Oct	Nov	Dec	Jan	Feb	Mar	Apr
1	8	59	56	30	19	1	9	2

Although birds were recorded at a number of widely scattered localities between Chichester Harbour in the west and Rye Harbour in the east, most occurred at Pagham Harbour (23), Beachy Head (19), Littlehampton West Beach (12) and Thorney Island (10). The highest counts were of four at Thorney on 30 October 1992, of which three remained until 20 November and two until 24 November, and five at Beachy Head during early November 1994. The table above shows a clear peak in autumn, suggesting that most birds move on. In some years, however, overwintering has occurred, most frequently at Pagham Harbour and Thorney Island, but also in a Lewes garden from 15 November 1971 to 22 February 1972 and in an isolated patch of gorse at Sheepcote Valley, Whitehawk in 1992/93. Birds have occasionally been noted in spring at sites where they have not overwintered. Such records have included singles at Pagham Harbour on 15-16 April 1968, 24 March 1978 and 11 March 1990, Steyning Round Hill on 31 March 1974 and 4 March 1994, West Wittering on 17 March 1989, Selsey Bill on 1 March 1992, Rye Harbour on 6 and 8 March 1993 and Shoreham Beach on 24 March 1993.

Mike Scott-Ham

Subalpine Warbler   *Sylvia cantillans*

Status:- A very rare vagrant (seven records).

One was recorded before 1962 (des Forges & Harber), a male on the beach to the east of the mouth of Pagham Harbour on 17 May 1961 (*SxBR* 14: 17).

Since 1962 a further six have been accepted, including four during 1992-94:

1984:   A singing male at Fairlight early on the morning of 22 April.
1988:   A singing male holding territory at the top of Cow Gap, Beachy Head from 9 to 13 May.
1992:   A female at Hodcombe, Beachy Head briefly on both 21 and 22 May.
1993:   A juvenile male in hedgerows at Sidlesham Quay, Pagham Harbour from 9 to 16 October.
1994:   A female briefly at Hodcombe, Beachy Head on 31 May.
         A male at Hodcombe, Beachy Head during the morning of 13 June.

Records are for April, May (4), June and October. Four were at Beachy Head, two at Pagham Harbour and one at Fairlight. The Cow Gap individual of 1988 showed the characteristics of the strongly contrasted Balkans race *S.c. albistriata* (Rogers *et al* 1989) but rarely allowed observers sufficient views to determine this.

A male seen well, but briefly, at Belle Tout, Beachy Head on 21 April 1992 (C F Winyard *pers. comm.*) has not, to date, been submitted and is excluded from the above totals.

There were nearly 320 records of this delightful small *Sylvia* warbler in the British Isles during 1962-94. It breeds in northwest Africa and from Iberia to western Turkey wintering in the Sahel.   *Richard Fairbank*

Sardinian Warbler   *Sylvia melanocephala*

Status:- A very rare vagrant (three records).

First recorded in 1976, there have been two records since:

1976:   A male to the west of Birling Gap between 23 August and 30 October was the sixth British record.

1990:   An adult female trapped at Icklesham on 3 July had a brood patch. It was not
        seen in the field.
1994:   An elusive male at Shooters Bottom, Beachy Head between 28 August and 11
        September and again on 27 and 29 September.

Although mainly confined to one large patch of scrub, the long staying
Birling individual was usually very difficult to see (Cooper 1976b), only
becoming marginally easier towards the end of its stay when it was more
mobile, possibly as food became harder to find.

There were over 40 records of this skulking *Sylvia* warbler in the British
Isles during 1962-94. It breeds around the Mediterranean wintering mainly in
northern Africa.   *Richard Fairbank*

Barred Warbler   *Sylvia nisoria*

Status:- A very scarce autumn visitor (36 records).

Three were recorded before 1962 (des Forges & Harber), one trapped at
Shoreham-by-Sea on 31 August 1959 and individuals seen at the Crumbles on
10 September 1959 (*SxBR* 12: 17) and at Holywell, Eastbourne on 3 September
1961.

Thirty-three have been recorded since the beginning of 1962, including
four in 1969 and three in five other subsequent years (fig. 89).

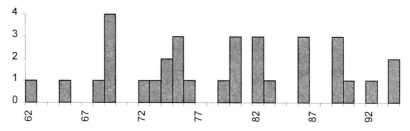

Figure 89. Annual totals of Barred Warblers, 1962 - 94.

All records have been of single individuals in autumn. The earliest were
trapped at Icklesham on 23 August 1994, seen at Watch Cottages, Rye
Harbour on 24 August 1979 and trapped at Whitbread Hollow, Beachy Head
on 25 August 1986 while the latest were trapped at Whitbread Hollow on
9 October 1974 and at Hodcombe, Beachy Head on 12 October 1989. Five
were seen in August, 29 in September and two in October, most being in
early to mid-September (fig. 90).

Over two-thirds of all records have been at Beachy Head (26) with three at
Icklesham (6-7 September 1986, 28 September 1989 and 23 August 1994) and
two each at Littlehampton West Beach (17 September 1983 and from 22 to 27
September 1992) and Rye Harbour (24 August 1979 and 4 September 1980).
Of the remaining records, two were in 1959 (detailed above) and one was seen
at Selsey Bill (29-30 September 1962). Those at Beachy Head include all four
recorded in the county in 1969 (three being trapped at Hodcombe), three in
both in 1975 and 1982 and two in 1974, 1980, 1986 and 1989. Twenty-one
have been trapped in total including 17 of those recorded at Beachy Head.

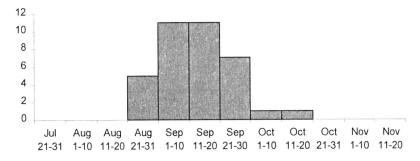

Jul 21-31 | Aug 1-10 | Aug 11-20 | Aug 21-31 | Sep 1-10 | Sep 11-20 | Sep 21-30 | Oct 1-10 | Oct 11-20 | Oct 21-31 | Nov 1-10 | Nov 11-20

Figure 90. Cumulative arrival dates of Barred Warblers (all records).

There were between 68 and 164 records of this large, clumsy looking, *Sylvia* warbler in the British Isles each year during 1986-92 (Fraser & Ryan 1994). It breeds from northern Italy and Poland to Mongolia wintering in East Africa.   *Richard Fairbank*

Lesser Whitethroat   *Sylvia curruca*
Status:- A common summer visitor and passage migrant.

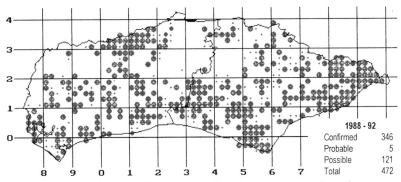

1988 - 92	
Confirmed	346
Probable	5
Possible	121
Total	472

The Lesser Whitethroat breeds in tall rather dense scrub and overgrown hedgerows. As the Atlas map shows, it is patchily distributed in Sussex, occurring most commonly on the Downs and in the northwest and far east of the county. It is, however, largely absent from heavily-wooded areas, heathlands and the centres of population. Of the four common members of the genus *Sylvia* which breed in Sussex, it is the least abundant.

The species breeds at low densities throughout the county and there is little survey data available from which to estimate the size of the breeding population. The use of national CBC data for woodland and farmland habitats in 1989 (New Atlas) indicates a county population of 2000-3000 pairs, a figure similar to the range of 2500-3000 pairs given for neighbouring Hampshire (Clark & Eyre 1993). Nationally, population levels have shown irregular fluctuations with no long-term trend (Marchant *et al* 1990) although the species has clearly extended its range since the 68-72 BTO Atlas (New Atlas).

After the war, the demise of sheep grazing and the plague of myxomatosis which substantially reduced rabbit populations allowed the encroachment of scrub on the Downs to begin. Much of this scrub is now of suitable size for Lesser Whitethroats and in downland sites they may outnumber Whitethroats (*SxBR* 37: 46). Ringing results from Beachy Head more closely reflect the national trend, showing large fluctuations but no obvious change. However, there has been a great decline in the number of Lesser Whitethroats trapped at Icklesham, where there has been relatively constant ringing effort in recent autumns. The number of birds ringed in the county fell from 627 in 1989 to 308 in 1992 but recovered slightly to 394 in 1993.

Lesser Whitethroats arrive from mid-April onwards, peaking in early May. During 1965-93, first arrival dates fell between 4 and 30 April with the average 16 April. The earliest ever were singles at Moulsecoomb Wild Park on 4 April 1989 and 8 April 1973 and at Beachy Head on 7 April 1973. Numbers of spring migrants are generally low. There have been only four counts of over 20, the highest of which were 30 at Church Norton on 10 May 1985 and 35 at Beachy Head on 27 April 1989.

Post-breeding dispersal commences in late July or early August and by early September the main movement is over. Exceptionally large numbers occur at Beachy Head where day totals of 100 or more were recorded in 12 autumns between 1979 and 1993. Totals of 150 were recorded on 1 September 1980, 5 September 1982, twice in September 1984 and 27 August 1988 and 200 on 28-29 August 1982. During 1965-93, last dates varied between 29 September and 13 November, with the average 13 October. The latest recorded were singles at Beachy Head on 27 October 1979 and 28 October 1971, at Church Norton on 13 November 1988 and at Burgess Hill from 12 to 21 November 1957. The 1971 bird was trapped and found to show characteristics of the eastern race *S.c. blythi*.

The Lesser Whitethroat migrates southeast, through Italy to winter in Ethiopia and returns via the Middle East. Fifteen birds ringed in Sussex have been recovered abroad. Of these, two were in northern Italy and seven in Egypt in autumn and three in Lebanon and singles in Israel, Cyprus and France in spring. One of the birds recovered in Egypt, ringed at the Crumbles in 1965, was the first British-ringed Lesser Whitethroat to be found in Africa. A bird controlled at Beachy Head in September 1989 had been ringed near Bootle, Cumbria on the 15 July of that year, an area where the species is expanding its breeding range (New Atlas).   *Robert D M Edgar*

Whitethroat   *Sylvia communis*

Status:- A very common summer visitor and passage migrant.

The Whitethroat is essentially a bird of low hedges and scrub favouring tangles of hawthorn, bramble and sometimes gorse, often with tall herbaceous vegetation. Much in the way that the Peregrine was the classic indicator of the effects of agricultural pesticides, so the Whitethroat has demonstrated the acute effect of the Sahel drought on migratory birds (Winstanley, Spencer & Williamson 1974). As the Atlas map shows, the species is still widespread in Sussex, particularly on the Downs, but the numbers are greatly reduced from those pre-1969. The *Sussex Bird Report* for that year states that "the breeding population (at Beachy Head) was estimated to be at least one-third lower than usual, at Alfriston a 75% decrease was noted and a 50% decrease was noted in parts of West Sussex". On a 98 ha farm at Sidlesham, between 14-19 pairs were present in 1962 and 1964, but none in 1973 and only four pairs in 1978. At Beachy Head the numbers of birds ringed in autumn declined from a quarter of all birds trapped there in 1968 to less than 4% in 1985 (Edgar 1986). Changes in the annual ringing totals at this site during 1962-85 mirrored almost exactly the changes in the CBC Population Index for this species over the same period. Evidence of a slight recovery since the mid-1980s is provided by an increase in the proportion of Whitethroats ringed at Beachy Head from a low of 4.7% in 1987 to 12.4% in 1992, with an average for the period 1986-92 of 8.1%. Although the landscape changed significantly between the late 1960s and early 1990s, there remains a great deal of unoccupied habitat should numbers ever fully recover.

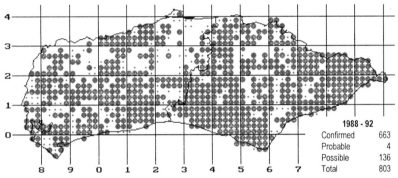

1988 - 92	
Confirmed	663
Probable	4
Possible	136
Total	803

The Woodland Survey that covered the period 1963-74 found that Whitethroats were the 11th most frequently encountered species in woodlands on clay. However, in a survey of 40 semi-natural broadleaved woodlands on Wealden clay in West Sussex in 1981, it was the 42nd most frequently encountered species at an average density of only 1.1 pairs per km² (Bealey & Sutherland 1983). Densities on farmland are higher, as shown by censuses of the bird communities at the Brinsbury Estate in 1980 and at Plumpton in 1982 which revealed densities of 8 pairs per km² and 7.5 pairs per km² respectively (Prater 1982, 1983b). Censuses of breeding birds in defined areas carried out during the 1980s produced a wide range of average densities from a high of 27 pairs per km² in young coniferous plantation at Finche's Wood, Nuthurst to a low of 4.6 pairs per km² in mixed scrub and woodland at Moulsecoomb Wild Park. Estimating the size of the county population is difficult, given the wide range of breeding densities, but the use of national CBC data suggests a figure in the range 10,500-12,700 pairs. However, breeding densities in Sussex appear to be higher than the national average (except in woodland) so a range of 10,000-15,000 pairs may be more appropriate. The national population was estimated to be 660,000 pairs (New Atlas).

The first Whitethroats usually arrive in mid-April. During the period

1965-93, earliest dates varied between 24 March and 23 April, with the average 10 April. The earliest ever was one at Southease on 19 March 1966 though others were recorded at the Crumbles on 24 March 1989, Hastings on 25 March 1954, Beachy Head on 26 March 1967 and Seaford Head on 30 March 1990. Falls are rare in spring although there were 100 at Beachy Head on 27 April 1981 and 180 there on 18 May 1975. Arrival may continue into June in some years.

Post-breeding dispersal commences in mid-July but emigration does not reach a peak until mid to late August. Day totals of over 100 are regular at Beachy Head; 300 were recorded there in 1974, 1989 and twice in August 1992, 400 in both 1968 and 1969 and 500 on 29 August 1992, the latter the highest total for the county. A few birds remain into October. During 1965-93, latest dates varied between 5 October and 17 December, with the average 19 October. The latest ever, at Darwell Reservoir on 17 December 1972, was presumably wintering. If it is excluded, the average moves to 17 October. There have been six November records for the county up to 16th (1958, Crumbles and 1994, Belle Tout).

Ringing has shown that the birds that pass through Sussex in autumn come from a wide area of Britain extending north to Scotland. There have been seven recoveries of Sussex-ringed Whitethroats in Portugal indicating that our birds head southwest towards Iberia after leaving the county. That two of the recoveries were over a month after the birds have been ringed, another after three weeks and one after two weeks indicates that the migration of this species may be fairly leisurely. There have been no recoveries, as yet, from south of the Mediterranean.   *Robert D M Edgar*

Garden Warbler   *Sylvia borin*

Status:- A very common summer visitor and passage migrant.

	1988 - 92
Confirmed	410
Probable	7
Possible	182
Total	599

The Garden Warbler inhabits deciduous woodland and scrub, with dense ground cover for nesting. In farmland areas they occur in small copses and clumps of hawthorn or blackthorn (New Atlas). Despite the comment in Shrubb about the similar distribution of this species and the closely related Blackcap, the Atlas map clearly shows that the Garden Warbler is an inhabitant of the Weald, with few occurring on the Downs or coastal plain.

The scrub that has developed on the downland slopes post-myxomatosis is clearly not to its liking.

The Woodland Survey that covered the period 1963-74 indicated that Garden Warblers were very scarce or absent in woodlands near the coast and two or three times as numerous in woodlands on clay soils than chalk or sand. They were half as numerous as Blackcaps except on clay soils where the position was reversed (Shrubb). Bealey & Sutherland (1983) found the species in 32 of the 40 semi-natural broadleaved woodlands they surveyed in West Sussex at an average density of 10.7 pairs per km², a figure similar to the density reported for Blackcap of 10.3 pairs per km². Combining the results of a number of censuses of breeding birds in defined areas carried out during the 1980s, in which densities varied between 1.5 pairs per km² (on farmland at Plumpton) and 16 pairs per km² (in Finche's Wood, Nuthurst), gives an average of 5.1 pairs per km². Applying this figure to the 417 tetrads in which breeding was confirmed or probable during the Atlas Survey indicates a county population of about 8500 pairs. Nationally, numbers have increased steadily since the mid-1970s when the population was at a low point (Marchant *et al* 1990). There is insufficient data available for Sussex to identify any population trends although the number of birds ringed in the county has increased by 50% since 1989.

A few Garden Warblers arrive from mid-April onwards, but the majority during the first half of May. During 1965-93, first arrival dates fell between 1 April and 2 May with the average 15 April. The earliest ever was one at Seaford Head on 1 April 1990 though there have been five other records for the first week of that month. Numbers of spring migrants are generally very small, indeed there have been only six records of 20 or more including an exceptional one of 100 at Pebsham on 11 May 1969.

Emigration occurs between mid-August and early October. Counts of this inconspicuous bird are typically low and rarely are more than ten recorded, except at Beachy Head where day totals of 100 or more were estimated on ten dates in six of the autumns during 1970-93, including counts of 100-120 on four dates in August 1989 and maxima of 200 on 6 September 1984 and 8 September 1986. During 1964-93, latest dates varied between 1 October and 7 November with the average 20 October. The latest ever was one at Beachy Head on 7 November 1968, where three were present on 3 November 1974.

Some Garden Warblers that pass through Sussex in autumn are of continental origin. Evidence for this is provided by four recoveries: one ringed at Beachy Head on 14 September 1976 and controlled in the Halle region of eastern Germany, 828 km east, on 4 June 1979; one ringed at Beachy Head on 16 September 1970 and controlled at Linburg, Belgium, 358 km east, on 16 July 1971; one ringed at Beclers, Belgium on 12 August 1988 and controlled at Beachy Head, 229 km west, on 11 September 1988; and one ringed near Rohrbach, Austria on 22 August 1992 and controlled at Icklesham, 987 km WNW, on 28 September of that year. The first two birds were presumably on breeding territories when controlled whereas the latter two were most likely on passage when first ringed, indicating an origin further to the east. Sussex-ringed birds have also been recovered in France, Spain, Portugal and Morocco.

Robert D M Edgar

Blackcap   *Sylvia atricapilla*

Status:- A very common summer visitor and passage migrant; small numbers winter.

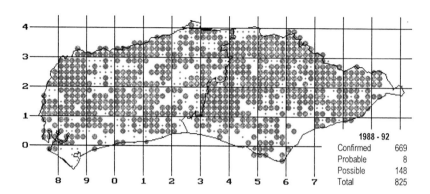

1988 - 92	
Confirmed	669
Probable	8
Possible	148
Total	825

The Blackcap breeds in deciduous woodland throughout the county. As the Atlas map shows, the most obvious gaps in its distribution were the Selsey peninsula and the levels in the vicinity of Pevensey and Rye, reflecting the lack of suitable habitat in these areas. Numbers in Britain have been increasing from at least the mid-1950s (Marchant *et al* 1990) although the reasons are not known (New Atlas). No breeding data are available to show long term trends in Sussex. However, the number of birds ringed at Beachy Head during 1962-84 closely mirrored the increase in the increase shown by the CBC Population Index over the same period (Edgar 1986).

The Woodland Survey that covered the period 1963-74 indicated that Blackcaps were widespread in the county and most numerous in woods on the chalk and near the coast (Shrubb). Bealey & Sutherland (1983) reported an average density of 10.3 pairs per km² based on their survey of semi-natural broadleaved woodlands in West Sussex in 1982. This figure was marginally lower than the density they reported for Garden Warblers, whereas in most areas the Blackcap considerably outnumbers the Garden Warbler. Given that the 1963-74 Woodland Survey found Blackcaps to be at least twice as numerous as Garden Warblers, except on clay soils where the situation was reversed, it may be significant that the woods surveyed by Bealey & Sutherland all lay on Wealden clay. Densities on farmland are lower, as shown by censuses of the bird communities at the Brinsbury Estate in 1980 and at Plumpton in 1982 which revealed densities of 4.5 pairs per km² and 4.8 pairs per km² respectively (Prater 1982, 1983b). Combining the results of a number of censuses of breeding birds in defined areas carried out during the 1980s, in which average densities varied between 1.3 pairs per km² (in downland scrub at Lullington Heath NNR) and 13.2 pairs per km² (in coniferous woodland at Finche's Wood, Nuthurst) gives an average of 8.2 pairs per km². Applying this figure to the 677 tetrads in which breeding was confirmed or probable during the Atlas Survey indicates a county population of about 22,000 pairs, although if the tetrads in which possible breeding was recorded are included, the figure rises to 27,000 pairs. The national population was estimated to be 580,000 pairs (New Atlas).

The presence of wintering Blackcaps masks the arrival of birds in early spring although it would appear that the breeding population arrives from mid to late March onwards. Arrival peaks between mid-April and early May but spring passage is usually unexceptional with low numbers recorded at the coast. In autumn, however, prodigious numbers may occur at both downland and coastal sites where there are berry-bearing shrubs. The numbers are highest at Beachy Head where counts of up to 500 in a day are regular in autumn and peaks of 1000 or more were recorded on 20 September 1980 and 8 September 1984. Large numbers are ringed in Sussex including nearly 5000 in 1992 alone. At Beachy Head, it has been found that 99% of all birds ringed are in their first year and that there are 8.6% more females than males (Edgar 1986). An explanation is provided by Davis (1967) who found that at seven British bird observatories males exceeded females by 9%, suggesting that the sexes must take slightly different migration routes. Although the bulk of birds pass through the county in September, there is some movement at the coast as early as late July. Whether there are significant numbers in October depends on the incidence of easterly winds which 'drift' birds of continental origin westwards, as in 1984 when 140 were recorded at Beachy Head on 11 October, an unusually large number for this late in the year. A few birds, presumably arriving to winter, are always recorded at coastal sites in late October and early November.

Wintering birds are of regular occurrence and generally appear to be increasing, although the exact numbers involved are not clear. Following the first report of overwintering in the county in 1947/48, Blackcaps were recorded almost annually in the winter months during the 1950s but the reports involved less than five birds each year. In 1959/60 the unprecedented total of nine was reported, followed by a modest increase in winter records during the 1960s. As in many other counties there was a dramatic increase during the 1970s, with no fewer than 71 recorded in an enquiry organised by the BTO during the winter of 1978/79 (Hughes 1980). Subsequent recording has been less rigorous but at least 48 were reported in early 1985 and 58 in late 1993. Most reports are of one or two birds although parties of five were recorded near Ditchling in 1959 and at Alexandra Park, Hastings in 1991. Rather more Blackcaps winter in coastal areas than inland but reports from the interior have become more frequent. In neighbouring Hampshire, there has been a similar marked increase in wintering birds since the early 1970s (Clark & Eyre 1993) although the numbers recorded there have been far higher.

Ringing has provided clues to the origin of Blackcaps that winter in Sussex. A male ringed at Revtangen, Klepp, Norway on 15 October 1982 was found dead at Steyning, 950 km SSW, on 17 December the same year, a female ringed at De Panne, Belgium on 6 October 1984 was found dead at Worthing on 28 January 1985 and one ringed at Icklesham on 19 September 1990 was controlled at Inglostadt-Zuchering, Oberbayern, Germany, 807 km SSE, on 12 June 1994. Wintering birds are not necessarily faithful to the same area as is indicated by a male ringed in East Cosham, Hampshire on 27 December 1983 and controlled at Patcham, Brighton on 4 February 1985. Return passage eastwards is shown by a female ringed at Worbarrow, Dorset on 14 November 1982 and found dead at Brighton on 28 March 1983. Most British birds winter around the Mediterranean and there have been at least nine midwinter recoveries of Sussex-ringed Blackcaps in Algeria, with others in Spain, Portugal and Morocco. A notable first was a bird ringed at Beachy Head on 12 September 1977 and found in Senegal that November. Although it had been assumed that some of our Blackcaps crossed the Sahara, this was the first proof that they did so.

Ringing has also shown that birds originating from a wide area of Britain, as far north as Islay, pass through Sussex in autumn. The breeding populations in Europe show a migratory divide, those west of 12°E heading chiefly southwest to southern France and Iberia, those east of 12°E chiefly southeast towards Cyprus and Levant (BWP). A few 'cross-over' as shown by a female ringed at Beachy Head on 25 September 1981 and controlled at Vach, Suhl, eastern Germany on 9 July 1983 and another female ringed at the same site on 10 September 1963 and killed in Lebanon on 19 October the same year. Other noteworthy recoveries include a male ringed at Beachy Head on 29 August 1966 and controlled at Strathvaich, Highland, 835 km NNW, on 21 November 1971 and a first-year male ringed at Icklesham on 14 October 1991 and controlled in Belgium, 201 km east, the following day. Another first-year male ringed at Beachy Head on 22 September 1977 was found freshly dead in Cadiz, Spain on 6 June 1988 (when it should have been breeding). The 10 years 8 months and 14 days between ringing and recovery established a longevity record for this species. *Robert D M Edgar*

Greenish Warbler   *Phylloscopus trochiloides*

Status:- A very rare vagrant (two records).

First recorded in the county in 1981, there has been one since:

1981:   A male in Belle Tout Wood, Beachy Head on 19 May was singing for much of the day.
1995:   One in a hedge immediately to the west of the Beachy Head Hotel on 10 September.

The individual seen in 1995 was part of the biggest national influx yet recorded with 32 reported, mainly from the east coast, during 2 to 20 September (*Birding World* 8: 328).

Previously published records from the Crumbles on 10 September 1959, 19 October 1962 and 17 September 1965 and at Selsey Bill on 27 September 1962 are no longer considered to be acceptable following a review (Dean 1985, Rogers *et al* 1985).

There were nearly 240 records of this species in the British Isles during 1962-94, the majority in autumn but, in recent years, an increasing number in spring, although with ten records from Kent up to 1990 (Evans 1994b) more might have been expected in the county. It breeds from Germany and Finland to central Asia wintering in southern Asia.   *Richard Fairbank*

Pallas's Warbler   *Phylloscopus proregulus*
Status:- A very scarce visitor (34 records, nearly all in late autumn).

First seen in the county at Beachy Head in October 1968, there have been records in 14 subsequent years including four in 1974, 1986 and 1987 and at least seven in 1994 (fig. 91).

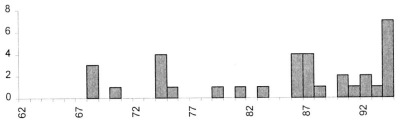

Figure 91. Annual totals of Pallas's Warblers (all records).

One in Lucerne Close, Aldwick, Bognor Regis between 14 and 23 March 1992 (*Birding World* 5: 88) was the first British record outside the period 23 September to 28 December. Occurrences are generally later than those of the superficially similar, but duller, Yellow-browed Warbler (fig. 92). Earliest in autumn were individuals at Hodcombe, Beachy Head from 11 to 13 October 1970 and at the Severals, Church Norton on 11 October 1987, while the latest were seen at Hodcombe on 19-20 November in 1981 and at Atherington on three dates between 11 November and 7 December 1986 and on 5-6 December 1987. One at Friston Forest on 25 and 28 December 1987 was the latest British record.

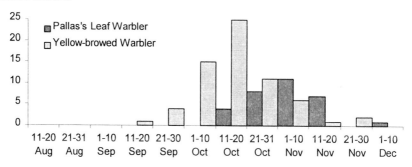

Figure 92. Cumulative 'autumn' arrival dates of Pallas's and Yellow-browed Warblers in Sussex (all records).

Over half have been seen at Beachy Head (19) with five at Church Norton or the Severals (1979, 1986, 1987, 1988 and 1994), four at Atherington/Littlehampton Golf Course (1986, 1987, 1993 and 1994), two at Balsdean (6 November 1986 and 12 November 1990) and singles at Aldwick (March 1992), East Brighton (Sheepcote Valley on 22-23 October 1994), Friston Forest (December 1987) and Hastings (East Hill on 3 November 1994). That two should have been seen at Balsdean, where there are very few trees, is particularly surprising, contrasting with the lack of records from Selsey Bill. This is presumably due to the lack of any suitable habitat that is readily viewable at Selsey, although the Aldwick individual often frequented shrubs in open plan gardens.

Three were seen at Beachy Head in October 1968, four there in 1974 (including two in Belle Tout Wood from 17 to 19 November, one remaining to 21st, although they were only ever seen together once) and three in 1994. Nine of those seen at Beachy Head have been in Belle Tout Wood, seven at Hodcombe, two in Whitbread Hollow and one at both Birling Gap and Long Down. The first to be seen in the county, on 18 October 1968, was trapped at Whitbread Hollow and subsequently released at Belle Tout Wood where it remained to 20th. It has been included in the above totals for both locations.

Despite over 800 records of this hyperactive gem in the British Isles during 1962-94 it remains one of the most sought-after autumn vagrants. It is perhaps surprising that none were found in the county in 1982, a year when over 120 were recorded in Britain (Howey & Bell 1985) while the seven recorded in 1994 were part of the largest national influx to date with 180 reported from 14 October to mid-November (Nightingale & Allsopp 1995). It breeds in Siberia from the Altai to Manchuria wintering in South-East Asia. Other races breed in the Himalayas and southern China. *Richard Fairbank*

Yellow-browed Warbler   *Phylloscopus inornatus*

Status:- A very scarce visitor (69 records, mostly in autumn).

First recorded in the county at Belle Tout Wood, Beachy Head on 24 October 1965, with seven seen during the 1960s and 11 during the 1970s. Since then, records have increased dramatically with 33 during the 1980s, including eight in 1985 and seven in 1988, and an average of nearly four per year since (fig. 93).

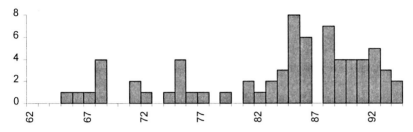

Figure 93. Annual totals of Yellow-browed Warblers (all records).

All records relate to single individuals, although two were present at different areas of Beachy Head on 20 October 1968 (Long Down and Belle Tout Wood, the latter having been present the previous day) and on 17 October 1992 (Whitbread Hollow and Belle Tout Wood, the latter from 16 to 18 October).

Records have been in September (5), October (51), November (9), December (1), January (1), March (1) and April (1). They include one in the churchyard at Thorney Island between 10 January and 26 April 1975, one at Westdean, Friston Forest from 28 March to 20 April 1975 and one at Church Norton on 12 April 1971.

Usually earlier than the more active Pallas's Warbler, there is a distinct peak in mid-October (fig. 92). The earliest autumn arrivals were at Birling Gap on 18 September 1988 and Church Norton on 26 September 1990 and Hodcombe, Beachy Head on 26 September 1994. The latest records were in Belle Tout Wood, Beachy Head on 24 November 1991 and 30 November 1968, and in an alder wood on Amberley Wild Brooks on 20 December 1986.

Over half the records have been at Beachy Head (38) with four each at Atherington/Littlehampton West Beach, Church Norton and the lower Cuckmere Valley. Three have been seen in the Brighton area (including one at Patcham Place on 15 October 1967 and one at Balsdean), three at Thorney Churchyard and two at both Rye Harbour (15 October 1985 and 1 October 1988) and Shoreham-by-Sea (both in October 1985). There are single records from Aldwick (5 November 1989), Amberley Wild Brooks (the furthest inland), Combe Haven (29 September 1984), Icklesham (trapped on 16 October 1992), Pagham Lagoon (29-30 October 1988), Rustington (29 October 1977), Seaford Head (20 October 1990), Selsey Bill (1 October 1994) and Westdean (March-April 1975). The record of one at Selsey Bill on 17 September 1961, at the time the first county record, is no longer considered to be acceptable.

One at Belle Tout Wood, Beachy Head from 13 to 17 November 1966 was potentially the first British occurrence of a bird showing the characteristics of Hume's Yellow-browed Warbler *P. (i.) humei* (Quinn & Clement 1972, Scott 1979) although the *BOURC* recommended a less formal treatment of subspecies, commenting that there was a broad zone of integration but that "some vagrants of unknown provenance appear to approach *humei*" (*BOURC* 1980). Its view appears to be changing, with consideration currently being given to granting *humei* full species status. In this context the above record is about to be re-examined and, if found acceptable, will be the first for Britain. Those overwintering at Thorney Island and Westdean in early 1975 were widely regarded as showing some of the characteristics associated with *humei*.

There have been between 250 and 350 records of this species in the British Isles in most years since the early 1980s, with 615 in 1985, 553 in 1986 and an impressive 771 in 1988 (Fraser & Ryan 1994), the years with most records in the county to date. The nominate race breeds from the Urals east across Siberia, while *humei* breeds from central Asia to the Himalayas. Both winter in southern Asia.   *Richard Fairbank*

Radde's Warbler   *Phylloscopus schwarzi*

Status:- A very rare vagrant (four autumn records).

First recorded in 1974, a further three were seen during 1991-94:

1974: One trapped at Hodcombe, Beachy Head on 18 October was the 14th British record.
1991: One in a hedge adjoining the southern part of Grafton Road, Selsey Bill, during the morning of 21 October.
1992: One trapped at Icklesham on 30 September.
1994: One in gardens at Reigate Road, Worthing on 26-27 October.

That at Icklesham was attracted to a multi-species audio tape played in the hope of luring a Yellow-browed Warbler and was not seen in the field. The individual in Worthing was an exceptional garden bird being about 1 km from the coast.

There were nearly 150 records of this leggy, stout-billed *Phylloscopus* warbler in the British Isles during 1962-94, but only two earlier occurrences. It breeds across southern Siberia to North Korea wintering in South East Asia.

Richard Fairbank

Dusky Warbler   *Phylloscopus fuscatus*

Status:- A very rare vagrant (three autumn records).

First recorded in 1974, two have been seen since:

1974: One trapped at Whitbread Hollow, Beachy Head on 18 October (*Brit. Birds* 68: plate 45) was the 16th British record.
1991: One skulking in gorse at Shooters Bottom, to the southeast of Hodcombe, Beachy Head from 27 to 30 October.
1992: One at Combe Haven on 26 October.

These records are in exactly the same years as, but generally slightly later than, the first three Radde's Warblers. Did another lurk unfound in late

October 1994? In complete contrast, Kent recorded 14 Dusky Warblers but only three Radde's up to 1990 (Evans 1994), suggesting that more of the former might have been expected in the county.

There were just over 150 records of this skulking warbler in the British Isles during 1962-94, but only two earlier occurrences. More readily heard than seen, it breeds from western to northeast Siberia and southern China wintering in northeast India and South East Asia (Harrison 1982).

Richard Fairbank

Bonelli's Warbler *Phylloscopus bonelli*

Status:- A very rare vagrant (seven records).

First recorded in 1970, five more were seen during 1970s but there has only been one since. Records are:

1970:   One at Hodcombe, Beachy Head on 25 August.
1972:   One at Whitbread Hollow, Beachy Head on the morning of 9 April.
1973:   One in gardens at Alfriston for ten minutes on 7 August.
1977:   One trapped at Whitbread Hollow, Beachy Head on 15 September.
1979:   One at Cow Gap, Beachy Head on the morning of 5 May.
        One in the wood at Rye Harbour from at least 28 August to 1 September.
1986:   One trapped at Hodcombe, Beachy Head on 30 September.

Two were in spring (April and May) and five in autumn (August and September). All have been seen in East Sussex, five at Beachy Head and one each at Alfriston (the only record away from the coast) and Rye Harbour.

The very pronounced decline in the number of records in the county since the 1970s has not been matched nationally, occurrences remaining fairly constant. The six above in the 1970s represent *ca.* 16% of the British total during that decade, the Sussex share falling to *ca.* 2.5% in the 1980s. Those reported in 1972 and 1973 were the earliest British spring and autumn records respectively.

There were just over 120 records of this species in the British Isles during 1962-94. It breeds from northwest Africa to northern France and Turkey, wintering along the southern edge of the Sahara.

Richard Fairbank

Wood Warbler *Phylloscopus sibilatrix*

Status:- A very scarce summer visitor and passage migrant.

Wood Warblers are frequently associated with damp oak woodland such as occurs in the western half of the British Isles. The species appears never to have been common in Sussex and there is evidence of a decline in the last 25 years or so. Shrubb reported a county population of the order of 150 pairs between 1965-69 but survey work in 1982 and 1983 found only 44 and 42 pairs respectively (Bealey & Sutherland 1983, Prater 1986b). Since then, the number reported in any year has again fallen to an all time low of only eight in breeding habitat in 1992 and ten in 1993. The species is mainly found at sites on the sandstone ridges and in association with birch, beech and oak woodland, especially in Ashdown Forest which, until recently, was a stronghold for Wood Warblers in the county. However, even here the population has decreased drastically and barely 1-2 pairs breed currently. The reason for this decline is not known. The Atlas map unfortunately gives a distorted picture for any one year and shows the species to be more widespread than it is in reality, an impression exaggerated by the addition of the records (as open circles) for the years 1976-87.

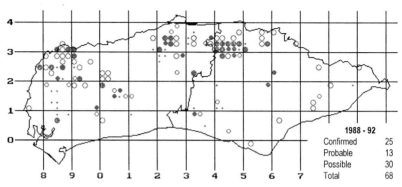

1988 - 92	
Confirmed	25
Probable	13
Possible	30
Total	68

Wood Warblers are one of the later summer migrants to arrive. Although singles were recorded at Wiggonholt Common on 7 April 1985 (the earliest county record) and Sidlesham Ferry on 9 April 1982, in some years none are seen until early May. During 1965-94 arrival dates varied between 7 April and 11 May with the average 22 April. Very few are seen on spring passage and totals of 21 in 1991 and 18 in 1993 are the largest recorded in the county. Five at Church Norton on 21 April 1988 is the highest day-count for a single site. Birds normally continue to arrive until mid-May but in some years later migrants are recorded, such as one at Beachy Head on 31 May 1975. One at this site on 26 June 1987 was indicative either of very late spring arrival or early post-breeding dispersal.

Wood Warblers are equally scarce on autumn passage which usually extends from late July into August and occasionally September. One at Littlehampton Golf Course on 1 October 1992 is by far the latest county record, exceeding that at Rye Harbour on 21 September 1986 by ten days. The number of birds reported in autumn in recent years has varied between just two in 1985 and 1991 and 17 in 1987. Most records are of single birds although there were five at Beachy Head on 11 August 1968.

Fewer than 100 Wood Warblers have been ringed in Sussex from which there have been no recoveries. However, one ringed as a nestling in the New Forest, Hampshire in June 1981 was controlled at Partridge Green, 97 km east, six weeks later while another ringed at Aldershot, Hampshire in June 1989 (also as a nestling) was found dead at Cuckfield, 55 km ESE, also six weeks later.   *Mike Scott-Ham*

Chiffchaff   *Phylloscopus collybita*

Status:- A very common summer visitor and passage migrant; small numbers winter.

The Chiffchaff is primarily a bird of deciduous woodland, requiring tall trees in its breeding habitat. It can also be found in farmland copses and shaws but is usually absent from scrub that is not of sufficient age to possess mature trees. The Atlas map shows that it is well distributed throughout most of Sussex, being absent only from treeless areas such as parts of the eastern Downs and the coastal levels. It is rather more widespread in the wooded High Weald than the Willow Warbler.

1988 - 92	
Confirmed	704
Probable	8
Possible	133
Total	845

The Woodland Survey that covered the period 1963-74 indicated that Chiffchaffs were two to five times scarcer than Willow Warblers and comprised about 2-5% of the total bird population (Shrubb). Densities were higher on clay soils than in other areas. Bealey & Sutherland (1983) reported a density of 11.1 pairs per km² based on their survey of semi-natural broadleaved woodlands in West Sussex, a figure significantly lower than the national average of 25.71 pairs per km² (New Atlas). The species was also much less common than the Willow Warbler for which a density of 31.6 pairs per km² was reported. Combining the results of a number of censuses of breeding birds in defined areas carried out during the 1980s, in which densities varied between 1.76 pairs per km² (on farmland at the Brinsbury Estate) and 23.1 pairs per km² (at West Dean Woods), gives an average of 8.6 pairs per km². Applying this figure to the 712 tetrads in which breeding was confirmed or probable during the Atlas Survey indicates a county population of about 25,000 pairs, an estimate which may be too high given the wide variation in breeding densities in different habitats.

The earliest dates for spring arrival are confused by the presence of wintering birds though some birds undoubtedly arrive in the first ten days of March, as shown by a high count of 14 at Seaford Head on 10 March 1990. The peak numbers tend to occur in early April although the presence of 60 at Selsey Bill on 7 May 1991 shows that arrival may continue for at least another month.

The main autumn departure is rather later than that of Willow Warblers but one on a boat 11 km south of Brighton on 23 July must have been going somewhere! Very large numbers may be recorded in September at coastal sites, especially at Beachy Head, where there have been many records of 400 or more. Larger totals at this site include 700 on 14 September 1989, 900 on 14 September 1985, 1000 on 16 September 1985, 2000 on 24 September 1989 and 1200 on 29 September 1987.

Walpole-Bond referred to a wintering bird in December 1875 and two in

January 1882, but by 1960 des Forges & Harber knew of only 14 records for December, about 18 for January and 18 for February. Numbers of wintering birds have subsequently increased although there is much variation from winter to winter. In early 1980, for example, only three were recorded compared with 32 at the beginning of January 1987. A cold spell later in the month reduced the total to seven. Nearly all wintering birds are found at or near the coast in scrub close to water. A total of 36 birds at 23 sites in January 1993 was the largest recorded since January 1987. This is in marked contrast to neighbouring Hampshire where over 100 have been recorded in some winters, including up to 26 at one site alone (Clark & Eyre 1993). The most reported at any one site in Sussex in winter was five at Pagham Harbour in January 1985, Rye Harbour in January 1992 and Seaford Head in February 1992.

That the county is an important staging area for migrant Chiffchaffs is shown by the control of no less than five Sussex-ringed birds in Senegal, West Africa in mid-winter. All had been ringed in September (two at Icklesham and one each at Beachy Head, Charleston Reedbed and Cissbury Ring). The bird ringed at Beachy Head in 1989 was nearly three and a half years old and was still in Senegal as late as 10 March. Less surprisingly, Sussex-ringed birds have also been recovered in Spain and Morocco in winter. Some individuals have demonstrated the unexpected, such as a bird ringed at Charleston Reedbed in September 1989 which was still in central Sweden in November of the following year. This apparently healthy individual had most likely summered further north (where most Swedish Chiffchaffs breed) but it seems surprising that it had not already departed. Birds from as far west as County Kerry, Ireland have reached Sussex and one ringed in Eastbourne was recovered on Heligoland, Germany in May.

Very small numbers of birds showing characters of either the Scandinavian race *P.c. abietinus* or, less frequently, the Siberian race *P.c. tristis* are recorded almost annually, most regularly in late autumn but also in the winter months. One such bird remained at Ifield Mill Pond from November 1990 to 29 March 1991.   *Robert D M Edgar*

Willow Warbler   *Phylloscopus trochilus*

Status:- An abundant summer visitor and passage migrant.

The Willow Warbler is our most widely distributed and abundant summer visitor. During the Atlas Survey, it was found in 872 tetrads (87%) and, as the map shows, it was absent from only a few inland areas (possibly due to lack of coverage) and from parts of the eastern Downs and coastal plain, where their is a lack of suitable habitat in the form of scrub, woodland edge and young plantations.

The Woodland Survey that covered the period 1963-74 showed this to be the fourth most numerous species breeding in the woodlands of Sussex and that it comprised on average 7-10% of the total bird populations recorded, except near the coast, where it comprised about 5% (Shrubb). Bealey & Sutherland (1983) reported a density of 31.6 pairs per km² based on their survey of semi-natural broadleaved woodlands in West Sussex, a figure rather higher than that of 24.7 pairs per km² obtained by averaging the results of a number of surveys of breeding birds in defined areas carried out during the 1980s. Densities recorded by these latter surveys varied between 9.4 pairs per km² (at Moulsecoomb) and 117.4 pairs per km² (at West Dean Woods). Applying a figure of 24.7 pairs per km² to the 711 tetrads in which breeding was confirmed or probable during the Atlas Survey indicates a county population in excess of 70,000 pairs. However, this estimate may again be too high allowing for the wide variation in breeding densities in different habitats.

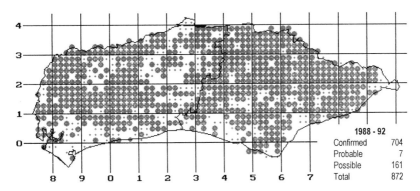

1988 - 92	
Confirmed	704
Probable	7
Possible	161
Total	872

The first Willow Warblers are usually recorded in the last week of March though the majority of birds do not arrive until the second half of April and early May. During 1964-93, first arrival dates fell between 4 March and 2 April with the average 24 March. The earliest ever reported were a male singing at Duddeswell, Ashdown Forest on 4 March 1993 and one at Seaford Head on 7 March 1992. Other very early birds were recorded at Beachy Head on 12 March 1967 and at Icklesham on 14 March 1989. The appearance of birds well inland in March is not unusual. Falls of up to 300 birds at coastal sites in spring are not infrequent, but one of 800 at Beachy Head on 15 April 1970 was exceptional. Numbers at inland sites are never as great but 150 at Bewl Water on 19 April 1983 was noteworthy.

Dispersal, probably of young birds, commences in mid-July. A count of 200 at Beachy Head on the 26 July 1977 was exceptional although, had it been made at this site in August, it would not have been considered unusual. Indeed 500 or more were recorded there 16 times between 1968 and 1972, with 1000 on 7 August 1985 and 10 August 1977 the largest counts recorded in the county. Numbers dwindle rapidly after mid-September and few are recorded in October. There are six records for November, the latest being at Hurst Green on 24 November 1980 (a bird thought to be of the northern race *P.t. acredula*) and at Cobnor, Chichester Harbour on 27 November 1991. There are old records of birds said to have been "obtained" on 9 December 1859 and 26 December 1892 (des Forges & Harber) and Hudson (1973) lists a record of one at Whyke from 11 to 26 December 1949.

Birds showing the characteristics of the race *acredula* are rarely seen in spring, but a small number are recorded in many autumns. Singles were trapped at Plumpton on 23 August and 7 and 17 September 1987 and, at

Beachy Head, 70% of the 250 present on 24 August of that year were thought to be of this race.

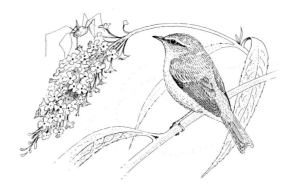

There have been no less than 115 recoveries of Willow Warblers ringed in Sussex. These include one ringed at Beachy Head on 20 August 1972 that was found freshly dead in Cambridgeshire, over six and a half years later, on 12 May 1979. Five have been recovered in North Africa (four in Morocco and one in Algeria). Singles found dead in Castellan, Spain on about 15 February 1986 and in Morocco on 8 February 1989 were presumably early spring migrants as Willow Warblers winter south of the Sahara in tropical Africa. Although no foreign-ringed birds have been recovered in Sussex, one ringed at Ashcombe Bottom as a juvenile on 12 June 1982 was controlled in Aland, Finland on 17 May 1983, an apparent case of a spring migrant overshooting. Over half the recoveries of Sussex-ringed Willow Warblers have been at least 100 km away including a total of 20 in northern England and Scotland, five in Wales and three in Ireland. Of birds ringed outside the county and recovered in Sussex, 27 were from northern England and Scotland, four from Wales and two from Ireland.   *Robert D M Edgar*

Goldcrest   *Regulus regulus*

Status:- A very common breeding resident, common passage migrant and winter visitor.

The Atlas map shows the Goldcrest to be widely distributed in the north of the county, in the woodlands of the High Weald and in central West Sussex. It is virtually absent from the coastal plain, most of the downland in East Sussex (except Friston Forest) and from the river valleys and levels, a distribution that reflects the species' preference for coniferous woodland.

In Britain the distribution of the Goldcrest has changed little since 1968-72 (New Atlas). There is little available breeding data for the years prior to the Atlas Survey except for CBC counts from defined areas and the results of two woodland surveys. Although no significant trends can be evaluated from these studies, they do provide some information about breeding densities. During the 1963-74 Woodland Survey, Goldcrests were found to be relatively more abundant in woodlands on sand compared with those on clay, chalk and the coastal plain. The same survey suggested that at least 20 other species were more abundant than Goldcrest in the 23 woodlands visited whereas Bealey & Sutherland (1983) showed this species to be the fourth most numerous in their survey of 40 semi-natural broadleaved woodlands in West Sussex. The latter study revealed an average density of 68.5 pairs per km², the highest figure reported in Sussex. Other breeding surveys in the county, which have recorded Goldcrests, have found widely varying densities ranging from an average of only 0.3 pairs per km² in 240 ha at Moulsecoomb Wild Park to 25.6 pairs per km² in a 50 ha coniferous plantation at Finche's Wood, Nuthurst. Estimating the size of the county population from such diverse and rather sparse information is difficult. Rough extrapolation of the data from the 1982 woodland survey would suggest that in that year there may have been in excess of 20,000 pairs in the woodlands of West Sussex alone. Combining the results of the other breeding surveys gives an average density of about 8 pairs per km², a figure which if applied to the 420 tetrads in which breeding was confirmed during the Atlas Survey, would give a population estimate of about 13,000 pairs, rising to nearly 19,000 pairs if all the tetrads in which Goldcrests were recorded are included. It is likely these estimates are on the high side but they are similar to Clark & Eyre's (1993) estimate of 20,000 pairs in neighbouring Hampshire.

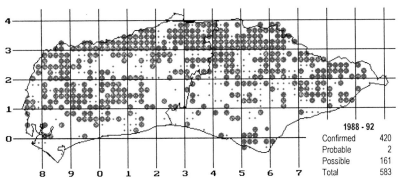

	1988 - 92	
	Confirmed	420
	Probable	2
	Possible	161
	Total	583

Numbers of Goldcrests may be severely depleted by severe weather. In 1963, for example, following the previous harsh winter, only two breeding pairs were recorded, although others were undoubtedly not reported. Numbers had largely recovered by 1967 and the results of the 1963-74 Woodland Survey suggested an increase of over 500% between 1963 and 1974 (Shrubb).

Spring passage begins in February but the main movement occurs between mid-March and mid-April with smaller numbers through until early May. The largest day totals in spring were of 100 at Pagham Harbour on 26 March 1974, 70 at Rye Harbour on 17 April 1975 and 60 at Beachy Head on 29 March 1971.

Autumn passage, which usually commences in early September, is markedly heavier than that in spring. Between late September and early November, large numbers may be recorded at coastal localities, where some spectacular falls have occurred. Prior to 1970, no three-figure counts had been recorded but in that year there were 100 at Beachy Head on 13 October. Large numbers were again recorded there the following autumn with maxima of 200 and 250 on 7 and 29 October respectively. The largest count in 1973 was of 100, again at Beachy Head, on 26 September while counts at this site in October 1974 included 105 on 1st, 120 on 10th and 200 on 18th. The best year of that decade was 1975 when exceptional numbers were recorded at Beachy Head as follows:

September					October				
28th	29th	30th	2nd	9th	14th	16th	25th	27th	28th
100	170	100	100	80	250	180	300	260	120

Although 150 were recorded on 19 October 1976 and 125 on 13 October 1977, the numbers recorded at Beachy Head in the next three autumns were more normal. In 1979, however, there was a dramatic slump with no more than six being recorded on any one day. The largest falls in the 1980s were in 1982, when counts included 500 and 200 at Beachy Head on 6 and 20 October respectively, and 1989 when an estimated 1000 were thought to be in the Cissbury area (including a total of 95 trapped) on 30 September. This remains the largest day total for the county. A number of large counts at Beachy Head in 1990 included 100 on 29 September, 200 on 14 October, 150 on 18 October and 350 on 25 October while notable concentrations at other sites included 130 at Seaford Head on 20 October, 100 at Hollingbury Camp on 25 October and 100 at Goring on 27-28 October. In 1991, however, very few were reported with 40 at Seaford Head on 11 October the sole count in double-figures. Numbers remained low in 1992 and 1993, the largest count being of 90 at Beachy Head on 11 October 1992.

Large concentrations have occasionally been noted inland during the winter, for example, 110 at Ambersham Common in December 1982 and 90 at Old Lodge, Ashdown Forest in December 1984.

There have been 28 recoveries of Sussex-ringed Goldcrests, seven within the county, 11 elsewhere in southern England, two in Scotland, one in both Wales and Ireland, two in the Netherlands and four in France. Six birds ringed elsewhere in the country have been recovered in Sussex and one from West Germany.

Tim Parmenter

Firecrest   *Regulus ignicapillus*

Status:- A rare breeder and scarce passage migrant and winter visitor.

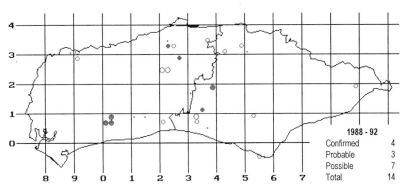

	1988 - 92	
	Confirmed	4
	Probable	3
	Possible	7
	Total	14

Prior to 1973, the Firecrest was recorded only as a passage migrant in spring and autumn and as an occasional winter visitor. In that year, an adult feeding young in Ashdown Forest on 19 July constituted the first breeding record for the county, eleven years after Firecrests bred for the first time in Britain in Hampshire in 1962 (Adams 1966). Two singing males were recorded in the same general area in 1974 and, although there was no indication of breeding in 1975, single pairs were located at two new sites near Lower Beeding in 1976. Breeding was again suspected in 1979 and 1981, then in 1982, a total of at least 11 singing males was found at four sites, mainly as a result of survey work by Bealey & Sutherland (1983) in West Sussex. Three colonies, comprising two, three and five singing males, were found in two woods where the birds showed a preference for the edges of mature spruce plantations. Although the 1982 records suggest a significant increase in the population at that time, it is quite likely that the birds had previously been overlooked. Since then, breeding was confirmed in 1983 and suspected in 1987-89, 1991 and 1993.

However, the species may well be under-recorded given that there are a number of suitable areas in the county for Firecrests which are rarely searched. The Atlas map shows both the results of the 1988-92 Atlas Survey and also those tetrads (as open circles) where Firecrests were recorded in the period 1976-87 but not in 1988-92. In 1988-91, the British population was estimated to be in the range 80-250 pairs (New Atlas) so Sussex holds only a small proportion of the national total.

The number of Firecrests recorded outside the breeding season has increased significantly in recent years (fig. 94).

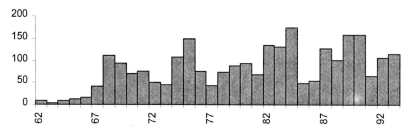

Figure 94. Annual totals of Firecrests, 1962 - 93.

There has also been a marked change in the occurrence of birds in spring and autumn. des Forges & Harber referred to a total of 220 Firecrests up to 1960 and, of those recorded after 1946, 66 were in spring, 44 in autumn and six in winter. Shrubb, however, reported a total of 820 birds between 1961 and 1976, almost equally divided between spring and autumn, whereas the cumulative monthly totals for 1983-93 shown below indicate that the autumn now produces the most records.

Aug	Sep	Oct	Nov	Dec	Jan	Feb	Mar	Apr	May	Jun
4	152	410	228	63	67	53	216	173	23	2

In spring, the presence of overwintering birds makes it difficult to establish early dates for genuine migrants. In some years, however, passage may start in late February as shown by the occurrence of Firecrests at sites where none had been recorded earlier in the winter. The main arrival is in March although birds may be recorded until early May or even later. Most are seen at coastal sites, especially Beachy Head, where there were 15 on 24 March and 11 on 20 April 1968. Totals for the whole county vary considerably from year to year; in 1962 there were just two whereas in 1975 a minimum of 90 was recorded.

Autumn passage usually commences in early September and continues through to December. Arrival dates during 1965-93 varied between 22 August and 26 September, with the average 9 September. The earliest were singles at Church Norton on 22 August 1988 and at Balsdean on 24 August 1981 with seven others recorded in that month between 1962 and 1993. The largest numbers occur in October, especially at Beachy Head, where 16 on 30 October 1982 and 14 on 30 September 1979 are the highest daily counts so far recorded in autumn. As in spring, the totals recorded vary considerably from year to year; over 100 were reported in 1982, 1984, 1989 and 1990.

Most of the Firecrests recorded in December and January are at coastal sites, with more in West than East Sussex.

There have been three recoveries of Firecrests ringed at Beachy Head. One controlled at Bournemouth, Dorset on 2 March 1980 had been ringed on 12 October 1979, one found dead at Burford, Oxfordshire on about 25 February 1983 had been ringed on 30 October 1982 and one controlled on Lundy, Devon on 26 October 1988 had been ringed 11 days previously on 15 October. *Tim Parmenter*

Spotted Flycatcher

Muscicapa striata

Status:- A fairly common summer visitor and passage migrant.

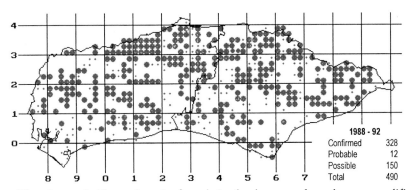

	1988 - 92
Confirmed	328
Probable	12
Possible	150
Total	490

The Spotted Flycatcher is found in both natural and man-modified habitats. In the former, it is a bird of the woodland edge, often choosing trees at the edge of lakes and ponds which are rich in insect life. Preferred habitats in the latter category include orchards, farmyards, large gardens, churchyards and parkland (68-72 BTO Atlas). The Atlas map shows that the species is widely distributed in Sussex, particularly in the north of the county. A number of gaps near the coast include the Selsey peninsula and the levels in the vicinity of Pevensey and Rye, reflecting the lack of mature trees in these areas. The Common Birds Census has shown that numbers have declined nationally since the 1960s to nearly a quarter of what they were (Marchant *et al* 1990). The cause of this decline is uncertain but is thought to be partly attributable to droughts in the Sahel region, south of the Sahara, through which Spotted Flycatchers pass to and from their wintering grounds in southern Africa (New Atlas).

During the Woodland Survey that covered the period 1963-74, the species was recorded in 12 out of the 23 sites visited. However, even in these, it was only found in just over half the years the sites were surveyed, and usually comprised under 0.5% of the total bird population recorded (Shrubb). A survey of semi-natural broadleaved woodlands in West Sussex in 1982 recorded an average density of 2.6 pairs per km² (Bealey & Sutherland 1983) while a survey of farmland bird communities at Plumpton (400 ha) in 1982 recorded a density of 1.0 pairs per km² (Prater 1983b). Other reported densities include six pairs in 55 ha at Fore Wood in 1981, two pairs in 7.5 ha at Hoads Wood, Fairlight in 1982, 16 pairs in 180 ha of mixed habitat around Bewl Water in 1984, three pairs in 40 ha at Hesworth Common in 1985, two pairs in 200 ha in Ashdown Forest in 1986, two pairs in 280 ha at Moulsecoomb Wild Park and three pairs in 60 ha at West Chiltington in 1988. The size of the breeding population in Sussex is difficult to assess as it is likely that some pairs were missed in towns and villages during the Atlas Survey. Applying a density of 2 pairs per km² to the 340 tetrads in which breeding was confirmed or probable indicates a county population of about 2600 pairs. The British total was estimated at 120,000 pairs (New Atlas).

The Spotted Flycatcher is one of the later summer migrants to arrive. The earliest county record is of one near Hastings on 8 April 1909 though others were recorded in the Cuckmere Valley on 11 April 1981, at Worthing on 14 April 1980 and Falmer on 14 April 1987. Arrival dates during 1965-93 varied between 11 April and 9 May, with the average 28 April. The main influx is in early to mid-May though arrivals can continue into early June. Numbers recorded in spring are typically low but occasional falls have been recorded, for example, 50 at Beachy Head and 62 at Sidlesham on 18 May 1975, 30 at Pebsham on 20 May 1969, and 25 at Beachy Head on both 20 May 1968 and 27 May 1970. Such falls have not been repeated, more recent concentrations rarely reaching double figures.

The main autumn movement usually begins in late August although individuals can be seen at the beginning of that month or even in late July. Counts of 15-25 are regular but larger falls occur from time to time (table 77).

Date	Locality	No. of birds
30 Aug. 1970	Beachy Head	50
16 Sep. 1971	Beachy Head	25
	Church Norton	23
7 Sep. 1976	Cissbury	47
29 Aug. 1977	Cissbury	50
8 Sep. 1977	Beachy Head	60
26 Sep. 1977	Church Norton	40
30 Aug. 1979	Cissbury	102
20 Sep. 1980	Beachy Head	75
21 Sep. 1980	Beachy Head	105
22 Sep. 1983	Beachy Head	67
26 Aug. 1985	Beachy Head	63
2 Sep. 1990	Sompting	91

Table 77. Peak autumn counts of Spotted Flycatchers.

During 1970-93, last dates varied between 28 September and 18 November, with the average 13 October. The latest ever recorded was one at Maynards Green on 18 November 1979 while the only other record for the month was of one at Beachy Head on 5 November 1975.

Ringing has shown that Spotted Flycatchers from as far north as central Scotland pass through Sussex, as shown by the recovery of a bird ringed at Icklesham on 2 September 1987 at Perth, Grampian on 16 June 1989. Birds from Ireland also pass through the county, as shown by one found injured at Robertstown on 5 July 1962 that had been ringed at Eastbourne on 16 September 1961 and one found dead at Ballymena, Antrim on 12 June 1964 that had also been ringed at the same site on 23 August 1963. There have been four foreign recoveries of Sussex-ringed birds comprising one ringed at Marley Common on 15 June 1964 and found dead at Agambuja, Portugal on 13 September of that year, one ringed at an unspecified locality on 3 September 1968 and controlled at Calais, France on 24 May 1970, one ringed at an unspecified locality on 18 September 1972 and found at Cadiz, Spain, 1685 km SSW, on 1 November 1972, and one ringed at Shoreham Sanctuary on 3 September 1980 and found dead at Seuta, Spanish Morocco, 1711 km SSW, on 27 September 1982. The recoveries from Spain, Portugal and Morocco indicate that Spotted Flycatchers head southwest after leaving Sussex.

Tim Parmenter

478

Red-breasted Flycatcher — *Ficedula parva*

Status:- A rare autumn vagrant (22 records).

One was recorded before 1962 (des Forges & Harber), a female seen briefly near Handcross on 29 April 1948 (Ferguson-Lees 1949). It is not only the sole spring record to date but also the only individual to be recorded away from the coast.

Twenty-one have been recorded since the beginning of 1962:

1967: One trapped at the Crumbles on 21 October.
1968: One trapped at Hope Gap, Seaford Head on 4 September.
      One at Belle Tout Wood, Beachy Head on 20 October.
      One above Whitbread Hollow, Beachy Head on 20 October.
1970: One at Belle Tout Wood, Beachy Head on 29 September.
1973: One at Hodcombe, Beachy Head on 11-12 October.
      One trapped at Whitbread Hollow, Beachy Head on 16 October.
1975: One at Church Norton on 27-28 September.
1976: One at Belle Tout Wood, Beachy Head on 25 September.
1977: One at the western end of Littlehampton Golf Course from 27 September to 1 October
      One at Went Hill, Birling Gap on 8 October.
1982: One at Belle Tout Wood, Beachy Head on 4 September.
1983: One at Hodcombe, Beachy Head on 4 October.
1984: One near Whitbread Hollow, Beachy Head on 22 September.
      One at Church Norton on 7 October.
1986: One at Church Norton on 2 November.
1989: One trapped at Icklesham on 21 September.
      One trapped at Hodcombe, Beachy Head on 29 September.
      One at Belle Tout Wood, Beachy Head on 7-8 October.
1991: One at Belle Tout Wood, Beachy Head on 6-7 October.
1994: One at Belle Tout Wood, Beachy Head on 1 October.

Records have been fairly constant throughout the period, with peaks of three in 1968 and 1989 (fig. 95).

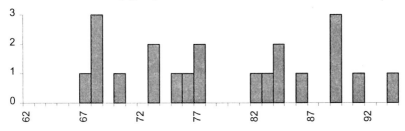

Figure 95. Annual totals of Red-breasted Flycatchers, 1962 - 94.

All were in autumn with nine in September (from 4th), eleven in October and one in early November (on 2nd). Most arrived in late September and early October (fig. 96).

Over half (14) have been in the Beachy Head area, with three at Church Norton (but none at Selsey Bill) and singles at the Crumbles, Handcross, Icklesham, Littlehampton Golf Course and Seaford Head.

There were between 67 and 136 records of this endearing small flycatcher in the British Isles each year during 1986-92 (Fraser & Ryan 1994). It breeds from Denmark and Austria east across Siberia, wintering in southern Asia.

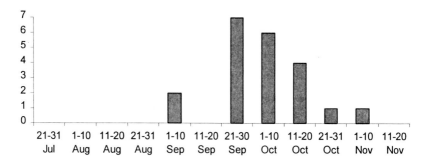

Figure 96. Cumulative 'autumn' arrival dates of Red-breasted Flycatchers (all records).

Richard Fairbank

Pied Flycatcher   *Ficedula hypoleuca*

Status:- A scarce passage migrant, more numerous in autumn than spring. Has bred.

Pied Flycatchers have bred in Sussex on three occasions: at West Broyle, Chichester prior to 1900, near the Ouse below Shortbridge about 1905 and near Southease in 1991. Unpaired males were recorded in the interior of the county from 4 May to 8 June 1975, 7 May to 5 June 1976, during May 1989, for about a month up to 21 May 1992 and at the same site as in 1992, on 5 May 1993. The slight expansion of range that has occurred in this species, with more breeding records from southeast England, is possibly due to the increased availability of nest boxes (New Atlas).

The earliest ever recorded in spring were singles at Kidds Hill, Ashdown Forest on 3 April 1994, The Pells, Lewes on 5 April 1994 and at Angmering on 8 April 1965. During 1962-93, first dates varied between 8 and 30 April, with the average 19 April. Spring passage peaks between mid-April and early May but few are seen thereafter. Totals have varied between one in 1965 and 31 in 1985. Shrubb reported an average of less than ten per spring for the period 1947-76, whereas the average for the period 1977-93 was 15, an increase that may largely be attributable to greater observer activity. Most records are of single birds, but there were three at Church Norton on 9 May 1965, Beachy Head on 23 April 1983 and Hollingbury Camp on 8 May 1988 and four at Church Norton on 18 April 1987, increasing to six the following day. A total of ten was recorded in the county on 18 April 1987 and nine on 17 April 1988.

des Forges & Harber referred to an average of about 13 birds per autumn in the period 1947-60, but between 1961 and 1976 the autumn average was about 100 birds, an increase that Shrubb attributed to greater coverage, especially at Beachy Head but possibly also to a change in the species' migration pattern. Since 1976, however, numbers have fallen, the average for the period 1977-92 being 60. No longer are day totals of 30-50 birds recorded at Beachy Head, the highest count there in recent years being of 25 on 6

September 1984, an autumn in which an above average total of 175 was recorded in the county.

The main autumn movement usually begins in early August although there are a few records of juveniles in July, the earliest being at Portslade on 13 July 1957. Large numbers have occurred in early August in some years. In 1967, for example, there were 50 at Beachy Head on 10th (the largest day total for the county), where at least 60 were trapped in the first two weeks of the month. In 1967, a total of *ca.* 150 was recorded there between 1st and 15th, with 50 trapped. Notable concentrations later in the month, all at Beachy Head, have included 30 on 25 August 1970, 30 on 23 August 1971, 42 on 19 August 1979 and 15 on 24 August 1984. In September, numbers tend to decrease as the month progresses, but in eight of the years between 1981 and 1993, more were recorded in that month than August. During 1962-93 last dates fell between 26 September and 1 November, with the average 10 October. One at Beachy Head on 1 November 1968 is the latest county record.

The numbers of birds reported each autumn is dependent on the incidence of favourable winds to drift birds westwards across the North Sea. Evidence that some of the Pied Flycatchers that occur in Sussex in autumn are of continental origin is provided by the control of a bird at Beachy Head on 20 August 1978 that had been ringed on Heligoland, Germany on 8 August of that year. One ringed at Beachy Head on 12 August 1973 was found nesting at Leominster, Herefordshire on 20 June 1974 while another ringed at Beachy Head on 16 August 1977 was found dead almost three weeks later at Cascais, Portugal on 5 September of that year.

A male with abnormally large amounts of white on its tertials (recalling Semi-collared Flycatcher *F. semitorquata*) was trapped at Beachy Head on 9 August 1987 (Mild 1995).   *Tim Parmenter*

Bearded Tit   *Panurus biarmicus*

Status:- A very scarce breeder, scarce passage migrant and winter visitor.

Sussex lost its original breeding stock of this species in the middle of the 19th century, largely as a result of the "rigorous reclamation of our really big reedbeds" (Walpole-Bond). Little is known about its former distribution, but Walpole-Bond mentioned five probable breeding areas: Amberley Wild Brooks, the Adur Valley, Lewes Brooks, Pevensey Levels, and near Winchelsea. Following a series of regular autumn irruptions from 1959 onwards, involving annual totals of 20 to 80 birds, a small population became re-established, with breeding suspected in 1971 and finally proven in 1972 (Shrubb). Nesting was irregular thereafter until 1980, since when it has become annual. Nesting has only occurred at four sites but up to 49 young have fledged in a single year. Bearded Tits are susceptible to hard weather and numbers can fall markedly following a succession of cold, snowy winters (68-72 BTO Atlas). Despite recent increases, the Sussex breeding population (currently less than ten pairs) remains somewhat tenuous and could shrink to the point of extinction following periods of prolonged snow cover.

The likely source of the influxes in the 1960s was the massive populations that became established on the newly created polders in the Netherlands (Axell 1966). Also, a series of milder winters, following the hard winter of 1962/63, allowed the breeding population in eastern England to flourish. In Kent, for example, there was an increase from seven pairs in 1963 to 70 pairs in 1965 (Taylor, Davenport & Flegg 1981). Although the change map in the New Atlas does not show as much change as might have been expected for this dynamic species, there has been a marked range expansion along the south coast of England. However, breeding numbers there remain low.

Date	Ringing site	Recovery site	Date	Distance
Jan. 1966	Chichester GP	Minsmere, Suffolk	Sep. 1966	
Jun. 1967	Minsmere, Suffolk	Crumbles	Oct. 1967	
Jul. 1967	Minsmere, Suffolk	Crumbles	Oct. 1967	
Aug. 1967	Minsmere, Suffolk	Crumbles	Oct. 1967	
Nov. 1973	Filsham	Kleimeer, Koedjik, Netherlands	May 1975	
Aug. 1978	Bradwell, Essex (2)	Pett Level	Nov. 1978	
Sep. 1978	Fordwich, Kent	Pett Level	Nov. 1978	54 km
Oct. 1978	Corsham, Wilts	Pett Level	Nov. 1978	205 km
Jun. 1979	Radipole, Dorset (4)	Thorney Island	Jan. 1980	110 km
Apr. 1981	Tilbury, Essex	Filsham	Oct. 1981	71 km
Sep. 1981	Stodmarsh, Kent	Filsham	Nov. 1984	69 km
Oct. 1987	Westbere, Kent	Icklesham	Oct. 1988	59 km
Sep. 1988	Stodmarsh, Kent	Icklesham	Oct. 1988	56 km
Sep. 1988	Sandwich, Kent	Icklesham	Oct. 1988	62 km
Jan. 1989	Icklesham	Walberswick, Suffolk	Jun. 1989	166 km
Oct. 1988	Titchfield, Hants (2)	Icklesham	Nov. 1989	135 km
Oct. 1989	Icklesham	Stodmarsh, Kent	May 1990	
Oct. 1989	Icklesham	Seine Maritime, France	Mar. 1990	145 km

Table 78. Ringing recoveries of Bearded Tits, 1966 - 89.

Small parties of Bearded Tits may be recorded at coastal sites in autumn, particularly in October, the main month for movement into the county. In 1972, about 110 were recorded in October-November including a flock of 15 at Beachy Head on 15 October that departed northwest. Totals in other autumns have been lower.

The winter population is considerably lower than that in autumn. In the winter of 1972/73, for example, a party of ten was recorded at one locality on 9 December but there were no other records for the month. In the early part of 1973 there were records totalling about ten birds at five localities. Occasional birds may sometimes be recorded far inland, as at Warnham Mill Pond where five appeared in March 1989 and four in January 1990, and Ifield Mill Pond where there was one in December 1989.

As the species is very much associated with reedbeds, its distribution in Sussex is fairly restricted. In autumn and winter, small parties may occur away from the primary habitat, feeding on weed seeds. Just such a loose flock of 50-60 birds appeared in 1978 at Pett Level, from October onwards, feeding on seeds of fat hen and willowherb. Trapping revealed that 12 of these had been ringed further to the east, including eight at nearby Dungeness, Kent. Ringing has also shown that some of the birds that visit Sussex in autumn arrive from the west (table 78).

Between 1990 and 1992, a large number of birds from north Kent were retrapped at Icklesham. These included 27 (mainly juveniles) from Stodmarsh, two from Westbere (59 km distant), three from Sturry (55 km), two from Faversham (47 km), and two from Chilham (44 km). Of the birds ringed at Stodmarsh, 19 were controlled at Icklesham in the period 4 to 27 October 1991. These had been ringed between June and September of that same year on their breeding grounds, and appear to have formed part of an irruptive movement. One ringed at Westbere on 26 September 1991 was controlled at Thorney Island on 7 August 1993.   *John E S Cooper*

Long-tailed Tit   *Aegithalos caudatus*

Status:- A very common resident.

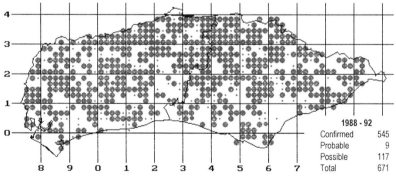

1988 - 92	
Confirmed	545
Probable	9
Possible	117
Total	671

Long-tailed Tits are usually encountered in small flocks in woodland, especially where a secondary shrub layer exists, but they are equally at home in large overgrown hedgerows or extensive areas of scrub. The preferred tree species for feeding are oak and hawthorn, but most deciduous varieties are acceptable, whence the birds obtain their insect diet, primarily from the outermost twigs (Perrins 1979). Such habitats and tree species are plentiful in the interior of the county and, as can be seen from the Atlas map, breeding pairs are widely distributed, with a preponderance of records away from the coast. Conifer woods are largely avoided.

No recent species survey has been undertaken, but from the general census data for predominantly farmland sites throughout the county for the period 1980-88, population densities were extrapolated at 3.62 pairs per km². This density was also recorded during a full survey of an area of mixed farmland and copse at the Brinsbury Estate, where 3.6 pairs per km² were found (Prater 1982), but a similar census the following year at Plumpton suggested only 1.75 pairs per km² (Prater 1983b). In contrast, however, a detailed study of semi-natural broadleaved woodlands in the West Sussex Weald (Bealey & Sutherland 1983) revealed a much higher average density of 32.2 pairs per km², giving an indication of the value of such habitat. Allowing for the large area of suitable woodland in the county, it is likely that the breeding population is in the order of 10,000-15,000 pairs.

As with all very small resident birds, the number of pairs available for breeding each spring is greatly dependent on the severity of the preceding winter. This is supported by the annual ringing totals for Sussex (1979-92) where the mean was 195, but such totals dropped substantially following prolonged or severe cold spells in winter, e.g. down to 121 in 1986. A run of mild winters soon redresses the population deficit, thus from 1987-90 the annual ringing totals increased in increments to 325 before numbers reduced sharply to 167 following extremely low temperatures in February 1991.

A general lack of ringing recoveries, from within or outside the county, indicate that this species is very sedentary, its winter distribution being similar to that of summer (Winter Atlas). Winter flock territories in woodland may be 20-25 ha in extent (Perrins 1979). Small flocks, usually consisting of extended family groups, then join with other tits and forage through woods and along hedgerows for insects, following regular daily routes. Within a roving mixed feeding flock, Long-tailed Tits are often in the vanguard, and the incessant contact calls herald their arrival and subsequent progress, a sound typical of Wealden woods in autumn and winter. Exceptionally, groups of 40-50 Long-tailed Tits have been recorded, but more usually they number less than 15. In recent years, the largest gathering was of 83 birds at West Chiltington on 22 September 1982.

For such a small bird, individual longevity can be surprising, and ringing studies at Ashcombe and Weir Wood Reservoir have shown retraps of 3-4 years old to be not unusual. Such birds would, of course, be very aware of territory food resources and, therefore, would be better able to survive occasional cold winters.

Although primarily insectivorous, they have been noted as occasional visitors to garden feeders in late winter in recent years.

Records refer to the British race *A.c. rosaceus* although des Forges & Harber list six occurrences of birds showing characteristics of one or other of the white-headed races, *A.c. caudatus* (Scandinavia) or *A.c. europaeus* (western Europe), the last being in 1958. Since then the only record has been of one trapped at Ashcombe Bottom on 9 May 1987.   *John E S Cooper*

Marsh Tit

Parus palustris

Status:- A common resident.

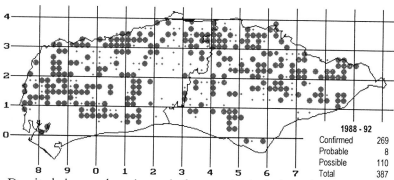

	1988 - 92
Confirmed	269
Probable	8
Possible	110
Total	387

Despite being unobtrusive and often overlooked, the Atlas map shows the species to be widely distributed in the county, in wooded areas away from the coast.

It is easily, and often, confused with its close relative, the Willow Tit, and separation in the field is best achieved by listening for the distinctive calls of each species. Ringing studies at sites where both species occur have shown that, even in the hand, it is necessary to take detailed measurements in order to determine species. This is especially applicable to juveniles prior to their first autumn moult. It is just possible, therefore, that a few records refer to birds that have been incorrectly identified.

In general, Marsh Tits frequent drier habitats, and are more likely to be found in mature deciduous woodland, especially where a shrub understorey exists, as most feeding occurs at this level. Conifer woods are generally avoided, but larger gardens are often visited in winter, with individuals coming to feeders. Pairs occupy large breeding territories of 2-6 ha in extent, which are maintained in winter also (Perrins 1979). Thus the species is very sedentary, with few movements nationally of ringed birds exceeding 10 km (Mead & Clark 1993), and the ringing recoveries from Sussex, or lack of them, tend to confirm this. A nestling ringed at Haslemere, Surrey in 1966 and retrapped at Fernhurst later that year is the most venturesome having travelled 6 km.

Ringing studies have shown that Marsh Tits can be long-lived. As well as the 9 year old bird at Possingworth Park in 1970 (Shrubb), another even older individual, colour-ringed at Fairlight in March 1984, was still present at this site in May 1994, establishing a longevity record for the species. At Weir Wood Reservoir, birds of 4-5 years old have been retrapped regularly.

Abundance is greatest in old Wealden woods to the north of the county as shown by a study of such woods in 1982 which recorded an average density of 23.3 pairs per km² (Bealey & Sutherland 1983). A survey of farmland at Plumpton (400 ha) revealed only five pairs (Prater 1983b). From other general records submitted during 1980-88, based on a few wooded sites, a density of 4.8 pairs per km² was extrapolated. It is probable, therefore, that the county breeding population is about 5000 pairs.

Nest-boxes are occasionally used but extensive studies in the High Weald (Cooper *unpubl.*) and at Bosham (Cross *unpubl.*) showed that occupation rarely amounted to more than 1-2% of those available. This may be a result of the species preference for using holes at or below 1 m height (68-72 BTO Atlas), whereas nest-boxes are generally sited at 2-3 m off the ground to restrict unwanted human interference.

County ringing totals for 1979-92 show Marsh Tits to be slightly more numerous than Willow Tits, but as only small numbers are caught each year from an even smaller number of sites, these totals probably do not reflect the true relative status of either species. Indeed, many ringing sites have a bias towards damp habitats, which would tend to exaggerate numbers of Willow Tits. *John E S Cooper*

Willow Tit   *Parus montanus*

Status:- A fairly common resident.

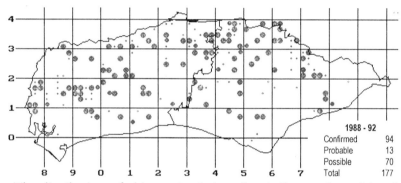

1988 - 92	
Confirmed	94
Probable	13
Possible	70
Total	177

The distribution of this species is broadly similar to that of its close relative, the Marsh Tit, except that sightings are more occasional. It is very uncommon near the coast and most are to be found in the northern half of the county (New Atlas).

Despite the possibility of confusion with Marsh Tit during fieldwork, it is probable that Willow Tits are genuinely scarcer as their preferred habitat of damp scrubby woodland and carr is not widespread or extensive. Where such habitat does occur, particularly around reservoirs, ponds and streams inland, the species can be locally numerous. The most common nesting trees reported for the species are birch, willow and alder and with all these being prone to rot before maturity, they can provide suitable small-diameter stumps in young scrubbier copses and carrs.

There have been no county surveys which give a good picture of Willow Tit numbers, as it does not fit neatly into the broad categories of farmland or woodland species. Where it has been noted as occurring during general habitat surveys, numbers located were very low and thus they may be unrepresentative. Bealey & Sutherland (1983) and Prater (1983b) both found densities of 0.5 pairs per km² in semi-natural broadleaved woodland and on farmland respectively. Applying this figure to the 177 tetrads in which the

486

species was recorded during the Atlas Survey indicates a county population of about 350 pairs. This estimate may well be on the low side given that densities are probably higher in optimum habitat.

Conifer woods may be used for feeding where these occur within a breeding territory, which can be of 20-30 ha in extent (Perrins 1979) but is often much smaller in favoured carr areas. Birds have been noted excavating nest holes in quite small rotten stumps in downland scrub, so dry habitats are not shunned entirely, and some pairs in copses and taller hedgerows in the under-watched areas of Wealden farmland may also go unrecorded. Gardens may occasionally be visited but Willow Tits are not noted as regularly attending bird-feeders, in contrast to other members of their family.

County ringing records for 1979-92 show the species to be trapped nearly as regularly as Marsh Tit, but this is almost certainly because of a bias created by the preferred habitat of ringers, i.e. reedbeds and willow scrub, rather than a true reflection of relative status. There are no recent ringing records of any movement in excess of 5 km, which confirms the bird's sedentary nature.

In contrast to the habits of most other tits, nest-boxes are almost never used as the bird excavates a new nest hole each year in a rotten tree stump. It appears unwilling to adopt the custom of utilising any ready-made cavity, be it natural or man-made. Certainly in the species' stronghold of the northern Weald, very extensive nest-box studies carried out during 1980-93 did not produce a single instance of occupation by Willow Tits.   *John E S Cooper*

Coal Tit   *Parus ater*

Status:- A very common resident.

1988 - 92	
Confirmed	483
Probable	1
Possible	119
Total	603

Coal Tits are associated with conifers much more than other members of the tit family, but may be present in deciduous woods at a lower density. The expansion of conifer plantations this century has doubtless increased the breeding population in Sussex, although this may prove to be of a locally temporary nature dependent upon the felling regimes of each tract of woodland.

From the Atlas map, it can be seen that breeding Coal Tits were found more commonly away from the coast, especially along the northern county boundary and in the High Weald. Shrubb gave evidence of it being four times commoner on sandstone soils than on chalk or clay, and this is confirmed by the abundance map in the New Atlas. The majority of conifer plantations and also clumps of the native Scots pine are mostly located on sandy soils in Sussex.

Within large areas of mature coniferous woodland, Coal Tits may reach breeding densities of up to 100 pairs per km² (Perrins 1979). In 1980, local census data from mixed woods across the county produced an extrapolated density of 11.6 pairs per km². In semi-natural broadleaved woodland in West Sussex, Bealey & Sutherland (1983) found an average density of 52.5 pairs per km². Farmland, by comparison, supports very few breeding pairs and surveys at the Brinsbury Estate and at Plumpton (Prater 1982, 1983b) revealed only 3.1 pairs per km² and 0.75 pairs per km² respectively. Even then, the small areas of woodland present at Brinsbury were mostly coniferous and thus probably gave a positive bias to the resultant data. Even in coniferous woods, there can be marked fluctuations in breeding numbers between years (Perrins 1979), and so the county population probably lies between 10,000 and 18,000 pairs.

In winter, the species' diet becomes more seed-based. This leads it to frequent garden feeders regularly, especially in years with poor crops of beech-mast (Glue 1982), and appearances in urban areas are not uncommon. Large gatherings in autumn and winter are often noted, possibly again related to local mast abundance, and loose flocks exceeding 100 have occurred on Ashdown Forest and Ambersham Common.

County ringing totals for 1979-92, by the amalgamation of nestlings ringed in nest-box schemes, tend to have distorted annual figures so that any population trends are difficult to determine. Ringing recoveries do, however, give an indication of some movement by this species. In 1986, one bird ringed as a nestling at Pippingford Park was controlled later that same autumn in Hertfordshire. The majority of ringing records refer only to local wanderings, suggesting that Coal Tits are essentially sedentary, and a comparison of the distributions shown by the Winter Atlas and the New Atlas would tend to confirm this.

Nest-box use can be variable, but is highest where boxes are sited in conifers. Extensive studies in the High Weald during 1980-93 (Cooper *unpubl.*) showed regular use of boxes until 1988 when, following the storm of October 1987 and the devastation of large areas of shallow-rooted conifers, many territories were lost. The boxes used prior to that time were almost always those sited among or on firs, preferably at 1-2 m height. It had been found that breeding success in boxes was very good, often with 100% fledging success at some sites, and second broods were not uncommon. Since 1988, and the subsequent clearance of windblown areas, the use of nest-boxes has been spasmodic as those remaining are now in tracts of predominantly deciduous woodland surrounded by new plantings.

There have been a number of records showing the characteristics of the brighter and greyer continental race *P.a. ater*. Prior to 1962, there was one at the Crumbles on 22 October 1952 and three at Selsey Bill on 29 October 1961. The latter may have been those seen at East Head the same day. During 1962-93 there were nine records comprising 11 individuals as follows:

1963: One at Fairlight on 13 October.
1970: Two at Beachy Head on 26 September.
　　　Two at Beachy Head on 11 October.
1971: One at Beachy Head on 4 October.
1979: One at Crowborough on 4 March.
　　　One at Bewl Water on 13 April.
1980: One at Holywell, Eastbourne on 9 November.
1988: One at Newmarket Hill on 19 September.
1993: One at Birling Gap on 18 September.

John E S Cooper

Blue Tit   *Parus caeruleus*

Status:- An abundant resident.

	1988 - 92
Confirmed	897
Probable	0
Possible	82
Total	979

Found throughout the county, in rural and urban locations alike, wherever there are shrubs or trees. The species is familiar to all watchers, so confirmation of occurrence was almost certainly complete. Comparison of the Atlas map with that for Great Tit reveals a very similar distribution pattern of unconfirmed breeding, which may be real for both species or perhaps a reflection of observer coverage.

Breeding density is at a peak where mature tree cover is greatest, especially oak, and this occurs in the extensive woods of the Weald, as is admirably demonstrated by the abundance maps of the New Atlas. In prime oakwood habitats, densities can reach 250 pairs per km² (Perrins 1979), and census data from Fore Wood revealed 178 pairs per km². Bealey & Sutherland (1983), in their study of semi-natural broadleaved woodlands in West Sussex, found Blue Tits present at a mean density of 103.9 pairs per km², a clear indication of the richness of such sites. Similar numbers of pairs can sometimes be found in the gardens of suburbia, attracted by the provision of food in winter, but clutch and brood sizes are usually substantially smaller than those of their woodland counterparts, with a higher proportion of young failing to fledge. Farmland tree belts support pairs also, but at a much reduced overall density, as shown by Prater (1982, 1983b) in his studies at the Brinsbury Estate and at Plumpton where 23.8 pairs per km² and 9.5 pairs per km² respectively were located. The extensive yew woods of Kingley Vale are not attractive to Blue Tits, with as few as 4 pairs per km². Within the county, there may be 120,000 to 170,000 breeding pairs.

Outside the breeding season, Blue Tits are less territorial and form loose flocks in autumn/winter with other *Paridae* searching for food in gardens and woods, particularly where beech occurs. In years of high beech-mast production, such flocks often comprise in excess of 100 birds, and winter survival is greatly enhanced (Perrins 1979).

Sussex ringing totals are inflated somewhat by the large numbers of nestlings ringed in various nest-box schemes across the county. Recoveries from such schemes have provided evidence of occasional movements, perhaps necessitated by local food shortages, as exemplified by the nestling from Possingworth Park found in Leicester, 205 km away, in 1982. In 1986, a second successive year of poor beech-mast production, three Sussex birds travelled to east Kent, while in the same year, two birds ringed at Beachy Head in late September were trapped at Shoreham-by-Sea early in October, showing coastal movement westwards.

Since 1979, several birds have been recovered in the Greater London area, but no clear pattern of movement is apparent. Other than one bird from Lancashire (351 km) in 1968, there have been no recent occurrences to match those records of birds ringed in the winter of 1957/58 and which were later found in Sussex, having flown from counties as distant as Cleveland (435 km), Warwickshire (215 km), Oxfordshire (134 km) and two from Buckinghamshire (113 and 103 km). No ringing records are known of migration to or from the near Continent that affect Sussex.

Longevity in the species is also evident from ringing activities. At East Grinstead and Weir Wood Reservoir, studies have shown that birds aged 5-7 years are not unknown.

Nest-boxes are extensively used, and have formed the basis for many studies of the species. Indeed, they are undoubtedly responsible for the species' high density in some areas where natural cavities may be at a premium, for example, in young plantations and suburban gardens.

No birds showing characters of the brighter continental race *P.c. caeruleus* have been noted since one at the Crumbles in 1959 (des Forges & Harber).

John E S Cooper

Great Tit   *Parus major*

Status:- An abundant resident.

Primarily a bird of woodland, it is much less arboreal in its feeding habits than other members of the tit family, due to larger size and lack of agility, and is often to be seen among fallen leaves searching for tree seeds in the winter months. While deciduous woods are the preferred habitat, especially where a shrub layer is present, conifers are not avoided, although densities in such areas are much lower (Perrins 1979). Great Tits are also to be found regularly in gardens, particularly the more wooded type, as these approximate closely to the favoured open woodland with scrub.

In both open woodland and gardens, breeding densities may exceed 80 pairs per km² (Perrins 1979). At Fore Wood, a 55 ha area of mature mixed wood with coppice, censuses have indicated densities in excess of 100 pairs per km², although this may have been influenced somewhat by the provision of

nest-boxes. In the old deciduous woods of the High Weald, Bealey &
Sutherland (1983) found an average density of 66.5 pairs per km², while
surveys of farmland at the Brinsbury Estate in 1980 and at Plumpton in 1982
found densities of 8 pairs per km² and 15 pairs per km² respectively, where
most were located in copses (Prater 1982, 1983b). Allowing for the widespread
distribution, as shown on the Atlas map, the county breeding population may
number between 55,000 and 80,000 pairs.

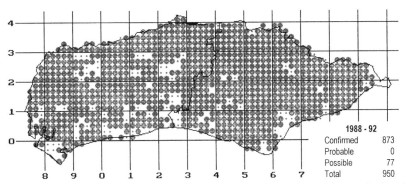

1988 - 92	
Confirmed	873
Probable	0
Possible	77
Total	950

Breeding numbers in spring have been shown to be affected greatly by the
availability of beech-mast in the preceding winter (Perrins 1979). As mast is
not produced annually, the population levels of Great Tits rise and fall in
consequence, being greatest in autumns following a "mast winter". It is then
that large roaming flocks appear looking for alternative food sources. The
storm of 1987 uprooted a substantial proportion of beech trees in parts of
Sussex, thus diminishing the potential supply of mast, and it remains to be
seen whether this will have any long-term effect on local population levels.

Great Tits will readily occupy nest-boxes, being able to dispossess the
much smaller Blue Tit in ownership disputes. Where boxes are in short
supply, the latter species is better equipped to utilise smaller natural sites with
narrow entrances. Nest-box studies in the High Weald have shown that Great
Tits have less preference than Blue Tits for the presence of oaks and will nest
in a wide range of woodland habitats (Cooper *unpubl.*). In coniferous woods,
second broods are often produced because the caterpillar food supply, though
less abundant, is available over a longer period in such habitat (Perrins 1979).

As with Blue Tits, annual county ringing totals are greatly influenced by
the activities of nest-box ringers, and do not give a reliable guide to any
fluctuations in population levels. Since 1979, only five birds have been
recovered in excess of 50 km from the site of original capture. The furthest
travelled individuals were both young females: one ringed at East Grinstead in
December 1985 that was controlled at Sandwich Bay, Kent, 99 km distant, in
March 1986 and one ringed at Bognor Regis in April 1986 and recovered at
Shorne, Kent the following April.

In the High Weald, ringing studies in gardens and woodland have shown
that some birds may attain life-spans of 5-7 years.

There have been no sightings of birds showing characters of the smaller-
billed continental race, *P.m. major*, since one was controlled at Fairlight in

1974 having been ringed at Eprave, Belgium in May 1973 (Shrubb). Melanism is not uncommon in this species and such birds have been regularly recorded across the county.

John E S Cooper

Nuthatch

Sitta europaea

Status:- A very common resident.

The Nuthatch is a bird very much associated with mature deciduous woodland, especially of oak and beech. In Sussex it is primarily to be found in the northern half of the county, as a glance at the Atlas map will show. Indeed, the woods of the High Weald are a stronghold for the species in Britain, as shown by the abundance map in the New Atlas. Its winter distribution is identical to that of summer (Winter Atlas), showing the bird's sedentary nature, and pairs are often seen together throughout the year. Conifer woods do not appear to be favoured, possibly because of lack of suitable food supply, although pine bark chips are often used to line the nest cavity.

Few recent studies have been undertaken, and for a bird known to be widespread in Sussex woods there is little accurate information on numbers. General records imply densities in deciduous woodland of the order of 10-15 pairs per km² but some favoured areas may exceed this figure. Bealey & Sutherland (1983), in their study of semi-natural broadleaved woodlands in West Sussex found an average density of 16.2 pairs per km². On farmland, as would be expected, birds numbered much less than 2 pairs per km² (Prater 1982, 1983b). The Sussex population probably numbers between 6000-8000 pairs. Shrubb suggested that a decrease in population levels, but expansion in range, might have occurred since 1965 but there is no recent evidence that this has continued.

Because of the species' sedentary disposition, territories may be quite large in order to encompass a sufficient supply of nuts, acorns and mast. In autumn and winter, Nuthatches will join foraging flocks of tits, and it is then that the species will most commonly appear in gardens in search of peanuts. Often such birds will be local pairs extending their more restricted summer range or young birds seeking a vacant territory. At this time also, sightings may occur nearer the coast, most probably being birds of the latter category.

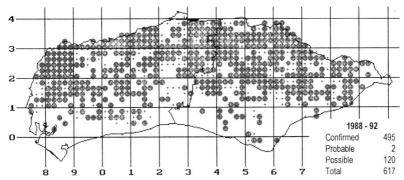

1988 - 92	
Confirmed	495
Probable	2
Possible	120
Total	617

Breeding numbers in spring are very dependent on local food availability in the preceding autumn and the severity of the winter (New Atlas). Nestboxes are often used but local studies have shown that these are preferred when erected at 3 m or higher (Cooper *unpubl.*). Copious quantities of mud are plastered around the entrance hole to restrict unwanted visitors, a practice that is extended to internal joints of box-lids. Retrapped nesting birds have provided examples of territorial fidelity. At Chelwood Vachery, one female successfully used the same nest-box for three consecutive years, and at the same site another was found using a box four years after being originally ringed there as a nestling.

County annual ringing totals are not high, occasionally exceeding 100, of which half might consist of nestlings. This is probably a reflection of the species' preference for mature inland woodland, where there is little ringing carried out. Distant recoveries are non-existent, again reflecting its sedentary nature, and recoveries from anywhere are few. The furthest wanderer in recent years was a bird ringed at Horsted Keynes in May 1984 and found dead at Horley, Surrey, 20 km away, a month later. One bird ventured a distance of 11 km from Friars Gate, Crowborough to Tunbridge Wells in 1984, and another travelled 10 km from Streat to Ringmer in 1986. All three birds were ringed as nestlings and probably represented juvenile dispersal in search of territory. On a national basis up to 1991, only 28 birds had ever been recovered more than 10 km from their site of capture (Mead & Clark 1993).

One recorded in atypical habitat in a hawthorn hedge near Sidlesham Ferry on 26 August 1993 flew off high to the east.   *John E S Cooper*

Wallcreeper   *Tichodroma muraria*

Status:- A very rare vagrant (three records).

Two were recorded before 1962 (des Forges & Harber): one was seen on the ruins of Greyfriars' Chapel at Winchelsea and promptly shot, probably in late spring 1886 (Walpole-Bond); the other worked its way up and down the undercliff at Rottingdean on about 4 June 1938 (Nicholl 1939). They were the third and sixth British records.

A superb male in summer plumage on the cliffs at Ecclesbourne Glen, Hastings from 6 to 10 April 1977 is the only recent record and one of the most celebrated rarities of all time. It appeared very tired when first found but was much more lively subsequently, feeding actively on the cliff face, often not far above the beach. At 07:00 hrs on 10 April it flew strongly south out to sea (Bonham 1977). Indelibly engraved on the memories of those who saw it, it was the ninth British record.

There have been ten records of this stunning species in Britain, four during 1962-94. That Sussex should have hosted three of them is especially pleasing, a high proportion that it is hoped will be maintained. It breeds in montane regions discontinuously from the Cantabrians of northern Spain to eastern China and is usually an altitudinal or short-distance migrant (BWP).

Richard Fairbank

Treecreeper   *Certhia familiaris*
Status:- A very common resident.

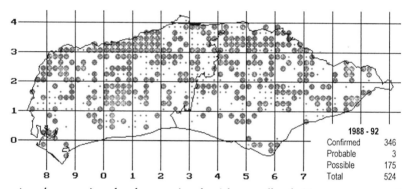

	1988 - 92	
Confirmed	346
Probable	3
Possible	175
Total	524

Another species closely associated with woodland, Treecreepers are less confined to mature deciduous trees and may be found in conifers, though in much smaller numbers. The Atlas map shows a similarity in distribution to that of Nuthatch but with fewer records in total. This latter fact is almost certainly more apparent than real, due to the likelihood of Treecreepers being under-recorded during surveys. The bird is notoriously difficult to detect as it ascends tree trunks, while its song and calls are high-pitched and not far-carrying. Being at its most vocal in early spring prior to the breeding season does little to assist detection during later surveys. The abundance map in the New Atlas shows that the woodlands in the north of the county have some of the highest concentrations of Treecreepers in Britain (New Atlas).

Records of confirmed breeding on the Atlas map are proportionately less for this species, doubtless due to the difficulties of locating the well-hidden nests of such an unobtrusive bird. From general census data of various woodland and scrub habitats submitted between 1980-88, population densities were extrapolated at 7.9 pairs per km². In the prime habitat of mature deciduous woodland in the West Sussex Weald, Bealey & Sutherland (1983) found an average density of 21.1 pairs per km². Prater (1982, 1983b), in his studies of bird communities on farmland, established that overall densities were much lower at 3.6 pairs per km² and 0.5 pairs per km² at the Brinsbury Estate and Plumpton respectively. Considering the high proportion of woodland in the county, the breeding population probably numbers between 8000-12,000 pairs. Shrubb referred to an apparent increase in numbers in Sussex during the 1970s. National CBC data would appear to confirm this trend that continued at least into the next decade (New Atlas). There is, however, some indication that a reversal of fortunes may have occurred early in the 1990s.

Breeding Treecreepers generally require the presence of an over-mature or damaged tree in woodland to provide a nesting crevice behind loose bark, but they will also nest behind large ivy stems and have been recorded using gaps in various man-made structures, such as sheds, where these are adjacent to wooded areas. Nest-boxes of the specialised types approximating to bark cavities are sometimes used but natural sites seem generally to be preferred where available. Studies in the High Weald (Cooper *unpubl.*) have shown the use of these specialised boxes at some sites to be regular but never extensive. Occupation of the standard type of tit-box is very uncommon.

Annual ringing totals for the county are never high, usually numbering less than 100, and the reasons proffered for the low totals of Nuthatch can probably be applied to Treecreeper as well. Another woodland species of very sedentary habit, the only recent record of any movement is of a bird from Marley Common killed by a cat in Woking, Surrey, 31 km away, in 1983. In autumn, Treecreepers will join foraging flocks of tits as they pass through woods and scrub. They may occasionally appear in gardens, and, uncommonly, have been noted venturing onto bird-tables, but this source of food supply does not appear to hold any lasting attraction.   *John E S Cooper*

Penduline Tit
Remiz pendulinus

Status:- A rare vagrant (nine records involving 13 individuals).

Thirteen have been seen including four in both 1987 (when first recorded) and 1989 and three in 1994:

1987: One beside Pett Level Pools on the afternoon of 4 October (Bale 1989).
   Two adults and a juvenile at Filsham Reedbed on 26 and 27 October.
1988: A female trapped at Icklesham on 15 October.
1989: A first-winter trapped at Icklesham on 7 October.
   A male trapped at Icklesham on 24 October.
   An adult and a juvenile at the 'long pool' near the northwest corner of Pagham Harbour on the morning of 1 November.
1993: A juvenile trapped at Icklesham on 21 October.
1994: Two adults at the 'long pool' near the northwest corner of Pagham Harbour on the morning of 15 October.
   A juvenile male trapped at Icklesham on 18 October.

All records have fallen between 4 October and 1 November, with all but those at Pagham Harbour being in the east of the county. The 1988 female was controlled while nesting at Örebro in southern Sweden, 1309 km northeast, on 3 May 1989 (Rumsey 1990).

First recorded in Britain in 1966, those in Sussex in 1987 were the 13th and 14th British records, although over 90 had been seen in Britain up to the end of 1994. It breeds around the north Mediterranean and from eastern Europe to Manchuria. Its range has expanded in the north and west with, for example, 100 to 150 pairs in the Netherlands in 1990 compared with only one in the 1970s (BWP).   *Richard Fairbank*

Golden Oriole
Oriolus oriolus

Status:- A very scarce passage migrant and summer visitor. May have bred.

There is no conclusive evidence that Golden Orioles have bred in Sussex despite a number of records from suitable habitats that suggest the possibility of breeding. The most indicative was in 1965 when a pair was recorded in a large wooded estate near Rake. The male vigorously defended a territory throughout the summer and returned again the following year.

Between 1962 and 1994 Golden Orioles were recorded in all but five years (fig. 97). At least 12 occurred in 1984, the best year since 1866 when there were ten (Walpole-Bond). There is also an unlikely and undated record of 14 in a single bush reported by Borrer (1890).

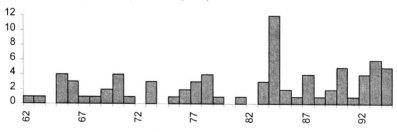

Figure 97. Annual totals of Golden Orioles, 1962 - 94.

The total of 80 recorded between 1962 and 1994, comprised mainly single birds and the majority were in May and June. The following table shows the cumulative monthly totals for this period.

Apr	May	Jun	Jul	Aug	Sep
2	48	23	6	-	1

The two earliest were a female at Icklesham on 27 April 1988 and a male at Beachy Head on 30 April 1984 whilst the only recent autumn record was of an immature male at Church Norton on 10 September 1991. Over 60% of those recorded were at sites within a few miles of the coast, including no less than 23 at Beachy Head, and over 70% were in East Sussex. This trend is to be expected, given that birds recorded in the county may be on passage to the species' East Anglian stronghold, and it ties in well with findings in neighbouring counties. In Hampshire a total of 46 was recorded in the 42 years up to 1992 (Clarke & Eyre 1993) whereas in Kent there were 80 in just 25 years between 1952 to 1976 (Taylor, Davenport & Flegg 1981). Records of males (65) considerably outnumber females (12) due, undoubtedly, to their clear fluty calls announcing their presence whilst quieter, less brightly coloured females pass unnoticed.

Apart from the pair near Rake the only other records involving more than one bird were of two flying over Pett on 7 July 1970, three at Combe Haven on 18 May 1984 and a pair there on 21 May, and two at Beachy Head on 28-29 May 1993 and 31 May 1994.

Although populations in many European countries have declined (BWP), the number of orioles breeding in Britain is reported to be increasing (Spencer *et al* 1993). The number of birds seen in Sussex is small, and any changes that have occurred may merely reflect an increase in observers. The totals recorded in the past three decades do, however, suggest that a small increase may have taken place:

1960-69	1970-79	1980-89	1990-94
13	19	26	21

des Forges & Harber recorded 90 in the 130 years up to 1937 but just two more up to 1960. They also referred to an old record for the early date of 12 April (1854, Battle) and to three sightings in August.   *John Newnham*

Isabelline Shrike   *Lanius isabellinus*

Status:- A very rare vagrant (one record).

A male, occasionally in song, at Pagham Harbour between 1 March and 20 April 1975 (*Brit. Birds* 69: plate 35a) showed characteristics closest to the race *L.i. isabellinus*. It was the sixth British record although the possibility of its being an escape from captivity could not be completely excluded (Dymond *et al* 1976). It was usually to be found in gorse along the north-western edge of Pagham Harbour, close to Sidlesham Ferry.

There were 36 records of this rufous-tailed shrike in the British Isles during 1962-94. Formerly regarded as conspecific with Red-backed Shrike, it breeds from Iran to Mongolia, wintering in northeast Africa and southwestern Asia.

The race *isabellinus* occurs in the more northwesterly part of its range (Sinkiang), wintering west to Iraq (BWP).   *Richard Fairbank*

Red-backed Shrike   *Lanius collurio*

Status:- A very scarce passage migrant; formerly a breeding summer visitor.

The sad decline of this attractive species in Britain has been well documented (e.g. Peakall 1962, Ash 1970, Bibby 1973, New Atlas). Walpole-Bond described Red-backed Shrikes as breeding generally throughout Sussex in suitable habitat but he noted them as becoming progressively scarcer during the 1930s. Although the numbers breeding in the county were never large, as recently as 1949 they were said to be increasing in places. Unfortunately, virtually no nesting records were retained in the county files for the period 1947 to 1958 (Shrubb) so it is only possible to chart the progress of the last few known pairs. By 1960 only three pairs were known to be present and in 1963 there were none. A pair that bred in Ashdown Forest annually from 1964 to 1968 was the last confirmed breeding record for the county. More recently there were unconfirmed reports of breeding near Broad Oak until about 1973 and also four records of pairs in late spring but with no signs of nesting. These were at Slaugham on 15 May 1977, the Midrips on 28 May 1977, at Heathfield on 12 June 1981 and at Combe Haven on 4-5 June 1993. Records of a singing male at Old Lodge, Ashdown Forest on 21 June 1987, a female at Hamsey on 16 June 1988 and a female at Rackham on 29 June 1991 probably relate to wandering individuals which had failed to find a mate.

The Red-backed Shrike has declined in most countries in northwest Europe. The causes of its demise are unknown despite various studies. The

498

main factor suggested is a reduction in the availability of large insects, the shrike's main prey item, brought about by climatic change. However, Bibby could find no consistent climatic trend over a period of 50 years in which the species had declined continuously. Indeed a period of warm and dry summers through the 1930s and 1940s ought to have been beneficial to the Red-backed Shrike, as had been noted in Sweden (Svardson & Durango 1950). At a local level other factors including habitat loss through scrub clearance and the use of herbicides, and egg-collecting may have been significant. In Sussex suitable habitat remains and the shrike's decline in the county must, therefore, be attributable to external factors. The New Atlas suggests that there has been a contraction in range with birds opting for preferred habitats further south and east in Europe after a shorter migration.

Apart from breeding birds, a total of about 128 presumed passage migrants was recorded between 1962 and 1994, of which 74% were in autumn (August-November). The cumulative monthly totals are shown below.

May	Jun	Jul	Aug	Sep	Oct	Nov
14	13	5	29	50	18	3

Most spring birds have occurred in the last week of May and first week of June. The pair at Slaugham on 15 May 1977 and males on 17 May at Cuckmere Haven in 1981 and Balsdean in 1982 are the only recent birds to have occurred earlier. However, pairs that formerly bred in Sussex were known to have established territories in early May and the earliest for the county were singles at Lidsey on 14 April 1945 (Hudson 1973), Steyning on 18 April 1948 and at Selsey on 20 April 1958. The above five July records all occurred between 1976 and 1978; all were adults, and probably wandering non-breeders. In autumn most have occurred at the end of August and in early September. The extreme dates are 11 August 1973 at Rottingdean and 16 November 1991 at Selsey Bill, the latter present since 6 November. The totals per decade for passage migrants are shown below.

1960-69	1970-79	1980-89	1990-94
24	59	33	15

Apart from in 1977, when about 26 were recorded, no more than seven have occurred in any one year, with an average of three per year. The total for 1977 included eight different individuals at Beachy Head with four there on 4 September.

Most passage migrants have been recorded at sites on or near the coast. Of these, 34 have been at Beachy Head, while other well-watched coastal sites such as Climping, Pagham Harbour, Rye Harbour and Selsey Bill have produced the majority of the rest. Of those recorded inland, most occurred between May and July with just five birds in autumn. Whereas many older records of passage birds may have related to the dispersal of the British breeding population, recent sightings are probably of birds originating from Fenno-Scandinavia. Red-backed Shrikes are known to exhibit loop migration, whereby their northward passage in spring follows a more easterly course than the return passage in autumn (BWP). Thus most records would be expected in the east of the county in autumn; indeed 64% of records of passage migrants were for East Sussex, often associated with easterly winds.

Furthermore, this pattern is shown in neighbouring counties with 46 passage migrants recorded in Hampshire between 1957 and 1992 (Clark & Eyre 1993) and about 150 in Kent in the 20 years up to 1976 (Taylor, Davenport & Flegg 1981).

There has been only one ringing recovery of a Red-backed Shrike in Sussex; a juvenile found dead at Winchelsea on 30 July 1948 had been ringed in the nest at Lyndhurst, Hampshire on 22 June.

The Red-backed Shrike has long been lost as a breeding bird in Sussex and it is now approaching extinction in Britain; any recovery now seems, unfortunately, most unlikely. *Michael Prince*

Lesser Grey Shrike *Lanius minor*

Status:- A very rare vagrant (six records).

One was recorded before 1962 (des Forges & Harber), a juvenile shot at Bosham on 14 October 1905. It is in the Booth Museum (BoMNH 208064).

Five have been seen since the beginning of 1962, the most recent in 1982:

1962: One, unaged, at Sidlesham Ferry on 1-2 July.
1969: An adult at Whitbread Hollow, Beachy Head during the early morning of 25 May.
1973: A juvenile at Oakhurst Farm, Sidlesham on the morning of 6 September.
1977: An adult at Rye Harbour on 3 June.
1982: An adult male at Birling Gap from 23 to 25 July (*Brit. Birds* 76: plate 222).

Records have fallen in May, June, July (2), September and October with four of the five since 1962 in either the Beachy Head area or at Sidlesham.

There were nearly 110 records of this long-winged shrike in the British Isles during 1962-94. It breeds from northeast Spain to Afghanistan and winters in sub-Saharan Africa. It is in decline over most of Europe (Tucker & Heath 1994). *Richard Fairbank*

Great Grey Shrike *Lanius excubitor*

Status:- A very scarce winter visitor and passage migrant.

Between 1961/62 and 1993/94, Great Grey Shrikes were recorded every winter, the best being 1974/75 when 22 were reported. The total for this period was about 228 birds (fig. 98), although the number of individuals involved was probably less due to wandering birds and those returning to the same locality in successive winters.

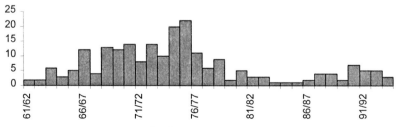

Figure 98. Winter totals of Great Grey Shrikes, 1961/62 - 93/94.

des Forges & Harber reported a consistent average of two or three birds per year prior to 1962. Thus a significant increase occurred, with an average of about 13 per winter in the period from 1966/67 to 1978/79, but numbers then dropped back to an average of about three per winter. Annual fluctuations are believed to be due to differences in breeding success and summer survival, linked to the availability of small rodents. Harsh winters may also force more birds to abandon their main wintering area of south central Sweden for more favourable conditions in Britain and the near continent (Winter Atlas). Scandinavia is the likely origin of most, if not all, Great Grey Shrikes in Sussex; the northernmost breeding populations are entirely migratory whereas birds from elsewhere in Europe are mainly sedentary. Although there are no ringing recoveries involving birds in Sussex, three of the four long distance British recoveries have been of birds from Scandinavia, including two from Norway (BWP).

Records of overwintering individuals indicate that their arrival dates typically fall between mid-October and the end of December, the mean date being 14 November. Departures are generally in March and early April, with a mean date of 17 March. The earliest in autumn was one at Belle Tout from 26 to 28 September 1989, although there is an old record for 7 September at the Crumbles in 1899. The latest recorded during 1962-94 was in Ashdown Forest in 1978, where one of three present there in March was last seen on 2 May. The latest ever was one at Rye Harbour on 14 May 1950.

In recent years the earliest and latest dates mentioned above are the only records which fall outside the period October to April, as the following table of cumulative monthly totals for the period 1962-94 shows.

Sep	Oct	Nov	Dec	Jan	Feb	Mar	Apr	May
1	73	57	54	53	52	62	16	1

des Forges & Harber mention a pair obtained at Hailsham during the summer of 1851 and four other in June and July.

The table shows that consistent numbers have been recorded in each of the months from November to February. The peaks in October and March correspond to periods when birds are likely to be passing through the county. This is clearly demonstrated by considering the records for the two main sites for the species in Sussex, Beachy Head and Ashdown Forest, which together are responsible for 35% of the birds recorded in recent years. Cumulative monthly totals for Beachy Head show that 60% of the birds there have been seen in October and November, whereas in Ashdown Forest they have been fairly even distributed in each of the months between November and April.

Birds have occurred at widely scattered localities in the county with a tendency for those on passage to be recorded at coastal sites, such as Beachy Head. Wintering individuals, however, occur inland to a greater extent, favouring habitats that include heaths and commons, downland and wet grassland. A similar pattern has been observed nationally (Winter Atlas) and it may be explained by considering the behaviour of the species. Birds typically hunt from a perch, adopting 'sit and wait' tactics. Their favoured wintering haunts are therefore characterised by good hunting areas, plenty of prominent and well scattered hunting perches, and good cover in case of danger. They are strongly territorial throughout the year and in winter they occupy a large territory. Thus it would seem that birds that arrive on the coast in autumn may soon move inland in search of territories. Shrubb concluded that the relative paucity of records from large areas of forestry plantations may have reflected a lack of observer activity in such areas in winter. While this may be true to a certain extent, it is known that the species shows a preference for deciduous trees in winter owing to the greater field of vision they afford (Winter Atlas).

There are a number of instances of birds returning to the same area for several winters in succession. For example, two returned to Worthing refuse tip each winter from 1968/69 to 1970/71, one was seen at Glynde Level each winter from 1969/70 to 1974/75 and, more recently, at least one has occurred at regular sites in Ashdown Forest in all but one winter since that of 1986/87.

Most records are of lone individuals although there are a few instances of two birds together, mostly on autumn passage. In 1970 there were many reports of up to three at Beachy Head from 17 to 31 October, probably involving six different individuals. A bird at Beachy Head in late October 1966 was seen to chase and catch a House Martin. BWP considers that Great Grey Shrikes catching birds is "rather exceptional" although it does acknowledge records of hirundines being taken in flight.   *Michael Prince*

Woodchat Shrike   *Lanius senator*
Status:- A rare vagrant (39 records).

Seventeen were recorded prior to 1962 (des Forges & Harber), although two or three spring records have not been traced. Most were in May (8), June (4) and September (3), with an adult at Mill Creek, Newhaven on 24 April 1957 and a juvenile in a Portslade garden from 7 to 9 October 1958. Records include adults seen at Climping on 5 June 1922 (Dallas 1922) and Bremere Rife, Sidlesham, on 16 May 1934 (Crowe 1934), with a pair at Pagham Harbour on 19 May 1950 and two juveniles near Shoreham-by-Sea on 12 September 1956, one near the railway bridge and the other below Mill Hill. An adult female obtained at Preston, near Brighton on 4 May 1866 is in the Booth Museum (BoMNH 208059).

Twenty-two have been recorded since the beginning of 1962:

1967: An adult female at Gallows Hill, Graffham on 26-27 May.
1972: An adult at Crowlink on 16 June.
1976: A juvenile west of Birling Gap on 22 August.
       A juvenile at Merston, Chichester between 11 and 25 September.
       A juvenile east of Birling Gap on 16 October.
       A juvenile at Sidlesham Ferry from 24 October to 2 November (the latest county record).
1980: A juvenile at Selsey Bill from 16 to 18 October.
1981: An adult at Belle Tout, Beachy Head on 31 May.
       An adult in Hove from 10 to 13 June.
1982: An adult female at Combe Haven between 20 June and 21 August.
1983: A juvenile at Selsey Bill on 6-7 September.
1987: A juvenile southeast of Sidlesham Ferry on 14-15 August.
1988: An adult male between the Pagham Harbour Information Centre and Sidlesham Quay on 16 May.
       An adult at Cuckmere Haven on 27 May.

1989: An adult at Westmeston, near Ditchling, on 20 May.
1990: An adult at Littlehampton Golf Course from 22 to 24 April (the earliest county record).
An adult female near Thorney Island yacht club on 11 May.
An adult at Rackham on 14 September.
1991: An adult at Pulborough Brooks on 26-27 May.
An adult in the Argos Hill area, near Mayfield, on 5 and 15 July.
1993: An adult at Church Norton on 7 June.
An adult at Selsey Bill on 25 June.

The increase in records since the mid-1970s (fig. 99) probably reflects observer coverage as the population is in decline in most of Europe (Tucker & Heath 1994).

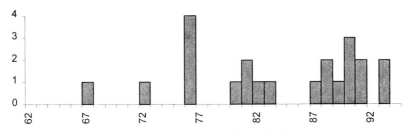

Figure 99. Annual totals of Woodchat Shrikes, 1962 - 94.

Since 1962 the proportion of autumn records has increased slightly, but only due to the four juveniles seen in 1976. All records have fallen between 22 April (1990) and 2 November (1976) with recent occurrences in summer falling outside normal periods of passage. This is particularly true of those in July 1991 and late June 1993 while the summering female at Combe Haven in 1982 was especially unusual. Only three have been seen at Beachy Head, a very low number compared with most other scarce passerines. This total is equalled by Selsey Bill and exceeded by the four around Pagham Harbour. The high number of occurrences away from the coast is also noteworthy. The cumulative monthly totals of all records are shown below.

	Apr	May	Jun	Jul	Aug	Sep	Oct
before 1962	1	8	4	-	-	3	1
1962-94	1	7	5	1	2	3	3

There were between seven and 27 records of this showy shrike in the British Isles each year during 1962-94 (Fraser & Ryan 1994). It breeds from northwestern Africa and Iberia to Poland and Iran, wintering in sub-Saharan Africa north of the Equator (BWP).   *Richard Fairbank*

Jay   *Garrulus glandarius*

Status:- A very common resident; passage migrant and winter visitor.

The Jay is found mainly in deciduous woodland, acorns and beechmast being important food items. However, it also breeds in coniferous woodland, although in smaller numbers. In recent times the Jay has moved into urban parks and suburban areas where there are mature trees. On farmland, Jays are associated mainly with shelter belts and copses.

The presence of woodland is central to its distribution and the abundance map in the New Atlas confirms that the greatest concentration occurs in Hampshire, Sussex and Kent, which form the most heavily wooded region of Britain (Locke 1987). The Atlas map shows that it is noticeably absent or scarce in the urbanised coastal strip between Newhaven and Bognor Regis and in poorly wooded areas of the Downs. Jays are also absent from Pevensey Levels.

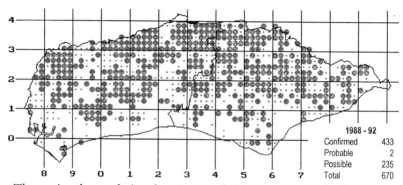

1988 - 92	
Confirmed	433
Probable	2
Possible	235
Total	670

The national population has increased this century, with the decline of gamekeeping, but in recent years it has stabilised (Marchant et al 1990). Information on breeding densities in the county is limited and certainly insufficient to show any long-term trends. Bealey & Sutherland (1983) found an average density of 15.6 pairs per km² in their survey of semi-natural broadleaved woodlands in West Sussex in 1982, a figure significantly higher than the national average for woodland of 8.83 pairs per km² (New Atlas). Surveys of the bird communities of farmland at the Brinsbury Estate in 1980 and Plumpton in 1982 found densities of 3 pairs per km² and 1.5 pairs per km² respectively (Prater 1982, 1983b), again higher than the national average for farmland of 0.9 pairs per km² (New Atlas). Combining the results of a number of censuses of breeding birds in defined areas carried out during the 1980s gives an average of 5.5 pairs of Jays per km², a figure which if applied to the 435 tetrads in which breeding was confirmed or probable during the Atlas Survey, indicates a county population of about 9500 pairs. This compares with a total for Britain and Ireland of 160,000 pairs (New Atlas).

In most autumns small numbers of birds are found in unusual locations, indicating that movements have occurred. The failure of the acorn crop over a large part of northwest Europe in the autumn of 1983 brought about eruptive movements of birds of both British and continental origin (John & Roskell 1985). The movement along the south coast was detected in Sussex in late September. The peak occurred in early October, when a number of flocks of 100 or more birds were seen on the coast or the Downs. At Cissbury 417 flew north in four hours on 2 October and 733 were recorded from nine sites flying south or west on 4 October. The latter included 300 at Beachy Head, 165 at East Brighton Golf Course, 122 over north Brighton and 113 at Parham.

Spring movement was noted in 1958 (des Forges & Harber) but was more recently seen to occur in 1982, when 41 were recorded from coastal localities, between 18 April and 15 May including nine over Worthing on the 24 April, ten over Beachy Head on the 12 May, nine over Selsey Bill on the 13 May and three which flew in from the sea at Beachy Head on 14 May.

Among 22 recoveries of Sussex-ringed Jays, only one was found outside the county. A young bird ringed at East Grinstead in August 1983 was killed near Andover, Hampshire, 94 km west, in May 1984. There is only one record of a bird ringed elsewhere being found in the county, namely one ringed near Portsmouth, Hampshire in January 1984 and killed at Billingshurst, 45 km ENE, the following April. Both these records occurred following the unprecedented eruption of Jays in October 1983, mentioned above, and may have been involved in that movement (Mead & Hudson 1984).   *Matthew Sennitt*

Magpie   *Pica pica*

Status:- A very common resident.

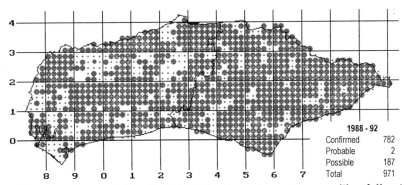

1988 - 92	
Confirmed	782
Probable	2
Possible	187
Total	971

The Magpie population in Britain has been increasing steadily, following the decline in gamekeeping since the beginning of the century. In the 1950s, there was a decline in the Magpie population, particularly in agricultural areas, probably due to the use of organochlorine pesticides. A recovery followed, though there was an unexplained decrease in Magpie breeding success in the period 1966-70 (O'Connor & Shrubb 1986). However, since the 1970s the population has been rising steadily (Marchant *et al* 1990), particularly in southern England.

The Magpie is found in a wide variety of habitats, requiring only suitable trees or shrubs for nesting. In the 1940s Magpies moved into suburban areas, and have since taken up residence in urban districts. Population densities in urban areas may exceed those for woodland or farmland (Tatner 1982)

Magpies are conspicuous nest predators, which together with their close proximity to man has resulted in their being implicated in the decline of some small songbirds. However, Baillie, Gooch & Birkhead (1993) found no evidence to support this. Furthermore, Tatner (1983) found vestiges of birds or eggs to occur in only a small number of samples of urban Magpie gizzards, or their faeces. In summer more than 70% of their diet was invertebrate, while in winter over 70% was plant material.

The Atlas map reflects the ubiquitous nature of the Magpie. During the Atlas Survey, birds were seen in 98% of tetrads and breeding was proved in 75%. The areas of low density in seemingly suitable habitat are likely to be those where game keeping is depressing the population. Information on breeding densities in the county is limited. Bealey & Sutherland (1983) found an average density of 8.7 pairs per km² in their survey of semi-natural broadleaved woodlands in West Sussex in 1982 while censuses of the bird communities of farmland at the Brinsbury Estate in 1980 and Plumpton in 1982 found densities of 6 pairs per km² and 5 pairs per km² respectively (Prater 1982, 1983b). Combining the results of a number of censuses of breeding birds in defined areas carried out during the 1980s gives an average of 6.7 pairs of Magpies per km², a figure which if applied to the 784 tetrads in which breeding was confirmed or probable during the Atlas Survey, indicates a county population of about 21,000 pairs. This compares with a total for Britain and Ireland of 590,000 pairs (New Atlas).

During the autumn and winter months, Magpies may be found in feeding and roosting flocks, often associated with areas of thick scrub. Since 1980, flocks of more than 100 have been seen at Moulsecoomb Wild Park and Eridge Park, with concentrations in excess of 50 at Chalvington, Midhurst, Sidlesham, Washington Gravel Pits and Whitbread Hollow.

No Sussex-ringed birds of this sedentary species have been recovered outside the county, and only one ringed elsewhere has been found here. This had been ringed as a nestling in Essex in May 1976 and was found near Cooksbridge, 100 km south, in April 1978. *Matthew Sennitt*

Nutcracker *Nucifraga caryocatactes*

Status:- A very rare vagrant (nine records).

Five were recorded before 1962 (des Forges & Harber). Individuals were shot at Litlington on 26 September 1844 (now in the Booth Museum, BoMNH 204086), near Chichester on 3 November 1893, at Chilgrove on 21 December 1900 and a female near Pulborough on 19 October 1913 (Ticehurst 1914). One was seen briefly two miles west of Turners Hill on 18 December 1946 (Ferguson-Lees 1948a).

Since the beginning of 1962 four have been seen, the most recent in 1970:

1968: One at Hailsham from 25 (when trapped) to 31 August (*Brit. Birds* 63: plate 63).
One flying west over Hodcombe, Beachy Head on 2 October.
A first-year female shot at Coldwaltham on 16 October had been mistaken for a Jay.
1970: One flying west over Whitbread Hollow, Beachy Head on 22 August.

Records have been in August (2), September, October (3), November and December (2). Those in 1968 were part of a large irruption into Europe which included 315 in Britain (between August and October), 800 in Belgium and 6000 in the Netherlands (Hollyer 1970).

Those recorded at Coldwaltham, Hailsham, Litlington and Pulborough were of the 'slender-billed' race *N.c. macrorhynchos* while that at Chilgrove was the second, and most recent, British record of the 'thick-billed' race *N.c. carycatactes*.

There were just over 350 records of this heavily spotted corvid in the British Isles during 1962-94, all but 35 arriving during 1968. The mainly resident race *carycatactes* breeds in the mountains of central and eastern Europe and in southern Scandinavia while the eruptive *macrorhynchos* breeds right across Siberia and in Japan. Other races occur in the Himalayas and China. *Richard Fairbank*

Chough

Pyrrhocorax pyrrhocorax

Status:- Formerly a breeding resident.

The Chough once bred on all the sea-cliffs of Sussex (White 1789), with its stronghold at Beachy Head. Consistent with a decline in the British Isles and areas of mainland Europe (Voous 1960), the Sussex population became extinct in the 19th century. Walpole-Bond concluded that this occurred about 1830 and that all subsequent records related to escapes. Neighbouring populations, in Kent and the Isle of Wight, were also extinct by the end of the 19th century (Kelsall & Munn 1905, Ticehurst 1909) and the remaining English populations lost in the 1960s (Darke 1971). Choughs in the British Isles are now confined to Wales, Scotland, Ireland and the Isle of Man.   *Matthew Sennitt*

Jackdaw

Corvus monedula

Status:- A very common resident.

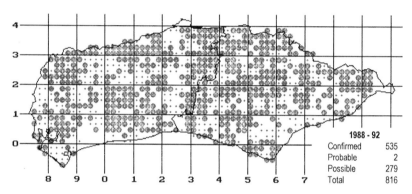

1988 - 92	
Confirmed	535
Probable	2
Possible	279
Total	816

The Jackdaw population has shown an upward trend, nationally, for most of this century, with only transient changes in fortune (Marchant *et al* 1990), though the numbers may now have stabilised. The increases have been observed in both woodland and farmland populations of Jackdaws.

The reasons for the long-term changes are not understood. The feeding preferences of farmland Jackdaws are not dissimilar to those of Rooks, with grain, weed seeds and invertebrates being the main food items, but the Jackdaw is a more generalised feeder utilising a wider range of foods. This may have diminished the negative effects of some of the modern farming techniques on the Jackdaw population, while the increase in cereal growing may have been beneficial (O'Connor & Shrubb 1986).

In 1938, half the Sussex population was thought to be housed in the chalk cliffs, but changes such as those brought about by increased urbanisation may have produced an increase in suitable nest sites.

The Atlas map shows the Jackdaw to be widely dispersed in Sussex, the gaps in its distribution presumably reflecting availability of nest sites. Information on breeding densities in the county is, however, very limited. Bealey & Sutherland (1983) found an average density of 3.4 pairs per km² in their survey of semi-natural broadleaved woodlands in West Sussex in 1982 while surveys of farmland bird communities at the Brinsbury Estate in 1980 and Plumpton in 1982 revealed densities of 5 pairs per km² and 0.75 per km² respectively (Prater 1982, 1983b). Assuming an average density of 3 pairs per km² indicates a county population of about 6500 pairs, compared with a British total of 390,000 pairs (New Atlas).

Movements of Jackdaws are infrequently recorded in Sussex. In 1983 a record immigration of Jackdaws in Kent resulted in a westerly movement. In late October, 120 were seen flying west over Brighton, while 120 were recorded in Slinfold. In November, 126 were observed at Pett and 100 flew west over Pagham.

Immigration is rarely seen. In 1982 a total of 11 birds were recorded in late April and early May, flying in off the sea at Selsey Bill, while one was also noted at Beachy Head. In 1983, a total of four flew in off the sea during March and April at Brighton Marina.

In winter large flocks gather to feed or roost, often with other corvids. A roost in excess of 2000 has regularly been recorded at West Chiltington, and flocks of similar size have been seen at Hurstpierpoint and North Stoke. Since 1980, flocks of 1000 or more have been observed at Bewl Water, Gatwick and Iping Common.

Of the 35 recoveries of Sussex-ringed Jackdaws, only three have been found outside the county and none had dispersed more than 100 km.

Matthew Sennitt

Rook   *Corvus frugilegus*

Status:- A very common resident.

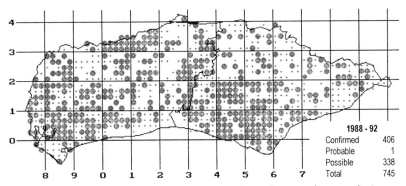

1988 - 92	
Confirmed	406
Probable	1
Possible	338
Total	745

Until the late 1950s it was thought that the Rook population was increasing (des Forges & Harber). However a survey in 1975 (Merritt 1978) found only 18,180 nests, a decline of some 42% in the Sussex breeding population since the national Rook Investigation of 1944-46. A similar change was found nationally (Sage & Vernon 1978). However, in 1980 a survey based on randomly selected 10-km squares (Sennitt 1981) found the Sussex population to have stabilised, despite a continuing downward trend in southern England (Sage & Whittington 1985).

The decrease in the Rook population appears to have been accompanied by a reduction in average rookery size as is evident from a series of surveys carried out by the Hastings and East Sussex Natural History Society from 1939 to 1975 (Merritt 1978), the results of which are given below.

Year of survey	1935	1945	1965	1975
Number of nests	2502	3223	1532	1311
Number of rookeries	24	29	44	45
Average size	104	111	35	29

However, the decrease in rookery size may have been exaggerated by differences in methods of rookery counting as well as observer coverage, between early and recent surveys.

Rooks use a large number of tree species for nesting. In Sussex most are in oak, pine and ash (Merritt 1978, Sennitt 1981). The loss of elms in the 1970s is not thought to have had more than local effects on the Rook population, for example the extinction of 12 rookeries in the Littlehampton area between 1975 and 1980.

It is likely that food supply is the major factor limiting the Rook population. This is influenced by farming practice. Brenchley (1984) found that Rooks are most successful where farms contain a similar proportion of pasture and tillage. In Sussex, the ratio of pasture to tillage fell most dramatically between 1939 and 1959, but continued to fall more slowly thereafter. Recently, intensification of cereal growing and the use of pesticides have reduced the availability of cereals and invertebrate foods, while food supply during the breeding season has been depressed by the change from spring to autumn sowing (O'Connor & Shrubb 1986).

Merritt (1978) found the highest breeding densities of Rooks on neutral or alkaline soils where arable farming was most prevalent, such as in the Chichester area and on the Downs between Lewes and Eastbourne. In contrast, well wooded regions on acid soils, such as the forest ridges between Crawley and Battle, and the high Weald north of Petworth and Midhurst, had the lowest densities. A similar picture is shown by the Atlas map, with an increase in distribution in the northwest of the county, since 1975, but a loss of some rookeries in the area to the north of Selsey. An absence of rookeries along the urban coastal strip, between Brighton and Littlehampton, is also evident.

Outside the breeding season, Rooks may gather in large numbers, to roost or take advantage of abundant food supplies. In November 1987, 400 were recorded in maize fields near Icklesham. Regular winter roosts are used, often in the company of other corvids. One such roost in West Chiltington regularly holds 1000-2500 birds during the winter months, while in 1983 pre-roost gatherings of 6000 and 5000 were recorded at Westhampnett and Arlington respectively.

No Rooks ringed in Sussex have been found outside the county. Five others ringed elsewhere have been recovered but all came from less than 100 km distant within southern England.   *Matthew Sennitt*

Carrion Crow   *Corvus corone*

Status:- A very common resident.

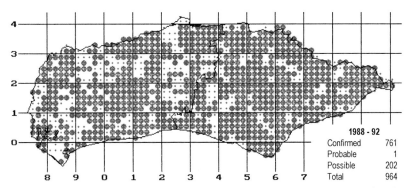

	1988 - 92
Confirmed	761
Probable	1
Possible	202
Total	964

In common with other corvids, the Carrion Crow population has been increasing nationally since the reduction in gamekeeping pressures at the beginning of the century. Despite its feeding habits, its population increase was unchecked by the era of organochlorine pesticides, which decimated many carrion feeders. In recent times it has spread into urban areas and will breed wherever there are suitable nest sites.

In the Atlas Survey, the Carrion Crow was found to be well distributed in Sussex, but the Atlas map shows that it was relatively thinly spread in some central and western areas of the county. These gaps mirror those of the Magpie and may well represent current areas of game keeping. Information on breeding densities in the county is very limited, especially in suburban areas. Bealey & Sutherland (1983) found an average density of 9.7 pairs per km² in their survey of semi-natural broadleaved woodlands in West Sussex in 1982 while surveys of farmland bird communities at the Brinsbury Estate in 1980 and Plumpton in 1982 revealed densities of 3.7 pairs per km² and 1.75 per km² respectively (Prater 1982, 1983b). Assuming an average density of 5 pairs per km² indicates a county population of about 15,000 pairs, compared with a British total of 790,000 pairs (New Atlas).

Outside the breeding season, sizeable flocks of Carrion Crows may be found scavenging at rubbish tips and along the shoreline. Up to 350-400 regularly visited Pebsham tip in the winter months of 1988, 300 were recorded at the Sompting tip in January 1982, and 198 at the Washington tip in June 1989. On Goring Beach up to 176 were recorded in December 1992, 101 in May 1991 and 87 in August in both 1980 and 1990. At Bewl Water, concentrations of 140 were noted in March 1980 and March 1991.

Immigration is rarely observed although a total of 26 arrived from the sea at Beachy Head between 3 and 20 May 1975 and a few immigrants were reported at both Beachy Head and Selsey Bill in March and April 1982.

Three Sussex-ringed birds have been recovered outside the county, all within southern England.

The Hooded Crow *C.c. cornix* occurs in Britain in the Isle of Man and north of a line which runs from southwest to northeast Scotland. It is also found throughout the whole of Ireland, where it has increased markedly since 1924 (Hutchinson 1989). In Sussex, a pair bred in Tilgate Forest in 1906, and a Hooded Crow mated with a Carrion Crow in St Leonard's Forest in 1908, but it now occurs as a very scarce winter visitor and probable passage migrant. Most birds in recent years have occurred in the period October to May as shown by the cumulative monthly totals for the period 1962-93 below.

Oct	Nov	Dec	Jan	Feb	Mar	Apr	May	Jun
11	20	25	18	21	11	12	10	1

One at Rye Harbour intermittently from 26 May to 16 June 1978 was the latest for the county since 1948 when one summered at Birling Gap.

des Forges & Harber recorded a marked decline in Hooded Crows in winter compared with the late 19th century. This decrease has continued with about 63 recorded between October and March in the 1970s but only ten in the 1980s. There were none in 1990 or 1991, while in 1992 the only record was of one that flew in off the sea at Beachy Head on 1 May, which may have been that seen feeding in nearby fields on 16 May. In 1993, one flew east at Glyne Gap, Bexhill on 13 March and there was one at Selsey Bill on 10 April.

Usually only single birds are seen, but seven were recorded at Pebsham in November-December 1969. *Matthew Sennitt*

Raven *Corvus corax*

Status:- A rare visitor which was formerly a breeding resident.

The Raven once bred throughout the county. Breeding ceased inland by 1880 and was then confined to the coast, where it continued for a further 15 years. Walpole-Bond listed 18 inland localities and ten along the coast where nesting was known to have occurred.

In Sussex, escaped or released birds cannot be ruled out when Ravens are seen. At least one of a pair which bred between 1938 and 1945, at Seaford Head and then Beachy Head, had escaped from captivity. A survivor of this pair remained until 1950.

Most Ravens have occurred in autumn or winter and between 1946 and 1961 there were only six such records, including one which flew in from the sea at Holywell, Eastbourne on 9 October 1958 (des Forges & Harber). During the period 1962-94 just 5-7 were recorded as follows:

1963: One over Chichester Harbour on 31 March.
1976: One at Beachy Head from 10 April to 1 May 1977.
    One flying east at Beachy Head on 18 September may have been different to that above.
1977: One near Steyning on 15 January.
1987: One at Combe Haven on 24 October.
1994: One at the North Wall, Pagham Harbour on 9 August departed north.
    One, presumably the same, roosted on Pilsey Sands on 23 August before departing.

Three were released at Pippingford Park, Ashdown Forest in May 1973, five in July 1973 and two in August 1976.

Nationally, the Raven is now confined to upland and sea cliff habitats, where rock nesting predominates. The population is stable, but the range has expanded slightly. This expansion has been accompanied by increased nesting in trees (Sitters 1988). Factors currently involved in determining population are persecution, farming practices, particularly sheep farming, patterns of afforestation and recreational activities.   *Matthew Sennitt*

Starling   *Sturnus vulgaris*

Status:- An abundant resident, passage migrant and winter visitor.

Starlings are both one of our most familiar and widespread birds; being cavity nesters, they will breed wherever there are mature trees, buildings, or other natural or man-made sites. They breed throughout the county, the highest densities occurring in urban and suburban areas, and the lowest on the large treeless areas of monocultural agriculture on the Downs.

There is evidence of a recent marked decline in breeding populations in farmland and woodland, as indicated by the national CBC indices (Marchant *et al* 1990). Reasons advanced for this decline include changing farm practices, particularly the increased use of pesticides (O'Connor & Shrubb 1986). However, the Common Birds Census does not include urban and suburban habitats and there appears to have been little population monitoring of Starlings in towns and cities, so it is difficult to tell whether a decrease has also occurred in these habitats. The recent CBC indices have certainly been mirrored abroad where breeding populations in northern Scandinavia and Russia have fallen markedly in recent years (Feare 1984). As many of our wintering birds originate from these areas, it may be that there has also been a decline in our wintering population.

Despite these declines, the Starling is plainly still an abundant breeding and wintering bird in Sussex. Recent surveys of various farmland and woodland sites in the county indicate an average of 10.5 pairs per km² in semi-natural broadleaved woodland (Bealey & Sutherland 1983) and densities of 13 pairs per km² on mixed farmland at the Brinsbury Estate in 1980 and 10.5 pairs per km² in similar habitat at Plumpton in 1982 (Prater 1982, 1983b). A total of 17 pairs was found in 45.3 ha at Grantley Farm, Maynards Green in 1992 but only three pairs in 67.5 ha at Marsh Farm, Binsted in 1993. Combining the results of these surveys indicates an average breeding density of about 15 pairs per km², a figure which if applied to the 876 tetrads in which breeding was confirmed indicates a county population of over 50,000 pairs. The national total was estimated at 1.1 million pairs (New Atlas).

1988 - 92	
Confirmed	876
Probable	0
Possible	94
Total	970

Post-breeding roosts, comprising largely juveniles, build up from early May onwards. At Rye Harbour, for example, numbers increased from 6000 on 29 May 1970 to 10,000 on 19 June and from 2000 on 2 May 1985 to 4000 on 26 May, 6000 on 30 July and 8000 on 9 October. A roost at Cissbury Ring held 17,000 birds in June 1965 and 50,000 the following June.

Diurnal movements were noted in most years up to the mid-1970s, mainly in October and November at coastal sites. Peak counts at Beachy Head included 3000 north on 19 November 1966, 4000 north on 5 November 1967 and 1000 west on 9 October 1976. At Portslade there were 4000 west on 21 November 1974. Since the mid-1970s, very few movements have been reported but whether this represents a genuine decrease or less rigorous recording is not known.

Very large roosts form in winter. The largest gathering recorded was of 75,000 at Lancing Shooting Range on 14 March 1968 but other notable concentrations include 50,000 at Shoreham in October 1977, at Berwick in December 1984 and at Portslade in January 1985, 40,000 at Upper Beeding in January 1970, 30,000 at Ovingdean in February 1968, 20,000 in a reedbed at Thorney Deeps in December 1990 and 12,000 at Chyngton Farm, Seaford in December 1988 and January 1989. Roosts of 10,000 were recorded at Pett Level in October 1969, Itchenor in November 1976, central Brighton in November 1986, Rye Harbour in October 1988 and Chichester Gravel Pits in October 1991. The roosts at Pett and Chichester were both in reedbeds.

Large movements may occur in cold weather. "Many thousands" flew west at Aldwick on 13 January 1964, 5000 flew west at Brighton in 3.5 hours on 15 January 1966, 90,000 flew west along the coast at Southwick in 2 hours on 9 December 1967 and 6500 flew east at Cissbury on 17 February 1969. At Plumpton, 2500 were grounded by bad weather on 13 March 1984.

Spring passage is indicated by a movement of 1150 southeast at Glyne Gap in 15 minutes on 7 March 1993.

There have been over 750 recoveries of Starlings ringed in Sussex which were summarised by Leverton (1989). Of these, about 80% were recovered within the county, 9% elsewhere in Britain and 11% on the Continent. In addition, 161 Starlings ringed elsewhere in Britain, and 41 ringed on the continent, have been recovered in Sussex. As would be expected, most movements involved an interchange of birds with Kent and Surrey and, to a lesser extent, with Hampshire. However, there were no movements between Sussex and Scotland, Wales or Ireland and only single movements to or from Cornwall, Devon, Wiltshire, Suffolk and Norfolk. After a relatively short period of parental care, young Starlings become independent, dispersing over a wide area during the summer months. Ringing has shown that Sussex-bred juveniles disperse not only to neighbouring counties but also across the Channel to France and Belgium. The Starlings that winter in Sussex originate mostly from eastern Europe (eastern Germany, Poland, Latvia, Estonia, Lithuania and the adjacent part of Russia) rather than from Scandinavia. Birds from Norway and Sweden winter mainly in northern England and Scotland, crossing the North Sea directly, and there is no evidence that they ever reach Sussex. There have, however, been three recoveries from Finland, with two movements the other way, indicating that they follow a different route to Britain, via the Baltic and North Sea coasts. A number of notable recoveries include one ringed at Southwick on 18 March 1958 and recovered at Cherikov, USSR in May of that year, a juvenile ringed at Hodcombe, Beachy Head on 10 August 1969 and found dead in Sweden on 20 May 1972 and a bird ringed at Alfriston on 2 February 1972 which was found at Arkhangelsk, USSR, 2903 km distant, in May the same year, close to the northern limit of the species range.   *Jon Curson*

Rose-coloured Starling   *Sturnus roseus*

Status:- A rare vagrant (23 records).

Eighteen, virtually all adults, were recorded before 1962 (des Forges & Harber). Three were undated, the others arriving in February (2), May, June (2), July, August (6) and November (3). Four of these were in August 1858 (at Blatchington, Piddinghoe, Tarring Neville and Worthing), one was present in a garden at Fishbourne from 22 February to 8 March 1929 while another was in a Lower Beeding garden from November 1933 to March 1934. A juvenile clap-netted at Rottingdean on 18 November 1910 is in the Booth Museum (BoMNH 207902), as is one of two shot near Brighton on 20 August 1870 (BoMNH 207903), having been feeding on flies from the back of a sheep at the time of its demise (Walpole-Bond).

Five have been seen since the beginning of 1962:

1970:   An adult in a garden in New Place, Eastbourne on 1 December.
1983:   An adult in a Hassocks garden on 22 July.
1984:   An adult at Birling Gap from 24 to 26 August.
1994:   An adult at Birling Gap from 11 to 15 June (*Birding World* 7: 222 and 493, *Brit. Birds* 88: plates 191 and 192).
        An adult at Sidlesham Ferry briefly on 18 September.

That all recent records and, as far as can be determined, all but one of the older records refer to adults is somewhat unusual, although juveniles are more readily overlooked. Perhaps more surprising is that April and particularly

October, generally good months for stray migrants, are the only months with no records. It is likely that several of the adults may relate to escapes from captivity.

There were nearly 250 records of this species in the British Isles during 1962-94 including a record 26 in 1994 (Rogers *et al* 1995). It breeds from southeastern Europe to southwest Asia and winters mainly in the Indian sub-continent. *Richard Fairbank*

House Sparrow *Passer domesticus*

Status:- An abundant resident.

Little attention is generally given to this familiar species and, as a consequence, few records are submitted. It is found throughout the county in close proximity to man, nesting in holes in buildings and roosting communally in parks and gardens. The ubiquitous nature of the species is shown by the results of the Atlas Survey, in which there were records in 927 (92%) tetrads, with breeding confirmed in 832 of these. Although the breeding population in Sussex is clearly very large, it is not possible to estimate its size, given that information on breeding densities is non-existent.

Recent literature has suggested that the national population may be falling (Marchant *et al* 1990) and that changes in farming practices, such as the increased use of chemical sprays, may have seriously affected the amount of weed seeds and invertebrate food available (New Atlas). Although little is known about population trends in the county, a marked decline was noted in the number of pairs at Bewl Water in 1992.

Large flocks may form after the breeding season, particularly on farmland, although few are ever reported. Notable exceptions have included 300 at Newhaven Tide Mills on 3 August 1987 and a roost of 900 at Brighton in January 1973.

Although the House Sparrow is regarded as a very sedentary species and hence not a target for ringing, a bird ringed at Litlington in August 1973 was recovered in Portsmouth, Hampshire, 85 km away, seventeen months later. Even more surprising was the 363 km travelled by a Yorkshire-ringed bird that was found dead at Bognor Regis in 1962.

A bird identified as a hybrid House x Tree Sparrow was trapped at Charleston Reedbed on 14 August 1973. *Val Bentley*

Tree Sparrow *Passer montanus*

Status:- A scarce and declining resident, passage migrant and winter visitor.

The Tree Sparrow has a very patchy distribution in Sussex. It nests singly or in small colonies, usually in holes in scattered trees, especially willow, but also oak, ash, birch and other species. Holes in sand and gravel pits, chalk quarries and buildings have also been used, as have nest-boxes at Pagham Harbour and Rye Harbour.

The history of the Tree Sparrow in Sussex has been summarised by Hughes & Dougharty (1975). At the end of the 19th century it was well distributed, if somewhat local, over most of England. However, during the first half of the present century it decreased throughout England, so that by 1935 Walpole-Bond knew of only two regular breeding colonies in the county. In the late 1950s this situation was being reversed and by 1961, des Forges & Harber were able to report that the numbers nesting in the county, although small, were definitely increasing. The population continued to increase thereafter so that by 1973 breeding had been reported from 155 tetrads. A detailed examination of the pattern of colonisation showed a correlation between new sites and the main river systems.

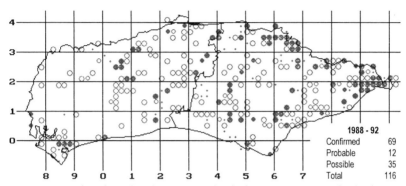

More recently, there has been a steady decline since 1978 which shows no sign of being reversed. Evidence of this decrease is provided by the results of the Atlas Survey, in which there were records in 116 tetrads, of which only 69 were of confirmed breeding. The Atlas map, which shows the tetrads in which the species was recorded during the Atlas Survey and also those (as open circles) in which it was found during 1961-87 but not during 1988-92, probably exaggerates the latest position. This is because the species has now disappeared from a number of tetrads where it had been found during 1988-92. In 1991, birds were absent from a farm at West Chiltington for the first time in 30 years, while in 1992, they were also absent for the first time in recent years at Bewl Water, although in 1993, the site was recolonised.

Various explanations have been offered to account for the fluctuations in this species. Summers-Smith (1989) concluded that upsurges in the British population were the result of autumn immigration from the continent when population levels were high there. A major factor in the recent decline may be modern farming methods that have encouraged greater weed control and autumn sowing of crops, reducing the availability of seeds, though the decrease early this century is more puzzling.

Large scale movements in autumn were evident in the 1960s and 1970s; about 1000 flew west at Selsey Bill on 18 October 1964, 2900 west at Beachy Head between 10 and 26 October 1971 and 1500 west at the same locality on 10 October 1976. In the 1980s, the largest movement recorded was one of 500 west at Hastings on 19 October 1983 while 13 over Fairlight on 10 October 1992 is the largest movement so far reported in the current decade.

There has been a similar fluctuation in the number of Tree Sparrows seen in winter. Large flocks were regular in the early 1970s; up to 500 were recorded on the Downs west of Brighton in the first two months of 1972, but a flock greater than 100 has not be reported since 1987. In 1992 and 1993 the largest winter flocks were just 27 and 28 respectively. The recent downward trend in both autumn and winter numbers is shown in fig. 100.

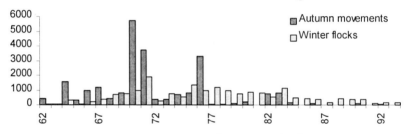

Figure 100. Autumn movements and winter totals of Tree Sparrows, 1970/71 - 92/93.

Only ten ringing recoveries have been reported and eight of these were within Sussex. The two longest movements, both just over 100 km, were for birds ringed in January 1962 and 1976 and subsequently found dead in Hemel Hempstead, Hertfordshire and Kent respectively. *Val Bentley*

Chaffinch *Fringilla coelebs*

Status:- An abundant resident, passage migrant and winter visitor.

The conclusions of the Woodland Survey covering the period 1963-74, the results of which were reported by Shrubb, are still valid today in that the species is one of the three most abundant and widely distributed woodland birds in the county. The Chaffinch can exploit almost any habitat where there are trees or bushes to provide a nest site and it will eat a wide variety of seeds, though the young are fed on small caterpillars and insects. Its ubiquitous nature is clearly demonstrated by the results of the Atlas Survey in which there were records in 984 (97%) tetrads with confirmed breeding in 896 tetrads. Only in a few tetrads in the heavily urbanised coastal strip near

Southwick, on the levels east of Rye and in a few poorly covered inland areas was the species not recorded.

The breeding population in Sussex probably does not fluctuate greatly and has possibly shown a slight increase in the last decade in line with national trends (Marchant *et al* 1990). In the 1963-74 Woodland Survey it was found that the Chaffinch accounted for about 9% of the total bird population in the 23 woods surveyed while Bealey & Sutherland (1983), in a more extensive survey of 40 semi-natural broadleaved woodlands in West Sussex found it to be the second most numerous species, comprising about 10.5% of the total bird population. This latter survey recorded an average breeding density of 90.8 pairs per km². Other breeding surveys of smaller defined areas have produced a range of breeding densities from an average of 15.3 pairs per km² on a 55 ha plot on the Adur Levels to over 125 pairs per km² in a small 12.1 ha portion of West Dean Woods. Combining the results of these smaller surveys gives an average density of 32 pairs per km², a figure which if applied to the tetrads in which breeding was confirmed, indicates a county population of about 115,000 pairs. Clark & Eyre (1993) estimated about 130,000 pairs in Hampshire compared with a total British population of 5.4 million pairs (New Atlas).

During late September and October, the resident population is joined by a marked influx of immigrants from the continent. Only small movements are recorded in most autumns and, with the exception of 500 that flew south out to sea at Selsey Bill on 18 October 1968, all the larger movements have been to the north or west. At Beachy Head, 4000 arrived from the south in just two hours on 14 October 1971 and 1000 on 8 October 1974. An unusually large movement was recorded on 12 October 1980, involving totals of more than 1500 at Beachy Head, 2100 at Maynards Green, 950 at Cissbury and 120 at Newmarket Hill. Interestingly, on the same day, only 67 were recorded at Selsey Bill compared with over 20,000 at Dungeness, Kent, thus reinforcing the notion that these movements involve birds of continental origin. During the early 1980s, movements were recorded annually in mid-October, the largest of which included 540 northwest at Cissbury on 19 October 1981, 784 over Pett on 20 October 1982, 600 over Hurst Green on 24 October 1982, 1854 west over Hurst Green and Crowborough on 20-21 October 1983 and

600 over Swanborough Hill, also on 20 October 1983. Since 1983, movements have been on a smaller scale although in October 1993, 575 were recorded at Hollingbury Camp on 15th, 400 flew west at Bewl Water on 17th and 650 did likewise at Seaford Head on 23rd.

Flocks of several hundred birds may occur during the winter months. The largest was one of 1000 at Graffham on 25 January 1986 though other notable concentrations have included 680 at Eridge Park on 31 December 1982, 800 at Stanmer Park on 2 January 1984 and 700 in an overgrown vineyard at North Marden on 4 January 1991.

There is very little evidence of spring passage although 600 at Chanctonbury Ring on 23 March 1969 may have been migrants while 610 which flew east at Rye on 11 April 1971, 350 at Beachy Head on 7 March 1976 and 100 birds per hour over Pett on 3 April 1983 definitely were.

Ringing recoveries have confirmed that some wintering birds are of continental origin. Individuals ringed in Holland were found in Hartfield in November 1966 and East Grinstead in January 1979 while birds ringed in Sussex during the winter were recovered during the breeding season in Finland in 1965, Belgium in 1966 and 1969, Denmark in 1974 and 1987, Germany in 1968 and Norway in 1985.

Albino individuals were recorded at Chidham in March and June 1966 and at Ditchling on 26 February 1978.   *Val Bentley & John Newnham*

Brambling   *Fringilla montifringilla*

Status:- A fairly common winter visitor and passage migrant.

Breeding in the birch woods of Fenno-Scandinavia, this close relative of the Chaffinch winters in southern and western Europe, normally arriving in Britain in October or November. Excluding 1964, when none were recorded in autumn, arrival dates during the period 1962-93 fell between 17 September and 21 October, with the average 5 October. The earliest ever recorded was one at Church Norton on 17 September 1988. Passage peaks between mid-October and early November, when diurnal movements may be noted, mainly at coastal sites. Day totals of more than 50 are rare though 120 were recorded at Beachy Head on 15 October 1993 and, exceptionally, *ca.* 500 arrived there on 10 November 1971.

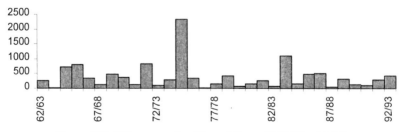

Figure 101. Winter totals of Bramblings, 1962/63 - 92/93.

The number of Bramblings recorded annually in Sussex varies considerably from year to year (fig. 101). More are recorded in very cold weather, as in early March 1965, when flocks totalling *ca.* 700 were seen in the Pagham/Selsey area, and January 1966, when a total of *ca.* 740 was recorded, including flocks of *ca.* 350 at Worthing and *ca.* 250 at Shoreham. A further influx occurred in severe weather in January 1987 with flocks of 100 at Brooklands, Worthing, 56 at Climping and 30 at Rye. There were, however, no significant influxes in the harsh winters of 1962/63 and 1978/79 and the two best recent winters for Bramblings, 1974/75 and 1983/84, were not particularly cold.

Most winter flocks are of up to 100 birds; larger flocks not previously mentioned include 160 at Little Common, Bexhill on 12 February 1969, 150 at the University of Sussex, Falmer on 9 February 1975 and 150 in Ashdown Forest on 10 January 1976. Many flocks remain for short periods only but a gathering of *ca.* 200 at Stanmer Park in November 1983 remained there or at nearby Withdean Park throughout the winter. An estimated 535 were present in the Brighton area on 29 February 1984.

The largest concentration of Bramblings in Sussex was that recorded by Guy Mountfort, then President of the SOS, who wrote that "On 9 January (1975), three large flocks of Bramblings passed over Possingworth Park, flying from the coast due north at an altitude of 25 m. The first was about 500 birds, the second of about 300, and the third about 400. The flocks were compact, flying in broad horizontal lines about 6-8 birds deep. A fourth flock of about 400 alighted in a beech coppice near my house and settled on the adjacent lawn and shubberies; feeding on beechmast and the berries of several large bushes of *Cotoneaster watereri*. Many of the males were in an unusually advanced state of breeding plumage with heads almost completely black. Part of the flock was still present on 20 January".

Bramblings favour beechwoods, where they are often seen in the company of Chaffinches, but once supplies of beech-mast are exhausted, they occupy a wider range of habitats such as open farmland, where they feed on cereal and weed seeds (Winter Atlas). Unusually, a flock of 20-40 fed regularly on peanuts in a garden in Brighton from January to April 1982.

A small spring passage is evident from mid-February onwards though numbers vary considerably. In 1977, for example, just three migrants were recorded, whereas in 1970 a marked passage in March included flocks of 20 west at Beachy Head and 39 northwest at Cuckmere Haven on 5th, *ca.* 100 at Rye Harbour on 8th and 30 at Worthing on 14th. During 1964-93, the average last date was 17 April. A female in Ashdown Forest on 7 May 1974 and a singing male at Belle Tout, Beachy Head on 12 May 1993 are the latest recorded in recent years, although des Forges & Harber referred to a few records for early May.

The cumulative monthly totals for 1962-76 and 1977-93, shown below, suggest that Bramblings may be now be arriving earlier in the autumn and in greater numbers but that fewer are now recorded in spring than previously.

	Sep	Oct	Nov	Dec	Jan	Feb	Mar	Apr	May
1962-76	1	506	808	231	3115	977	1587	369	1
1977-93	16	1417	805	710	1479	1372	638	226	1
Total	17	1923	1613	941	4594	2349	2225	595	2

There have been two recoveries of Sussex-ringed Bramblings. One ringed at an unspecified locality on 9 March 1973 was controlled in Texel, the Netherlands, 436 km NNE, on 24 April 1973 and a second-year bird ringed at Ashcombe, near Lewes, on 28 March 1975 was found dead in Italy in November 1983. The latter recovery demonstrates that Bramblings do not necessarily return to winter in the same country. One ringed at Lewell, Dorset on 22 November 1993 was controlled at Marley Common, 120 km ENE, on 3 April 1994. *Val Bentley & John Newnham*

Serin   *Serinus serinus*

Status:- A very scarce passage migrant. Has bred.

Following the first British breeding record in Dorset in 1967, a pair bred in Ashdown Forest in 1969, which may possibly have escaped from captivity (Shrubb). There have been no further confirmed breeding records for the county although a male was present at East Dean from May to July 1972, a pair at Beachy Head on 5 May 1973, a "confiding" pair there from 5 May to 14 June 1976, a pair at Birling Gap on 13 May 1977, a pair at Slinfold on 14 April 1982, a singing male in a garden at Pebsham from 24 April to 4 May 1983, and at least four individuals at Selsey Bill between 21 April and 31 May 1992, including two males and a female on 5 May.

Prior to 1962, there were about 13 records of 22 birds, all before 1933 except for one at Langney Point on 2 November 1954 (des Forges & Harber). Since the beginning of 1962, a total of about 125 birds has been recorded (fig. 102), including no less than 43 males. The most in any one year was 14 in 1972 and 15 in 1994. This is in marked contrast to neighbouring Hampshire where just 14 were recorded during 1962-92 (Clark & Eyre 1993).

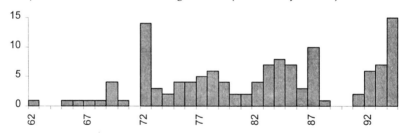

Figure 102. Annual totals of Serins, 1962 - 94.

This increase which has occurred, particularly since 1972, is in line with the national trend and is probably due to the extension that has occurred in the species' breeding range on the continent.

Serins are essentially passage migrants. Of the 125 recorded during 1962-94, 98 (78%) arrived in the period March to June, with six in March, 28 in April, 50 in May and 14 in June. The earliest recorded were singles at Beachy Head on 6 March 1983 and at both Birling Gap and Goring on 19 March 1994. The cumulative monthly totals for the period 1962-94 are shown below:

Jan	Feb	Mar	Apr	May	Jun	Jul	Aug	Sep	Oct	Nov	Dec
1	1	7	29	53	19	5	4	2	12	3	1

No less than 115 (92%) of those recorded during 1962-94 were at localities on or near the coast, notably Beachy Head (64) and Selsey (29). The only inland records, apart from those mentioned above, were of two males at Lewes from 5 to 12 April 1984, a male at Chichester Gravel Pits on 8 April 1984, a juvenile at Haywards Heath from 29 August to 10 September 1984, one at Arundel on 19 April 1986 and a male at Weir Wood Reservoir on 12 May 1993.

Of 24 recorded in the period July to November, 12 occurred between 8 and 21 October and 15 at Beachy Head.

There have been only two recent records for the period December to February although des Forges & Harber refer to 7-8 old records for February and three or more for December. One was recorded at Selsey Bill on 3 December 1967 and a male was present at Mewsbrook Park, Littlehampton from 14 January to 2 May 1978 where there was a second male from 9 to 28 April. *John A Hobson*

Greenfinch *Carduelis chloris*

Status:- A very common resident, passage migrant and winter visitor.

The Greenfinch breeds in all of the 10-km squares in Sussex. Favoured nesting habitats include young plantations, shrubby parks and gardens, and the fringes of woodland. Like other finches, they tend to nest in loose colonies, but range over large areas to obtain their food (New Atlas). During the Atlas Survey, Greenfinches were found in 864 (86%) tetrads, with breeding confirmed in 714 of these. The Atlas map shows the species to be widespread except in the northwest of the county where it is more patchily distributed. Very little information on numerical abundance is available, but Shrubb reported densities of about 120 pairs per 2500 acres on farmland. This might suggest a population as low as 4000 pairs in the county but this is very likely a significant underestimate as the species reaches its highest density in suburban areas. Given that Clark & Eyre (1993) estimated that there were

20,000-30,000 pairs in neighbouring Hampshire where birds were found in 991 tetrads, a range of 17,000-26,000 pairs seems appropriate for Sussex. Following a reduction in the 1960s due to the use of dieldrin and other organochlorine pesticides to treat spring-grown cereal grains, population levels in Britain have remained stable. Birds have, however, become much less abundant on farmland, and more numerous in towns and villages where more food has become available because of the increased planting of seed-bearing trees and shrubs, and the deliberate feeding of birds by householders (New Atlas). During 1988-91 there were an estimated 530,000 Greenfinch territories in Britain with greatest densities being reached in the south and east (New Atlas).

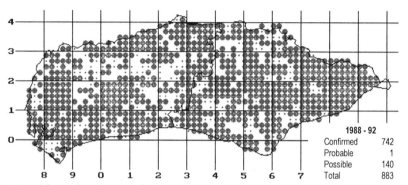

1988 - 92	
Confirmed	742
Probable	1
Possible	140
Total	883

Sizeable and rather confusing movements may occur in autumn and these are most obvious at coastal localities. Regular observations at Selsey Bill between 1963 and 1969 showed most movement in October and November, with emigration predominating in October, and coasting movements, usually westerly, predominating in November (Shrubb). Significant day totals have included 561 west at Bracklesham Bay on 29 November 1981, 371 west at Seaford Head on 19 October 1991, 300 west at Selsey Bill on 17 November 1974 and a total of 401 east between Littlehampton and Lancing during 16-19 October 1988.

Large flocks may appear from July onwards and these are supplemented by the arrival of autumn immigrants. Between 1967 and 1986, there were nine reports of 1000 or more including 1270 at Rye Harbour in November 1983 and at Cissbury, 1200 on 29 July 1976 and 1100 in October to December 1967. The absence of similarly sized flocks in more recent years is most likely due to changes in farming practices, especially the use of herbicides to control favoured weed seeds.

Ringing has shown that fewer than 7% of Greenfinch recoveries were for birds that had travelled more than 100 km from the Sussex ringing site. Since 1960 there have been three foreign recoveries in France while two birds ringed in Channel Islands have been controlled in Sussex.

Studies at an East Grinstead site, where 8000 Greenfinches have been ringed since 1979, have shown a regular movement through the area, usually from mid-February to mid-March. They have also shown that some of the birds that winter in Sussex move into north Kent and East Anglia for the breeding season. Of 66 birds that were recovered more than 20 km away between April and September, the predominant direction was between north and east and the average distance from the ringing site was 63 km. The furthest recovery was 171 km away in Norfolk. The paucity of recoveries to the south and west, suggests that the birds that move through north Sussex in early spring have probably wintered in the county.

Ringing of Greenfinches at this site, mainly between November and March, has also shown a reduction in the number of birds wintering, as follows:

	Total number of birds ringed	Average ringed per year
1979-83	3530	706
1984-88	2873	574
1989-93	2109	422
1989, 1991-93	1975	494*

* excludes 1990 data, when ringing was not on a comparable basis to other years.

Roy Sanderson

Goldfinch   *Carduelis carduelis*

Status:- A common resident and partial migrant.

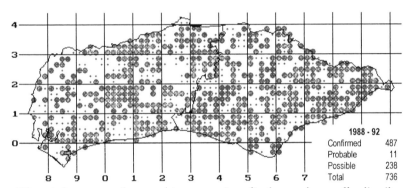

1988 - 92	
Confirmed	487
Probable	11
Possible	238
Total	736

The Atlas map shows this attractive finch to be well distributed throughout Sussex. Although the species was recorded in 73% of the county's tetrads, nearly a third of the records were of possible breeding only. Goldfinches nest in loose colonies and move over large areas to find food, hence these records may refer to feeding rather than breeding birds. Breeding data for the county are lacking. Only small numbers have been recorded in various censuses of breeding birds in defined areas. The Woodland Survey that covered the period 1963-74 found 30 species more common in the 23 woods surveyed (Shrubb) while a survey of semi-natural broadleaved woodlands in West Sussex in 1982 revealed an average density of 1.6 pairs per km² (Bealey & Sutherland 1983). Breeding densities on farmland are also low as shown by the presence of only four pairs in 227 ha (1.8 pairs per km²) at the Brinsbury Estate in 1980 and five pairs in 400 ha (1.3 pairs per km²) at Plumpton in 1982 (Prater 1982, 1983b). Using these data indicates a county population of about 6000 pairs compared with an estimated 7000-10,000 pairs in neighbouring Hampshire (Clark & Eyre 1993) where Goldfinches were recorded in 23%

more tetrads than in Sussex. The national population was estimated at 220,000 pairs (New Atlas).

It is reported that a total of 132,000 Goldfinches was captured on downland near Worthing in 1860 and undoubtedly trappers contributed significantly to the decrease of this species. Large scale bird-catching for commercial purposes ceased after legislation in 1933 and numbers in Britain increased in the following decades, until a decline, particularly in eastern and southern England, became apparent in the 1980s (Marchant *et al* 1990). Although many observers acknowledge that this species has declined in Sussex, a lack of records makes this difficult to prove. Leverton (1988) showed a significant reduction in the numbers of Goldfinches trapped for ringing at three downland sites between 1970 and 1987 and, although recognising that several factors may have been involved, he felt that changes in agricultural practice, particularly the increased use of herbicides were largely responsible for this decline.

There is no doubt that Goldfinches are most abundant during the autumn when large flocks can be found, particularly where there are bountiful supplies of dandelion and thistle seeds, on which the species feeds. Such gatherings regularly reach three-figures and there have been four reports of 500 or more comprising 500 at Amberley Wild Brooks on both 3 October 1976 and 14 September 1990, 1000 at Beachy Head on 8 October 1977 and 800 there on 17 October 1988.

Diurnal movements are recorded almost annually in autumn at coastal sites, particularly Beachy Head. These movements have been recorded in all directions although most passage occurs along the coast. Emigration is observed mainly from the headlands but very few birds have been noted arriving from the south. Numbers vary from year to year and, although passage is evident from early September to November, the largest movements generally occur in October (table 79).

Eastward		Westward	
Selsey Bill	1020, 21 Sep.1963	Beachy Head	1500, 17 Nov. 1974
Beachy Head	2000, 15 Oct. 1970	Beachy Head	1000, 1 Oct. 1975
Beachy Head	5500, 6 Oct. 1973	Beachy Head	2000, 9 Oct. 1982
Beachy Head	1000, 8 Oct. 1976	Beachy Head	1500, 11 Oct. 1987
Beachy Head	1000, 12 Oct. 1985	Beachy Head	1000, 22 Oct. 1987
Seaford Head	1278, 8 Oct. 1988	Beachy Head	1000, 29 Sep. 1988
Climping	1200, 16 Oct. 1988	Seaford Head	1150, 5 Oct. 1991
Climping	1254, 17 Oct. 1988		

Table 79. Peak autumn movements of Goldfinches, 1962 - 93.

There have also been a number of records that, regrettably, are unclear as to whether they involved feeding flocks, passage birds or a combination of both. All these were from Beachy Head including 1200 on 25 September 1971, 1150 on 24 October 1971, 2000 on 16 October 1973 and 1000 on 8 October 1977.

Those Goldfinches still present in the county in winter feed predominantly on seeds of alder, birch and teasel. Flocks are usually small and scattered and often mixed with other finches. Three-figure flocks are rarely recorded in winter; just six were noted between 1965 and 1976 (Shrubb) and eight between 1977 and 1993. The largest winter flocks recorded in recent decades were 250 at Weir Wood Reservoir in 1970 and 200 at Wiggonholt on 29 December 1978 and Rye Harbour on 17 February 1980. Winter movements in response to hard weather are seldom recorded, but occasional small parties have been noted, the largest of 40 flying west at Brighton on 15 January 1966.

Even fewer large flocks have been recorded in spring, the most notable being 500 at Chidmere Pond on 9 March 1974, 150 at Rogate Common on 11 March 1991, 140 in Tilgate Forest on 28 April 1979 and 100 at Stansted Forest on 3 April 1991. Spring passage extends from March until mid-May although most visible movements are noted between mid-April and mid-May. During these months small parties are often noted arriving from the sea or passing along the coast. Although numbers vary from year to year, they are usually very much smaller than those in the autumn. An exceptional arrival occurred in inclement weather on 13 April 1990 when 1500, many exhausted, were recorded with other passerines at Selsey Bill. Over half of the Goldfinches observed flying over this site in spring during the 1960s passed out to sea, a feature not noted in recent years.

Although present throughout the year, up to 80% of British Goldfinches winter in Belgium, France and Iberia (Newton 1972); ringing recoveries indicate that the most important wintering areas for locally bred birds are southwest France and northwest Spain. A total of 42 Sussex-ringed Goldfinches have been recovered in France and Spain; one ringed at Beachy Head in October 1969 reached northern Spain just 16 days later.

A leucistic bird, showing a hint of yellow in the wing, was seen at Chichester Gravel Pits on 16 September 1970 and one was among a flock of normal Goldfinches at Selsey on 8 September 1979.

Val Bentley & John Newnham

Siskin   *Carduelis spinus*

Status:- A common winter visitor and passage migrant. Probably now a very scarce breeder.

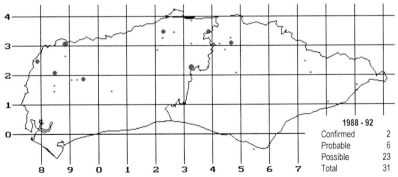

1988 - 92	
Confirmed	2
Probable	6
Possible	23
Total	31

Although Siskins were reported from an number of inland localities in Sussex during the summer months from 1979 onwards, breeding was not confirmed in the county until 1989. During the Atlas Survey, there were records in 31 tetrads but it is likely that many of those recorded in the 'possible' category referred to lingering winter birds rather than actual breeders. The New Atlas shows that the species has increased its breeding range in recent years, particularly in Wales, the Borders and parts of southern England, notably Dorset and the New Forest. Siskins nest mainly in coniferous forests and the recent population increase has been linked to the age-class of these woodlands. The amount of coniferous forest in Britain has doubled in the last 20 years, so providing substantial amounts of additional tree seeds, the Siskin's principal food. The population in Sussex, currently less than ten pairs, is very small compared to that in neighbouring Hampshire where an estimated 170-270 pairs were present in 1986-91 (Clark & Eyre 1993). The British population was estimated at 300,000 pairs (New Atlas).

There is a heavy autumn passage in some years, with diurnal movements regularly observed at coastal sites. Although migrants have been noted as early as 21 July, the main passage is from mid-September onwards. Very large numbers occurred in 1985, 1988, 1991 and 1993. In 1985, totals of 1900 and 1850 were recorded in September and October respectively while in 1988, passage was heaviest during the periods 15-22 September, 28 September-3 October and 15-20 October involving 2250, 2250 and 1000 birds respectively. The largest movement was of 1500 flying west at Beachy Head on 29 September 1988. In 1991, the totals for September and October were 2223 and 2095 respectively while in 1993, a minimum of 3500 was recorded in October including 445 at Church Norton on 14th and 400 at Beachy Head on 15th. At Seaford Head, a total of 1440 flew west between 23rd and 28th.

In winter, flocks of Siskins are often encountered feeding in alders, especially along rivers. During the 1960s, the largest flock reported between November and March was that of 78 at Black Down on 11 February 1967. In the 1970s, six flocks of 100 or more were reported in the same period, including 262 at Copthorne on 1 January 1972 and 250 at Warningcamp on 21 and 29 March 1971. Between 1980 and 1993, there were reports of 21 flocks of 100 or more in winter, the largest being 500 at Battle Great Wood on 4 March 1984, 304 at Littlehampton West Beach on 25 December 1993 and two flocks totalling 600 in the Midhurst area on 24 February 1985. Further evidence of the increase that has occurred in the wintering population is provided by a comparison of the average number of birds reported between January and March in 5-year periods from 1978 to 1992:

1978-82	508
1983-87	833
1988-92	845

As the winter progresses, there is an increasing tendency for Siskins to visit gardens to feed on peanuts, probably as natural food sources become depleted. The habit was first noted in the county in 1969, after which it spread rapidly. Birds were reported from three garden feeding sites in 1970 and from a further six in 1971, 27 in 1972 and 45 in 1973, a total of 81 gardens in all (Hughes 1974). In the East Grinstead area, Siskins arrive in gardens to feed on peanuts from late December onwards, although the dates and the numbers involved vary considerably from winter to winter. In some years it is not until February that the first birds are seen. Numbers varying from one or two up to a dozen or more feed together daily.

Most Siskins have left by late April although apparent migrants have been noted at coastal sites as late as early June. At Rye Harbour, a total of 79 flew east between 11 and 27 April 1971 but few other diurnal movements have been reported at this time of year. The presence of large flocks in spring, for example, 100 at the Isle of Thorns, Ashdown Forest on 1 April 1967, 100 in Friston Forest on 4 April 1973 and 450 at Buchan Park, Faygate on 6 April 1982 may, however, be indicative of spring passage.

Ringing studies in an East Grinstead garden between 1979 and 1993, in which over 2200 birds were trapped, have shown that the departure dates of Siskins in spring vary from year to year (Cooper 1987). In the week or two before they migrate, it has been shown that there is a period of rapid weight gain, indicating an increase in fat reserves in readiness for long-distance migration (Cooper 1985). Ringing recoveries show that some birds move rather rapidly from Sussex to Scotland, indeed one controlled in Highland had been ringed at East Grinstead just four days earlier. Recoveries in the West Midlands, Shropshire, Cheshire and Merseyside indicate the probable route taken from Sussex to Scotland. The wintering population does not only originate from Scotland. There is a possibility that some birds now stay in the county and nest, certainly many start singing before they leave the area. In some autumns there is an influx from the Continent, as shown by the recovery of birds from East Grinstead in the Low Countries and Scandinavia, including one in Finland. A comparison of the average number of birds ringed at this site in 5-year periods from 1979 to 1993 provides further evidence of the recent increase in the wintering population in the county:

	Total number of Siskins ringed	Average per year
1979-83	370	74
1984-88	771	154
1989-93	1140	228
Total	2281	

The 1994 total was 253, continuing the upward trend.   *Roy Sanderson*

Linnet   *Carduelis cannabina*

Status:- A very common resident and partial migrant.

The Linnet is a locally common bird of downland, heathland and farmland thickets and hedges but it is also increasingly reported from suburban gardens. The Atlas map shows the species to be unevenly distributed in the county with over 61% of the confirmed breeding records in East Sussex. The main concentrations are on the Downs from Brighton to Beachy Head and from Bexhill east to the Kent border. Conversely, there were several areas in West Sussex, notably southwest of Horsham and in the extreme northwest of the county, where Linnets were not recorded during the Atlas Survey.

Like the Goldfinch, this species increased in numbers following the cessation of large scale trapping earlier this century and as a result of the abundance of weed seeds available during agricultural recession between the two World Wars. Shrubb reported no change in the breeding population in the years to 1979. However, increased use of herbicides and loss of habitat doubtless contributed to a steep decline in numbers during the 1980s as indicated by the national CBC index (Marchant *et al* 1990). There are few breeding data for the county which span sufficient years to show changes. However, at Lullington Heath NNR there were 150 occupied territories in a 62 ha CBC plot in 1964, 100 in 1965, 42 in 1972, but only five in 1986 and four in 1987 (Bowley 1994). Although many of the censuses of breeding birds in defined areas during the 1980s reported few Linnets, surveys at Moulsecoomb Wild Park (240 ha) and the Adur Levels (55 ha) revealed average densities of 4.2 pairs per km² and 27.2 pairs per km² respectively. A study of the bird communities at the Brinsbury Estate (227 ha) in 1980, within an area of sparse distribution as shown by the Atlas map, found only one pair while a similar study at Plumpton (400 ha) in 1982 found 14 pairs (Prater 1982, 1983b). Although Linnets were reported from slightly fewer tetrads than Goldfinches, their breeding densities would appear to be higher. It is likely, therefore, that the population in Sussex is slightly larger than that of the Goldfinch, in the region of 5000-8000 pairs. This compares with an estimated 6000-10,000 pairs in Hampshire (Clark & Eyre 1993) and a British population of 520,000 pairs (New Atlas).

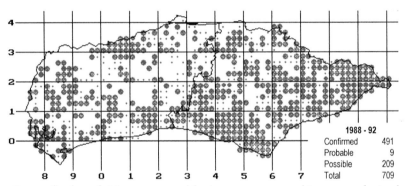

1988 - 92	
Confirmed	491
Probable	9
Possible	209
Total	709

Large flocks of Linnets assemble in autumn, reaching a peak in late September and October. Numbers then decline as emigration continues into November. During 1962-93, there were 17 reports of flocks of 1000 or more (table 80), although none were recorded between 1978 and 1986, a period in which the British breeding population was in steep decline. As the table shows, most large flocks have been in East Sussex, mainly in October. The only four-figure flock recorded in early autumn was that of 1000 feeding on linseed at Harbour Farm, Rye Harbour in August 1990.

Very large diurnal movements of Linnets have been recorded in some autumns, principally at Beachy Head and Selsey Bill. Most passage is along the coast although large numbers of birds have been observed flying out to sea at the latter site on a number of occasions (table 81). Some of the largest movements have coincided with heavy passage of Goldfinches, as on 15 October 1970, 9 October 1982 and 11 October 1987.

Beachy Head	1500, 9 Oct. 1965	Beachy Head	2000, 17 Oct. 1988
Lullington Heath	1000, 7 Oct. 1971	Rye Harbour	1000, 14 Oct. 1989
Beachy Head	3000, 15 Oct. 1971	Rye Harbour	1000, Aug. 1990
Beachy Head	2000, 7 Oct. 1973		2000, Sept. 1990
Beachy Head	1200, 9 Oct. 1974	Beachy Head	1000, 11 Oct. 1990
Beachy Head	3000, 21 Oct. 1975	Sompting Brooks	1074, 26 Sept. 1991
Littlehampton West Beach	1500, 8 Oct. 1977	Rye Harbour	1000, 2 Oct. 1991
Cooden Golf Course	1000, 27 Oct. 1977	Church Norton	1100, 1-31 Oct. 1993
Beachy Head	1000, 11 Oct. 1987	Selsey West Fields	1000, 2 Oct. 1993

Table 80. Peak autumn flocks of Linnets, 1962 - 93.

Large flocks have been recorded in a number of winters at both coastal and downland sites, feeding in kale, stubble and maize fields. There have, however, been only six reports of flocks of 1000 or more, comprising 1500 at Stump Bottom on 8 February 1969, 1000 at Cradle Valley, Seaford on 21 January 1975, 1500 at Shoreham Sanctuary on 24 January 1979, 2500 at the Devil's Dyke on 25 February 1979, 1000 at Pagham Harbour on 13 February 1991 and 1000 at Rodmell Brooks on 27 December 1993. Large flocks were not reported during the 1980s and it remains to be seen whether the higher numbers recorded in the winter of 1993/94 represent a genuine increase due to recent changes in agricultural policy. Cold weather movements of Linnets are occasionally recorded, the largest of which were of 200 and 250 flying west at Brighton on 15 January 1966 and 8 February 1969 respectively.

Eastward movements		Westward movements	
Beachy Head	3000, 11 Oct. 1994	Beachy Head	3000, 9 Oct. 1982
Beachy Head	2000, 15 Oct. 1970	Hastings	1700, 19 Oct. 1983
Beachy Head	5800, 11-15 Oct. 1972	Beachy Head	1000, 14 Oct. 1984
Beachy Head	1000, 16 Oct. 1973	Beachy Head	2000, 11 Oct. 1987
Beachy Head	1000, 12 Oct. 1986	Seaford Head	1100, 8 Oct. 1993
Beachy Head	1000, 11 Oct. 1982		

Southward movements	
Selsey Bill	3760, 19 Oct. 1963
Selsey Bill	4350, 15-16 Oct. 1966
Selsey Bill	1245, 21 Oct. 1967
Selsey Bill	1040 SE, 8 Oct. 1977

Table 81. Peak autumn movements of Linnets, 1962 - 93.

Although 1670 flew east at Rottingdean on 4 March 1965, spring passage normally occurs between mid-March and early May, with the main influx during the first half of April. The largest numbers are recorded at Beachy Head and Selsey Bill but the totals involved are generally smaller than those in autumn. At the former site, totals of 1120 east, 830 west and 100 north were recorded in 1962 and 1300 north and 1150 west between 11 and 22 April 1971. At Selsey Bill, a total of 1023 flew north in spring 1981 with a peak of 520 on 7 April. By far the largest influx recorded at this site was during wet weather on 13 April 1990 when a large fall of passerines included 1820 Linnets. Apart from the movement in early March at Rottingdean, the largest coastal movement away from Beachy Head and Selsey Bill was of 607 flying east at Glyne Gap, Bexhill on 13 April 1993. Although small parties are frequently encountered in the spring, there have been few reports of large flocks.

Exceptions include 300 at Rye Harbour on 17 April 1972, 1000 at Camber on 23 April 1976 and 700 Church Norton on 1 April 1993.

Ringing has shown that Sussex-bred Linnets winter in western France and northern Spain from where there have been 15 and four recoveries respectively.   *Val Bentley & John Newnham*

Twite   *Carduelis flavirostris*

Status:- A scarce winter visitor and passage migrant.

The Twite, a breeding bird of moorland habitats in northern Britain and Scandinavia, is found in small numbers along the Sussex coast in winter, feeding mostly upon areas of saltmarsh.

Shrubb noted a continuing recovery in the period 1962-74 (fig. 103) from the low numbers referred to by des Forges & Harber between 1947 and 1956. The graph shows the approximate number of birds recorded each winter and includes those on passage in October. The totals are the sum of the maxima recorded at each site during the winter; thus some duplication is possible where birds moved from one site to another. The graph also shows a marked decline which commenced in 1975/76 and was still continuing in the early 1990s. A similar decrease has also occurred in neighbouring Hampshire since the late 1970s (Clark & Eyre 1993).

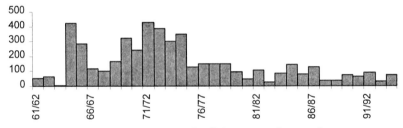

Figure 103. Winter totals of Twite,1961/62 - 93/94.

In the peak years, several large flocks were reported. In October 1964, for example, there were parties of 35 at Bracklesham and 45 at Selsey in mid-month while, in East Sussex, there were 100 at Beachy Head and 50 at Cuckmere Haven on 24th, 60 at Rye Harbour and 30 at the Midrips on 26th and 50 at Newhaven Tide Mills on 28th. Between the mid-1960s and mid-1970s large wintering flocks could be found at several sites in the county, particularly on the saltings between Rye Harbour and Camber where there were 150 on 18 January 1966, 200 on 11 November 1969, 107 on 18 November 1972 and 200 in late 1974. In several other years, up to 100 was recorded at this locality. At other sites in the county, numbers were lower with peaks of 75 at Chidham on 18 January 1973, 60 at Selsey West Beach on 11 November 1973, 60 at Pagham Harbour on 22 December 1973 and 7 March 1986, 70 on the Adur Estuary in February 1973, 70 at Cuckmere Haven on 24 October 1977 and 50 at the Midrips on 9 December 1962. Since 1980, the largest gatherings have been of 57 at Cobnor on 30 October 1991 and 70, with Linnets and Greenfinches, at Thorney Island airfield on 5 October 1993.

The cumulative monthly totals for the periods 1962-76 and 1977-94, shown below, confirm the decline in numbers since the mid-1970s.

	Sep	Oct	Nov	Dec	Jan	Feb	Mar	Apr
1962-76	1	1145	1299	1380	1157	567	250	6
1977-94	15	403	552	282	557	484	154	8

The earliest autumn record is of a single bird at Pagham Harbour on 15 September 1984 but, as the table shows, Twite are rare in this month. des Forges & Harber mentioned an old record for 22 September 1906 near Eastbourne but nothing is known of the September record tabulated by Shrubb, except that it occurred in 1967. Subsequent to Shrubb's analysis and additional to the Pagham individual, were three at Rye Harbour on 30 September 1979 and a party of 11 at Cuckmere Haven on 23 September 1990. Although fewer Twite have been noted in autumn in recent years, the records suggest that they may be arriving slightly earlier. During 1977-94, the average first date was 13 October compared with 20 October for the years between 1962 and 1976. The main arrival period, however, is the last two weeks of October.

The preceding table also suggests there may have been a change in the pattern of occurrence. The data for 1962-76 show that numbers remained fairly constant from October to January followed by a decline in February as overwintering birds started to leave. Records for 1977-94 show reduced numbers in December but an increase in January and a higher proportion remaining into February. Twite were recorded in March in 23 of the 32 years between 1962 and 1994; most, however, were early in the month with only a handful in late March. There were records in April in five of the years during 1962-94, totalling 14 individuals. The latest were three at Beachy Head on 19 April 1970.

There have been only a few records of movements of Twite, mostly involving small numbers. All were in the autumn, the most notable being 14 flying east at Selsey Bill on 1 November 1964, parties of 35 and 15 arriving at Beachy Head on 8 October and 22 October 1974 respectively, 38 flying east during a finch movement at Cuckmere Haven on 3 November 1989 and 21 flying west at the same site on 5 October 1991.

Although most records have been for the immediate vicinity of the coast, there have been a number of inland sightings. Those from the river valleys may refer to birds that had previously been feeding in more typical habitat near the mouth of the river; thus a party of eight at Lewes Brooks on 28 December 1971 and one there on 22 October 1988 may have come from Newhaven. Similarly, the small flocks recorded at Arlington Reservoir on 15 October 1972 and 27 November 1988 and at Litlington on 16 January 1982 may have come from Cuckmere Haven. Single Twite were recorded on downland at Bignor Hill on 31 October 1970, at Mile Oak near Portslade on 14 October 1973, at Lewes race course on 17 October 1989 and four, with Linnets, at Newmarket Hill on 2 November 1992. Other inland records include three at Swanbourne Lake, Arundel on 6 February 1989 and one in song at Runcton, near Chichester on 7 March 1974, while further inland were four at Selsfield Common, near East Grinstead, on 5 February 1969 and one at

Bewl Water on 18 January 1981. The largest inland party was of 42 at Chichester Gravel Pits on 6 February 1985.

Very few Twite have been ringed in Sussex and none in recent years. There have been no recoveries, thus the origin of birds passing through and wintering in Sussex is unknown.   *Val Bentley & John Newnham*

Redpoll   *Carduelis flammea*

Status:- A fairly common breeder, passage migrant and winter visitor.

Walpole-Bond described the Redpoll as "excessively local, with breeding pairs or small colonies of not more than eight separated by several miles from others of their kind". He also recorded that numbers of breeding pairs were subject to fluctuation from year to year and that some sites which still appeared suitable were abandoned for several years at a time. Although he did not give or estimate numbers, the county population at the time was probably fewer than 50 pairs. The main breeding area was given as a rough oblong with Loxwood, Storrington, Heathfield and Tunbridge Wells at its corners.

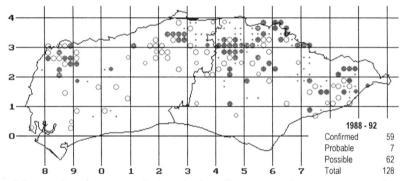

	1988 - 92
Confirmed	59
Probable	7
Possible	62
Total	128

The results of a survey during the breeding seasons in 1976, 1977 and 1978 indicated a county population of at least 372 pairs, although a full census was not undertaken in any one of the survey years (Houghton 1979). This figure suggested a seven-fold increase in the species since the 1930s. The survey, however, was carried out at a time when the national population was at a high level following a four-fold increase during 1964-74 (68-72 BTO Atlas). The Atlas map shows a total of 27 tetrads in which breeding was confirmed within the oblong described by Walpole-Bond and a further 31 outside it, mainly in the northwest and southeast of the county, indicating a considerably expansion in range since the 1930s. Casual records suggest a decrease in the Sussex breeding population since about 1984 with only 17 pairs or displaying males reported in 1988 and 15 in 1990. There was, however, a welcome increase to 44 pairs in 1992.

In some years, there is a considerable influx in autumn, characterised by westward movements at coastal sites and the appearance of occasional large flocks, such as 300 at Fairlight on 5 November 1982 and Icklesham on 28 October 1993. At Beachy Head, where diurnal movements are often observed, totals of 2600 and 2220 were recorded in the autumns of 1970 and 1971 respectively. Fewer have been reported from this site in recent years, although 500 were noted there on 26 October 1991. At least 500 flew west at Pett Level in one hour on 8 October 1977. Large flocks have also been recorded at inland localities in autumn, for example, 350 at Crowborough on 29 September 1985.

Redpolls are typically associated with birch and alder trees, wintering flocks occurring on heaths and in river valleys, often in the company of Siskins. The numbers wintering in the county show little correlation with the numbers reported in the preceding autumn. However, a poor autumn passage is often followed by low wintering numbers, as in 1987/88 when totals of 203 were reported in October, 200 in November, 59 in December, 52 in January, 80 in February and just nine in March. In other winters, numbers may be far larger as in 1985/86 when 600 were reported in December, 233 in January, 584 in February and 170 in March. Wintering flocks rarely comprise more than 50 birds although larger numbers are occasionally recorded, for example, 350 at Buchan Park, Crawley in November 1991, 325 in Brantridge Forest on 1 February 1986 and 300 in Ashdown Forest on 15 February 1992. Some flocks may linger well into April or even May, as in 1986 when there were 150 at Paddockhurst Estate on 2 May, 300 at Old House Warren on 8 May and 200 at Verdley Wood on 10 May. It seems likely, however, that these birds were on passage given that the March total for the whole county in that year was 170.

Spring passage at coastal sites is rarely marked, normally comprising nothing more than a handful of singles, mainly in May. The highest counts for coastal localities in spring appear to be those of 45 that flew north over Brighton on 1 May 1980 and 22 at Beachy Head on 9 May 1981.

Ringing recoveries, which are few and far between, suggest that some of the Redpolls that visit Sussex originate from northwest England. Of those birds ringed in Sussex and found on the continent, five were in Belgium and one each in France and Germany, the latter a movement of 775 km east.

The Redpolls that breed in Britain are of the race *C.f. cabaret*. There are, however, occasional reports of larger, paler birds showing the characteristics of the continental race, the Mealy Redpoll *C.f. flammea*. There have been seven records since the beginning of 1962, as follows:

1964: One-two at Sidlesham on 19 October.
       One at Shoreham rubbish dump on 25 October.
       One at Warminghurst, Washington in November.
1968: One trapped at Marley Common on 27 February.
1972: One trapped at Marley Common on 29 December.
1991: One in Ashdown Forest on 3 January.
1994: One trapped at Icklesham on 13 November.

Mike Scott-Ham

Crossbill   *Loxia curvirostra*

Status:- A scarce visitor occurring in large numbers in irruption years. Breeds occasionally.

Feeding almost exclusively in conifer woodlands, Crossbills have been recorded in Sussex in all of the last 33 years except 1970 and 1976. Annual totals have ranged from just one in 1989 to about 1200 in 1991, the latter the largest county total since the winter of 1909/10 when flocks of several hundred were seen in many areas (Walpole-Bond). The large numbers recorded in some years (fig. 104) follow periodic westward eruptions from the forests of northern Europe. These probably result from high population levels coinciding with poor or moderate seed harvests (BWP). Other individuals may come from established populations in the New Forest and on the Hampshire/Surrey border.

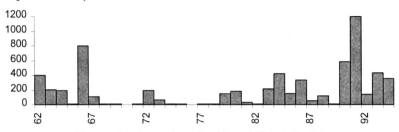

Figure 104. Annual totals of Crossbills, 1962 - 94.

During these influxes, a few large flocks have been recorded. Those of 100 or more have included at least 120, perhaps 200, in Friston Forest on 29-30 June 1962 (with 100 still there on 4 July), 100 in the Ardingly/Paddockhurst Estate area in early 1984, 100 at Balcombe in July-August 1990, 100 at Lavington Common on 9 March 1991 and 155 at West Dean Woods on 17 May 1991.

The graph above shows the years in which irruptions occurred. Following such influxes, some Crossbills may stay to breed in almost any month of the year where there is suitable habitat. Breeding in the county was confirmed or probable in 1963, 1967, 1973, 1979, 1980, 1984, 1991 and 1994. The Atlas map shows both the tetrads in which the species was recorded in the 1988-92 Atlas Survey (mainly in 1991) and also those tetrads (as open circles) where Crossbills were recorded in the period 1976-87 but not in 1988-92. During the former period, breeding was confirmed or probable in just eight tetrads, only one of which also held Crossbills in 1991. Most recent breeding records have been for Ashdown Forest and the West Sussex commons.

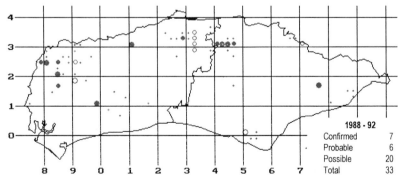

In invasion years, birds start to arrive in June but the largest numbers may be recorded at any time between July (as in 1990) and October-November (as in 1979). Shrubb referred to "no particular pattern of occurrence" outside the irruption years "except that nearly all records were for the period July to April". The cumulative monthly totals for the period 1962-94, shown below, suggest that most are recorded in July and fewest in April and May.

Jan	Feb	Mar	Apr	May	Jun	Jul	Aug	Sep	Oct	Nov	Dec
981	862	1035	542	513	754	1326	971	555	648	565	661

Val Bentley & John Newnham

Parrot Crossbill   *Loxia pytyopsittacus*

Status:- A very rare vagrant (one old record).

One was shot in St Leonard's Forest in March 1870 (des Forges & Harber). It is in the Booth Museum (either BoMNH 208120 or 208121).

There were over 470 records of this species in the British Isles during 1962-94, over half during the invasion of 1990-91. It breeds in Scandinavia and western Russia, periodically irrupting southwestwards.   *Richard Fairbank*

Trumpeter Finch   *Bucanetes githagineus*

Status:- A very rare vagrant (one record).

One at Church Norton from 19 to 23 May 1984, when it was taken by a Sparrowhawk, was the fourth British record (James 1986). It consorted with Linnets and alternated between feeding on the beach and in an adjoining short grassy field. The latter was probably its undoing, its pale coloration making it too obvious to predators.

There have been seven records of this sandy finch in Britain up to the end of 1994, the first in 1971. It breeds from the Canary Islands and extreme southern Spain across north Africa to southwest Asia.   *Richard Fairbank*

Scarlet Rosefinch   *Carpodacus erythrinus*

Status:- A rare, but increasing, vagrant (21 records).

One was recorded before 1962 (des Forges & Harber): a female caught alive close to Brighton during the last week of September 1869. It was the first British record and was kept in an aviary until it died in June 1876, nearly seven years later (Walpole-Bond).

Records since 1962 are as follows:

1974: One trapped at Hodcombe, Beachy Head on 1 October.
1976: A juvenile or female trapped at Whitbread Hollow, Beachy Head on 21 October.
1980 One trapped at Whitbread Hollow, Beachy Head on 24 September.
1983 An adult male in song at Hodcombe, Beachy Head on 2 June.
1985: A juvenile in the garden of the Beachy Head Hotel on 13 October.
1986: One between Beachy Head Hotel and Hodcombe on 11 October.
1987: An adult male in song at Hodcombe, Beachy Head on 29 May.
1989: A first-summer male at Icklesham on 2 July.
1990: An adult male at Icklesham on 29 May.
          A first-summer male at Cow Gap, Beachy Head on 10 June.
          One at Belle Tout Wood, Beachy Head on 14 October.

1991: An adult male in song at Hodcombe, Beachy Head on 28 May.
An adult male in song near the Pagham Harbour Information Centre at
Sidlesham Ferry on 4 June.
A first-summer male in song at Hodcombe, Beachy Head on 19 June.
1992: An adult male in song at Selsey Bill early on the morning of 25 May.
A female or first-summer male at Littlehampton West Beach on 14 June.
1993: A female or first-summer male above Whitbread Hollow, Beachy Head on 29
May.
1994: A first-summer male in song at Belle Tout, Beachy Head on 12 June had earlier
been singing in scrub southeast of Hodcombe.
A female or first-summer male at Birling Gap on 19 June.
One at Hodcombe, Beachy Head and in scrub to the southeast on 14
September.

The recent increase, a reflection of the species changing status in Western
Europe, is most pronounced with more than half of all records being during
1990-94 (fig. 105).

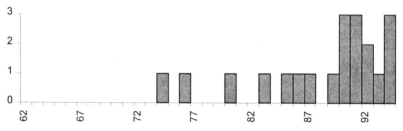

Figure 105. Annual totals of Scarlet Rosefinches, 1962 - 94.

Occurrences in spring have been between 25 May and 19 June with one in
July and those in autumn between 14 September and 21 October. Six of the
first seven records were in autumn but there have only been two autumn
occurrences since. The cumulative monthly totals are shown below.

	May	Jun	Jul	Aug	Sep	Oct
before 1990	1	1	1	-	2	4
1990-94	4	6	-	-	1	1

Fifteen have been seen at Beachy Head, two at Icklesham and one each at
Brighton, Littlehampton West Beach, Selsey Bill and Sidlesham. Short stays
are the norm with most of those recorded in the county quickly moving on,
although that seen on 12 June 1994 was present for most of the day.

This plain-faced finch is becoming more frequent, particularly in spring
and although most records relate to drab first-summer males they are
generally very vocal. Females, however, can be particularly unobtrusive.
There were between 70 and 135 records in the British Isles each year during
1986-91 with 217 in 1992 (Fraser & Ryan 1994), although only 70 in 1993
(Dawson & Allsopp 1994). It breeds from eastern Europe right across Russia
and is spreading into western Europe. In recent years breeding has been
recorded in the Netherlands with 45+ pairs in 1992 (Clement, Harris & Davis
1993) while breeding was first proved in France in 1993 (*Ornithos* 1: 44-45)
with 34 to 37 singing males in 1994 (Dubois 1994). Five pairs nested in
England in 1992 and between five and 20 in 1993 (Ogilvie *et al* 1995).

Richard Fairbank

Bullfinch

Pyrrhula pyrrhula

Status:- A very common resident

Though the male of this species has very striking plumage, the Bullfinch is an unobtrusive and retiring species which is easily overlooked unless its distinctive call is heard. It excites little interest from those submitting records due to its generally sedentary nature.

1988 - 92	
Confirmed	471
Probable	3
Possible	196
Total	670

The Atlas map shows that the Bullfinch is patchily distributed in Sussex. It is absent from the levels in the vicinity of Pevensey and Rye, which lack suitable habitat, and is thinly distributed on parts of the intensively cultivated chalk Downs and the densely populated coastal strip. There are, however, several areas in Wealden Sussex where suitable habitat exists but Bullfinches were not recorded. This may reflect, at least partly, the inconspicuous nature of the species which may result in it being under-recorded. Significantly, 30% of the registrations shown on the Atlas map are for possible or probable breeding only.

The Bullfinch is less common than either the Greenfinch or Chaffinch though, as the abundance map in the New Atlas shows, southeast England is among the areas of Britain with the highest population density. It is generally absent from intensive arable farmland, preferring woodland or farmland with mature hedgerows and a supply of weed and tree seeds, especially ash. When these foods are insufficient to sustain the population through the winter, attention is directed towards fruit buds, including those in orchards, and conflict with commercial interests can occur (Newton 1972). Newton also noted that Bullfinch numbers in southeast England increased substantially during the 1950s but suffered a decline from the mid 1970s, a trend borne out by national CBC data (Marchant *et al* 1990). He suggested that these fluctuations may be connected to the severe reduction in the Sparrowhawk population during the era of organochlorine pesticides, followed by its recovery two decades later, although the New Atlas cites hedgerow removal as the most likely factor causing this decline. Shrubb, however, found little evidence for any marked population trend in Sussex to 1976, and counts in defined areas during the period 1981-88 also showed no significant trends. Cooper (1975), in analysing the ringing data over a 10-year period at Beachy Head, suggested that Bullfinches had not suffered as much as other resident species in the severe winter of 1962/63 and that the low number trapped in one year (1968) was due to a poor breeding season.

During the Woodland Survey that covered the period 1963-74, Bullfinches were recorded in 20 of the 23 woods studied but were encountered less frequently on sandy soils than elsewhere. Information on breeding densities in the county is limited. However, Bealey & Sutherland (1983) found the species in 33 of the 40 broadleaved woodlands they surveyed in West Sussex at an average density of 7.5 pairs per km². A slightly higher density of 9.8 pairs per km² was reported for CBC plot at Kingley Vale and similar figures of 7.1 pairs per km² and 6.2 pairs per km² in farmland surveys at Maynards Green and West Chiltington respectively. Lower densities have, however, been recorded at other sites including 2.3 pairs per km² at Lullington Heath and only 1 pair per km² in 280 ha of mixed scrub and woodland at Moulsecoomb Wild Park. Combining the results of surveys of eight sites that have recorded Bullfinches over several years gives an average of about 5 pairs per km², a figure which if applied to the 671 tetrads in which the species was recorded during the Atlas Survey indicates a county population of 10,000-15,000 pairs. The British population was estimated to be 190,000 pairs (New Atlas).

Although the winter distribution closely matches that in the breeding season and ringing recoveries show that birds rarely move more than a few km (Winter Atlas), there are a number of records that suggest that some autumn movement occurs. Records for Beachy Head in the 1960s indicate that small influxes, totalling perhaps 40-50 birds, occurred in late October. More direct evidence of passage include records of eight arriving from the sea at Beachy Head on 20 November 1966 and 20 moving west there on 29 October 1967. One which flew in from the sea at Selsey Bill on 28 March 1964 is the only record suggestive of a spring passage.

Sussex ringing data confirm that local birds do not move far; of 129 ringed and recovered, only one, ringed at Beachy Head in October 1970 and found in Essex in June 1971, had moved more than 100 km.

British Bullfinches, belonging to the race *P.p. pileata*, differ from those of the nominate race *P.p. pyrrhula*, originating from northern and eastern Europe, by being smaller (BWP). One showing characteristics of the race *pyrrhula* was obtained at St Leonards on 7 January 1897 (des Forges & Harber).   *Val Bentley & John Newnham*

Hawfinch   *Coccothraustes coccothraustes*

Status:- A scarce breeding resident and very scarce passage migrant.

The Hawfinch is an elusive species found in mixed deciduous woodland. Its breeding density throughout its range in Britain is very low, with evidence of some decline since 1968-72 (New Atlas).

The Atlas map, which shows both the tetrads in which the species was recorded during the Atlas Survey and also those tetrads (as open circles) where Hawfinches were recorded during 1976-87 but not 1988-92, reveals a scattering of breeding records in both East and West Sussex. Hawfinches are not easily found, probably explaining why two-thirds of the registrations during the Atlas Survey were in the "seen" category only. However, even if these records are included, the species was recorded in just 2.1% of the county's tetrads during this 5-year period. A similar survey in Hampshire recorded Hawfinches in 10% of the county's tetrads during 1986-91 (Clark & Eyre 1993) while a breeding survey in Kent covering the period 1967-73 recorded the species in 8% of that county's tetrads (Taylor, Davenport & Flegg 1981). In the 12 years preceding the Atlas Survey, Hawfinches were recorded in 62 (6.1%) tetrads, mainly in northern West Sussex, particularly in the vicinity of Fernhurst. A survey of semi-natural broadleaved woodlands in the Midhurst and Horsham/Crawley areas in 1982 found single pairs in eight of the 40 woods visited, despite the survey being carried out after the main period of territorial activity, which usually occurs in March and early April (Bealey & Sutherland 1983). Most birds were present in woods with a dense, fairly uniform canopy, where mature oak was dominant, or oak with beech, often with hazel or rhododendron abundant in the shrub layer. An association with cherry was also found.

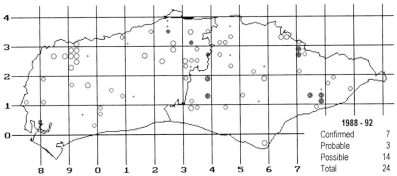

	1988 - 92	
	Confirmed	7
	Probable	3
	Possible	14
	Total	24

The number of Hawfinches recorded in Sussex has fluctuated annually (fig. 106) although this apparent variation is partly explained by chance sightings of large flocks, as in 1968, 1972 and 1979. The graph shows considerably more variation in annual totals since the early 1980s, from a low of just seven in 1992 to 61 in 1991, the latter figure including a flock of 35 at Horsham on 15 April. During 1965-93, an average of 24 birds was recorded per year. In some years, such as 1993, there were no reports of confirmed breeding, but in other years, for example 1970, 1978-81 and 1984, from one to five pairs were known to have bred. From the limited data available, it is difficult to estimate the size of the breeding population in Sussex.

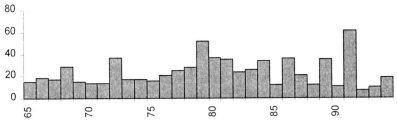

Figure 106. Approximate annual totals of Hawfinches, 1965 - 94

The results of the Atlas Survey and casual records submitted to the SOS indicate a population of between 20 and 50 pairs though the results of Bealey & Sutherland's survey in 1982, which looked at only about 5% of the woodland in West Sussex, suggest that this may be an underestimate. It is clear, however, that the breeding population in Sussex is considerably less than that in neighbouring Hampshire where the population is estimated to be 275-500 pairs, including 150-250 pairs in the New Forest alone (Clark & Eyre 1993). Outside the breeding season, large flocks are encountered regularly in both the neighbouring counties of Hampshire and Kent, indeed Clark & Eyre reported 49 flocks of ten or more birds in the New Forest during 1977-92. A roost at Bedgebury, Kent, just over the county boundary, has regularly held 20-50 birds since 1966 (Taylor, Davenport & Flegg 1981). Although Walpole-Bond once saw a flock of 200 Hawfinches, there have been only seven records of flocks of more than ten in the county since the beginning of 1962 as follows:

Date	Locality	
27 June 1965	Pease Pottage	13, including five or six juveniles
15 April 1968	Horsted Keynes	flock of *ca.* 20
26 December 1972	Flimwell	flock of 30
20 May 1979	Possingworth Park	flock of 20 in rural garden for 30 minutes
15 March 1980	Wakehurst Place	minimum of 17 in pinetum
January-February 1981	Cowfold	feeding party of 12-15
15 April 1991	Horsham	35 that alighted briefly on a beech hedge

All the above flocks occurred between late December and June, so inflating the cumulative totals for these months shown in the table below. Winter and spring are clearly the most likely seasons in which to encounter Hawfinches in Sussex.

Jan	Feb	Mar	Apr	May	Jun	Jul	Aug	Sep	Oct	Nov	Dec
80	87	97	138	117	84	34	12	21	36	25	91

Most British birds are considered to be resident although some migration may occur, particularly in continental and northern populations (BWP). Most sightings of presumed migrants have been in the autumn with seven birds recorded at Beachy Head and five in the Selsey/Pagham area during September-October; indeed 11 of the 35 recorded in October were at coastal localities. Possible spring migrants include singles at Beachy Head on 11 April 1970 and 1 April 1976 and at Selsey Bill on 7 April 1974 and 6 and 7 May 1991. The 1974 bird arrived from the west while those in 1991 flew in from the southeast.

Only two Hawfinches were ringed in the county between 1979 and 1993 and there have been no recoveries of Sussex birds.

Val Bentley & John Newnham

Blackpoll Warbler   *Dendroica striata*

Status:- A very rare vagrant (one record).

One was present at Bewl Water from at least 10 to 21 December 1994. It was very confiding and frequented the strip of woodland near the hide, to the east of Chesson's Farm, often favouring three thick sallows at the edge of the reservoir (*Birding World* 7: 465, *Brit. Birds* 88: plate 193).

This is the most frequent American warbler to be recorded in the British Isles with 31 previous records, although the first was as recently as 1968. This was the first in southeast England, the first away from the coast and the first to fall outside the period mid-September to 1 November. It breeds across Canada and winters in northern and central South America (Curson, Quinn & Beadle 1994).   *Richard Fairbank*

Slate-coloured Junco   *Junco hyemalis*
Status:- A very rare vagrant (one record).

An approachable male in an area of coastal scrub and shingle to the east of Winchelsea Beach on 12 February 1972 is the only record. Very recently accepted, it becomes the sixth to be recorded in Britain, the previous five all having been in May.

Including this one, there were 16 records in the British Isles during 1962-94 (falling between December and June). These include occurrences in Dorset (3), Hampshire and the Isle of Wight, while one of the two earlier records was in Kent. It is likely that, in keeping with other American sparrows in Britain, most have crossed the Atlantic with some degree of ship assistance. It breeds across northern North America and winters mainly in the USA.

Richard Fairbank

White-throated Sparrow   *Zonotrichia albicollis*
Status:- A very rare vagrant (one record).

A first-year at Belle Tout Wood, Beachy Head between 19 and 30 October 1968 is the only record. At times very elusive, it was the seventh British record.

A female netted with Yellowhammers at Bevendean, Brighton on 22 March 1872 was not included as a genuine wild bird by Walpole-Bond, as "in all probability it was an escaped importation". Clearly the problem presented by potential escapes is not a recent phenomenon.

There were 17 records of this yellow-lored Emberizid in the British Isles during 1962-94. The proximity of many to docks make it likely that most have arrived with ship assistance for at least part of their Atlantic crossing. It breeds in Canada wintering mainly in the USA.   *Richard Fairbank*

Lapland Bunting   *Calcarius lapponicus*
Status:- A very scarce passage migrant and winter visitor.

Of all the species which frequent coastal habitats in winter, the Lapland Bunting is one of the most difficult to locate and most likely to be overlooked, unless its distinctive call is known. It is normally present in only small numbers, it is shy and, on the ground, moves with a quick run which enables it to find rapid concealment.

Between 1947 and 1961 the species was recorded annually in Sussex except in 1949-51. Numbers ranged from one to 15, except in 1956 when 60-80 were reported (des Forges & Harber). Since the beginning of 1962 no less than 197 birds have been recorded, with a maximum of 36 in the winter of 1986/87 (fig. 107). The total for Sussex is nearly four times greater than that for neighbouring Hampshire, where only 50 were recorded in the period 1961/62-91/92 (Clark & Eyre 1993), but is significantly less than that for Kent, where 214 were recorded in the winter of 1956/57 alone (Taylor, Davenport & Flegg 1981).

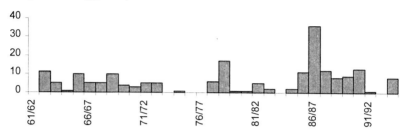

Figure 107. Winter totals of Lapland Buntings, 1961/62 - 93/94.

Prior to 1962, des Forges & Harber noted that most Lapland Buntings were recorded in winter, particularly January and February. Shrubb, however, showed that numbers recorded during the winter months declined sharply during 1962-76, so much so, that he considered the species to be "now virtually only an autumn passage migrant". A comparison of the cumulative monthly totals for the periods 1962-76 and 1977-94, shown below, reveals that January is now the peak month. This suggests that the species is no longer a predominantly autumn migrant and that there has been a return to the pattern of occurrence pre-1962.

	Sep	Oct	Nov	Dec	Jan	Feb	Mar	Apr
1962-76	5	16	20	18	8	0	0	1
1977-94	7	22	20	19	48	19	2	0
Total	12	38	40	37	56	19	2	1

The earliest recorded was one at Beachy Head on 10 September 1968. The records suggest that there is a small passage through the county in autumn and that birds do not stay for any significant period. Of those recorded during the period 1962-94, 85% were noted on only one day while on only five occasions did birds appear to stay for longer than five days. The longest stays recorded include a flock of *ca.* 40 at Beachy Head from 27 October to early December 1956 and up to three at the same locality between 12 November and 3 December 1967. Those in winter have often appeared following the onset of harsh weather. In 1986/87, for example, the exceptional total of 36 was recorded including a flock of up to 28 at Hooe Level in January 1987.

On migration and in winter, Lapland Buntings frequent rough grassland, weedy and grassy fields, bare open cultivated areas away from shrub thickets and trees, grain stubbles and open grassy areas bordering coasts and estuaries. They feed almost entirely on seeds taken from the ground or from low-lying plants, though they may feed on the shore, picking through the drift line. Nearly all of those recorded during 1962-93 were on or near the coast, with the majority at Beachy Head, Pevensey Levels and between Pett Level and the

Midrips. A total of 169 birds (86%) was recorded from east of Brighton to the Kent border, nine (5%) from between Brighton and Climping and 16 (8%) from west of Climping to the Hampshire border. The only records away from the vicinity of the coast were of singles at Arlington Reservoir (10 km inland) on 9 February 1991 and flying over Bewl Water (30 km inland) on 4 November 1982 and Pulborough Brooks (17 km inland) on 2 December 1990.

Unfortunately, there are no ringing recoveries to indicate either the origins of our birds or where passage birds go to for the remainder of the winter. However, it has been suggested that the Lapland Buntings wintering in Britain originate from Scandinavia supplemented, in some years, by larger influxes from Greenland (Winter Atlas). *John A Hobson*

Snow Bunting *Plectrophenax nivalis*

Status:- A scarce passage migrant and winter visitor.

In Sussex, as elsewhere in southern Britain, Snow Buntings are almost entirely confined to coastal sites with a marked preference for sandy shores.

The number of birds recorded in the county has decreased in recent years from a peak in the late 1950s and early 1960s (fig. 108). A similar trend is also apparent in neighbouring Hampshire (Clark & Eyre 1993). About 200 were recorded in Sussex in the winter of 1961/62, 194 in 1962/63 and 113 in 1963/64 but, since then, the only winter in which more than 100 was reported was 1971/72 when there were at least 124. Only six were reported in 1974/75 and 1979/80 and five in 1986/87.

The records suggest that flocks of appreciable numbers in one area are generally winter residents. The largest numbers formerly occurred between Winchelsea Beach and the Midrips, especially at Camber Sands. In the 1950s and 1960s, flocks in excess of 30 were often seen in this area and flocks of 50 to 100 were recorded in nine winters. However, concentrations of this size have been conspicuous by their absence since the last was recorded in 1971. Furthermore, there appears to have been a general reduction in flock size, with no party larger than ten recorded in the county since 1981. Further evidence of the decrease that has occurred in the wintering population is provided by a comparison of the average number of birds recorded in 5-year periods from 1948/49 to 1992/93:

Winter	Average	Winter	Average
1948/49 - 52/53	29	1973/74 - 77/78	45
1953/54 - 57/58	70	1978/79 - 82/83	28
1958/59 - 62/63	132	1983/84 - 87/88	16
1963/64 - 67/68	79	1988/89 - 92/93	34
1968/69 - 72/73	72		

Birds have apparently arrived in the county in every month from September to May. There have also been two records for June and one for July, possibly relating to injured birds (des Forges & Harber). The earliest in autumn was one at the Midrips on 13 September 1958 but few are recorded before November. The latest (apart from the June and July records) was one at Pagham on 6 May 1962. The monthly patterns of arrival (i.e. new birds not previously recorded) for the periods 1948-61 and 1962-94 are shown below:

	Sep	Oct	Nov	Dec	Jan	Feb	Mar	Apr	May
1948-61	3	21	476	145	106	81	56	1	-
1962-94	4	77	398	570	332	178	70	6	1
Total	7	98	874	715	438	259	126	7	1

These data suggest a change in the pattern of occurrence in recent years. Before 1962, the main influx was in November but, since then, it has been in December.

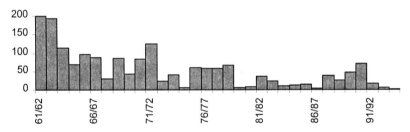

Figure 108. Winter totals of Snow Buntings, 1961/62 - 93/94.

During 1962-94, there were 28 records of birds away from the immediate vicinity of the coast involving about 75 individuals, all between 9 October and 11 April. Of these, 63 birds were on the Downs including parties of *ca.* 30 at Woodingdean from 14 to 19 December 1966 and nine at Harting Down on 2 December 1965. The furthest away from the coast were singles at St Leonard's Forest (27 km inland) on 29 October 1963, Bewl Water (30 km inland) on 25 October 1983 and 30 March 1988, and Marley Common (35 km inland) from 7 to 10 November 1984. The cumulative monthly totals of all records away from the coast during 1962-94 are shown below.

Oct	Nov	Dec	Jan	Feb	Mar	Apr
9	13	45	3	-	4	1

The breeding distribution is circumpolar, with populations from Greenland, Iceland and northern Europe moving into Britain and Ireland each winter (Winter Atlas). *John A Hobson*

Yellowhammer

Emberiza citrinella

Status:- A very common resident.

1988 - 92
Confirmed	666
Probable	1
Possible	159
Total	826

The Yellowhammer is widely distributed throughout Britain favouring highly productive farmland, heaths, commons and the edges of woodland. In Sussex, as the Atlas map shows, it is apparently absent from the heavily built-up coastal strip between Littlehampton and Brighton and the levels in the vicinity of Pevensey and Rye and, curiously, is patchily distributed in an area extending from Midhurst to Cuckfield.

The Common Birds Census has shown that, nationally, numbers have remained relatively stable on farmland but have declined in woodland (Marchant *et al* 1990). During the Woodland Survey that covered the period 1963-74, Yellowhammers were found in 70% of the areas visited. They showed a marked preference for young forestry plantations, where they comprised up to 10% or more of the total bird populations recorded (Shrubb). Limited information on breeding densities in woodland was available though counts in north-central Sussex in 1969 which gave a range of densities from 10 to 75 pairs per km² and an average density of 18 pairs per km². The few counts available for farmland at that time indicated much lower densities of around 7.5 pairs per km².

Censuses in various habitats during the late 1970s and 1980s have provided further information about population trends and breeding densities. Increases were recorded in the number of occupied territories at Iping Common (77 ha), following a fire in July 1976, from nine in 1977 to 23 in 1982 (Hughes & Griffiths 1983) and at Lullington Heath NNR (62 ha) from four in 1979 to 17 in 1988 (Bowley 1994). The maxima recorded at these sites give densities of 30 pairs per km² and 27 pairs per km² respectively. Surveys of farmland bird communities at the Brinsbury Estate (227 ha) in 1980 and at Plumpton (400 ha) in 1982 recorded densities of 5.7 pairs per km² and 12.5 pairs per km² respectively (Prater 1982, 1983b). A survey of semi-natural broadleaved woodlands in West Sussex in 1982 recorded an average density of 2.2 pairs per km² (Bealey & Sutherland 1983). Assuming an average of 10 pairs per tetrad in which breeding was confirmed indicates a county population in excess of 25,000 pairs. The British total was estimated at 1.2 million pairs (New Atlas).

Outside the breeding season, large flocks of 100 or more may form.

Shrubb referred to eight flocks of over 100 between 1965 and 1976, nearly all from the Downs, the largest of which was of 400 at Ashcombe Farm in January 1975. More recent large gatherings have included a roost of 200 at Fairlight in January-February 1978, 220 at Ifield in January 1980, 170 at Cissbury on 14 November 1981, 150-200 at Storrington and 180 at Eridge Park on 29 December 1982, 121 at Pagham Harbour in February 1983, 150 at Cissbury on 18 September 1986, 350 at Plumpton on 27 December 1986, 100 at Nyetimber in January 1987, 140 at Washington in February 1987, 160 at Falmer in February 1988 and 102 at Flansham on 5 November 1990. The absence of three-figure flocks since 1990 may reflect the marked decline in weed-rich stubble fields or, alternatively the recent absence of harsh winters, when large flocks might be expected to gather.

Although small numbers are occasionally noted moving at coastal localities, for example, 30 flying west at Brighton in 3.5 hours on 15 January 1966, it is likely that our birds are resident. Indeed, analysis of ringing recoveries shows that of the 22 birds recovered in the county, none had moved more than 9 km. *Tim Parmenter*

Cirl Bunting *Emberiza cirlus*

Status:- Formerly a scarce resident; now extinct as a breeding species and not recorded since 1988.

A comparison of the distribution maps published in the 68-72 BTO Atlas and the New Atlas shows that the range of the Cirl Bunting has contracted markedly, so that it is now largely confined in Britain to the coastal strip of south Devon. A census in 1982 revealed a maximum of 167 pairs in England, mostly in Devon, a significant decline from the 250-300 pairs estimated at the time of the 68-72 Atlas (Sitters 1982). A further survey in 1991 recorded 229 pairs, 217 of them in Devon. This apparent increase was due to the discovery of previously unknown sub-populations and also to good breeding success in the summers of 1989 and 1990 (New Atlas). A breeding survey carried out in Sussex during the years 1971 to 1973 recorded a maximum of 28 breeding pairs from 20 sites (Wilson 1974), compared with 45-50 pairs from 35 sites during 1963-70. During the last year of the survey (1973), only 20 pairs were found.

The cause of the decline is still not entirely clear. Climatic factors may have played a part, as British Cirl Buntings are at the northern limit of the species' range, though recent research has suggested that habitat change and changes in farming practice are the primary cause (Evans 1992). The removal of hedges, the lack of availability of weed rich stubble fields in winter for food and the scarcity of invertebrate rich grassland in the breeding season have probably had an effect. In Sussex, another factor which probably contributed to the decline was the large scale development of housing estates and the building of new houses in the extensive gardens of older properties, particularly those backing on to the Downs, where the species would once have bred.

The favoured habitat of the Cirl Bunting in Sussex was always between the Downs and the sea, particularly in the lower river valleys. One of the strongholds was the Cuckmere Valley where there were ten occupied territories in 1968 and 1969, 15 in 1970, 12 in 1971 (following the hard winter of 1970/71) but only 5-6 pairs in 1972, when there were also five pairs at Beachy Head. In 1974 and 1975, there were records for the breeding season from Beachy Head, the Cuckmere Valley and Friston Forest. A total of 11 pairs was reported in 1976, including five pairs in the Cuckmere Valley and three pairs at Beachy Head but by 1977 the species was close to extinction in the county, with just 6-7 pairs known at possibly four sites. There were still two pairs at both Beachy Head and the Cuckmere Valley in 1978 but in 1979, the only known pair was at the former site. Pairs were present at Beachy Head and Holywell, Eastbourne in 1980 and breeding may have taken place at the latter site in 1981. A female seen carrying food near Exceat Bridge on 29 May 1982 was the last record of breeding in Sussex. The only subsequent records have been of single males at Glynde on 18 August 1983, Church Norton on 11 October 1987 and at Selsey Bill on 8 May 1988.

Outside the breeding season, birds were occasionally seen a short distance away from their breeding sites, often in small flocks, including 15-20 in a garden in Alfriston in late December 1970.

An unprecedented ringing recovery was that of a bird ringed at Hodcombe, Beachy Head on 22 July 1975 and controlled on the Isle of May, Scotland, 625 km NNW, on 11 June 1976. *Tim Parmenter*

Rock Bunting   *Emberiza cia*

Status:- A very rare vagrant (one record involving two individuals).

Two netted near Shoreham-by-Sea towards the end of October 1902 were the first to be recorded in Britain. One died shortly after capture, the other being seen alive in captivity two months later (Walpole-Bond).

There were just two records of this grey-headed Bunting in the British Isles during 1962-94 and three earlier occurrences, involving four individuals. It breeds in mountains from northwestern Africa and Iberia to the Himalayas and China, generally wintering at lower elevations. *Richard Fairbank*

Ortolan Bunting   *Emberiza hortulana*

Status:- A very scarce, mainly autumn, visitor (55 records involving 63 individuals).

Eighteen were recorded before 1962 (des Forges & Harber): in April (3), May (2), June, September (10) and October (2) and all between Brighton and Eastbourne. Extreme dates in spring were at Castle Hill on 21 April 1896 and in brick fields to the east of Eastbourne on 29 June 1896, a very unusual date. Both these, and one limed near Brighton on 30 September 1870 are in the Booth Museum (BoMNH 208111, 208112 and 208109 respectively). The earliest to be recorded in autumn was netted at Rottingdean on 5 September 1906 and the latest seen at the Crumbles on 5 October 1950 (Harber 1951). A record from between Brighton and Lewes in February 1877 (BoMNH 208110) was excluded by Walpole-Bond who had "little or no hesitation about relegating the specimen involved to the rank of an imported escape". Five were seen in 1961 (the best year to date), all at Seaford Head in September, with a male and three juveniles together there in stubble on 17th.

Forty-five have been seen since the beginning of 1962 including three in 1973, 1983, 1985 and 1993. Records have been fairly constant throughout the period (fig. 109); probably increased observer coverage offsetting the species decline in most of Europe (Tucker & Heath 1994).

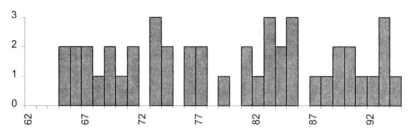

Figure 109. Annual totals of Ortolan Buntings, 1962 - 94.

Most records are of single individuals although two were seen at Beachy Head on 17 September 1967, 25-26 August 1971, 5-6 September 1976 and 10 September 1985.

Since 1962, records have been in April (1), May (2), August (13), September (26), October (2) and November (1).

Spring records account for under 7% of all occurrences since 1962, a significant reduction from earlier years when one-third were in April, May or June. All three recorded in spring since 1962 have been at Beachy Head, a female at Cornish Farm on 3 May 1969 and males at Hodcombe on 6 May 1983 and 27 April 1989.

Earliest autumn records were singles flying south over Combe Haven on 14 August 1987 and at Selsey West Fields on 15 August 1981 while the latest were at Hodcombe, Beachy Head from 8 to 10 October 1983 and in stubble near the Beachy Head Hotel on 3 and 4 November 1968. Most have been seen from late August to mid-September (fig. 110).

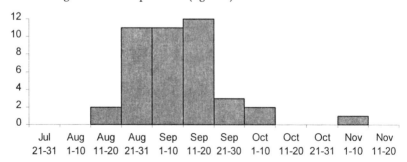

Figure 110. Cumulative 'autumn' arrival dates of Ortolan Buntings, 1962 - 94.

Since the beginning of 1962 nearly three-quarters of all records have been at Beachy Head (33) with five at Pagham Harbour/Sidlesham and two at

Combe Haven. Single individuals have been recorded at Atherington (24 September 1983), Patcham (trapped at Standean Farm on 13 September 1984), Selsey West Fields, Shoreham-by-Sea (trapped below Mill Hill on 11 September 1985) and on the Downs near Steyning Bowl (29 August 1982).

There were between 32 and 81 records of this pink-billed bunting in the British Isles each year during 1986-92 (Fraser & Ryan 1994). It breeds from Iberia and Scandinavia to Mongolia wintering in sub-Saharan Africa north of the Equator. *Richard Fairbank*

Rustic Bunting *Emberiza rustica*

Status:- A very rare vagrant (three autumn records).

One was recorded before 1962 (des Forges & Harber). It was trapped near the old naphtha works at Brighton, close to where Roedean School now stands, on 23 October 1867. It was the first British record and is in the Booth Museum (BoMNH 204074).

Two have been recorded since the beginning of 1962:

1983: A male at Hodcombe, Beachy Head from 8 to 12 October (*Brit. Birds* 78: plate 287).
1991: One at Littlehampton West Beach from 30 October to 1 November.

The Hodcombe individual frequented a ploughed field, at one stage consorting with an Ortolan Bunting, while that at Littlehampton was seen in the dunes to the southeast of the Golf Course.

There were over 280 records of this species in the British Isles during 1962-94, including a staggering 50 in 1993 (although none were seen in Sussex). It breeds from Sweden right across Russia and winters from Turkestan to eastern China. *Richard Fairbank*

Little Bunting *Emberiza pusilla*

Status:- A very rare vagrant (five records).

Two were recorded before 1962 (des Forges & Harber). One netted near the old naphtha works at Brighton, close to where Roedean School now stands, on 2 November 1864 was the first British record and is in the Booth Museum (BoMNH 207569). One netted at the Crumbles in autumn 1906 was kept in an aviary for some years and exhibited at the Crystal Palace (Arnold 1936).

Since the beginning of 1962 three have been seen:

1964: One at Langney Point on 15 October (*SxBR* 17: 30).
1987: One trapped at Charleston Reedbed on 4 October.
1994: One in fields to the southwest of Ifield Church from 11 January to at least 24 March.

Four were in autumn and one wintered (with a mixed flock of over 100 Yellowhammers and Reed Buntings). Two have been seen at Langney Point or the Crumbles but none at nearby Beachy Head or on the Selsey peninsula. One trapped at Icklesham on 8 November 1992 was surprisingly not accepted by *BBRC*.

There were about 550 records of this small, neat bunting in the British Isles during 1962-94. It breeds from eastern Scandinavia right across Siberia, wintering from Turkestan to South East Asia. *Richard Fairbank*

Reed Bunting *Emberiza schoeniclus*

Status:- A common resident, passage migrant and winter visitor.

The Atlas map shows that the main concentrations of Reed Buntings in the county are found in the river valleys and on coastal marshes, where stands of reeds and other rank vegetation provide nesting sites. Although traditionally a bird of wetland areas, they have expanded in to drier habitats including young forestry plantations, dry heathland, downland areas with gorse and farmland hedgerows and scrub.

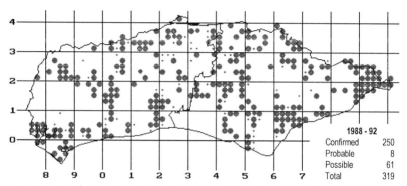

1988 - 92	
Confirmed	250
Probable	8
Possible	61
Total	319

In Britain, the results of the Common Birds Census indicate a recent steep decline in the Reed Bunting population. Despite the hard winters of the early 1960s, when numbers were severely reduced, the population remained at a relatively stable high level from the late 1960s into the mid-1970s. A decrease of more than 50% followed but, since the early 1980s, numbers have been fairly stable at a lower level (Marchant *et al* 1990). Information on population trends in Sussex is limited. At Rye Harbour LNR, numbers decreased from 40 pairs in 1984 to 24 pairs in 1987 but then increased to 38 pairs in 1989 and 48 pairs in 1992. In 1993, however, only 33 pairs were recorded. At Thorney Deeps, there was a marked decrease from 49-51 pairs in 1988 to 31 pairs in 1989 and 18 pairs in 1993.

Shrubb referred to breeding densities in wetland habitats of between 4.0 and 7.0 pairs per km² at Pevensey and Crowhurst Marsh and 10.5 pairs per km² at Amberley/Pulborough. Little information was available to indicate the number of pairs in drier habitats. However, a total of 23 singing males was found in Ashdown Forest in 1973 and a density of 1.5 pairs per km² was reported for young conifer plantations in the northwest of the county in 1970. Surveys of Pevensey Levels located 262 pairs in 1976 and 219 pairs in 1987 (Hitchings 1988), the latter figure giving an average of 5.4 pairs per km². Few of the censuses of breeding birds in defined areas carried out during the 1980s recorded Reed Buntings. In 1981, 20 pairs were located in both 875 ha of Brede Levels and 55 ha of the Adur Levels. Estimating the size of the county population is difficult given the wide range of breeding densities reported. Assuming an average of five pairs per occupied tetrad indicates a population of about 6400 pairs. The British total was estimated at 220,000 pairs (New Atlas).

In autumn, small scale movements are noted at coastal sites, mainly in late September and October. However, a much more marked passage involving up to 50 birds in a day was recorded at Selsey Bill between 1963 and 1969. Coasting movements predominated, accounting for 82% of the records, and about twice as many moved east as west. Emigration was noted annually but very few arrivals were seen (Shrubb). Very large numbers were recorded at Elms Farm, Icklesham in 1993, where it was estimated that well in excess of 500 birds passed through between 24 August and 5 November. The largest day totals were 300 on 7 October, 250 on 16 October and 80 on 28 October. Few other large concentrations have been recorded in autumn although there were at least 200 in a reedy ditch at Camber Castle on 26 September 1974.

Shrubb reported that Reed Buntings were decidedly scarce in Sussex in winter and thought it likely that most of our breeding birds left the county. He referred to only 13 records of winter flocks of 20 to 50 birds between 1965 and 1976, and one of 120 near Fairwarp, Ashdown Forest on 20 November 1971. A number of large concentrations have since been recorded in this area including 100 or more in January-February 1979 and roosts at Gill's Lap of 170 on 30 January 1983, 220 on 9 December 1984 and 250 on 1 February 1986. Large flocks at other sites in the county, most of which have occurred in harsh weather, have included 100-200 on a vegetable patch at Pett Level in January-February 1979, 125 at Chailey Common in early 1981, 50 at Pagham and 100 at Shoreham-by-Sea on 1 and 10 January 1982 respectively, 120-150 in the lower Cuckmere Valley on 7 January 1985 and 100 roosting at Woods Mill on 15 December 1990. The latter is the only three-figure gathering to be recorded in the county since 1986, reflecting the species' current lower density throughout Britain. Since the hard winter of 1978/79 and more especially that of 1981/82, more Reed Buntings have been observed at garden feeding stations in winter and in many areas of Sussex, this is now a common occurrence.

Shrubb stated that little visible migration had been noted at the coast in spring, but that quite large flocks may appear there in March and April, clearly indicating passage. Such records have included two flocks totalling 200 birds at Sidlesham on 2 April 1973 which appeared to be fresh arrivals, 25 at Barcombe Reservoir on 21 March 1980, 20 at Horse Eye Level and 25 at Langney Point the following day, and 20 at the latter site on 29 March 1981.

Analysis of ringing data shows that of the 42 recoveries of Reed Buntings ringed in Sussex, 22 were within the county, a further 18 elsewhere in southern England and singles in Belgium and France. Only five foreign-ringed birds have been recovered in Sussex, from Sweden (3) and Denmark and the Netherlands (1 each). These recoveries suggest that the local breeding population is largely resident, with some emigration in winter, and that some birds arrive from the continent to winter here.   *Tim Parmenter*

Pallas's Reed Bunting   *Emberiza pallasi*

Status:- A very rare vagrant (one record).

A first-winter male was trapped at Icklesham on 17 October 1990 (*Brit. Birds* 87: plates 148 and 149). It was not seen in the field and it was only identified two and a half years later from photographs and measurements (S J R Rumsey *in litt.*).

This was the third, and most recent, British record following occurrences on Fair Isle from 29 September to 11 October 1976 and 17-18 September 1981. It breeds in central and eastern Siberia wintering from Mongolia to Korea and southern China.   *Richard Fairbank*

Black-headed Bunting   *Emberiza melanocephala*

Status:- A very rare vagrant (two records).

One was recorded before 1962 (des Forges & Harber), an adult female shot while following Yellowhammers near the windmill at Brighton Racecourse on about 3 November 1868. It was the first British record and is in the Booth Museum (BoMNH 208127).

A male in a grazed grass field southeast of Castle Water, Rye Harbour on 8-9 September 1971 is the only comparatively recent record. It was seen on one occasion next to a Tawny Pipit which was present in the area from 6 to 9 September.

A female bunting at Birling Gap from 17 to 20 June 1994 was thought by many observers to be Black-headed, although the possibility of it being a female Red-headed Bunting *E. bruniceps*, which is extremely similar, is recognised (Fairbank 1994). The identification of this individual is currently being assessed by *BBRC*.

There were nearly 110 records of this species in the British Isles during 1962-94. It breeds from Italy to Iran and winters in western India.

Richard Fairbank

Corn Bunting   *Miliaria calandra*

Status:- A fairly common but decreasing resident.

The Corn Bunting is strongly associated with agriculture, especially arable farming, with a strong correlation between populations and the proportion and area of tillage (Donald 1994). In Sussex, the breeding population is now virtually restricted to open downland and the coastal plains of the Selsey peninsula and the Rye area. Its fortunes have fluctuated considerably in relation to the state of arable farming. Walpole-Bond regarded it as "a common bird in Sussex but on the whole much less so than it was, say, twenty years ago". Following the agricultural revival of the 1940s, the species increased to a high point in the late 1970s, since when the population has declined considerably. Reduction in food availability is probably a key factor in the decline of populations, with a need for invertebrates in summer and weed seeds in winter. This has been exacerbated by the increased use of inorganic fertilisers, insecticides and herbicides up to the mid-1980s and the change to autumn ploughing with the consequent loss of winter weedy stubbles.

In the early 1960s, des Forges & Harber referred to the species as breeding mainly on the open Downs, particularly in the east of the county, and in their vicinity down to the coast. They also reported that it had been spreading in the extreme east of the county, resulting in nesting along the coast from Rye Harbour to the Kent boundary. Shrubb's comment that "the breeding population is mainly concentrated along the whole length of the Downs" suggests that there had been some expansion on the Downs in the west of the county. At that time, there was still a substantial breeding population on the coastal plain to the south of Chichester and there were also breeding records from several localities north of the Downs.

Results from the BTO Common Birds Census between 1973 and 1993 and the BTO Farmland Bunting Survey (Donald 1994) indicated that there had been a 75% reduction in the British population to 20,000 territories and a contraction in its range. The situation in Sussex is somewhat less clear cut. The results of a breeding survey of this species in 1993-94 yielded a total of 660 singing males (equated with 'territories') in 239 1-km squares (Manns 1996b). Taking the downland figures separately gave a total of 479 territories in 151 1-km squares (an average of 3.2 territories per km^2). In the 'lowland' (coastal) areas, there were 181 territories in 88 1-km squares, an average of 2.1 territories per km^2, 34% less than the downland average. The area of downland 'available' to Corn Buntings (i.e. unwooded land) was calculated from Ordnance Survey maps to be approximately 381 km^2. This gave an average density of 1.26 territories per km^2, compared with an average density of 3-4 territories per km^2 on the Downs calculated by Shrubb. Even allowing for a 10% error in arriving at the area of available downland, and taking Shrubb's minimum figure of 3 territories per km^2, there appears to have been a reduction in the downland population of between 53% and 62% since the mid-1970s. As far as the coastal population is concerned, a valid comparison with Shrubb's estimate of 6 territories per km^2 could not be made, as it was not possible to calculate the area of 'available' land. Given that the 1993-94 survey, taking only the 1-km squares which held singing males, had produced an average density which was 34% less than on downland, it seems likely that the reduction in the coastal populations has been very much greater, possibly even as high as 86%. Densities of singing males vary widely from place to place, ranging from 1 per km² up to a maximum of 19 per km², the latter at Steep Down, Lancing. This variation is not new, having been noted by both Walpole-Bond and Shrubb.

The map below shows the records of singing males from the 1993-94 survey as solid circles and the additional breeding season records from the period 1976-92 (including the Atlas Survey) as open circles.

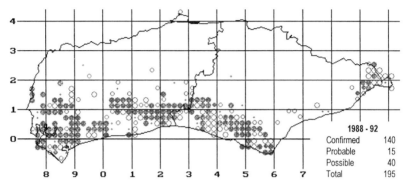

1988 - 92	
Confirmed	140
Probable	15
Possible	40
Total	195

Even allowing for the more intensive coverage in the breeding survey, the map demonstrates the contraction in range that has occurred. The small and scattered breeding populations to the north of the Downs have been lost and the population in the far east of the county is now concentrated at Rye Harbour, East Guldeford Level and the Rother Levels.

There are few records in the county files of counts made in the 1970s and 1980s of singing males in specific areas. Consequently, only a few significant comparisons can be made with the results from the 1993-94 survey (table 82).

Locality	Year	No. of singing males	No. of singing males in 1993
Thorney Island	1989	12	8
Goodwood	1986	6	0
Wepham Down	1976	16	5
Chantry Hill, Storrington	1975	20	7
Cissbury Ring	1976	11	4
Mile Oak, Portslade	1975	12	9
Pyecombe Golf Course	1985	8	3
Plumpton Plain	1984	10	4
Beachy Head area	1975	40	7
Rye Harbour LNR	1979	16	3

Table 82. Counts of singing male Corn Buntings.

The 1993-94 survey also recorded data on the use of different habitat and song post types (table 83). Despite the conversion of considerable areas of downland from arable to grassland with sheep and cattle grazing, singing males still show a preference for cereal crops in fields with adjacent song-posts, these being of a wide variety, such as hedgerows, trees, fences and power-lines. Tall weeds within fields or even the crop itself may also be used. However, in the absence of ideal conditions, there is a willingness to accept alternative farm crops, such as oil seed rape, linseed and peas, ungrazed grassland and areas under rotational set-aside. The data on usage of song post types should be treated with some caution as they probably reflect song post availability, particularly on the Downs, rather than actual preference.

Habitat types	%	Song post types	%
Cereals	50.5	Hedge	6.4
Grassland	23.4	Hedge with trees	3.9
Oilseed Rape	6.3	Tree line, no hedge	2.3
Root crops	0.8	Isolated bush	24.6
Other green crops	10.0	Wire fence	37.3
Other crops	6.9	Overhead wire	9.8
Other farming	1.2	Other types	15.8
Non-farming	0.6		

Table 83. Usage of habitat and song post types by Corn Buntings, 1993/94.

Outside the breeding season, Corn Buntings gather in flocks for feeding and roosting. Up until the mid-1980s, these were often large but, recently, they have been generally much reduced (table 84). Results from the BTO Winter Corn Bunting Survey (Marchant & Gregory 1993, Donald 1994) indicate that for winter feeding, weedy stubbles are more valuable, holding twice the number of flocks and birds as 'clean' stubble. Sussex records indicate that birds find their food in winter in cereal stubbles (including maize), kale, ploughed land and grazed pasture, and are also prepared to take advantage of cattle food, duck feed, partridge feeders and, in severe weather, bird seed in suburban parks and gardens.

Locality	Date	Count	Date	Count
Pagham Harbour	Dec. 1975	250	Feb. 1991	322
Lower Adur Valley	Aug.1975	250	Mar. 1993	12
Upper Beeding	Sep. 1981	550	Dec. 1991	500
Lower Cuckmere Valley	Feb. 1975	100	Oct. 1993	34
Beachy Head	Sep. 1971	200	Aug. 1993	50
Rye Harbour	Nov. 1975	200	Feb. 1993	97

Table 84. Counts of flocks of Corn Buntings.

In winter, birds roost communally, often in reedbeds, previously in considerable numbers but now much reduced. At Striven's Reedbed, Steyning, up to 500 were recorded roosting in 1976 but only 70 in 1993. Another reedbed roost at Thorney Deeps held maxima of 51 in 1983 and 37 in 1993. At Rye Harbour, where birds roost regularly on the saltings, there were peaks of 125 in 1979 and 55 in 1982.

There is little evidence of migration beyond the county. Shrubb wrote that "there have been occasional records of movements at the coast in spring and autumn, but these have involved only a few individuals". The only more recent records which indicate passage are of 15 flying west at Selsey Bill on 18 October 1980 and 12 flying in from the sea at Beachy Head on 8 March 1985.

All recoveries of Sussex-ringed Corn Buntings have been within the county. Most had travelled less than 10 km from their ringing site, but one ringed at Castle Hill was found breeding 15 km away at Seaford Head in 1985.

Leonard Manns

Northern Oriole   *Icterus galbula*

Status:- A very rare vagrant (one record).

An adult male at Whitbread Hollow, Beachy Head on 5-6 October 1962 was the second British record (Harber 1963), although the possibility that it might have been an escape from captivity could not be excluded at the time (Harber & Swaine 1963). That it was an adult is particularly unusual, nearly all autumn vagrant nearctic passerines being juveniles. It is currently under review.

There were 17 records of this bright Icterid in the British Isles during 1962-94. It breeds in USA and southern Canada wintering from Mexico to northern South America. The race recorded in Britain, 'Baltimore Oriole' *I.g. galbula*, occurs in eastern and central parts of its range and was formerly regarded as distinct from its western counterpart 'Bullock's Oriole' *I.g. bullockii*.

Richard Fairbank

Appendix One. Category D Species and Other Escapes and Exotics.

Until 1975 the Sussex Ornithological Society did not collect or publish records of species which were considered to have escaped from captivity or had been intentionally released into the wild. In the 1975 *Sussex Bird Report* it was stated that "reports of escaped birds and of those released into the wild are always welcomed" and that "when a suitable opportunity occurs the records will be summarised and published in a future Report." Between 1978 and 1981 and from 1988 onwards, summaries of these records were published in the annual *Sussex Bird Report.*

The submission and collection of records of escaped birds in the county has been variable but by the end of 1993, the 'Escapes and Ferals' file held over 900 records. Of these, 78% were of wildfowl, particularly Barnacle Geese. The gathering of such records is of value in that it allows feral populations to be monitored and may be of use in assessing the origin of potentially true vagrants (Parkin & Knox 1994).

The following table lists some of the species which have been recorded in the county as presumed escapes using the English species names and taxonomic order in Howard & Moore (1984). Those that are also referred to in the systematic list are marked *. It should be noted, however, that records of escaped birds have not generally been subject to strict adjudication, unlike records of wild birds, and that some of the species listed may possibly have been wrongly identified.

English Name	Scientific Name	English Name	Scientific Name
Pink-backed Pelican	*Pelecanus rufescens*	Ferruginous Duck *	*Aythya nyroca*
Cattle Egret *	*Bubulcus ibis*	Barrow's Goldeneye *	*Bucephala islandica*
White Stork *	*Ciconia ciconia*	Black Vulture	*Aegypius monarchus*
Greater Adjutant Stork	*Leptoptilos dubius*	Harris's Hawk	*Parabuteo unicinctus*
Marabou Stork	*Leptoptilos crumeniferus*	Red-tailed Hawk	*Buteo jamaincensis*
Sacred Ibis	*Threskiornis aethiopious*	Lanner Falcon	*Falco biarmicus*
Spoonbill x African Spoonbill *	*Platelea leucorodia x alba*	Saker Falcon	*Falco cherrug*
Greater Flamingo *	*Phoenicopterus ruber*	Peregrine *	*Falco peregrinus*
Chilean Flamingo *	*Phoenicopterus chilensis*	Chukar Partridge	*Alectoris chukar*
Fulvous Whistling Duck	*Dendrocygna bicolor*	Silver Pheasant	*Lophura nycthemera*
White-faced Whistling Duck	*Dendrocygna viduata*	Reeves' Pheasant	*Syrmaticus reeves*
Black Swan	*Cygnus atratus*	Lady Amherst's Pheasant *	*Chrysolophus amherstiae*
Black-necked Swan	*Cygnus melanocoryphus*	Common Peafowl	*Pavo cristatus*
Whooper Swan *	*Cygnus cygnus*	Sarus Crane	*Grus antigone*
Bean Goose *	*Anas fabilis*	Crowned Crane	*Balearica pavonina*
Pink-footed Goose *	*Anas brachyrhynchus*	Barbary Dove	*Streptopelia roseogrisea*
White-fronted Goose *	*Anser albifrons*		*risoria*
Lesser White-fronted Goose	*Anser erythropus*	Laughing Dove	*Streptopelia senegalensis*
Bar-headed Goose	*Anser indicus*	Sulphur-crested Cockatoo	*Cacatua galerita*
Snow Goose *	*Anser caerulescens*	Cockatiel	*Nymphicus hollandicus*
Emperor Goose	*Anser canagicus*	Budgerigar	*Melopsittacus undulatus*
Canada Goose *	*Branta canadensis minima*	Grey Parrot	*Psittacus erithacus*
Barnacle Goose *	*Branta leucopsis*	Grey-headed Lovebird	*Agopornis cana*
Black Brant *	*Branta bernicla nigricans*	Black-headed Lovebird	*Agopornis nigrigenis*
Red-breasted Goose *	*Branta ruficollis*	Alexandrine Parakeet	*Psittacula eupatria*
Magellan Goose	*Chloephaga picta*	Ring-necked Parakeet *	*Psittacula krameri*
Egyptian Goose *	*Alopochen aegyptiacus*	Buffon's Macaw	*Ara ambigua*
Ruddy Shelduck *	*Tadorna ferruginea*	Nanday Conure	*Nandayus nanday*
South African Shelduck	*Tadorna cana*	Black-headed Caique	*Pionites melanocephala*
Paradise Shelduck	*Tadorna variegata*	Yellow-crowned Amazon	*Amazona ochrocephala*
Australian Shelduck	*Tadorna tadornoides*	Eagle Owl *	*Bubo bubo*
Muscovy Duck	*Cairina moschata*	Hummingbird species	
Comb Duck	*Sarkidiornis melanotos*	Trumpeter Hornbill	*Bycanistes bucinator*
Ringed Teal	*Callonetta leucophrys*	Red-whiskered Bulbul	*Pycnonotus jocosus*
Wood Duck	*Aix sponsa*	Blue Rock Thrush *	*Monticola solitarius*
Maned Goose	*Chenonetta jubata*	Pekin Robin	*Leiothrix lutea.*
American Wigeon *	*Anas americana*	Black-headed Bunting *	*Emberiza melanocephala*
Chiloe Wigeon	*Anas sibilatrix*	Red-headed Bunting	*Emberiza bruniceps*
Baikal Teal *	*Anas formosa*	Red-crested Cardinal	*Paroaria coronata*
Green-winged Teal *	*Anas crecca carolinensis*	Canary	*Serinus canaria*
Chilean Teal	*Anas flavirostris*	Black-headed Siskin	*Serinus nigriceps*
Sharp-winged Teal	*Anas flavirostris oxypterum*	Yellow-fronted Canary **	*Serinus mozambicus*
Cape Teal	*Anas capensis*	Red-billed Fire Finch	*Lagonostricta senegala*
Chestnut-breasted Teal	*Anas castanea*	Common Waxbill	*Estrilda astrild*
Laysan Teal	*Anas platyrhynchos laysanensis*	Zebra Waxbill	*Amandava subflava*
		Java Sparrow	*Padda oryzivora*
Spotbill Duck	*Anas poecilorhyncha*	Pin-tailed Whydah	*Vidua macroura*
Phillippine Duck	*Anas luzonica*	Sudan Golden Sparrow	*Auripasser luteus*
Chilean Pintail	*Anas georgica spinicauda*	Black-headed Weaver	*Ploceus melanocephalus*
Bahama Pintail	*Anas bahamensis*	Red-headed Weaver	*Anaplectes melanotis*
Red-billed Pintail	*Anas erythrorhyncha*	Red-billed Quelea	*Quelea quelea*
Versicolor Teal	*Anas versicolor*	Red-crowned Bishop	*Euplectes hordeacea*
Puna Teal	*Anas versicolor puna*	Red Bishop	*Euplectes orix*
Hottentot Teal	*Anas punctata*	Red-shouldered Glossy Starling	*Lamprotornis nitens*
Blue-winged Teal *	*Anas discors*	Common Mynah	*Acridotheres tristis*
Cinnamon Teal	*Anas cyanoptera*	Indian Tree Pie	*Dendrocitta vagabunda*
Red-crested Pochard *	*Netta rufina*		
Rosybill	*Netta peposaca*		

The following summaries refer to some of the more interesting and regularly reported species which do not feature in the systematic list.

Black Swan   *Cygnus atratus*

A few were recorded almost annually between 1978 and 1993, mainly singles and often associating with Mute Swans. Pairs bred at Hastings in at least three of the years between 1980 and 1984, a pair raised four cygnets at Maresfield Park in March 1978 and four juveniles were seen at Ardingly Reservoir on 25 August 1980.

Lesser White-fronted Goose   *Anser erythropus*

A single bird was recorded with Canada Geese in Petworth Park on 6 June 1988 and 23 March 1989.

Bar-headed Goose   *Anser indicus*

Records in the Society's files suggest that there were several at liberty in the county during the late 1970s. Subsequent reports have been of ones and twos, usually in the company of either Greylag or Canada Geese. There have been records from 24 sites, mainly in areas such as the Arun Valley where large flocks of feral geese regularly occur. Four in Chichester Harbour on 17 and 31 March 1979 and at Beeding Brooks on 8 November 1992 were the largest parties recorded.

Wood Duck   *Aix sponsa*

This attractive North American perching duck is commonly kept in wildfowl collections in Europe. Although it was first introduced into England in the 1870s, it has not been as successful in colonizing Britain as its close relative the Mandarin and, as yet, it has not been admitted to the British List.

A comparison of the maps published in the 68-72 BTO Atlas and the New Atlas shows that the species has extended its range from its original strongholds in Surrey and Berkshire into surrounding counties, including Sussex. It cannot, however, be considered a successful colonist in Sussex since there are only two sites in the county at which it has been recorded regularly. At Swanbourne Lake, Arundel, where there were 14, including eight young, on 9 January 1984 and 17 on 13 December 1992, pairs were reported annually between 1978 and 1993, with breeding proved in five of these years. It is likely, however, that this colony is not truly self-sustaining as the nearby WWT reserve is an obvious source of supplementary food and shelter. At Dower House Farm, Blackboys there were ten on 15 January 1984, up to 12 regularly throughout 1985 and eight during May and June 1988.

With the exception of a party of six at Hampden Park, Eastbourne on 15 January 1984 and pairs at Mannings Heath on 11 April 1983, Icklesham on 18 November 1989 and Malthouse Farm, Wisborough Green on 17 June 1991, the other records have been of single birds at about 20 other sites in the county. A most unusual record was that of a bird found exhausted at Selsey Bill on 11 November 1991.   *Tony Cook*

Cockatiel   *Nymphicus hollandicus*

This Australian parrot, which is commonly kept in captivity, is the most frequently recorded escaped cage bird in Sussex. The 44 records up to the end of 1993 have all been of single birds, well distributed throughout the county. As the following table shows, most have occurred between March and October, suggesting that few survive for long in the cold winter months.

Jan	Feb	Mar	Apr	May	Jun	Jul	Aug	Sep	Oct	Nov	Dec
1	-	5	4	4	4	3	7	7	7	1	1

Red-headed Bunting   *Emberiza bruniceps*

des Forges & Harber stated that there was no reason to believe that the Red-headed Buntings that had occurred in Sussex prior to 1962 were anything other than escapes from captivity. Since the beginning of 1962, there have been at least nine records of males in the county as follows:

1962:   One at Atherington on 15 September.
1969:   One at Chichester Gravel Pits on 7 June.
1971:   One at East Head, West Wittering on 26-27 May.
1973:   One at Beachy Head on 14 July.
1974:   One at Rottingdean on 18 April.
1975:   One at Galley Hill, Bexhill on 6 July.
1979:   One at Church Norton from 5 to 7 October.
1990:   One in a garden at Ashington from 15 to 19 January.
1990:   One at St Leonards on 19 September.

Once again, all were thought to be escapes.   *John Newnham*

Appendix Two. Early and Late Dates for Summer Migrants.

The following table gives the earliest arrival and latest departure dates for 48 species of summer migrants. In compiling this information, reference has been made to a number of sources, principally des Forges & Harber, Shrubb, the *Sussex Bird Report* 1948-94 and Hudson (1973). Omitted from the table are details of birds known to have definitely overwintered in the county and also a number of species which, although primarily summer migrants, overwinter too often to allow the earliest and latest dates to be identified. These are Avocet, Whimbrel, Greenshank, Common Sandpiper, Lesser Black-backed Gull, Black Redstart, Blackcap and Chiffchaff.

Species	Earliest Date	Locality	Latest Date	Locality
Garganey *	21 January 1994	Icklesham	13 December 1994	Bewl Water
Honey Buzzard	9 May 1971	Beachy Head	1 November 1979	Maynards Green
Montagu's Harrier	17 April 1955	Broomhill Level	22 October 1972	Steyning
Osprey	24 March 1993	Bewl Water	9 December 1994	Arlington Res.
Hobby	12 April 1971	Midrips	31 October 1965	Selsey Bill
Quail *	21 March 1921 & 21 March 1973	St Leonards & Lancing		
Corncrake	9 April 1961	Selsey Bill	28 December 1908	Hardham
Stone Curlew *	8 March 1969	West Chiltington	1 December 1958	Burpham
Little Ringed Plover	6 March 1990	Fishbourne	8 October 1983	Chichester GP
Kentish Plover *	13 February 1982	West Wittering	14 December 1963	Chichester Hbr
Dotterel *	22 March 1853	East Blatchington	10 November 1875	Sidlesham
Temminck's Stint *	19 March 1975	Thorney Island	21 October 1975	Sidlesham Ferry
Wood Sandpiper	11 February 1967	Iford	3 November 1976	Newhaven
Sandwich Tern *	10 February 1990	Selsey Bill	20 December 1972	Southwick
Roseate Tern	17 April 1968	Beachy Head	30 September 1965	Langney Point
Common/Arctic Tern	21 March 1981	Beachy Head	30-31 December 1966	Pagham Hbr
Little Tern	3 April 1985	Worthing	4 November 1991	Selsey Bill
Black Tern	4 April 1957	Chichester GP	13-21 November 1954	Cuckmere Valley
Turtle Dove	22 March 1966	Plumpton	12 November 1978	Pagham
Cuckoo	15 March 1936	Fairlight Cove	11 November 1928	Goodwood
Nightjar	8 April 1912	Pulborough	5 November 1961	Worthing
Swift	10 April 1989	Cuckmere Valley	22 November 1994	Church Norton
Hoopoe	ca. 1 March 1932	St. Leonards	14 December 1897	Hartfield
Wryneck	9 March 1908	Pulborough	5 November 1947	Crumbles
Sand Martin	5 March 1994	Chichester GP	5 December 1911	?
Swallow	4 February 1967	Langney Point	28 December 1974	Church Norton
House Martin	1 February 1975	Petworth	22 December 1894	Fishbourne
Tree Pipit	17 March 1922	Bexhill	9 November 1980	Bexhill
Yellow Wagtail*	12 March 1990	Sidlesham Ferry	21 November 1926	Hove
Nightingale	21 March 1988	Littlehampton	19 October 1943	North Bersted
Redstart	13 March 1993	Bognor	29 November 1989	Pett Level
Whinchat	17 March 1968	Weir Wood Res.	2 December 1981	Shoreham
Wheatear*	13 February 1934	Midrips	31 December 1987	Littlehampton
Ring Ouzel	2 February 1905	Mannings Heath	26 December 1992	Wilmington
Grasshopper Warbler	4 April 1965 & 4 April 1972	Beachy Head & Devil's Dyke	1 November 1969	Beachy Head
Savi's Warbler	10 April 1961	Selsey Bill	25 October 1988	Icklesham
Sedge Warbler	27 March 1977	Arundel Park	29 October 1961	Pett Level
Marsh Warbler	8 May 1923	?	6 October 1991	Seaford Head
Reed Warbler	9 April 1966 & 9 April 1981	Selsey Bill & Chichester GP	13 November 1994	Beachy Head
Lesser Whitethroat	4 April 1989	Moulsecoomb	21 November 1957	Burgess Hill
Whitethroat	19 March 1966	Southease	17 December 1972	Darwell Reservoir
Garden Warbler	1 April 1990	Seaford Head	7 November 1968	Beachy Head
Wood Warbler	7 April 1985	Wiggonholt Common	1 October 1992	Littlehampton
Willow Warbler	4 March 1993	Duddeswell	26 December 1892 & 26 December 1949	? & Whyke
Spotted Flycatcher	8 April 1909	Hastings	18 November 1979	Maynards Green
Pied Flycatcher	3 April 1994	Ashdown Forest	1 November 1968	Beachy Head
Golden Oriole	12 April 1854	Battle	10 September 1991	Church Norton
Red-backed Shrike	15 April 1945	Lidsey	16 November 1991	Selsey Bill

* has or probably has overwintered

Tim Parmenter & Paul James

562

Gazetteer

Compiled by John Irons and John Newnham.

Section A

The Sussex Ornithological Society holds computerised records for more than 2600 sites, a considerable number of which have relatively few records and so have not been included in this section of the Gazetteer. The sites listed in Section A are those which, at the end of 1994, each held more than 30 records. While these sites tend to be those which are regularly watched, there are many others of considerable ornithological interest. The following sites vary enormously in size from extensive areas occupying several square kilometres to small pools or fields which are not shown on the Ordnance Survey maps 1:50,000.

Abbot's Wood, Hailsham	TQ5607	Beach Reserve, Rye Harbour LNR	TQ9317
Adur Levels, Upper	TQ1914	Beachy Head	TV5895
Adur Recreation Ground, Shoreham	TQ2004	Beauport Park, Hastings	TQ7814
Adur Valley, Lower	TQ2005	Beeding Brooks	TQ1911
Aldingbourne Rife, nr Bognor	SU9201	Beeding Hill	TQ2109
Aldsworth Pond	SU7608	Belle Tout, Beachy Head	TV5695
Aldwick, Bognor	SZ9098	Bepton	SU8618
Alexandra Park, Hastings	TQ8010	Berwick	TQ5105
Alfriston	TQ5103	Bewbush, Crawley	TQ2435
Amberley	TQ0213	Bewl Water	TQ6733
Amberley Mount	TQ0412	Bewl Water, Dam Area	TQ6733
Amberley Wild Brooks	TQ0314	Bexhill	TQ7307
Ambersham Common	SU9119	Bexleyhillnr Lodsworth	SU9125
Angmering Decoy Ponds	TQ0505	Bignor Park	SU9915
Apuldram Manor Farm	SU8303	Billingshurst	TQ0825
Apuldram, nr Chichester	SU8303	Bines Bridge, Ashurst	TQ1817
Ardingly	TQ3429	Binstead, nr Arundel	SU9806
Ardingly Reservoir	TQ3229	Birchgrove, Horsted Keynes	TQ3929
Arlington Reservoir	TQ5307	Birdham	SU8200
Arun Valley (Pulborough-Amberley)	TQ0215	Birling Gap, Beachy Head	TV5596
Arundel	TQ0107	Bishopstone, nr Seaford	TQ4701
Arundel Mill Stream	TQ0207	Black Down, nr Fernhurst	SU9130
Arundel Park	TQ0108	Blackwell, East Grinstead	TQ3939
Arundel Watermeadows	TQ0207	Blakehurst, nr Arundel	TQ0406
Arundel WWT	TQ0208	Bluebell Railway, Sheffield Park	TQ3726
Ashburnham Place, Battle	TQ6914	Bodiam	TQ7825
Ashcombe Bottom, Lewes	TQ3711	Bognor Golf Course	SU9501
Ashcombe Farm, Lewes	TQ3809	Bognor Regis	SZ9399
Ashdown Forest	TQ4332	Bolney	TQ2623
Ashdown Forest Centre	TQ4332	Bosham	SU8004
Atherington, nr Climping	TQ0000	Bosham Channel	SU7902
Balcombe	TQ3130	Bowders Farm, Balcombe	TQ3129
Balcombe Lake	TQ3131	Bracklesham Bay	SZ8096
Balsdean, nr Rottingdean	TQ3704	Bramber	TQ1810
Barcombe Mills	TQ4314	Brantridge Park, Balcombe	TQ2830
Barcombe Reservoir	TQ4314	Brede Levels	TQ8217
Barlavington Down	SU9615	Bremere Rife, Pagham	SZ8798
Barnham	SU9504	Brighton	TQ3104
Barns Copse, Binstead	SU9806	Brighton - at sea off	TQ3300
Barns Green	TQ1226	Brighton Marina	TQ3302
Barnsden, Ashdown	TQ4728	Brighton Woodvale Cemetery	TQ3205
Battle	TQ7416	Brinsbury Estate	TQ0622
Bayham	TQ6336	Broad Oak, Heathfield	TQ6022
Beach Field, Rye Harbour SSSI	TQ9217	Broadhurst, Horsted Keynes	TQ3830

Broadstone Warren, Ashdown	TQ4332	Cooden Beach Golf Course	TQ7006
Broadwater, Worthing	TQ1504	Cook's Pond, Milland	SU8326
Brooklands, Worthing	TQ1703	Cooksbridge	TQ4013
Broomhill Level	TQ9719	Copthorne Common	TQ3238
Buchan Park, nr Crawley	TQ2434	Copthorne, nr Crawley	TQ3139
Buckhurst Park, nr Withyham	TQ5035	Cotchet Farm, nr Fernhurst	SU9129
Burgess Hill	TQ3118	Cow Gap, Beachy Head	TV5995
Burgh Hill, Etchingham	TQ7227	Cripps Manor, Ashdown	TQ4032
Burpham	TQ0308	Crowborough	TQ5130
Burpham Levels	TQ0209	Crowhurst Marsh	TQ7610
Burton Mill Pond	SU9617	Crowlink, East Dean	TV5497
Burton Park, Duncton	SU9617	Crows Nest, Ashdown	TQ4728
Bury Watermeadows	TQ0212	Crumbles Gravel Pits	TQ6301
Buxted Park, nr Uckfield	TQ4822	Cuckmere Haven	TV5197
Byworth	SU9820	Cuckmere Lower Valley	TV5197
Camber Pit, Large	TQ9519	Cuckmere Upper Valley	TQ5204
Camber Pit, Small	TQ9419	Cuckoo Corner, Coombes	TQ2006
Camber Shore SSSI	TQ9618	Darch's Wood, nr Cross-in-Hand	TQ5621
Camp Hill, Ashdown	TQ4629	Darwell Reservoir	TQ7121
Carter's Pit, Rye Harbour LNR	TQ9319	Dell Quay	SU8302
Castle Farm, Rye Harbour LNR	TQ9118	Denton	TQ4502
Castle Hill, nr Falmer	TQ3706	Devil's Dyke	TQ2511
Castle Pit, Rye Harbour LNR	TQ9218	Ditchling	TQ3215
Castle Water, Rye Harbour LNR	TQ9218	Ditchling Beacon	TQ3313
Cattlestone Farm, West Chiltington	TQ1020	Ditchling Common	TQ3318
Chailey	TQ3919	Doomsday Green, Horsham	TQ1929
Chailey Common	TQ3820	Dover Woods, Angmering	TQ0506
Chalvington Sand Pit	TQ5209	Down Level, Pevensey	TQ6107
Chanctonbury Ring	TQ1312	Drayton Gravel Pit, Chichester	SU8804
Chantry Hill	TQ0812	Druids The, Ifieldwood	TQ2438
Chapel Common, Liphook	SU8128	Duddleswell, Ashdown	TQ4627
Charleston Reedbed, nr Litlington	TQ5201	Duncton Mill Pond	SU9616
Chelwood Beacon, Ashdown	TQ4229	Dunford Gravel Pit, nr Midhurst	SU8919
Chelwood Gate, Ashdown	TQ4130	Durrington, Worthing	TQ1104
Chelwood Vachery, Ashdown	TQ4330	Earnley, nr East Wittering	SZ8196
Chichester	SU8504	Easebourne Great Common	SU8824
Chichester Canal	SU8301	East Chidham	SU7903
Chichester Channel, Lower	SZ7799	East Dean (West Sussex)	SU9012
Chichester Channel, Upper	SU8001	East Grinstead	TQ3938
Chichester Gravel Pits	SU8703	East Guldeford Level	TQ9421
Chichester Harbour	SU7600	East Head, nr West Wittering	SZ7698
Chilver Bridge, Arlington	TQ5306	Eastbourne	TV6199
Chingford Pond, Duncton	SU9717	Ebernoe Common	SU9726
Chingford Trout Pond	SU9617	Ebernoe Furnace Pond	SU9727
Chingley Wood, Bewl Water	TQ6833	Ella Nore, nr West Wittering	SZ7799
Chithurst	SU8423	Ellison's Pond, Ashdown	TQ4628
Chithurst Hammer Pond	SU8423	Elms Farm, Icklesham	TQ8815
Church Farm, Climping	TQ0002	Emsworth Channel, Chichester	SU7402
Church Norton	SZ8795	Eridge Park	TQ5635
Church Norton - offshore	SZ8795	Eridge Park Lake	TQ5634
Church Norton, Shingle Spit	SZ8795	Etchingham	TQ7126
Chyngton Farm, Cuckmere	TV5098	Exceat Bridge, Cuckmere	TV5199
Cissbury Ring	TQ1408	Fairlight	TQ8611
Claphatch Hide, Bewl Water	TQ6731	Fairlight Country Park	TQ8511
Cliff End, Cuckmere Haven	TV5297	Fairlight Glen	TQ8510
Cliff End, nr Pett	TQ8813	Falmer Pond	TQ3508
Climping	TQ0001	Fen Place Mill, Crawley Down	TQ3536
Climping-Littlehampton Gap	TQ0101	Fernhurst	SU8928
Coates Common	TQ0017	Ferring	TQ0901
Cobnor Cottage, Chichester	SU7902	Ferring Rife	TQ0901
Cobnor Farm, Chichester	SU7902	Ferry Lagoon, Pagham	SZ8596
Cobnor Point, Chichester	SU7901	Filsham Reedbed LNR	TQ7709
Cold Coombes, nr Lewes	TQ3707	Finche's Wood, Nuthurst	TQ1927
Coldwaltham Brooks	TQ0215	Findon Valley, Worthing	TQ1306
Combe Haven	TQ7609	Firle	TQ4607

Firle Park	TQ4707	Holmbush Farm, Faygate	TQ2233
Fishbourne	SU8404	Holmbush Tip, Faygate	TQ2335
Fishbourne Channel	SU8303	Holme Farm, Mannings Heath	TQ2128
Fishbourne Sewage Works	SU8403	Honer Farm, Pagham	SZ8798
Five Hundred Acre Wood, Ashdown	TQ4832	Hooe Level, Pevensey	TQ6806
Folly Pond, nr Liphook	SU8229	Hook Straight, Bewl Water	TQ6732
Ford, Arun Valley	TQ0003	Hope Gap, Seaford	TV5097
Fore Wood, Crowhurst	TQ7513	Horam	TQ5717
Four Counties, Ashdown	TQ4631	Horder Centre, Ashdown	TQ4931
Friars Gate, Ashdown	TQ4933	Horse Eye Level, Pevensey	TQ6208
Friston Forest	TV5499	Horses Field, Church Norton	SZ8795
Gatwick Airport	TQ2740	Horseshoe Plantation, Beachy Head	TV5695
Giffard's Wood, West Hoathly	TQ3633	Horsham	TQ1730
Gills Lap, Ashdown	TQ4632	Horsted Keynes	TQ3828
Glebe Meadow, Church Norton	SZ8795	Horton Hall, nr Small Dole	TQ2011
Glynde	TQ4509	Hotham Park, Bognor	SZ9399
Glynde Levels	TQ4609	Houghton, nr Amberley	TQ0111
Glynde Reach Clay Pit	TQ4609	Hove	TQ2805
Glyne Gap Beach, Bexhill	TQ7607	Hove Lagoon	TQ2604
Glyne Gap Marsh, Bexhill	TQ7608	Hove Park	TQ2806
Glyne Gap, Bexhill	TQ7607	Hunston, nr Chichester	SU8601
Goat The, Ashdown	TQ4032	Hurst Green	TQ7327
Goodwood	SU8911	Hurstpierpoint	TQ2716
Goring Beach	TQ1001	Hutchinson's Farm, Wick	TQ0104
Goring Gap	TQ1001	Icklesham	TQ8716
Goring Wood	TQ1001	Ifield Mill Pond	TQ2436
Goring-by-Sea	TQ1102	Ifield, Crawley	TQ2537
Gossop Green Mill Pond, Crawley	TQ2436	Iford, nr Lewes	TQ4007
Gossops Green, Crawley	TQ2535	Inholmes Copse, nr Milland	SU8526
Graffham Common	SU9319	Iping Common	SU8421
Grantleys Farm, Maynard's Green	TQ5818	Isfield	TQ4417
Gravetye Lakes, nr West Hoathly	TQ3634	Isle Of Thorns, Ashdown	TQ4230
Great Wood, Stanmer	TQ3309	Ivy Lake, Chichester	SU8703
Greatham	TQ0415	Jury's Gap	TQ9818
Greatham Bridge	TQ0316	Kilnwood, nr Faygate	TQ2235
Greatham Common	TQ0415	King's Standing, Ashdown	TQ4730
Greenwood Clump, Ashdown	TQ4731	Kingley Vale	SU8110
Greyfriars, Winchelsea	TQ9016	Kings Barn Steyning	TQ1811
Guildenhurst, Billingshurst	TQ0625	Kingston Gorse	TQ0801
Hailsham	TQ5809	Knepp Estate	TQ1521
Halsey's Farm, Sidlesham	SZ8697	Kneppmill Pond	TQ1521
Hampden Park, Eastbourne	TQ6002	Knucker Hole, Lyminster	TQ0204
Hampers Lane, Storrington	TQ1014	Lancing	TQ1804
Hamsey, River Ouse	TQ4112	Lancing Clump	TQ1806
Harbour Farm, Rye SSSI	TQ9317	Lancing College	TQ1906
Harbour Shore, Rye SSSI	TQ9417	Langney Point	TQ6401
Harting Down	SU7918	Lavender Platt, Ashdown	TQ4033
Hassocks	TQ3015	Lavington Common	SU9418
Hastings	TQ8109	Leonardslee, nr Crabtree	TQ2225
Haywards Heath	TQ3324	Lewes	TQ4009
Heath Common, Storrington	TQ1114	Lewes Brooks	TQ4207
Hedgecourt Lake, Felbridge	TQ3540	Lewes Brooks, Lower Rise	TQ4207
Hellingly	TQ5812	Lewes Race Course	TQ3910
Henfield Levels	TQ1914	Lidsey Rife, Barnham	SU9502
Herstmonceux Castle	TQ6410	Limekiln Wood, Crowborough	TQ5331
Hesworth Common	TQ0019	Lindfield	TQ3425
Heyshott Common	SU9019	Lindfield Pond	TQ3425
High Salvington, Worthing	TQ1206	Litlington	TQ5201
Highdole Hill, Telscombe	TQ3904	Littlehampton	TQ0301
Highdown, nr Worthing	TQ0904	Littlehampton Golf Course	TQ0101
Hill Barn, Worthing	TQ1405	Littlehampton Marina	TQ0102
Hindleap Warren, Ashdown	TQ4132	Littlehampton West Beach	TQ0201
Hodcombe, Beachy Head	TV5795	Littleworth	TQ1920
Hollies, Ashdown	TQ4528	Loder Valley, Ardingly	TQ3329
Hollingbury Camp	TQ3207	Long Pit, Rye SSSI	TQ9217

Lullington Heath	TQ5401	Pagham Harbour, Intertidals	SZ8796
Lurgashall Mill Pond	SU9325	Pagham Harbour, North Wall	SZ8797
Lychpole Hill, nr Cissbury	TQ1507	Pagham Harbour, West Side	SZ8696
Lyminster	TQ0204	Pagham Lagoon	SZ8896
Mannings Heath	TQ2028	Pagham Village	SZ8897
Manxey Level, Pevensey	TQ6406	Palace Pier, Brighton	TQ3103
Marley Common	SU8831	Pannel Sewer	TQ8715
Marline Wood, Hastings	TQ7812	Parham	TQ0614
Marsh Farm, Yapton	SU9804	Parham House Lake	TQ0514
Marsham Valley, nr Pett	TQ8713	Park Wood, Hellingly	TQ6012
Maynard's Green	TQ5818	Partridge Green	TQ1919
Mens The, nr Bedham	TQ0223	Patcham, Brighton	TQ3008
Mewsbrook Park, Littlehampton	TQ0401	Patching Pond	TQ0805
Michelgrove, Patching	TQ0808	Pease Pottage	TQ2532
Middle Bridge, Pevensey	TQ6606	Peasmarsh Decoy Pond	TQ8725
Midhurst	SU8821	Pebsham	TQ7609
Midhurst Common	SU8721	Pells The, Lewes	TQ4110
Midrips The	TR0017	Peter Pond, Emsworth	SU7505
Mill Hill, Shoreham	TQ2107	Pett Level	TQ9015
Mill Pond Marsh, Pagham	SZ8597	Pett Level Pools	TQ9014
Millbrook, Ashdown	TQ4428	Pett Level Shore	TQ9014
Milton Hide, nr Arlington	TQ5608	Petworth Park	SU9721
Misbourne, nr Nutley	TQ4527	Petworth Park Lake	SU9722
Moneypenny Gravel Pit	TQ9420	Pevensey Bridge Level	TQ6504
Mountfield	TQ7320	Pevensey Levels	TQ6605
Muntham Court, Findon	TQ1109	Pheasantry, Wych Cross	TQ4431
Nap Wood, nr Frant	TQ5832	Piddinghoe Pond, nr Newhaven	TQ4302
Narrow Pit, Rye SSSI	TQ9318	Piddinghoe, nr Newhaven	TQ4302
New Bridge, Pevensey	TQ6209	Pilsey Island	SU7600
New Lake, Chichester	SU8702	Pilsey Sands	SU7600
New Salts Farm, Lancing	TQ2004	Pippingford Park, Ashdown	TQ4430
Newells Pond, Lower Beeding	TQ2026	Plashett Park, Isfield	TQ4616
Newhaven	TQ4400	Plumpton	TQ3613
Newhaven Cliffs	TV4499	Plumpton Green	TQ3616
Newhaven Fort	TQ4400	Poling, nr Arundel	TQ0404
Newhaven Harbour	TQ4400	Pond Lye, Goddard's Green	TQ2821
Newhaven Tide Mills	TQ4500	Pontin's Site, Selsey Bill	SZ8592
Newhaven West Pier	TV4599	Poplar Copse, Church Norton	SZ8795
Newick	TQ4121	Portfield Gravel Pit, Chichester	SU8805
Newmarket Hill, nr Falmer	TQ3607	Possingworth Park	TQ5321
Newtimber Hill, Poynings	TQ2712	Poundgate, nr Crowborough	TQ4928
No Mans' Land, nr Steyning	TQ1409	Poverty Bottom, Newhaven	TQ4602
Nook Meadows, Rye SSSI	TQ9217	Powdermill Reservoir	TQ7919
Normans' Bay	TQ6805	Press Ridge Warren, Ashdown	TQ4131
North Fields, Pagham Harbour	SZ8697	Preston Park, Brighton	TQ3006
North Stoke, Arun Valley	TQ0210	Pulborough	TQ0418
Northpark Wood, Parham	TQ0515	Pulborough Brooks RSPB Reserve	TQ0516
Northpoint Pit Small, Rye	TQ9419	Pulborough Mid Brooks	TQ0516
Northpoint Pit, Rye	TQ9319	Pulborough North Brooks	TQ0517
Nutbourne	SU7705	Pulborough Sewage Farm	TQ0618
Nutley	TQ4427	Pulborough South Brooks	TQ0516
Nutley Windmill	TQ4529	Rackham Woods	TQ0414
Nyewood Lakes, Rogate	SU8021	Redlands, West Wittering	SZ7999
Offham	TQ0208	Rewell Wood, nr Arundel	SU9808
Offham, nr Lewes	TQ3911	Rickney, nr Pevensey	TQ6206
Old Airstrip, Ashdown	TQ4130	Ringmer	TQ4413
Old Lodge Reserve, Ashdown	TQ4530	Rise Barn, Lewes Brooks	TQ4208
Old Park Wood, Bosham	SU8202	River Adur, Shoreham	TQ2104
Ouse Valley, Lower	TQ4302	River Brede	TQ9119
Ouse-Glynde Confluence	TQ4307	River Ouse, Barcombe	TQ4213
Oving	SU9005	River Rother Estuary	TQ9319
Ovingdean	TQ3603	River Rother, West	SU8822
Pagham Beach	SZ8896	Robertsbridge	TQ7323
Pagham Harbour	SZ8796	Rock-a-Nore, Hastings	TQ8309
Pagham Harbour, Information Centre	SZ8596	Rock Common, Washington	TQ1213

Roedean, nr Brighton	TQ3403	Sompting Downs	TQ1605
Rogate	SU8023	South Ambersham	SU9120
Roman Road Area, Ashdown	TQ4729	South Heighton	TQ4502
Rookwood, West Wittering	SZ7899	South Stoke, Arun Valley	TQ0210
Rother Levels (East)	TQ9324	Southease	TQ4205
Rottingdean	TQ3602	Southwick Hill	TQ2307
Royal Military Canal, Pett	TQ8915	Sovereign Harbour Marina	TQ6402
Rudgwick	TQ0833	Sparrite Common, Parham	TQ0515
Runcton, nr Chichester	SU8802	Splash Point, Seaford	TV4898
Rye Bay Wood	TQ9217	St Helen's Wood, Hastings	TQ8111
Rye Bay, River Mouth	TQ9517	St Julien's, Coolham	TQ1222
Rye Bay, Sea / Offshore	TQ9415	St Leonard's Forest	TQ2231
Rye Harbour LNR	TQ9216	St Leonard's Hammer Pond	TQ2229
Rye Harbour SSSI	TQ9218	St Leonards	TQ7909
Rye Harbour Village	TQ9419	Stakes Island, Chichester	SU7801
Rye Saltings	TQ9320	Stakes Island, North	SU7801
Rye Town	TQ9120	Stakes Island, South	SU7701
Saltbarn, Playden	TQ9222	Standen Wood, Weir Wood	TQ3935
Saltdean	TQ3801	Stanmer Park, nr Brighton	TQ3309
Sandgate Park, Storrington	TQ1014	Stansted Forest	SU7511
Saunders Pit, Rye SSSI	TQ9318	Star Lock, Playden	TQ9322
Scaynes Hill	TQ3623	Stedham Common	SU8521
Scobell's Farm, Barcombe	TQ4216	Stedham Sand Pit	SU8521
Scotney Court Gravel Pit	TR0119	Steep Down, Lancing	TQ1607
Scrase LNR, Lindfield	TQ3424	Steyning	TQ1710
Seaford	TV4898	Steyning Round Hill	TQ1610
Seaford College, Duncton	SU9416	Storrington	TQ0814
Seaford Head	TV4997	Stoughton	SU8011
Selsey	SZ8593	Streele Farm, Billingshurst	TQ0624
Selsey Bill	SZ8592	Streele Lake, Billingshurst	TQ0624
Selsey East Beach	SZ8693	Stretham Manor, Henfield	TQ2013
Selsey West Beach	SZ8493	Strivens Reedbed, Steyning	TQ1811
Seven Sisters Country Park	TV5197	Stubbermere, nr Emsworth	SU7509
Severals, Church Norton	SZ8794	Stump Bottom, nr Steyning	TQ1509
Sharpthorne	TQ3732	Sullington Warren	TQ0914
Sheepcote Valley, Brighton	TQ3404	Sunnyside, East Grinstead	TQ3937
Sheffield Forest	TQ4226	Sutton	SU9715
Sheffield Park	TQ4123	Sutton End	SU9816
Sherman Bridge, Wilmington	TQ5305	Swanbourne Lake, Arundel	TQ0107
Shillinglee Lake	SU9631	Tarring Neville	TQ4403
Shooters' Bottom, Beachy Head	TV5795	Tas Combe, Willingdon	TQ5802
Shopham Bridge, nr Byworth	SU9818	Ternery Pool, Rye Harbour LNR	TQ9317
Shoreham Airport	TQ2005	The Mound, Church Norton	SZ8795
Shoreham Beach	TQ2204	Theale Farm, Slinfold	TQ1231
Shoreham Harbour	TQ2304	Thorney Airfield	SU7601
Shoreham Power Station	TQ2404	Thorney Channel	SU7700
Shoreham Sanctuary	TQ2106	Thorney Deeps	SU7503
Shoreham-by-Sea	TQ2105	Thorney Island	SU7602
Sidlesham	SZ8598	Thorney South-East Deeps	SU7603
Sidlesham Ferry	SZ8596	Three Corner Copse, Hove	TQ2807
Sidlesham Ferry Field	SZ8596	Tilgate Forest	TQ2733
Sidlesham Ferry Long Pool	SZ8696	Tilgate Lake	TQ2734
Sidlesham Ferry Pool	SZ8596	Tilgate Park, nr Crawley	TQ2734
Sidlesham Ferry Small Pool	SZ8596	Toot Rock, Pett	TQ8914
Sidlesham Mill Pond	SZ8697	Tortington, Arundel	TQ0005
Slaugham Furnace Pond	TQ2428	Townsend Car Park, Ashdown	TQ4432
Slaugham Manor	TQ2527	Trout Lakes, Chichester	SU8702
Slaugham Mill Pond	TQ2527	Uckfield	TQ4721
Slindon	SU9608	Union Canal, East Guldeford	TQ9322
Slinfold	TQ1131	University of Sussex, Falmer	TQ3409
Small Dole	TQ2112	Upper Beeding	TQ1910
Snowhill, West Wittering	SZ7798	Verdley Wood, nr Fernhurst	SU9026
Sompting	TQ1604	Wader Pool, Rye Harbour LNR	TQ9418
Sompting Abbotts	TQ1605	Wadhurst Park Estate	TQ6328
Sompting Brooks	TQ1604	Wakehurst Place	TQ3331

Wallers Haven, Pevensey	TQ6607	Whitbread Hollow, Beachy Head	TV5996
Warnham LNR	TQ1732	Whites Creek, Pagham	SZ8797
Warnham Mill Pond	TQ1632	Widewater, Lancing	TQ2004
Wartling	TQ6509	Wiggonholt Common	TQ0516
Washington Common	TQ1114	Wild Park, Brighton	TQ3207
Watch Cottage Pools, Rye SSSI	TQ9317	Willingdon, Eastbourne	TQ5802
Watch Cottages, Rye Harbour LNR	TQ9217	Willingdon Level, Eastbourne	TQ6101
Weir Wood Reservoir	TQ3834	Wilmington	TQ5404
Wepham Down	TQ0610	Winchelsea	TQ9017
West Chidham	SU7802	Winchelsea Beach	TQ9115
West Chiltington	TQ0816	Wiston Estate, nr Steyning	TQ1512
West Dean	SU8612	Withdean Park, Brighton	TQ3007
West Fields, Selsey	SZ8394	Woodingdean	TQ3505
West Harting Pond	SU7721	Woods Mill, Henfield	TQ2113
West Hove Golf Course	TQ2606	Woolbeding Common	SU8625
West Ifield, Crawley	TQ2437	Worth Forest	TQ3034
West Itchenor	SU7901	Worthing Beach	TQ1201
West Wittering	SZ7798	Worthing	TQ1402
West Worthing	TQ1302	Wrens Warren, Ashdown	TQ4732
Westbourne, nr Emsworth	SU7507	Wych Cross, Ashdown	TQ4131
Westdean Woods	SU8515	Wyckham Farm, Steyning	TQ1913
Westhampnet Gravel Pit, Chichester	SU8705	Yapton	SU9702
Whepley Level Pevensey	TQ6110		

Section B

The following sites are mentioned in the text but do not appear in Section A.

Adversane	TQ0723	Clayton Downs	TQ3013
Alder Shaw	TQ8520	Cocking	SU8717
Angmering	TQ0604	Coldwaltham	TQ0216
Ansty	TQ2923	Colgate	TQ2332
Argos Hill, nr Mayfield	TQ5728	Colworth, nr Chichester	SZ9190
Asham, nr Iford	TQ4007	Cooden	TQ7006
Ashington	TQ1316	Corkwood Farm, Iden	TQ9024
Barnhorn Level	TQ7008	Cornish Farm, Beachy Head	TV5696
Beckley	TQ8524	Cottendean, Stonegate	TQ6728
Beddingham	TQ4407	Covehurst Fairlight	TQ8510
Bevendean, Brighton	TQ3406	Cowbeech	TQ6115
Bignor Hill	SU9813	Cowdray Park	SU9022
Black Rock, Brighton	TQ3303	Cowfold	TQ2122
Boreham Street	TQ6611	Cradle Valley, Seaford	TQ5001
Brantridge Forest	TQ2831	Crowhurst	TQ7512
Brede	TQ8218	Cuckfield	TQ3024
Brede Valley	TQ8117	Cuilfail Cliff, Lewes	TQ4210
Brighton Racecourse	TQ3405	Dower House Farm, Blackboys	TQ5319
Broadbridge Heath	TQ1431	Dragon's Green	TQ1423
Bullock Hill, Woodingdean	TQ3606	Duncton	SU9517
Bulverhythe	TQ7708	East Blatchington	TQ4800
Burton Down	SU9613	East Brighton Golf Course	TQ3404
Burwash	TQ6724	East Chiltington	TQ3714
Bury	TQ0113	East Harting	SU7919
Buxted	TQ5023	East Preston	TQ0702
Camber	TQ9618	East Wittering	SZ8096
Camber Castle	TQ9218	Eastergate	SU9405
Carters Farm, Pett	TQ8814	Ecclesbourne Glen, Hastings	TQ8310
Catsfield	TQ7213	Edburton	TQ2311
Chalvington	TQ5209	Eridge Old Park	TQ5734
Charleston Bottom, Friston Forest	TQ5300	Fairwarp	TQ4626
Charleston Manor	TQ5200	Falmer	TQ3508
Chesson's Farm, Bewl Water	TQ6631	Faygate	TQ2134
Chichester Yacht Basin	SU8301	Filsham Farm, St Leonards	TQ7809
Chidmere Pond	SU7903	Finchdean	SU7312
Chilgrove	SU8314	Findon	TQ1208

568

Firle Beacon	TQ4806	Middleton-on-Sea	SU9700
Flansham	SU9501	Mile Oak, Portslade	TQ2407
Fontwell	SU9407	Mill Creek, Newhaven	TQ4500
Ford Aerodrome	SU9902	Milland	SU8427
Forest Mere	SU8130	Moorhead Farm, Horsham	TQ3032
Framfield	TQ4920	Mount Caburn	TQ4409
Friston	TV5598	Newick Park	TQ4219
Furnace Green, Crawley	TQ2835	Neylands Farm, Weir Wood Reservoir	TQ3834
Galley Hill, Bexhill	TQ7507	Northchapel	SU9529
Gallows Hill, Graffham	SU9319	Northease	TQ4106
Gillham's Moor, Liphook	SU8632	North Bersted	SU9201
Glynde Place	TQ4509	North Farm, Washington	TQ1210
Glynleigh	TQ6106	North Lancing	TQ1805
Goodwood Park	SU8808	North Marden	SU8016
Graffham Down	SU9116	Nyetimber	SZ8998
Great Park Wood, Udimore	TQ8518	Nyewood	SU8021
Great Sowdens Wood, Brede	TQ8519	Oakhurst Farm, Sidlesham	SZ8496
Great Wood, Battle	TQ7615	Old Tottingworth Farm, Broad Oak	TQ8219
Groombridge	TQ5236	Oreham Common	TQ2214
Ham Farm, Sidlesham	SZ8395	Orlton's Copse, Rusper	TQ2238
Hammer	SU8732	Paddockhurst Estate	TQ3233
Handcross	TQ2629	Parham Park	TQ0614
Hangleton	TQ2606	Patcham Place	TQ3008
Hardham	TQ0317	Peacehaven	TQ4101
Hartfield	TQ4836	Peasmarsh	TQ8822
Heathfield	TQ5821	Pett	TQ8713
Heathfield Park	TQ5920	Pevensey	TQ6404
Henfield	TQ2116	Pevensey Bay	TQ6504
Herstmonceux	TQ6312	Plaistow	TQ0030
High and Over, Seaford	TQ5101	Playden, Rye	TQ9121
High Hurstwood	TQ4924	Plumpton Agricultural College	TQ3513
Higham	TQ8225	Plumpton Bostall	TQ3612
Hoads Wood, Fairlight	TQ8612	Plumpton Plain	TQ3612
Hollingbury Park	TQ3207	Polegate	TQ5704
Hollycombe	SU8529	Portobello, Telscombe Cliffs	TQ3901
Holywell, Eastbourne	TV6096	Portslade-by-Sea	TQ2504
Hove Cemetery	TQ2705	Pound Hill, Crawley	TQ2937
Hurston Warren	TQ0617	Preston, Brighton	TQ3006
Iden	TQ9123	Priesthawes	TQ6005
Itchenor	SU7901	Pyecombe Golf Course	TQ3012
Itchingfield	TQ1328	Rackham	TQ0513
Itford Hill	TQ4405	Ripe	TQ5010
Kingston	TQ3908	Rodmell Brooks	TQ4206
Kirdford	TQ0126	Rogate Common	SU7912
Lancing Shooting Range	TQ1906	Rotherfield	TQ5529
Langney Fort	TQ6401	Runcton Lake, Chichester	SU8703
Laughton	TQ5013	Rushlake Green	TQ6218
Leasam Wood	TQ9021	Rustington	TQ0401
Little Common, Bexhill	TQ7108	Sailor's Copse Poling	TQ0406
Littleham Farm, Sidlesham	SZ8495	Sandy Point, Chichester Harbour	SZ7498
Lock Farm, Iden	TQ9123	Seaford Bay	TV4699
Lodsworth	SU9223	Sedgwick Park	TQ1826
Long Down, Beachy Head	TV5796	Sedlescombe	TQ7718
Long Furlong, Patching	TQ0907	Selmeston	TQ5006
Lower Beeding	TQ2227	Selsey Sewage Farm	SZ8494
Loxwood	TQ0331	Selsfield Common	TQ3434
Madehurst	SU9810	Shipley	TQ1421
Mallydams Wood	TQ8512	Shoreham Fort	TQ2304
Malthouse Farm, Wisborough Green	TQ0324	Shortbridge	TQ4521
Manhood End	SU8301	Shripney, nr Bognor Regis	SU9302
Maresfield	TQ4723	Sidlesham Quay, Pagham Harbour	SZ8697
Maresfield Park	TQ4624	Sidlesham Sewage Farm	SZ8496
Marker Point, Thorney	SU7402	Singleton Plantation	SU8712
Mayfield	TQ5926	Slaugham	TQ2528
Merston, Chichester	SU8903	Slindon Park	SU9508

South Harting	SU7819	Warnham Court Park	TQ1633
South Malling	TQ4111	Warningcamp	TQ0307
South Mundham	SZ8799	Washington	TQ1212
Southwick	TQ2405	Washington refuse tip	TQ1313
St John's Park, Burgess Hill	TQ3019	Went Hill, Birling Gap	TV5596
Standean Farm	TQ3111	Wepham Farm	TQ0408
Stedham	SU8622	West Blatchington	TQ2806
Steyning Bowl	TQ1609	West Broyle, Chichester	SU8406
Steyning Mill Pond	TQ1711	West Firle	TQ4707
Stopham	TQ0218	West Hoathly	TQ3632
Stoughton Down	SU8212	West Hove	TQ2605
Streat	TQ3515	West Kingston	TQ0702
Swanborough Hill	TQ3806	Westdean, Friston Forest	TV5299
Swanborough Sewage Farm	TQ4008	Westfield	TQ8115
Telscombe	TQ4003	Westham	TQ6304
Telscombe Cliffs	TQ4001	Westhampnett	SU8806
Tenant Hill	TQ2309	Westmeston, nr Ditchling	TQ3313
Tenants Hill, nr Worthing	TQ1407	Wet Level	TQ8726
Tern Island Pagham Harbour	SZ8795	Wicks, The	TR0118
Thakeham	TQ1017	Wiggonholt Brooks	TQ0516
Three Bridges	TQ2837	Winner Bank, Chichester Harbour	SZ7698
Turners Hill	TQ3435	Wisborough Green	TQ0524
Udimore	TQ8618	Wish Park, West Hove	TQ2704
Upwaltham Down	SU9513	Wiston	TQ1415
Vine's Cross	TQ5917	Wittersham Level	TQ9025
Waldron	TQ5419	Woodman's Green	TQ7619
Waltham Brooks	TQ0215	Woodmansgreen, Linchmere	SU8627
Wannock	TQ5703	Wyckham Wood	TQ1914
Warminghurst, Washington	TQ1116		

Bibliography

compiled by Barrie Watson

Adams, M C 1966. Firecrests breeding in Hampshire. *Brit. Birds* 59: 240-246.

Alder, L P 1950. Roller in Sussex. *Brit. Birds* 43: 301.

Alder, L P, Harber, D D and James, C M 1952. Balearic Shearwater off Sussex and Norfolk. *Brit. Birds* 45: 72.

Alder, L P and James, C M 1950. Bonaparte's Gull in Sussex. *Brit. Birds* 43: 134-5.

Alder, L P and James, C M 1952. Marsh Sandpiper in Sussex. *Brit. Birds* 45: 224.

Appleyard, I 1994. *Ring Ousels of the Yorkshire Dales*. Manley, Leeds.

Arnold, E C 1908. Aquatic Warbler in Sussex. *Brit. Birds* 2: 236.

Arnold, E C 1936. *Birds of Eastbourne*. Strange. Eastbourne.

Arnold, E C 1940. *Bird Reserves*. Witherby. London.

Arnold, E C 1945. Dipper in Sussex. *Brit. Birds* 38: 194.

Ash, J S 1970. Observations on a decreasing population of Red-backed Shrikes. *Brit. Birds* 63: 185-205, 225-239.

Aspinall, S J and Tasker, M L 1992. *Birds of the Solent*. Joint Nature Conservation Committee. Aberdeen.

Aspinall, S J, Taverner, J H and Wiseman, E J 1993. History of Black-headed Gull colonies in Hampshire and neighbouring counties. *British Birds* 86: 103-113.

Axell, H E 1966. Eruptions of Bearded Tits during 1959-65. *Brit. Birds* 59: 513-543.

Baatsen, R G 1990. Red-crested Pochard in Cotswold Water Park. *Hobby* 1990: 64-67.

Baillie, S, Gooch, S and Birkhead, T 1993. The effects of magpie predation on songbird populations. In *Britain's Birds in 1990-91: the conservation and monitoring review*. BTO and JNCC. eds Andrews, J and Carter SP. pp68-73.

Baines, R 1988. Black-eared Wheatear in Sussex. *Birding World* 1: 167.

Bale, J 1989. Penduline Tit at Pett Pools, October 1987 - new to Sussex. *Sussex Bird Report* 41: 88.

Barth, E K 1975. Taxonomy of *Larus argentatus* and *Larus fuscus* in north western Europe. *Ornis. Scand.* 6: 49-63.

Barthel, P 1991. Status of Ruddy Shelduck in Germany. *Birding World* 4: 175-176.

Batten, L A, Bibby, C J, Clement, P, Elliott, G D and Porter, R F 1990. *Red Data Birds in Britain*. Poyser. London.

Bealey, C E and Sutherland, M P 1983. Woodland Birds of the West Sussex Weald. *Sussex Bird Report* 35: 69-73.

Betts, A H 1952. Terek Sandpiper in Sussex. *Brit. Birds* 45: 36.

Bibby, C J 1973. The Red-backed Shrike: a vanishing British species. *Bird Study* 20: 103-110.

Bibby, C J 1981. Wintering Bitterns in Britain. *Brit. Birds* 74: 1-10.

Bibby, C J 1982. Polygyny and the breeding ecology of the Cetti's Warbler *Cettia cetti. Ibis* 124: 288-301.

Bibby, C J, Burgess, N D and Hill, D A 1992. *Bird Census Techniques.* Academic Press. London.

Biodiversity: The UK Steering Group Report (1995). *Volume 2: Action Plans.* HMSO. London.

Blake, E A, Blake, F W and Cawkell, H A R 1949. Bonaparte's Sandpiper in Sussex. *Brit. Birds* 42: 332-3.

Blurton Jones, N G 1956. Census of breeding Canada Geese 1953. *Bird Study* 3: 153-170.

Bonham, P F 1977. Those Hastings rarities again ... *Sussex Ornithological Society Newsletter* 61: 5.

Borrer, W 1891. The Birds of Sussex. Porter. London

BOURC 1978. Ninth Report of British Ornithologists Union Records Committee (April 1978). *Ibis* 120: 409-411.

BOURC 1980. Tenth Report of British Ornithologists Union Records Committee (March 1980). *Ibis* 122: 564-568.

BOURC 1992. Sixteenth Report of the British Ornithologists Union Records Committee. *Ibis* 134: 211-214.

BOURC 1993a. Eighteenth Report of British Ornithologists Union Records Committee (December 1992). *Ibis* 135: 220-222.

BOURC 1993b. Nineteenth Report of British Ornithologists Union Records Committee (May 1993). *Ibis* 135: 493-499.

BOURC 1994. Twentieth report of British Ornithologists Union Records Committee (December 1993). *Ibis* 136: 253-255.

Bourne, W R P 1967. Long-distance vagrancy in the Petrels. *Ibis* 109: 141-167.

Bourne, W R P 1988. The Status of Little, Audubon's and 'Levantine' Shearwater in Britain and Ireland. *Brit. Birds* 81: 401-402.

Bowley, A L 1994. The Birds of Lullington Heath National Nature Reserve (1964-88). *Sussex Bird Report* 46: 112-119.

Branson, N J B A and Minton, C D T 1976. Moult, Measurements and Migrations of the Grey Plover. *Bird Study* 23: 257-266.

Brenchley, A 1984. The use of birds as indicators of change in agriculture. In *Agriculture and the Environment.* ITE symp. 13: 1323-128. Ed. Jenkins. ITE/NERC. Cambridge.

Brown, L 1976. *British Birds of Prey.* Collins. London.

Brown, A F and Grice, P V 1993. Birds in England: Context and Priorities. *English Nature Research Reports* 62. English Nature.

Calvert, G W, Fitter, R S R and Hale, R W 1944. Black Redstarts breeding in Middlesex since 1925. *Brit. Birds* 37: 189-190.

Campbell, B and Lack, E 1985. *A Dictionary of Birds.* Poyser. Calton.

Carter, M J, Mead, C J and Sheldon, A B 1963. Stilt Sandpiper in Sussex. *Brit. Birds* 56: 64-66.

Cawkell, E M 1935. The Heronries of Sussex. *The Sussex County Magazine* 9: 483-486 569-572 639-642.

Cawkell, E M 1937. The Heronries of Sussex. *The Sussex County Magazine* 11: 594.

Cawkell, E M 1938. The Heronries of Sussex. *The Sussex County Magazine* 12: 818.

Cawkell, E M 1947. Ferruginous Duck in Sussex. *Brit. Birds* 40: 219.

Cawkell, E M 1948. The Heronries of Sussex. *The Sussex County Magazine* 22: 130-133.

Cawkell, E M 1982. Some Reminiscences of John Walpole-Bond. *Sussex Ornithological Society Newsletter* 82.

Cawkell, H A R 1968. A Brief History of Sussex Bird Historians from Markwick to Walpole-Bond. *Sussex Ornithological Society Newsletter* 25.

Cawkell, H A R 1969. Bristow and the Hastings Rarities Affair. *Sussex Ornithological Society Newsletter* 29.

Chandler, R and Wilds, C 1994. Little, Least and Saunders's Terns. *Brit. Birds* 87: 60-66.

Charlwood, R H 1964. A second Slender-billed Gull in Sussex. *Brit. Birds* 57: 81-82.

Clark, J M 1984. *Birds of the Hants/Surrey Border*. Hobby Books. Fleet.

Clark, J M and Eyre, J A (ed.) 1993. *Birds of Hampshire*. Hampshire Ornithological Society.

Clement, P, Harris, A and Davis, J 1993. *Finches and Sparrows: An Identification Guide*. Helm. London.

Cohen, E 1963. *Birds of Hampshire and the Isle of Wight*. Oliver and Boyd. Edinburgh.

Combridge, P and Parr, C 1992. Influx of Little Egrets in Britain and Ireland in 1989. *Brit. Birds* 85: 16-21.

Coombes, R A H 1970. The Hastings Rarities. *Brit. Birds* 63: 89-90.

Cooper, J E S 1985. Spring migration of Siskin in north Sussex during 1984. *Ringing & Migration* 6: 61-65.

Cooper, J E S 1987. The timing of Siskin migration through north Sussex, spring 1986. *Sussex Bird Report* 39: 88-91.

Cooper, J F 1975. Bird Population Trends as shown by Ringing. *Sussex Bird Report* 27: 57-64

Cooper, J F 1976a. An analysis of the spring sea-watches at Beachy Head, Sussex. *Sussex Bird Report* 28: 56-66.

Cooper, J F 1976b. That was the Sardinian that was. *Sussex Ornithological Society Newsletter* 59: 5.

Cooper, R H W 1988. Migration strategies of shorebirds during the non-breeding season with particular reference to Sanderling (*Calidris alba*). Unpublished PhD thesis, University of Durham.

Corrigan, C J 1993. The breeding waders of the Arun valley (1991). *Sussex Bird Report* 45: 90-96.

Cramp, S (Ed) 1977-94, *The Handbook of the Birds of Europe, The Middle East and North Africa: The Birds of the Western Palearctic*. Vols. 1-9. Oxford University Press. Oxford

Cramp, S, Bourne, W R P and Saunders, D 1974. *The Seabirds of Britain and Ireland*. Collins. London.

Cranswick, P A, Kirby, J S and Waters, R J 1992. *Wildfowl and Wader Counts 1991/92*. Wildfowl and Wetlands Trust. Slimbridge.

Cranswick, P A, Waters, R J, Evans, J and Pollitt, M S 1995. *The Wetland Bird Survey 1993-94: Wildfowl and Wader Counts*. BTO/WWT/RSPB/JNCC.

Crawley, D 1992. Ringing in Sussex in 1991. *Sussex Bird Report* 44: 76-80.

Crowe, G 1934. Woodchat seen in Sussex. *Brit. Birds* 28: 50.

Curson, J, Quinn, D and Beadle, D 1994. *New World Warblers*. Helm. London.

Dallas, J E S 1922. Probable Woodchat Shrike seen in Sussex. *Brit. Birds* 16: 48-49.

Darke, T O 1971. *The Cornish Chough*. Truro.

Davenport, D L 1989. Seabird movements in Kent: Autumn 1987. *Kent Bird Report* 36: 93-97.

Davis, P 1967. Migration seasons of the Sylvia warblers at British Bird Observatories. *Bird Study* 14: 65-95.

Davis, P G 1982. Nightingales in Britain in 1980 *Bird Study* 29: 73-79.

Dawson, I and Allsop, K 1994. The ornithological year 1993. *Brit. Birds* 87: 453-467.

Dawson, M J 1952. Squacco Heron in Sussex. *Brit. Birds* 45: 293.

Day, J C U 1981. Status of Bitterns in Europe since 1976. *Brit. Birds* 74: 10-16.

de Potier, A and Yates, B J 1994. Gulls roosting in Winter in Sussex in 1993. *Sussex Bird Report* 46: 123-125.

Dean, A R 1984. Origin and distribution of British Glaucous Gulls. *Brit. Birds* 77: 165-166.

Dean, A R 1985. Review of the British status and identification of Greenish Warbler. *Brit. Birds* 78: 437-451.

Delany, S 1990. *National Mute Swan Survey 1990 - Preliminary report to the Nature Conservancy Council*. Wildfowl and Wetlands Trust, Slimbridge.

Delaney, S 1993. Introduced and escaped geese in Britain in summer 1991. *Brit. Birds* 86: 591-599.

des Forges, G 1968. An old record of Laughing Gull in Sussex. *Brit. Birds* 61: 213-214.

des Forges, G 1982. A note on the breeding distribution of Woodcock in Sussex. *Sussex Bird Report* 34: 82-83.

des Forges, G (ed) 1987. *Birds in Sussex 1962-1987*. Sussex Ornithological Society.

des Forges, G and Harber, D D 1963. *A Guide to the Birds of Sussex*. Oliver and Boyd. Edinburgh.

des Forges, G and Paulson, C W G 1952. Marsh Sandpiper in Sussex. *Brit. Birds* 45: 223-224.

Devillers, P 1983. Yellow-legged Herring Gulls on southern North Sea Shores. *Brit. Birds*. 76: 191-192.

Donald, P 1994. Corn Buntings - old theories and new. *BTO News* 192: 6-7.

Donovan, J W 1958. Pratincole or Black-winged Pratincole in Sussex. *Brit. Birds* 51: 120.

Dougharty, F W and Hughes, S W M 1990. The Lesser Spotted Woodpecker in Sussex, 1964-1988. *Sussex Bird Report* 42: 76-86.

Douglas, C E 1951. Red-breasted Snipe in Sussex. *Brit. Birds* 44: 315-316.

Dubois, P J 1994. European News. *Brit. Birds* 87: 311-325.

Dymond, J N and the Rarities Committee. 1976. Report on rare birds in Great Britain in 1975. *Brit. Birds* 69: 321-368.

Dymond, J N, Fraser, P and Gantlett, S J M 1989. *Rare Birds in Britain and Ireland*. Poyser.

Edgar, R D M 1986. Some results of the study by ringing of Warbler migration at Beachy Head for 1960-1985. *Sussex Bird Report* 38: 76-84.

Edgar, R D M 1987. A survey of breeding Sand Martins in Sussex, 1985-1986. *Sussex Bird Report* 39: 62-65.

Edgar, R D M 1979. Bird Habitats in Sussex, in Shrubb, M 1979. *The Birds of Sussex, their present status*. Phillimore. Chichester.

Edwards, T J 1989. American Golden Plover at Church Norton, September 1988 - new to Sussex. *Sussex Bird Report* 41: 89.

Edwards, M and Hodge, P J 1993. *An entomological survey of the remaining heathlands of West Sussex. Technical Report for the West Sussex Heathland Forum*. West Sussex County Council.

Ellwood, J, Harrison J G, Mouland, H and Ruxton, J 1971. Greylag Geese in south-east England. *WAGBI Annual Report* 1970-71: 61-62.

Evans, A D 1988. *Individual differences in foraging behaviour, habitat selection and bill morphology of wintering Curlew Numenius arquata*. University of Edinburgh. Edinburgh.

Evans, A D 1992. The numbers and distribution of Cirl Buntings *Emberizia cirlus* breeding in Britain in 1989. *Bird Study* 39: 17-22.

Evans, L G R 1993a. *Rare birds in Britain 1992*. Published privately.

Evans, L G R 1993b. The Isles of Scilly Blyth's Pipit. *Birding World* 6: 398-400.

Evans, L G R 1994a. Ivory Gulls in Britain and Ireland. *Birding World* 7: 10-14.

Evans, L G R 1994b. *Rare birds in Britain 1800-1990*. Published privately.

Evans, L G R 1995. *Rare birds in Britain 1993*. Published privately.

Everett, M J 1967. *Scottish Birds* 4: 534-548.

Everett, M J and Prytherch, R 1993. News and comment. *Brit.Birds* 86: 338.

Fairbank, R J 1987. Scarce migrants in Sussex 1961-1985, in des Forges G. (ed.) *Birds in Sussex 1962-1987*. Sussex Ornithological Society.

Fairbank, R J 1991a. The Sussex List. *Sussex Bird Report* 43: 48 and i-iv.

Fairbank, R J 1991b. Great Spotted Cuckoo at Shoreham Airfield, April-May 1990. *Sussex Bird Report* 43: 89-91.

Fairbank, R J 1992. The Sussex List with Euring species codes. *Sussex Bird Report* 44: i-iv.

Fairbank, R J 1994. Black-headed Bunting identification. *Birding World* 7: 319.

Fairbank, R J 1995. The Sussex List, Recent Additions and Hypothetical Species. *Sussex Ornithological Society Newsletter* 134: 6.

Feare, C J 1984. *The Starling*. Oxford University Press. Oxford.

Ferguson-Lees, I J 1948a. Nutcracker in Sussex. *Brit. Birds* 41: 149.

Ferguson-Lees, I J 1948b. American Pectoral Sandpipers in Sussex. *Brit. Birds* 41: 186-7.

Ferguson-Lees, I J 1949. Red-breasted Flycatcher in Sussex. *Brit. Birds* 42: 182.

Ferguson-Lees, I J 1958. The identification of the White-headed and Ruddy Ducks. *Brit. Birds* 51: 239-240.

Ferguson-Lees, I J and Smith, J A 1948. Yellowshank in Sussex. *Brit. Birds* 41: 156.

Ferns, P N 1980. The spring migration of Sanderling (*Calidris alba*) through Britain in 1979. *Wader Study Group Bulletin* 30: 22-25.

Fisher, J 1952. *The Fulmar*. Collins. London.

Flint, V E, Boehme, R L and Kostin, Y V 1984. *A Field Guide to Birds of the USSR*. Princetown University Press.

Fluke, W G 1953. Baird's Sandpiper in Sussex. *Brit. Birds* 46: 304-305.

Forshaw, J M 1980. *Parrots of the World*. Lansdown. Melbourne.

Fraser, P A and Ryan, J F 1992. Scarce Migrants in Britain and Ireland. *Brit. Birds* 85: 631-635.

Fraser, P A and Ryan, J F 1994. Scarce migrants in Britain and Ireland (part 2). *Brit. Birds* 87: 605-615.

Fry, C H, Fry, K and Harris, A 1992. *Kingfishers, Bee-eaters and Rollers: A Handbook*. Helm. London.

Fuller, R J 1982. *Bird Habitats in Britain*. Poyser. Calton.

Galbraith, H 1988. Effects of agriculture on the breeding ecology of lapwings (*Vanellus vanellus*). *J. appl. Ecol.* 25: 487-503.

Game Conservancy Trust 1995. *The Game Conservancy Review of 1994 issue no. 26*. The Game Conservancy Trust. Fordingbridge.

Gantlett, S J M 1993. The status and separation of White-headed Duck and Ruddy Duck. *Birding World* 6: 273-281.

Gantlett, S J M and Millington, R 1993. The Oriental Pratincole in Norfolk. *Birding World* 6: 192-193.

Gibbons, D W, Reid, J B and Chapman, R A 1993. *The New Atlas of Breeding Birds in Britain and Ireland: 1988-91*. Poyser. London.

Gibbons, D W and Wotton, S 1995. The 1994 Dartford Warbler (*Sylvia undata*) survey. A Report to English Nature. RSPB.

Glue, D 1982. *The Garden Bird Book*. Macmillan. London.

Goss-Custard, J D and Moser, M E 1988. Rates of change in the numbers of Dunlin wintering in British Estuaries in relation to the spread of *Spartina anglica*. *Journal of Applied Ecology* 25.

Grant, P J 1983. Yellow-legged Herring Gulls in Britain. *Brit. Birds*. 76: 192-194.

Grant, P J 1986. *Gulls: a guide to identification*. Second Edition. Poyser. Calton.

Green, R E 1985. Estimating the abundance of breeding Snipe. *Bird Study* 32: 141-149.

Griffith, A F 1911. Sooty Tern in Sussex. *Brit. Birds* 5: 81.

HMSO 1992. *Office of Population Censuses and Surveys (1992) County Report: East Sussex (Part 1)*. HMSO.

HMSO 1993. *Office of Population Censuses and Surveys (1993) County Report: West Sussex (Part 1)*. HMSO.

Halls, J M 1993. The 1991-1992 Nightjar survey in Sussex. *Sussex Bird Report* 45: 88-89.

Harber, D D 1949. Cory's Shearwater off Sussex. *Brit. Birds* 42: 218-219.

Harber, D D 1950. Aquatic Warbler in Sussex. *Brit. Birds* 43: 58.

Harber, D D 1951a. Cory's Shearwater off Sussex. *Brit. Birds* 44: 284.

Harber, D D 1951b. Ortolan Bunting in Sussex. *Brit. Birds* 44: 310.

Harber, D D 1952a. Bonaparte's Gull in Sussex. *Brit. Birds* 45: 333.

Harber, D D 1952b. Gull-billed Terns in Sussex. *Brit. Birds* 45: 371-372.

Harber, D D 1953. Balearic Shearwaters off Sussex. *Brit. Birds* 46: 64.

Harber, D D 1955a. Special Review: The Birds of the Soviet Union. *Brit. Birds* 48: 218-224, 268-276, 313-319, 343-348, 404-410, 447-453, 505-511.

Harber, D D 1955b. Ivory Gull in Sussex. *Brit. Birds* 48: 546.

Harber, D D 1962. Slender-billed Gull in Sussex: a bird new to Britain. *Brit. Birds* 55: 169-171.

Harber, D D 1963. Baltimore Oriole in Sussex. *Brit. Birds* 56: 64-65.

Harber, D D 1964. Cetti's Warbler in Sussex. *Brit. Birds* 57: 366.

Harber, D D and the Rarities Committee. 1966. Report on rare birds in Great Britain in 1965. *Brit. Birds* 59: 280-305.

Harber, D D and Swaine, C M 1963. Report on rare birds in Great Britain in 1962. *Brit. Birds* 56: 393-409.

Harris, A, Tucker, L and Vinicombe, K E 1989. *The Macmillan Field Guide to Bird Identification*. Macmillan. London.

Harrison, C 1982. *An Atlas of the Birds of the Western Palearctic*. Collins. London.

Harrison, J M 1934. Buff-breasted Sandpiper in Sussex. *Brit. Birds* 28: 148.

Harrison, J M 1936. Audubon's Little Shearwater in Sussex. A new British Bird. *Brit. Birds* 30: 48-49.

Harrison, J M 1973. *A Wealth of Wildfowl* (second edition). Corgi. London.

Harrop, A 1991. The status of Red-crested Pochard. *Birding World* 4: 171-175.

Hayman, P, Marchant, J H and Prater, A J 1986. *Shorebirds: an identification guide to the waders of the world*. Croom Helm. London.

Higson, P and Urquhart, E D 1990. Crag Martins in Cornwall and East Sussex: new to Britain and Ireland. *Brit. Birds* 83: 155-159.

Hirons, G 1981. Sex and discrimination in the Woodcock. *Game Conservancy Annual Report* 1980. The Game Conservancy Trust. Fordingbridge.

Hitchings, S P 1988. The ornithological status of Pevensey Levels. *Sussex Bird Report* 40: 71-80.

Hollyer, J N 1970. The invasion of Nutcrackers in autumn 1968. *Brit. Birds* 63: 353-373.

Hoodless, A 1995. Studies of West Palearctic birds: 195. Eurasian Woodcock *Scolopax rusticola*. *Brit. Birds* 88: 578-592.

Horsfield 1824. *History of Lewes*. Lewes.

Hosking, E 1970. *An Eye for a Bird*. Hutchinson.

Houghton, J W 1979. The breeding season status of the Redpoll in Sussex. *Sussex Bird Report* 31: 68-74.

Houghton, J W 1980. Further Nightjar monitoring. *Sussex Bird Report* 32: 76-77.

Houghton, J W 1982. A further report on the breeding distribution and status of the Nightjar in Sussex. *Sussex Bird Report* 34: 75-78.

Houghton, J W 1983. The breeding distribution of the Redstart in Sussex. *Sussex Bird Report* 35: 64-68.

Howard, R and Moore, A 1984. *A Complete Checklist of the Birds of the World.* Academic Press. London.

Howey, D H and Bell, M 1985. Pallas's Warblers and other migrants in Britain and Ireland in October 1982. *Brit. Birds* 78: 381-392.

Hudson, A V, Stowe T J and Aspinall S J 1990. Status of Corncrakes in Britain 1988. *Brit. Birds* 83: 173-187.

Hudson, R 1973. *Early and late dates for summer migrants. BTO Guide 15.* BTO. Tring.

Hudson, R 1974. Feral parakeets near London. *Brit. Birds* 67: 33, 174.

Hudson, W H 1900. *Nature in Downland.* Longman Green & Co. London.

Hughes, S W M 1970. The decline of the Woodlark as a Sussex breeding species. *Sussex Bird Report* 22: 65-68.

Hughes, S W M 1971. Surveying a breeding population of Swifts. *Sussex Bird Report* 23: 61-69.

Hughes, S W M 1972. The breeding distribution and status of the Tree Pipit in Sussex. *Sussex Bird Report* 24: 68-79.

Hughes, S W M 1973. The Canada Goose in Sussex. *Sussex Bird Report* 25: 51-66.

Hughes, S W M 1975. Cormorants roosting on spire. *Brit. Birds* 68: 429

Hughes, S W M 1976. The Woodcock in Sussex: A review of recent records. *Sussex Bird Report* 28: 66-79.

Hughes, S W M 1980. Winter Blackcaps in Sussex - a review of recent records. *Sussex Bird Report* 32: 77-84.

Hughes, S W M 1982. Inland observations on Cormorants in Sussex. *Sussex Bird Report* 35: 74-80.

Hughes, S W M 1987a. Changes in the breeding status and habitat of the Great Crested Grebe in Sussex. *Sussex Bird Report* 39: 69-80.

Hughes, S W M 1987b. Feral Greylag Geese in Sussex. *Sussex Bird Report* 39: 91-96.

Hughes, S W M 1989. The Little Grebe in Sussex. Part I Breeding distribution and status 1966-1986. *Sussex Bird Report* 41: 78-87.

Hughes, S W M 1991a. The Little Grebe in Sussex. Part II Non-breeding distribution and status 1966-1989. *Sussex Bird Report* 43: 78-88.

Hughes, S W M 1991b. The 1990 Mute Swan census in Sussex. *Sussex Bird Report* 43: 91-96.

Hughes, S W M 1992. The changed distribution and status of Bewick's Swan in Sussex. *Sussex Bird Report* 44: 83- 92.

Hughes, S W M and Codd, D 1980. Feral Mandarins in Sussex. *Sussex Bird Report* 32: 72-76.

Hughes, S W M and Codd, D 1982. A further assessment of the status of the Mandarin in Sussex. *Sussex Bird Report* 34: 84.

Hughes, S W M and Dougharty, F W 1975. The recolonisation of Sussex by the Tree Sparrow. *Sussex Bird Report* 27: 67-69.

Hughes, S W M and Dougharty, F W 1979. A repeat census of the Kestrel in North West Sussex. *Sussex Bird Report* 31: 78-80.

Hughes, S W M and Griffiths, A J 1983. The Birds of Iping Common. *Sussex Bird Report* 35: 88-94.

Hughes, S W M, Houghton, J W and Blake, F W 1978. The breeding distribution of the Nightjar in East and West Sussex. *Sussex Bird Report* 30: 66-72.

Hughes, S W M and Shrubb, M 1974. The breeding distribution and status of the Stonechat in Sussex 1962-1973. *Susssex Bird Report* 26: 50-55.

Hughes, S W M and Watson, A B 1984. Censuses of the Mute Swan in Sussex in 1978 and 1983. *Sussex Bird Report* 36: 69-73.

Hughes, S W M and Watson, A B 1986. The distribution, status and movements of Sussex Canada Geese. *Sussex Bird Report* 38: 85-94.

Hume, R A 1993. Common, Arctic and Roseate Terns: an identification review. *Brit. Birds* 86: 210-217.

Hume, R A and Christie, D A 1989. Sabine's Gulls and other seabirds after the October 1987 storm. *Brit. Birds* 82: 191-208.

Hutchinson, C D 1989. *Birds in Ireland*. Poyser.

James, B and James, C M 1955. Alpine Accentor in Sussex. *Brit. Birds* 48: 373-374.

James, P 1981. Nesting of the Kittiwake in Sussex. *Sussex Bird Report* 33: 78-80.

James, P 1986. Trumpeter Finch in West Sussex. *Brit. Birds* 79: 299-300.

James, P 1987. Changes in the status of some breeding birds in Sussex over the past 25 years, in des Forges, G (ed) *1987. Birds in Sussex 1962-1987*: 9-13.

Janman, C R and Mitchell, O 1979-93. *Selsey Bill, West Susex: Bird Reports. 1979-1982*. West Sussex County Council. Chichester.

John, A W G and Roskell, J 1985. Jay movements in autumn 1983. *Brit. Birds* 78: 611-637.

Joy, N H 1939. Great Shearwater in Kent. *Brit. Birds* 32: 276-277.

Joy, N H 1949. Bee-eater in Sussex. *Brit. Birds* 42: 390.

Kelsall, J E and Munn, P W 1905. *The Birds of Hampshire and the Isle of Wight*. Witherby. London.

Kimmins, D E 1955. Bee-Eaters in Sussex, 1955; a first British breeding record. *Countryside* Winter 1955: 315-318.

King, B 1976. Association between male North American Ruddy Ducks and stray ducklings. *Brit. Birds* 69: 34.

Kirby, J S, Ferns J R, Waters R J and Prys-Jones, R P 1991. *Wildfowl and Wader Counts 1990-91*. Wildfowl and Wetlands Trust. Slimbridge.

Kitson, A, Marr, B A E and Porter, R 1980. Greater Sand Plover: new to Britain and Ireland. *Brit. Birds* 73: 568-573.

Knight, R and Cox, A 1996. A brief study of some West Sussex Cormorant roosts. *Sussex Bird Report* 47: 115-122.

Knox, A 1988. Taxonomy of the Rock/Water Pipit superspecies *Anthus petrosus, spinoletta and rubescens. Brit. Birds* 81: 206-211.

Knox, A E 1845. *Ornithological Rambles in Sussex*. London.

Lack, P 1986. *The Atlas of Wintering Birds in Britain and Ireland*. Poyser. Calton.

Lack, P 1992. Birds on Lowland Farms. HMSO. London.

Langton, H 1909. American Bittern in Sussex. *Brit. Birds* 3: 229.

Langton, H 1910. Short-toed Lark in Sussex. *Brit. Birds* 3: 63.

Leverton, R 1986. Passage of wintering thrushes at a downland site. *Sussex Bird Report* 38: 67-75.

Leverton, R 1987. Ringing in Sussex, 1962-1987, in des Forges, G 1987 (ed.) *Birds in Sussex 1962-1987*. Sussex Ornithological Society.

Leverton, R 1988. Ringing in Sussex in 1987. *Sussex Bird Report* 40: 67-70.

Leverton, R 1989. Movements of Starlings to and from Sussex as shown by ringing. *Sussex Bird Report* 41: 90-96.

Leverton, R 1990. Passage Ring Ousels in Sussex, 1992-1998. *Sussex Bird Report* 42: 87-92.

Leverton, R 1993. Migrant Ring Ousels at a stopover site on the South Downs. *Brit. Birds* 86: 253-266.

Leverton, R 1994. Downland, Scrub and Birds. *Sussex Bird Report* 46: 103-111.

Leverton, R and Haskell, C 1985. Wintering Long Eared Owls at a downland site. *Sussex Bird Report* 37: 81-83.

Lloyd, C, Tasker, M L and Partridge, K C 1991. *The Status of Seabirds in Britain and Ireland*. Poyser. London.

Locke, G M L 1987. *Census of woodlands and trees - 1979-82*. Forestry Commission Bulletin 63. HMSO. London.

Lord, R M and Janman, C R 1984. Wintering Hen Harriers on the Selsey Peninsula. *Sussex Bird Report* 36: 83-92.

MAFF, 1993. *Strategy for Flood and Coastal Defence in England and Wales*. Ministry of Agriculture, Fisheries and Food and the Welsh Office. HMSO. London.

MAFF, 1994. *The Habitat Scheme: Former Set-aside Land*. Information pack. Ministry of Agriculture, Fisheries and Food. HMSO. London.

Madge, S and Burn, H 1988. *Wildfowl: an identification guide to the ducks, geese and swans of the world*. Helm. London.

Manns, L 1996. The Corn Bunting Survey 1993-94. *Sussex Bird Report* 47: 133-137.

Marchant, J H and Gregory, R 1993 Seed-eater declines: new results from farmland CBC. *BTO News* 189: 8-9.

Marchant, J H, Hudson, R, Carter, S P and Whittington, P 1990. *Population trends in British Breeding Birds*. British Trust for Ornithology, Tring.

Markwick, W 1795. *Aves Sussexiensis* or *A catalogue of Birds found in the County of Sussex*. Transactions of the Linnaean Society. London.

Marr, B A E, Phillips, W W A and Sheldon, A B 1963. Four Cattle Egrets in Sussex. *Brit. Birds* 56: 293-4.

Mead, C J, Boddy, S and Watson, A B 1964. Sand Martins at Chichester, 1963. *Sussex Bird Report* 16: 52-55.

Mead, C J and Clark, J A 1993. Report on bird ringing in Britain and Ireland for 1991. *Ringing & Migration* 1993, 14: 1-72.

Mead, C J and Harrison, J D 1979. Overseas movements of British and Irish Sand Martins. *Bird Study* 26: 87-98.

Mead, C J and Harrison, J D 1979. Sand Martin movements within Great Britain and Ireland. *Bird Study* 26: 73-86.

Mead, C J and Hudson, R 1984. Report on bird-ringing for 1983. *Ringing and Migration* 5: 153-192.

Mead, C J and Wilson, J 1993. Up with the Larks in 1994. *BTO News* 188: 1.

Merritt, W 1978. The Rook in Sussex: The breeding population and its distribution in 1975. *Sussex Bird Report* 30: 56-65.

Merritt, W 1979. The Distribution and Population of the Nightingale in Sussex, 1974-77. *Sussex Bird Report* 31: 63-67.

Merritt, W, Greenhalf, R R and Bonham, P F 1970. A survey of the Grey Wagtail in Sussex. *Sussex Bird Report* 22: 68-79.

Metcalfe, B 1952. Short-toed Lark in Sussex. *Brit. Birds* 45: 28.

Mild, K 1995. The identification of some problem flycatchers. *Birding World* 8: 271-276.

Millais, J G 1905. Birds of Sussex. *Victoria History of the County of Sussex.* Constable. London.

Millais, J G 1907. Roller in Sussex. *Brit. Birds* 1: 189.

Millington, R 1990. Great Spotted Cuckoos in Spring 1990. *Birding World* 3: 140.

Mills, P R and Watson, A B 1958. Red-breasted Goose in Sussex. *Brit. Birds* 51:192-193.

Milne, B S 1974. Ecological succession and bird life at a newly created gravel pit. *Bird Study* 21: 263-278.

Milne, B S, Palmer, K H and Pilcher, E J 1955. Rufous Warbler on the Kent/Sussex border. *Brit. Birds* 48: 329-30.

Mitchell, O 1982. The Breeding Status and Distribution of Snipe, Redshank and Yellow Wagtail in Sussex. *Sussex Bird Report* 34: 65-71.

Mitchell, O 1991. *The Birds of Selsey Bill (West Sussex): a check list with notes.* West Sussex County Council. Chichester.

Moore, N W 1942. Baillon's Crake in Sussex. *Brit. Birds* 35: 230-231.

Moreau, R E 1951.The British status of the Quail and some problems of its biology. *Brit. Birds* 44: 257-276.

Moreau, R E 1972. *The Palaearctic-African Bird Migration Systems.* Academic Press. London.

Mortimore, R N 1983. The Geology of Sussex, in *Sussex Environment, Landscape and Society.* Sutton.

Mortlock, B M 1992. *Birds of Weir Wood Reservoir* 1954 -1989.

Mullens, W H and Ticehurst, N 1925. *Notes on Sussex Ornithology: being extracts from diaries (1845-1869) of Robert Nathaniel Dennis.* Witherby. London.

Newnham, J A 1981. The Population and Distribution of the Nightingale in Sussex during 1980. *Sussex Bird Report* 33: 89-91.

Newnham, J A 1984a. Some aspect of the sea bird movements observed from the Sussex coast during the spring 1983. *Sussex Bird Report* 36: 60-63.

Newnham, J A 1984b. Gulls roosting in winter in Sussex in 1983. *Sussex Bird Report* 36: 64-68

Newnham, J A 1985. Some aspects of the spring migration observed from the Sussex coast during 1984. *Sussex Bird Report* 37: 61-64.

Newnham, J A 1986a The Unsociable Rarity. *Sussex Ornithological Society Newsletter* 96: 2-3.

Newnham, J A 1986b. The origin and movements of Black-headed Gulls which have wintered in Sussex. *Sussex Bird Report* 1985: 59-65

Newnham, J A 1987. Movements of Fulmars, Gannets and auks observed from the Sussex coast, with particular reference to the spring of 1986. *Sussex Bird Report* 39: 81-87.

Newnham, J A (Ed) 1988. *The Birds of Shoreham and surrounding areas including Brighton, Steyning and Worthing.* Shoreham District Ornithological Society.

Newnham, J A and Watson, A B 1994. Wing measurements and movements of Common Gulls ringed in Sussex in relation to the addition of the subspecies *Larus canus heinei* to the British List. *Sussex Bird Report* 46: 120-122.

Newton, I 1972. *Finches.* Collins, London

Newton, I, Wyllie, I and Asher, A 1991. Mortality census in British Barn Owls (*Tyto alba*), with a discussion of aldrin - dieldrin poisoning. *Ibis* 133: 162-169.

Nichol, M J 1908. A Sussex Rufous Warbler. *Brit. Birds* 2: 201-202.

Nicholl, J B 1939. Wall-creeper seen in Sussex. *Brit. Birds* 32: 272-273.

Nicholson, E M and Ferguson-Lees, I J 1962. The Hastings Rarities. *Brit. Birds* 55: 299-384.

Nightingale, B and Allsopp, K 1993. Seasonal reports: autumn 1992. *Brit. Birds* 86: 323-337.

Nightingale, B and Allsopp, K 1994. Invasion of Red-footed Falcons in spring 1992. *Brit. Birds* 87: 223-231.

Nightingale, B and Allsopp, K 1995. The ornithological year 1994. *Brit. Birds* 88: 457-472.

Nisbet, I C T 1959. Bewick's Swans in the British Isles in the winters of 1954-55 and 1955-56. *Brit. Birds* 52: 393-416.

O'Connor, R J and Shrubb, M 1986. *Farming and Birds.* Cambridge University Press, Cambridge.

Ogilvie, M and the Rare Breeding Birds Panel 1994. Rare breeding birds in the United Kingdom in 1991. *Brit. Birds* 87: 336-393.

Ogilvie, M and the Rare Breeding Birds Panel 1995. Rare breeding birds in the United Kingdom in 1992. *Brit. Birds* 88: 67-93.

Olsson, V 1981. *Var Fagelvarld* 40: 447-454.

Osborne, P 1982. Some effects of Dutch Elm disease on nesting farmland birds. *Bird Study* 29: 2-16.

Owen, M, Atkinson-Willes, G L and Salmon, D G 1986. *Wildfowl in Great Britain.* 2nd Edition. Cambridge University Press. Cambridge.

Parkin, D T and Knox, A 1994. Occurrence patterns of rare passerines in Britain and Ireland; *Brit. Birds*; 87: 585-592.

Parmenter, T W 1982. The Grasshopper Warbler in Sussex: the results of a breeding survey during 1877-1980. *Sussex Bird Report* 34: 79-82.

Parmenter, T W 1992. Additional notes on the Pied Wheatear. *Sussex Bird Report* 44: 81-82.

Parrinder, E R 1949. First record of Little Ringed Plovers in Suffolk. *Brit. Birds* 42: 396.

Parslow, J L F 1973. *Breeding Birds of Britain and Ireland.* Poyser. Berkhampstead.

Payne, S and Pailthorpe, R (eds) 1989. *Barcley Wills' The Downland Shepherds*. Sutton. Gloucester.

Peakall, D B 1962. The past and present status of the Red-backed Shrike in Great Britain. *Bird Study* 9: 198-216.

Percival, S M 1990. Recent Trends in Barn and Tawny Owl populations in Britain. *BTO Research Report No. 57*. BTO Tring.

Percival, S M 1991. The BTO Tawny Owl survey of 1989 - the results. *BTO News* 177: 6-7.

Perkins, R 1992. Ruddy Shelducks in Britain. *Birding World* 5: 447.

Perrins, C M 1979. *British Tits*. Collins New Naturalist, London.

Piersma, T 1986. Breeding waders in Europe: a review of population size estimates and a bibliography of information sources. *Wader Study Group Bulletin* 48, Supplement.

Pilcher, R 1991. *A survey of breeding waders and wildfowl within the Arun Valley, West Sussex*. RSPB.

Porter, R F 1966. A Breeding Survey of the Sussex Cliffs in 1965. *Sussex Bird Report* 18: 56-57.

Porter, R F 1967. The Spread of the Collared Dove in Sussex. *Sussex Bird Report* 19: 63-68.

Porter, R F 1970. The Continued Spread of the Collared Dove in Sussex. *Sussex Bird Report* 22: 61-64.

Porter, R F 1978. The breeding status of the Black Redstart in Sussex. *Sussex Bird Report* 30: 65-72.

Porter, R F 1979. Roosting Gulls in Sussex in winter. *Sussex Bird Report* 31: 74-78.

Porter, R F 1981. Making a note of it. *Birds* Vol. 8 No. 7 (Autumn 1981): 48.

Potts, A S and Browne, J J 1983. The Climate of Sussex, in *Sussex Environment, Landscape and Society*. Sutton.

Potts, G R 1986. *The Partridge; Pesticides, Predation and Conservation*. Collins. London.

Prater, A J 1975. *Birds of Estuaries Enquiry 1974-75*. BTO/RSPB.

Prater, A J 1976. Breeding Population of the Ringed Plover in Britain. *Bird Study* 23: 155-161.

Prater, A J 1981. *Estuary Birds of Britain and Ireland*. Poyser, Calton.

Prater, A J 1982. The Birds of Brinsbury Estate, West Sussex. *Sussex Bird Report* 34: 60-64.

Prater, A J 1983a. Brent Goose feeding patterns for Chichester Harbour 1982/83. *Sussex Bird Report* 35: 87.

Prater, A J 1983b. Bird Communities and Farming Trends on the Downs and Weald at Plumpton. *Sussex Bird Report*. 35: 81-86.

Prater, A J 1985. Breeding Seabirds in Sussex. *Sussex Bird Report*. 37: 65-71.

Prater, A J 1986a. The decline to extinction of the Stone Curlew in Sussex. *Sussex Bird Report* 38: 65-66.

Prater, A J 1986b. The breeding distribution of Wood Warblers in Sussex. *Sussex Bird Report* 38: 95-96.

Prater, A J 1987. Coastal Wetlands and Waders in Sussex, in des Forges, G (ed) 1987. *Birds in Sussex 1962-1987* : 19-28.

Prater, A J 1988. The Breeding Population of Reed and Sedge Warblers in Sussex. *Sussex Bird Report* 40: 81-96.

Prater, A J 1989. Ringed Plover *Charadrius hiaticula* breeding population of the United Kingdom in 1984. *Bird Study* 36: 154-159.

Prestt, I 1965. An enquiry into the recent breeding status of some of the smaller birds of prey and crows in Britain. *Bird Study* 12: 196-221.

Pye, K and French, P W 1992. Targets for Coastal Habitat Recreation. *English Nature Science* 13. English Nature. Peterborough.

Quinn, A and Clement, P 1972. *The Beachy Head Bird Report 1960-1970.* Beachy Head Ringing Group.

RSPB, 1994. *Reedbed Habitat Action Plan.* Unpublished RSPB Report.

Rehfisch, M and Waters, R J 1995. Grey plovers continue to increase. *BTO News* 199: 1.

Rettke-Grover, R F and Hughes, S W M 1993. A survey of introduced geese in Sussex. *Sussex Bird Report* 45: 97-100.

Reynolds, R A W 1952. Great Reed Warbler in Sussex. *Brit. Birds* 45: 220-221.

Robertson, P A, Tapper, S C and Stoate, C 1989. *Estimating game densities in Britain from land use maps.* Game Conservancy Trust. Fordingbridge. Unpub. Report.

Robinson, D A and Williams, R G B 1983. Sussex coast, past and present, in *Sussex Environment, Landscape and Society.* Sutton.

Rogers, M J 1972. Franklin's Gull in Sussex. *Brit. Birds* 65: 81-82.

Rogers, M J and the Rarities Committee 1979. Report on rare birds in Great Britain in 1978. *Brit. Birds* 72: 503-549.

Rogers, M J and the Rarities Committee 1981. Report on rare birds in Great Britain in 1980. *Brit. Birds* 74: 453-495.

Rogers, M J and the Rarities Committee 1985. Report on rare birds in Great Britain in 1984. *Brit. Birds* 78: 529-589.

Rogers, M J and the Rarities Committee 1986. Report on rare birds in Great Britain in 1985. *Brit. Birds* 79: 526-588.

Rogers, M J and the Rarities Committee 1989. Report on rare birds in Great Britain in 1988. *Brit. Birds* 82: 505-563.

Rogers, M J and the Rarities Committee 1990. Report on rare birds in Great Britain in 1989. *Brit. Birds* 83: 439-496.

Rogers, M J and the Rarities Committee 1991. Report on rare birds in Great Britain in 1990. *Brit. Birds* 84: 449-505.

Rogers, M J and the Rarities Committee 1993. Report on rare birds in Great Britain in 1992. *Brit. Birds* 86: 447-540.

Rogers, M J and the Rarities Committee 1994. Report on rare birds in Great Britain in 1993. *Brit. Birds* 87: 503-571.

Rogers, M J and the Rarities Committee 1995. Report on rare birds in Great Britain in 1994. *Brit. Birds* 88: 493-558.

Rose, F 1992. *Report on the remaining heathlands of West Sussex 1991-92.* West Sussex County Council.

Round, P 1982. Inland feeding by Brent geese *Branta bernicula* in Sussex, England. *Biological Conservation* 23: 15-32.

Rumsey, S J R 1990. Sussex-ringed Penduline Tit recovered in Sweden. *Sussex Bird Report* 42: 73.

Rumsey, S J R 1991. Rye Bay Ringing Group, 1986-1990. *Sussex Bird Report* 43: 74-77.

Sadler, D 1988. Little Bittern in Sussex. *Birding World* 1: 120-122.

Sage, B L and Vernon, J D R 1978. The 1975 National Survey of Rookeries. *Bird Study* 25: 64-86.

Sage, B L and Whittington, P A 1985. The 1980 Sample Survey of Rookeries. *Bird Study* 32: 7-81.

Sandison, R J 1981. Barn Owls in Sussex - the last twelve years. *Sussex Bird Report* 33: 70-78.

Scott, R E 1968. Rough-legged Buzzards in Britain in the winter of 1966/67. *Brit. Birds* 61: 449-455.

Scott, R E 1978. Rough-legged Buzzards in Britain in 1973/74 and 1974/75 . *Brit. Birds* 71: 325-338.

Scott, R E 1979. Note on unusual Yellow Browed Warbler in Sussex. *Brit. Birds* 72: 124-126.

Self, M, O'Brien, M and Hirons, G 1994. Hydrological management on RSPB lowland wet grassland reserves. *RSPB Conservation Review 1994*. RSPB.

Sennitt, M V 1981. Sample survey of the breeding Rook population in Sussex, 1980. *Sussex Bird Report* 33: 80-84.

Sharrock, J T R 1974. *Scarce Migrant Birds in Britain and Ireland*. Poyser. Berkhamstead.

Sharrock, J T R 1976. *The Atlas of Breeding birds in Britain and Ireland*. British Trust for Ornithology. Tring.

Shrubb, M 1964. Stilt Sandpiper in Sussex. *Brit. Birds* 57:126-127.

Shrubb, M 1965. Report on breeding bird surveys 1964. *Sussex Bird Report* 17: 31-37.

Shrubb, M 1968. The Status and Distribution of Snipe, Redshank and Yellow Wagtail as Breeding Birds in Sussex. *Sussex Bird Report* 20: 53-60

Shrubb, M 1969. The present status of the Kestrel in Sussex. *Sussex Bird Report* 21: 58-69.

Shrubb, M 1979. *The Birds of Sussex, their present status*. Phillimore. Chichester.

Shrubb, M 1979. Blyth's Pipit; a bird new to Britain and Sussex. *Sussex Bird Report* 31: 55.

Shrubb, M 1982. Sussex breeding birds, past, present and future - a personal view. *Sussex Ornithological Society Newsletter* 81: 3-5.

Shrubb, M 1984. The Sparrowhawk in Sussex 1960-1983. *Sussex Bird Report* 36: 74-82.

Shrubb, M and Lack, P C 1991. The numbers and distribution of Lapwings V. vanellus nesting in England and Wales in 1987. *Bird Study* 38: 20-37.

Simmons, K E L 1974. Adaptations in the reproductive biology of the Great Crested Grebe. *Brit. Birds* 67: 413-437.

Simms, E 1953. Yellow-billed Cuckoo in Sussex. *Brit. Birds* 46: 218.

Sinton, R 1994. *Stone Curlews and the South Downs*. RSPB report.

Sitters, H P 1982. The decline of the Cirl Bunting in Britain, 1968-80. *Brit. Birds* 75: 105-108.

Sitters, H P 1986. Woodlarks in Britain 1968-83. *Brit. Birds* 79: 105-116.

Sitters, H P 1988. *Tetrad atlas of the breeding birds of Devon.* Devon Birdwatching and Preservation Society. Yelverton.

Smit, T and Piersma, T 1989. Numbers, mid-winter distribution and migration of wader populations using the East Atlantic Flyway. *Flyways and reserve networks for waterbirds.* IWRB Special Publication 9. Slimbridge.

Snow, D W (ed.) 1971. *The Status of Birds in Britain and Ireland.* BOU/Blackwell. London.

Spencer, R and the Rare Breeding Birds Panel 1991. Rare breeding birds in the United Kingdom in 1989. *British Birds* 84: 349-370, 379-392.

Spencer, R and the Rare Breeding Birds Panel 1993. Rare breeding birds in the United Kingdom in 1990. *Brit. Birds* 86: 62-90.

Stanley, P I, Brough, T, Fletcher, M R, Horton, N and Rochard, J B A 1981. The origins of Herring Gulls wintering inland in south-east England. *Bird Study* 28: 123-132.

Streeter, D 1983. Biogeography, ecology and conservation in Sussex, in *Sussex Environment, Landscape and Society.* Sutton.

Summers-Smith, J D 1989. A history of the status of the Tree Sparrow *Passer montanus* in the British Isles. *Bird Study* 36: 23-31.

Sussex Bird Reports 1-47. (ed.) des Forges, G 1948; des Forges, G and Harber, D D 1949-55; Harber, D D 1956-61; Sheldon, A B 1962-8; Bayliss-Smith, S 1969-75; Jackson, R J B 1976-80; Shrubb, M 1981-5; Bonham, P F 1986-90; Roberts, G C M 1991-3. Patton, S J 1994. Sussex Bird Reports 1948-94.

Sussex Wildlife Trust, 1996. *Vision for the Wildlife of Sussex.* Sussex Wildlife Trust. Henfield.

Sutherland, M P 1983. Presumed hybrid Glaucous x Herring Gulls in Kent. *Brit. Birds* 76: 83-85.

Sutton, G A 1958. White-winged Black Tern in Sussex. *Brit. Birds* 51: 160.

Svardson, G and Durango, S 1950. Spring weather and population fluctuations. *Proc. Int. Orn. Congr.* 10: 497-501.

Tatner, P 1982. Factors influencing the distribution of Magpies *Pica pica* in an urban environment. *Bird study* 29: 227-234.

Tatner, P 1983. The diet of urban Magpies (*Pica pica*). *Ibis* 125: 90-107.

Taverner, J H 1970. Mediterranean Gulls nesting in Hampshire. *Brit. Birds* 63: 67-79.

Taylor, D W, Davenport, D L and Flegg, J J M 1981. *The Birds of Kent: A Review of their Status and Distribution.* Kent Ornithological Society.

Ticehurst, N F 1907. *Hastings and East Sussex Naturalist* 1: 60-62.

Ticehurst, N F 1909. *History of the Birds of Kent.* 189-192.

Ticehurst, N F 1912. White-spotted Bluethroat in Sussex. *Brit. Birds* 6: 187.

Ticehurst, N F 1914. Slender-billed Nutcrackers in Kent and Sussex. *Brit. Birds* 7: 261-262.

Ticehurst, N F 1934. Broad-billed Sandpiper seen in Sussex. *Brit. Birds* 28: 209-210.

Ticehurst, N F and Morley, A 1937. Marsh Sandpipers seen in Kent and Sussex. *Brit. Birds* 31: 197-198.

Tittensor, R 1881. A sideways look at nature conservation in Britain. *Discussion Paper in Conservation* No. 29. UCL. London.

Tubbs, C R 1993. An introduction to Hampshire, in Clarke, J M and Eyre, J A 1993. *Birds of Hampshire*. Hampshire Ornithological Society.

Tucker, G M and Heath, M F 1994. *Birds in Europe: their conservation status*. Cambridge.

UK Biodiversity Steering Group 1995. *Biodiversity: The UK Steering Group Report 1995*. HMSO. London.

Urquhart, E D 1990. Crag Martin at Beachy Head, July 1988 - new to Sussex. *Sussex Bird Report* 42: 74-5.

Underhill, L G *et al* 1993. Breeding of waders (*Charadrii*) and Brent geese *Branta bernicla bernicla* at Prontishcheva Lake, northeastern Taimyr, Russia, in a peak and decreasing lemming year. *Ibis* 135: 277-292.

Veen, J 1977. *The Sandwich tern; functional and causal aspects of nest distribution*. Brill. Leiden.

Venables, L S V 1939. Bird distribution on the South Downs and a comparison of that of Surrey Greensand heaths. *J. Anim. Ecol.* 6: 227-237.

Vinicombe, K E and Chandler, R J 1982. Movements of Ruddy Ducks during the hard winter of 1978/79. *Brit. Birds* 75: 1-11.

Vinicombe, K E and Hopkin, P J 1993. The Great Black-headed Gull in Britain. *Brit. Birds* 86: 201-205.

Vinicombe, K E, Marchant, J H and Knox, A 1993. Review of status and categorisation of feral birds on the British List. *Brit. Birds* 86: 605-614.

Voous, K H 1960. *Atlas of European Birds*. Nelson. Amsterdam and London.

WSCC 1993. *The State of the West Sussex Environment*. Report to Strategic Planning Committee of WSCC 1993.

Walker, A F G 1970. The moult migration of Yorkshire Canada Geese. *Wildfowl* 21: 99-104.

Walker, F J 1953. Roosting Hen Harriers in Walland Marsh. *Kent Bird Report* 23: 15.

Walpole-Bond, J 1938. *A History of Sussex Birds*. Witherby. London.

Waters, R 1994. Wintering gulls 1953 - 1993. *BTO News* 190: 9-10.

Waters, R J and Cranswick, P A 1993. *The Wetland Bird Survey 1992-1993: Wildfowl and Wader Counts*. BTO, WWT, RSPB, JNCC.

Watson, A B 1992. Pied Wheatear at Newhaven, July 1990. *Sussex Bird Report* 44: 81.

Watson, J 1987. A survey of wintering Cormorants in Sussex, 1985/86. *Sussex Bird Report* 39: 65-68.

Welfare, M 1979. Hard weather movements, New Year 1979. *Shoreham Ornithological Society Report* 26: 49-54.

Whitbread, T and Curson, S 1992. *Wildlife Drying Up. An Action Plan to safeguard the water meadows and wildbrooks of Sussex*. Sussex Wildlife Trust.

White, C M N 1936. *Puffinus kuhlii* off the Sussex coast. *Brit. Birds* 30: 229-230.

White, G 1789. *The Natural History of Selborne*. London.

Wilkins, J P 1939. Aquatic Warbler seen in Sussex. *Brit. Birds* 32: 273.

Williams, R P 1931. Ivory Gull in Sussex. *Brit. Birds* 24: 299.

Williams, R G B and Robinson, D A 1983. The soils and vegetation history of Sussex, in *Sussex Environment, Landscape and Society*. Sutton.

Williamson, K 1977. Blyth's Pipit in the Western Palearctic. *Bull. BOC* 97: 60-61.

Williamson, R 1978. *The Great Yew Forest, the Natural History of Kingley Vale*. Macmillan. London.

Williamson, R and Williamson, K 1973. The bird community of Yew woodland at Kingley Vale, Sussex. *Brit. Birds* 66: 12-23.

Willsher, J 1995. A history of farm diversification and the development of a Nature Reserve at Elms Farm, Icklesham. In Montgomery, H (ed) 1995. *The Sussex Recorder. Proceedings from the Biological Recorders' Seminar February 1995*. Sussex Wildlife Trust.

Wilson, P J 1974. A survey of the Cirl Bunting in Sussex. *Sussex Bird Report* 26: 57-59.

Winstanley, D, Spencer, R and Williamson, K 1974. Where have all the Whitethroats gone? *Bird Study* 21: 1-14.

Witherby, H F 1927. Snowy Owls in the Atlantic. *Brit. Birds* 20: 228.

Witherby, H F, Jourdain, F R C, Ticehurst, N F and Tucker, B W 1940-1. *The Handbook of British Birds* (5 Volumes). Witherby. London.

Wynne-Edwards, V C 1962. *Animal Dispersion in Relation to Social Behaviour*. Edinburgh.

Yates, B J and de Potier, A 1994. Shelduck breeding survey in Sussex (1990-92). *Sussex bird Report* 46: 98-102.

Yates, B J and Taffs, H 1990. Least Tern in East Sussex - a new Western Palearctic bird. *Birding World* 3: 197-199.

Index

"In conclusion I will only add, that as I have found it a life long pleasure to investigate the works of the Creator, so wonderfully and beautifully displayed in the natural history of the 'fowls of the air' so I hope that the results of my studies, thus presented in this volume, may help those that come after me to enjoy the same pleasure."

(William Borrer - *The Birds of Sussex* 1891)